Innovations in Design: 1993 Ford Hybrid Electric Vehicle Challenge

SP-980

GLOBAL MOBILITY DATABASE

All SAE papers, standards, and selected books are abstracted and indexed in the Global Mobility Database.

Published by:
Society of Automotive Engineers, Inc.
400 Commonwealth Drive
Warrendale, PA 15096-0001
USA
Phone: (412) 776-4841
Fax: (412) 776-5760
February 1994

ISBN 1-56091-388-6
SAE/SP-94/980
Library of Congress Catalog Card Number: 93-84469
Copyright 1994 Society of Automotive Engineers, Inc.

Printed in USA

FORWARD

The papers in this Special Publication were originally developed as submittals for the Technical Report event at the 1993 Hybrid Electric Vehicle (HEV) Challenge. Held June 1 through June 6 in Dearborn, Michigan, the 1993 HEV Challenge was sponsored by a partnership of the Ford Motor Company, the U. S. Department of Energy (DOE), and the Society of Automotive Engineers (SAE). This competition was another in a series of Engineering Research Competitions supported by DOE and part of the Collegiate Engineering Design Competition Series sponsored by SAE. The papers presented here are enhanced and expanded versions of those prepared in advance of the competition by teams of participating student engineers. They describe the design elements and construction details of the largest field of HEVs yet assembled from some of the best engineering schools in North America. Special thanks and recognition are extended to the Ford Motor Company for its outstanding support of this competition.

Thirty colleges and universities from the U.S. and Canada were selected to participate in this HEV competition to explore the potential of this cutting-edge technology through a Request for Proposals process initiated in January, 1992. A letter announcing and soliciting interest in the competition was sent to all accredited engineering programs and two-year technical schools in both countries. It described the nature of the events and the two available classes in the competition: one required constructing a HEV from the ground-up and the other required converting a 1992 Ford Escort Wagon to hybrid operation. Sixty-seven schools submitted proposals that were evaluated by a team of judges from industry and government experts. From these proposals, twelve schools were selected to participate in the Ground-Up class and eighteen schools in the Escort Conversion class. Twenty-six of these schools were able to pass technical and safety inspections and qualify for the actual competition in June, 1993.

The Challenge consisted of a series of static and dynamic events designed to assess the quality of the student's efforts. The dynamic events measured the performance of the vehicles constructed by the teams of student engineers and the static events evaluated their engineering and communication skills. Each event was assigned a portion of the 1,000 available points in the competition according to Table 1. The Technical Report event served both as a way to emphasize the importance of communicating the content of and rationale for the team's design as well as to document the specifications of the competing vehicles. The Report was due one month before the competition to allow time to judge them. Teams of judges were assembled from industry and government sources to read and score the reports. At least five judges evaluated each report; their scores were normalized to a 75 point scoring range and then averaged to determine a rank order of schools in each class. Points were then assigned to the schools according to a pre-published schedule that allocated points according to the vehicle class and the school's overall rank.

Table 1. Competition Points	
Event Description	**Points**
Technical Report	75
Engineering Design Event	150
Oral Presentation	50
Acceleration Event	100
Emissions Event	150
Commuter Challenge Event	150
APU Efficiency Event	35
Range Event	75
Electric Efficiency Event	35
Overall Efficiency Event	55
Cost Assessment Event	125
Total Points	1,000

The complete results from the 1993 HEV Challenge, including the scores from the Technical Report event, can be found in Table 2 for the Ground-Up Class and Table 3 for the Escort Conversion Class. Many technical achievements and performance benchmarks for HEVs were set during this competition; a complete description of the competition's structure and outcomes, as well as an analysis of the results, will be published as a separate SAE paper.

On behalf of all the sponsors of the 1993 HEV Challenge, I thank you for your interest in the 1993 HEV Challenge. The impressive accomplishments of the teams of student engineers contained in this publication speak for themselves. If the reader has any questions concerning the organization of the competition or its outcomes, please contact me at 9700 S. Cass Avenue, Building 362-B209, Argonne, Illinois, 60440, USA.

Robert P. Larsen

Center for Transportation Research

Argonne National Laboratory

Table 2. **Final Scores for the 1993 Ford/DOE/SAE HEV Challenge** **Ground-Up Class**	Technical Report	Engineering Design Event	Oral Presentation	Acceleration Event	Emissions Event	Commuter Challenge	APU Efficiency Event	Range Event	Electric Efficiency Event	Overall Efficiency Event	Cost Assessment Event	Total Points
California Polytechnic - Pomona	18	52	9	34	0	73	6	18	10	32	83	335
California Polytechnic-San Luis Obispo	14	73	20	23	42	0	14	14	35	27	55	317
Cornell University	37	44	41	82	106	150	29	62	29	45	125	750
Lawrence Technological University	26	150	24	41	68	52	8	26	8	13	66	482
Michigan State University	62	124	34	41	99	124	20	51	17	19	60	651
New York Institute of Technology	11	0	5	0	0	0	0	0	0	0	25	41
University of California - Davis	51	87	11	79	77	102	24	75	24	37	108	675
University of California - Santa Barbara	75	36	14	31	85	61	12	43	12	16	93	478
University of Idaho/Washington State	8	102	7	84	48	44	10	31	14	55	44	447
University of Tennessee	43	22	29	63	111	87	17	37	20	22	74	525
University of Texas - Arlington	11	61	17	0	0	0	0	0	0	0	25	114
University of Tulsa	22	29	50	20	84	36	35	22	0	10	49	357

Table 3. **Final Scores for the 1993 Ford/DOE/SAE HEV Challenge** **Ford Escort Conversion Class**	Technical Report	Engineering Design Event	Oral Presentation	Acceleration Event	Emissions Event	Commuter Challenge	APU Efficiency Event	Range Event	Electric Efficiency Event	Overall Efficiency Event	Cost Assessment Event	Penalty Points	Total Points
California State University - Northridge	18	50	28	32	89	35	12	16	24	22	65		391
Colorado School of Mines	12	55	16	51	71	68	31	46	11	18	81		460
Colorado State University	34	84	34	8	74	45	22	38	8	20	50		417
Concordia University	75	103	10	78	82	76	35	34	9	48	101		651
Jordan College Energy Institute	14	35	18	44	0	55	8	24	22	28	53		301
Pennsylvania State University	0	25	8	56	67	103	14	42	18	14	61	(327)	81.2
Seattle University	28.5	61	25	48	97	131	20	57	35	25	75		602.5
Stanford University	51	115	5	24	0	61	0	18	27	12	47		360
Texas Tech University	24	45	20	0	56	0	11	0	0	0	44	(222)	(21.5)
United States Naval Academy	38	40	12	32	88	93	27	30	7	16	87	(10)	460
University of Alberta	46	131	43	88	71	150	24	75	14	38	94		774
University of California - Irvine	21	0	7	0	0	0	0	0	0	0	25		53
University of Illinois	65	150	31	52	73	40	9	27	12	42	57		558
University of Wisconsin	57	68	38	68	0	0	0	14	18	0	41		304
Washington University - St. Louis	0	0	6	0	0	0	0	0	0	0	0		6
Wayne State University	28.5	30	14	46	106	50	16	51	10	34	87	(240)	232.7
Weber State University	16	93	50	59	131	115	18	65	31	31	125		734
West Virginia University	42	76	22	44	48	84	10	21	18	55	70		490

TABLE OF CONTENTS

Design Reports

The University of Alberta Hybrid Electric Vehicle Project Final Technical Report

Vincent Duckworth, Ken Workun, David Checkel
University of Alberta

ABSTRACT

Utilizing the range benefits of an internal combustion engine in concert with the zero-emission characteristics of an electric motor/battery combination has the potential to change the long held belief that electric cars are not practical or marketable. Spurred on by the rising air pollution levels in cities like Los Angeles, the automotive industry has responded by upscaling research and development of a practical and consumer appealing electric automobile. Development is now underway by the world's leading car makers to produce and deliver a working hybrid electric vehicle - one that runs on electricity and gasoline utilizing the benefits of both. As part of that effort, the University of Alberta (U of A), along with 29 other schools and universities from across North America, has spent eighteen months modifying a 1992 Ford Escort Station wagon into a working hybrid electric vehicle. The results of this endeavor have determined that the hybrid concept is feasible, producible, and deliverable to the car buying public.

INTRODUCTION

The U.S Department of Energy, SAE, and Ford Motor Company have created a student design competition to develop hybrid electric automobiles, the Hybrid Electric Vehicle (HEV) Challenge. These hybrid vehicles must be capable of running a "reasonable" distance on battery power, (zero-emission mode), and of running extended distances using conventional liquid fuels, (gasoline, M85 or E100). This report details the technical design of the University of Alberta's hybrid electric vehicle, "EMISSION IMPOSSIBLE". The U of A team produced a hybrid electric vehicle by converting a Ford Escort station wagon to hybrid drive. Throughout the design process, the emphasis of the project team was to develop a car which was realistically manufacturable and marketable within the constraints of the competition guidelines. A few illustrations of this philosophy are: the U of A car is fueled with regular gasoline since that is the only fuel reliably available; the car retains all of the interior padding and sound damping material since the benefits to marketability far outweigh the costs to performance.

The major technical component of the hybrid vehicle is the hybrid electric drivetrain. This consisting of the battery pack, the electric motor controllers, the electric motors, the internal combustion engine, the transmission, and the coupler between the engine and the electric motors. The first section of this report covers the drivetrain design strategy, component selection, and drivetrain mounting and integration. This is followed by a section on operating modes, drivetrain control strategy, emissions control, and fuel and electrical consumption of the hybrid powerplant. Integrating this novel drivetrain into a stock vehicle body required significant modifications. The next section of the report covers the design of powertrain mounts, battery box, suspension modifications, and other necessary structural changes to the car. Finally, The experimental nature of the vehicle demanded additional operating instruments and controls. To produce an aesthetically pleasing driver environment, the U of A team developed a prototype console and instrument panel which incorporated the additional controls and display instrumentation.

POWERTRAIN CONFIGURATION

There are two primary coupling methods available when configuring the powertrain of a Hybrid Electric Vehicle; series and parallel.

SERIES CONFIGURATION - This configuration is common to many locomotives and commuter buses in use throughout North America. The premise behind this method is simple. An engine fueled by common combustibles is used to power an electric generator which in turn supplies the required electrical power to an electric drive motor.

The main advantage of this system is its simplicity. The power transfer between the combustion engine and the electric drive motor is independent of each respective unit. The internal combustion engine can be tuned to operate at its optimum speed and efficiency with a battery system in place to absorb the fluctuating power needs of the electric motors. This allows a substantial reduction in size of the battery (the limiting factor with purely electric vehicles) while still using of the near-ideal torque characteristics of the electric motors.

1

The series configuration has two main disadvantages. The combustion engine cannot be used to directly propel the vehicle which results in a loss of efficiency and a decrease in peak performance. Using an internal combustion engine to drive a generator, putting charge into the batteries which is then drawn by the electric motors is less efficient than using the internal combustion engine to supply power directly to the powertrain. Also, because the ICE cannot supply power directly to the drivetrain, the peak power of the HEV is limited by the electric motors.

PARALLEL CONFIGURATION - This method allows for either the internal combustion engine or the electric motor(s) to work independently as the primary drive unit. Additionally, this method has the ability to use both powerplants concurrently to drive the vehicle.

The advantage of this system is its functionality, having three distinct modes of operation: electric motor only, combustion engine only, or a combination of the two (hybrid mode).

The parallel configuration is not as simple to implement as a series system. A direct linkage is required between both the combustion engine and electric motor(s) and the final drive system. The need for, and the subsequent isolating effect of, a generator is lost when utilizing this system.

CHOSEN CONFIGURATION - Although more difficult to design and build, the University of Alberta HEV team opted for the parallel configuration. The performance, efficiency and the significant weight savings available with this system outweighed the simplicity of the series configuration.

Electric Motor Selection - Many different types of electric motors were investigated prior to the final selection. Included were DC Shunt Wound, DC Series Wound, and AC Synchronous. The critical factors considered were efficiency, durability, weight, output power, and cost.

The chosen electrical power unit is a set of two BRLS16, DC Brushless, Permanent Magnet motors manufactured by Solectria Corporation. These motors are lightweight (30 kg (64 lb) each for a total of 60 kg (128 lb)) and have a nominal power output of 12 kW (16 Hp) each. This output can be overrated to a maximum of 22 kW (30 Hp) each for one out of every three minutes of operation. Additionally, because of the lack of brushes they are considered to be low maintenance, robust motors.

Each of the motors has its own controller. The power is regulated by a pulse width modulated current signal at a nominal voltage of 144V. For an increase in power, the duty cycle is lengthened. The motors operate on three phases of modulated DC current and have a nominal draw of 83 Amps. The torque and speed range of these motors is not adequate to drive the vehicle directly. Therefore a transmission is necessary.

The motors/controllers have an inherent regenerative braking capability. With the parallel configuration, regenerative braking can be used in all three operating modes. The electric motors are permanently linked to the clutch input and rotate at the speed of the transmission input shaft whenever the clutch is engaged. If regenerative braking is enabled, operating the vehicle brakes switches the controllers into regenerative mode and the energy of the vehicle is dissipated by running the electric motors as DC generators. The generated power is used to recharge the battery pack.

These motors and their controllers were purchased at a cost of $10,000.00 each. This high cost is due to both the low production volume (< 200 units/year) and the high price attached to developing small, high flux density permanent magnets.

Auxiliary Power Unit - Studies of commuter driving patterns show the average commuter will drive less than 65 km (40 mi) in one day approximately 77% of the time. A pie chart showing the percentage breakdown from an SAE study done in 1975 is shown in Figure 1. With the predicted range of the battery system at just over 70 km, this means that, on average, the internal combustion engine of the HEV powertrain will see use only once every four days. This will occur when the operator wishes to drive to a location outside the 72 km (45 mi) range. Ideally, this duty cycle will occur at the steady speed and load associated with highway travel, thus maximizing the efficiency of the engine and reducing its horsepower requirements.

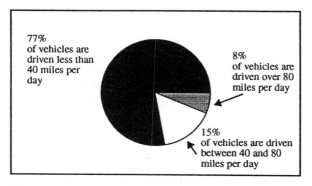

Figure 1: Driving Habits

Because the engine found in a stock Escort takes up the majority of the engine bay, a smaller engine was required to package all of the powertrain components within the same engine bay. Various motorcycle engines were considered because of their compact layout and high power/weight ratio. However, it was felt that the emissions control and electronic engine management systems for the motorcycle engines would require excessive engineering effort to achieve acceptable emissions and fuel economy driving a heavy automobile. For this reason, the search was directed to small automobile engines.

Two alternatives were investigated; the Honda VTEC engine out of the Honda Civic VX, and the engine out of a Suzuki Swift GA (the same engine can be found in the GEO Metro). The VTEC engine was preferred because of its high efficiency, due to its use of lean burn technology, and its output horsepower which was similar to the original Escort engine. A VTEC was procured but unfortunately proved to be too large to be successfully integrated within the drivetrain.

The internal combustion engine used in the U of A HEV is the Suzuki 1.0 L, three cylinder, four stroke gas engine. Because of its small physical dimensions, it was ideal for the chosen configuration, allowing both drives to be mounted within the engine bay. Additionally, it has an aluminum block giving a weight savings of over 68 kg (150

). This engine has an output power rating of 41 kW (55 Hp) making its power/weight ratio 0.65:1 (kW/kg) which is significantly better than the original Ford engine's ratio of 0.49:1. This engine has a fully mapped electronic fuel and spark control system and a catalyst system which allows it to meet California emissions standards in the small Suzuki Swift. Given the sophisticated engine control system, it was felt that the engine could be remapped to give adequate emissions performance with the heavier HEV. Unleaded, high octane gasoline is the preferred fuel type for this engine.

Coupling Mechanism & Transmission - The primary difficulty with the parallel configuration is the design of a coupling mechanism which allows full functionality in each of the three driving modes; electric, gas, and hybrid. The design must allow both the electric and gasoline powered units to drive the vehicle alone or in concert.

The U of A HEV design achieves this with an overrunning clutch mechanism called a mechanical diode. This device is manufactured by Epilogics Corporation in Los Gatos, California. It was originally designed to work within an dragster torque converter and can withstand up to 1100 ft. lbs of applied torque (30 times greater than required). It was created to replace traditional ramp and roller clutches and is therefore of similar dimensions. "The clutch consists of two disks; the carrier and the receptor. When the carrier spins in one direction, torque is transmitted between the disks. When the receptor spins faster than the carrier, the disks are disconnected and allowed to spin independently" (* as quoted in Mechanical Engineering Vol. 115/No.3, March 1993 issue).

In the U of A HEV, this mechanism is mounted between the engine crankshaft and the clutch. The mechanical diode free-wheels when the vehicle is in electric only mode (i.e. the gasoline engine remains stationary). In combustion only mode, this device engages, driving the clutch and spinning the electric motors in the process (thus maintaining the regenerative ability). In hybrid mode, the electric motors are initially spinning and applying power to the drivetrain. Once the output shaft of the gasoline engine reaches an equivalent speed, the mechanical diode engages, providing added torque to the drivetrain.

The mechanical diode is situated within a housing (the coupler) which is an extended transmission bell housing. The two electric motors have steel pulleys attached to them and apply power to the coupler through a wide, high efficiency cog belt.

As shown in Figure 2, the internal combustion engine is located on the passenger side of the engine bay and occupies approximately 1/2 of the available space in that compartment. The electric motors are mounted one above the other on the driver side of the engine bay directly in front of the transaxle. Their controllers have been fixed together and are mounted behind the motors, above the transaxle.

Due to the limited rpm range of both the ICE and the electric motors, it was determined that a transmission was necessary to achieve maximum performance. The transmission chosen for this design was the stock Escort five speed manual transmission. This transmission met all the needs of the design and was easily integrated using existing mountings. The small losses incurred by using a transmission were negligible when compared with the increased

performance benefits. The transmission is located on the driver side of the engine bay (its original location) directly below the electric motor controllers.

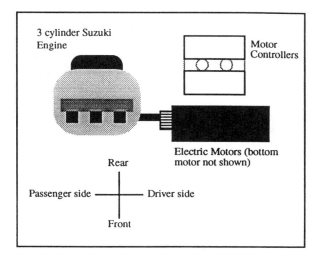

Figure 2: Engine Bay Schematic - Top View

Battery Pack - As with the electric motor selection, a great deal of time and effort went into the final choice of a battery. The battery was to be the single largest weight addition in the vehicle design and as such, the overriding criteria in this area were weight and energy density. Additional concerns included; safety, recyclability and cost.

Two common battery types evaluated were Lead Acid and Nickel Cadmium. Both of these cells are significantly less energy dense than most of the advanced types currently being researched. Many of these exotic cells, such as Zinc Air, Zinc Bromine, Nickel-Metal-Hydride, Lithium Permanganate, and Sodium Sulfur, were investigated to determine their usability. Both the Zinc Bromine and Sodium Sulphur cells were pursued vigorously but could not be acquired. With the safety concerns associated with the ZnBr cell, the manufacturer was reevaluating the production of this system and would not release the technology. The NaS battery system was unavailable to us due to a contract agreement between Ford and the manufacturer and Ford's request that these cells not be given for use in the HEV Challenge.

The chosen battery system for the U of A HEV consists of STM 1.60 Nickel Cadmium cells manufactured by SAFT NIFE Corporation in France. A diagram showing cell dimensions and key features can be seen in Figure 3. This cell is specifically designed for automotive uses. It utilizes a light plastic casing (replacing the traditional metal casing) and features a very high depth of discharge. This is important in an automobile where a fairly constant current draw is desirable throughout the discharge cycle. The entire pack is composed of 135 cells yielding a pack voltage of 170 Volts. The Amp-Hr rating on this pack is 61 Amp-Hrs which is predicted to yield a range of approximately 72 km (45 mi) on a single charge. The ideal operating temperature of the pack is 23 °C (60 °F).

Some additional features of these Nickel Cadmium cells include; self-watering ability, high energy density, and recyclable internals. The self-watering system attaches to the top of each cell with reservoirs located along the sides of the battery box. These cells are approximately 1.5

times as energy dense as conventional Lead Acid cells providing 50% greater vehicle range with similarly sized battery packs. Additionally, these cells perform slightly better than normal Lead Acid cells in cold weather (a concern in the Canadian climate). The metals found inside the cells, nickel and cadmium, are recyclable. They can be reconstituted and reused in another cell. Only minimal gases are emitted during a normal charging cycle and NiCads are much more robust than Lead Acid, with less damage to the cells if they are overcharged. These cells have a life of between 2000 and 3000 charge-discharge cycles which translates into five to eight years of daily charging.

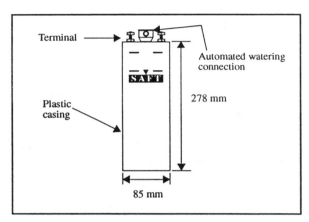

Figure 3: Chosen Nickel Cadmium Cell

The total weight of the battery pack is 272 kg (600 lb), and was purchased at a cost $25,000.00. As with the electric motors, this high cost is due mainly to the low production volume (< 100 packs/year) and the high price of cadmium.

The battery pack is situated in the space originally occupied by the rear seats. Rear seating is no longer available in this prototype hybrid. The cells are located in seven rows running the width of the vehicle inside a structurally and liquid-sealed containment box. Thermal management of the cells is achieved through intake vents located in the vehicle floorpan and exhaust vents located in the vehicle doors. Continuous digital monitoring of the battery temperature, state of charge, and current flow has been incorporated into the design.

CONTROLLER STRATEGY

The U of A HEV design, using the parallel configuration previously discussed, allows the vehicle to be propelled in three distinct modes; electric only, gasoline only, and a combination of the two. These modes are engaged manually using a multi-position rotary switch mounted on the dashboard. The switch is shown in Figure 4. It has four positions (in clockwise order); OFF, electric only mode (EM), hybrid mode (HEV), and combustion only mode (ICE).

ELECTRIC ONLY MODE - Electric only mode is the primary mode of operation for the vehicle. To engage, the driver must turn the ignition key to the ON position similar to operating a conventional vehicle. The Suzuki engine computer, fuel injector, and starter circuit are locked out in this

mode. At this time, the vehicle is ready for zero emissions operation.

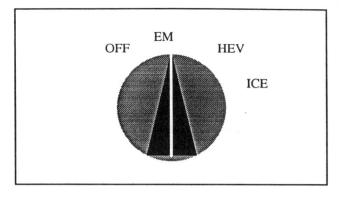

Figure 4: Mode Select Switch

Control of the electric motor speed and hence the vehicle speed is actuated through the conventional accelerator pedal. The actual mechanism beneath the accelerator pedal is a twinned potentiometer which will send an identical signal to each of the two motor controllers. As the accelerator pedal is depressed, the potentiometer voltage signal is increased which in turn instructs the controllers to supply more current to the motors. When changing between gears, the clutch pedal and accelerator pedal must be operated as in a conventional combustion vehicle (i.e. the clutch pedal is slowly released while the accelerator pedal is slowly depressed). It should be noted that the electric motors do not idle - no sound is heard from the engine bay when the vehicle is stopped. A low electrical whine (quieter than the normal combustion rumble) is noticeable when the vehicle is in motion. For the predicted performance figures in electric mode, see Figure 5.

HYBRID MODE - The hybrid mode of operation is useful when increased performance is desired. Its primary usage will be on the highway for passing or in hilly terrain. The hybrid option can be enabled either while the vehicle is at a standstill or while in motion. A standard mechanical linkage exists between the accelerator pedal and the throttle of the combustion engine and this regulates the flow of fuel/air mixture which in turn determines the engine power. The speed of the electric motors is regulated as before. When engaging the hybrid mode, the vehicle can be in either electric only mode - the primary case, or in gasoline only mode - the secondary case. The vehicle can also be started from hybrid mode.

In the primary case, the operator will turn the selector switch from electric only mode to the hybrid mode. The Suzuki engine computer, fuel injector, and starting circuit are re-enabled. All of the electric motor systems remain active and operational. The operator must now turn the ignition key to the START position to start the internal combustion engine as normal. The combustion engine will not couple with the transmission until its output shaft speed matches the rotational speed of the electric motor output shafts. Once the combustion engine has coupled with the transmission shaft, the torque from all three powerplants (two electric motors and one combustion engine) will be transmitted through the vehicle transmission providing added performance; a maximum of 86 kW (115 Hp).

4

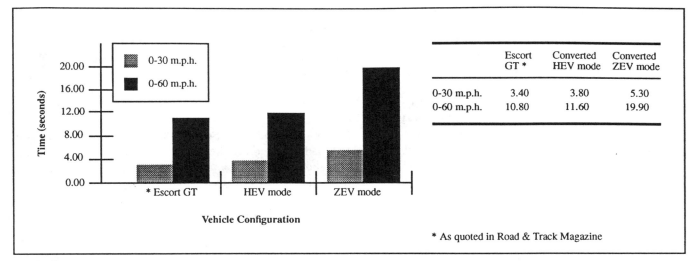

Figure 5: Projected Performance Comparison

	Escort GT *	Converted HEV mode	Converted ZEV mode
0-30 m.p.h.	3.40	3.80	5.30
0-60 m.p.h.	10.80	11.60	19.90

* As quoted in Road & Track Magazine

In the secondary case, the operator will be running the vehicle in internal combustion mode only with all of the previously mentioned combustion systems operational and all of the electric motor systems disabled. The driver will select the hybrid mode option by turning the selector switch counterclockwise one notch. Because of the nature of the coupling mechanism, the electric motors are already free-wheeling when the vehicle is in combustion mode only. This fact greatly simplifies and reduces the transition time between these modes. The additive torque from the electric motors is virtually instantaneous. This secondary case will be quite useful in a highway situation when instant "boost" for quick passing is desirable. The result is an approximate doubling of power. For the predicted performance figures in hybrid mode, see Figure 5.

COMBUSTION MODE ONLY - Combustion mode only is the auxiliary mode of operation for this vehicle. The operator has the option of either starting the vehicle in this mode or switching to this mode while the vehicle is in motion.

To start the vehicle in this mode, the operator selects the combustion mode on the Selector Switch by setting the switch to its extreme right. In this position, the primary combustion systems are enabled and no signal from the accelerator potentiometer reaches the electric motor controllers. The operator uses the ignition key to start the engine just as with a conventional automobile. Driving is also done as in a normal automobile.

To engage this mode while the vehicle is in motion (assuming that the car is currently operating in electric only mode), a short transition through the hybrid mode is recommended. This will allow the internal combustion engine to be started (as described above) without the loss of power while driving. The gasoline engine accelerates to match the electric motor speed at which time it will engage the transmission. Once this has occurred, a transition from hybrid to combustion only mode can be made safely and expeditiously.

BRAKING STRATEGY - The use of an electric motor as a primary powerplant within a vehicle allows for the use of a unique feature found in electric motor/controller systems; regenerative braking. It is available within the U of A HEV in all three of its operational modes.

In each of the three modes, regenerative braking takes the inertial energy of the vehicle and drives the motors as generators while slowing the vehicle down. It is engaged when the driver presses the brake pedal, with the first half of the of the pedal travel being regenerative and the last half applying the hydraulic brakes. This allows for the majority of braking energy to be reclaimed into the battery, while keeping the additional braking capacity of disk brakes. This feature is only enabled when the vehicle is in gear. No regeneration occurs while the vehicle is in neutral or when the clutch pedal is depressed. This is to prevent possible damage to the motors as a result of them coming to a halt too rapidly, and thus throwing a magnet.

In combustion only mode, regeneration allows power from the internal combustion engine to be transmitted into the battery pack. A red push-button on the vehicle dashboard gives the operator the option of using this feature. Furthermore, a potentiometer located on the dashboard allows the driver to select the level of regeneration available. This will be especially useful in the State of California where proposals are in place to have certain traffic zones designated zero emission zones. These zones will alternate with low emission zones. The use of the regeneration is ideal in such a setting. The operator can increase the battery potential by "topping up" the battery pack when driving through a low emission zone.

EMISSIONS CONTROL

Control and overall reduction of emissions from the U of A HEV was tackled in the following manner.

In selecting an internal combustion engine, the desirable characteristics included state of the art emission control and the ability to easily alter the engine control process. Both the Honda VTEC engine and the Suzuki 1.0 L engine have fully mapped electronic engine control.

The 1.0 liter Suzuki engine chosen will typically operate at a higher power level in the HEV than it would in its normal vehicle - a Suzuki Swift. For example, the maximum power requirement during the limited speed hot-505 emissions test cycle is approximately 16 kW (22 Hp) in a Swift (775 kg (1710 lb)) and approximately 33 kW (44 Hp) in the HEV (1575 kg (3472 lb)). This results in a need for some engine control changes and possibly additional catalytic converter volume. The engine control changes are to limit the high power enrichment and spark advance built into the Suzuki engine management system. These only come into effect when the engine is operating at high torque and engine speeds, well beyond the normal operating range for the Swift. The proposed changes push this enrichment closer to the extreme throttle position and engine speed limits. This leaves the maximum engine power the same, but lowers emissions in the normal operating range.

The empirical results of these proposed changes have yet to be explored or verified on the U of A HEV.

FUEL & ELECTRICAL POWER CONSUMPTION

At this stage of development, detailed fuel and power consumption measurements are not yet available. However, computer projections of the vehicle performance show the trends to be expected. The vehicle weight has been increased significantly (about 23%) from the weight of an empty, stock Escort wagon. This increase raises the tractive energy requirement due to increased inertial resistance and increased rolling resistance. A prediction based on tractive energy analysis of a speed-limited hot-505 emissions test cycle shows that the energy requirement should rise by 29% due to the greater vehicle weight. Since the vehicle is being driven through the same 5 speed transmission, it might be assumed that the power transmission and engine efficiency would remain the same as with the stock vehicle. However, the lower torque output of the Suzuki 1.0 L engine will require using lower gears and higher engine speeds during accelerations. This will reduce efficiency somewhat due to higher friction. Conversely, the Suzuki engine will operate at relatively high loads much of the time, thus increasing its Otto cycle efficiency. Assuming that these effects are approximately in balance, the HEV is expected to use about 29% more fuel when driving the same cycle as a (lighter) stock Escort wagon. The Suzuki Swift has a published fuel economy rating of 50 miles per gallon on the highway. With the predicted increase in fuel consumption, the U of A HEV may achieve between 35 and 39 miles per gallon when driving on gasoline alone in a highway situation.

In electrical mode, the electrical energy consumption should be reduced somewhat by regenerative braking. Cycle simulations using a relatively low regenerative braking level and typical battery charging efficiency show that an 8% reduction in energy consumption should be attainable with regenerative braking. The actual efficiencies of the components involved remain to be determined by testing but this gives a conservative estimate. Of course, the regenerative braking will be available in hybrid and combustion only modes as well, so that a similar savings in total energy consumption (but no savings in fuel consumption) can also be expected in these modes.

A comparison between the fuel economy of the gasoline engine and the electric motors is difficult since combustion and electrical efficiencies are vastly different. From a marketing standpoint, the consumer cares about fuel/electricity costs. The comparison on this level is much easier to quantify. The cost of gasoline in Edmonton is 45 ¢/liter ($1.90/gallon) and the cost of electricity is approximately 7 ¢/kW•hr. The range of the U of A HEV battery is approximately 72 km (45 mi) and its energy capacity is approximately 10 kW•hr. The cost to the consumer to travel 72 km in the HEV on combustion mode alone using a fuel economy of 16.2 km/litre (38 mi/gal) would be about $2.00CAN. This same distance travelled on electric power alone without regeneration would cost about 70 ¢CAN (approximately a savings of 65%). With regeneration, this savings would be slightly higher (68%).

VEHICLE STRUCTURE MODIFICATIONS

Since the U of A HEV is one of eighteen conversion vehicles in this design competition, very little structural modifications were made to the Escort chassis. The modifications that were undertaken were primarily in the engine bay and the passenger compartment.

ENGINE BAY - The powertrain mounting system is one of the most important parts of the U of A's HEV conversion. Two electric motors, their controllers, the Suzuki engine, and a variety of digital monitoring equipment all needed to be integrated within the confines of an engine bay originally designed to house the Ford 1.9 L engine. The complex geometry of this new powerplant combination and the need for precise alignment between each of the powertrain components required that these mounts be carefully designed and constructed.

The configuration and geometry of the various engine bay components was determined using dimensionally correct constructs of the Suzuki engine, the Ford transaxle, the electric motors, and the controllers. Once this geometry was fixed, a detailed loading and stress analysis was undertaken using Algor for stress analysis of major components. The results of this analysis laid the foundation for the mount design. To minimize the weight of the overall mounting system, many of the mounts are fabricated from aluminum. Where strength was critical, for example with the mounting plate between the two electric motors and the internal combustion engine, high strength steel was utilized.

The powertrain mounting points which existed in the engine bay prior to conversion were used for the new mounts as much as possible. All mountings were designed with attachment points flexible enough to allow minor misalignments to be corrected. The new mounts support the weight of all powertrain components and damp vibrations, allowing for smooth engine/motor operation. It is interesting to note that the aggregate weight of the new powertrain is very similar to the original engine bay components.

PASSENGER COMPARTMENT - The major modifications in this area were a box to accommodate the battery and a roll cage to meet competition safety requirements.

Battery Box - The battery and its enclosure weigh approximately 318 kg (700 lb). The rear passenger seat and the flooring between the side rails, aft of the front seats and forward of the rear cross member were removed to make way for the battery containment box. This section of flooring was removed only after a series of extensive strain gauge measurements and a complete finite element analysis, using ANSYS software, of the affected area was undertaken. This analysis showed that if the side rails and rear cross member were unaltered, the vehicle floor could be removed without compromising the structural integrity of the vehicle. To ensure rigidity, this section was replaced by the base of the battery box which was manufactured from a similar grade and gauge of steel to the original floor pan. A schematic of this replacement can be seen in Figure 6.

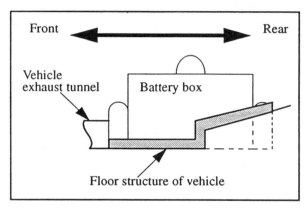

Figure 6: Battery Box-Vehicle Integration (driver side)

The battery box is structurally secure and will contain all fluids within its seals. This was done to protect the occupants from any hazardous materials present inside the box in the event of a collision. A heat shielded exhaust tunnel runs below the longitudinal center of the box. The box is designed to house 148 Nickel Cadmium cells in 7 rows as shown in Figure 7. Each of the rows is supported on a removable tray which is slotted into the side walls of the box. These trays rest on two longitudinal rails along each side of the box. The row alignment is maintained by nonconducting links placed between each row.

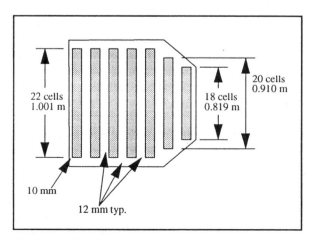

Figure 7: Cell placement in Battery Box

Cooling of the battery is achieved by drawing cool air from below the vehicle and exhausting the heated air out through a vent located in the center of the box lid. The exhaust is vented to the vehicle exterior by ducts which exit through the rear passenger doors.

<u>Additional Modifications</u> - Additional modifications to the passenger compartment were made for increased safety. Since the battery box is permanently mounted to the vehicle and may crush the vehicle in the event of a rollover, a rollbar has been installed to increase occupant safety. Two styles of roll bar bracing were investigated; cross bracing and parallel bracing. Finite element analysis revealed that cross bracing was the most effective with the U of A HEV design however due to the dimensions of the battery pack, parallel bracing was used. As with standard roll bar arrangements, the main hoop will support the roof of the vehicle in the event of a rollover. For additional structural stability and as a safety measure for the occupants, a parallel brace is attached to the main hoop just forward of the battery containment box. This ensures that in the unlikely event that the box broke its welds, both the driver and passenger would be shielded from harm. The main hoop is braced against the rear suspension mounts (aft of the battery box) to provide stability and increased structural stiffness.

Two racing seats with new mounts have been installed to provide higher occupant protection and to accommodate five point racing harnesses. The mounts for the new racing seats are manufactured from aluminum and bolt directly to the vehicle floorpan using the original Ford mounting points. These seats have been placed as far rearward as the rollbar bracing has allowed.

SUSPENSION MODIFICATIONS

The modified Escort designed and built by the U of A HEV project has a curb weight of approximately 1406 kg (3100 lb) which is 272 kg (600 lb) more than the stock Escort. The weight distribution has changed slightly from an approximate 60%/40% split on the front and rear axles respectively to an approximate 55%/45% split on the front and rear axles respectively. The vertical center of gravity of the vehicle has been maintained very near to the unconverted Escort.

Although within the standard vehicle's gross vehicle weight, the significantly higher weight of U of A HEV has necessitated some modifications to the vehicle suspension. Primarily, these changes result from the desire to maintain the original ground clearance and to increase spring stiffness to account for this greater weight. The existing springs were replaced with springs having an increased spring coefficient. The new front springs have a spring coefficient of 29.3 kN/m as compared with the original spring coefficient of 26.6 kN/m. The new rear springs have a spring coefficient of 18.8 kN/m as compared with the original spring coefficient of 15.6 kN/m. Their integration will return both the ride height and ride stiffness to approximately their original levels.

Since the U of A HEV can operate as a fully electric vehicle, it will not always have engine vacuum to operate the standard vacuum-boosted power brakes. The preferred solution was a manual braking system since it would eliminate components, thus reducing weight and increasing reliability. A performance test on the stock vacuum boost assembly showed that the unit could be replaced with a direct hydraulic system. The stock 22.2 mm diameter master cylinder was replaced with a 19.1 mm (3/4 inch) unit. The changes resulted in maximum brake performance being achieved with a pedal force of 373 N which falls within the regulated range of 67 to 535 N as specified in SAE J937b, *Service Brake System Performance Requirements - Passenger Car*. As well as the master cylinder replacement, the redesign required changes to the brake pedal lever, (the mechanical advantage was changed from 4.12/1 to 4.73/1), the brake pedal mounting bracket, the master cylinder mounting bracket, and the master cylinder pushrod.

With the increase in rear axle weight, consideration was given to replacing the rear drum brakes with disk brakes. Stock components are available for such a conversion but it was felt that the additional cost was not justified. Since the U of A HEV is within the normal GVW limit, no additional changes to the brake system should be required.

No other changes or modifications to the existing vehicle were necessary as the weight distribution has been improved and the vehicle center of gravity has remained low.

CHOICE OF MATERIALS

Three main areas of the U of A HEV design required careful thought and selection of materials; the engine bay mounts, battery containment box, and vehicle dashboard. Because this design is a conversion rather than a ground up design, the material selection for the remaining vehicle components including chassis and body panels was predetermined.

ENGINE BAY MOUNTS - The design criteria for the engine bay mounts centered around strength, weight, and cost. The major load structure within the engine bay is the main plate which connects and locates the electric motors and transmission to the internal combustion engine. This mount is manufactured from 6.35 mm (0.25 in) high strength steel plate and weighs approximately 10 kg (22 lb). The powertrain mounts are attached at their various points by either welds or bolts. The auxiliary mounts which attach and support the various powertrain components to the vehicle frame are manufactured from low weight aluminum. There are a number of miscellaneous mounts manufactured from 16-20 gauge mild steel which support peripheral engine bay equipment. These include a number of lightly loaded locational mounts for the electric motor controllers, clutch master cylinder, and digital equipment.

BATTERY BOX - The design criteria for this structure included: weight, corrosion resistance, and cost. The exterior of the box is manufactured from 20 gauge, mild steel closely matching the grade and gauge of the original Escort floorpan. The ideal material for the containment box is stainless steel which ensures corrosion resistance, however the cost was prohibitive and mild steel was chosen. To provide increased corrosion resistance, the interior of the box is coated with a thick layer of water resistant epoxy. The underside of the box, which is exposed to the elements, is painted with a protective layer of undercoating. The battery box is attached to the vehicle with continuous seam welds running the full length of all sides. These welds are predicted to withstand a 15g deceleration of the vehicle in the event of a collision. Important structures within the battery enclosure itself are the battery trays. Stainless steel was used for the construction of these trays. The need for these trays to remain undamaged by potential battery fluid spills offset the higher cost associated with using stainless steel.

VEHICLE DASHBOARD - A full discussion of the dashboard of the U of A HEV can be found under the BODY STYLING & ERGONOMICS section of this report. Material selection with respect to this component will be discussed here.

The vehicle dashboard is an important component as it houses the instrument cluster and provides the primary impact area for vehicle occupants in the event of a collision. The material chosen for this component had to be flexible enough to accommodate easy manufacture, into a surface which is relatively smooth and free from sharp edges. The chosen material for the U of A HEV dashboard is fiberglass. This dashboard is covered in vinyl upholstery with adequate padding underneath to provide a cushion in the event of an impact. The dashboard is attached to the original Escort dashboard subframe and incorporates all of instrumentation necessary in a hybrid vehicle.

VEHICLE MANUFACTURABILITY

The U of A HEV was designed to be put into production as a practical and market appealing automobile. Wherever possible, the modifications made to this Escort have incorporated ideas and methods that will lead to simple manufacture at a production level. The majority of the components used in the conversion are readily available and currently being produced. The more exotic and expensive components including the electric motors and batteries could become commonplace with increased demand. The market appeal of this vehicle is that it looks and drives much like a conventional automobile. All of the usual comforts and functional aspects have been retained. It has headlights, a horn, a normal steering wheel, one accelerator pedal, one brake pedal, all in their common locations, allowing the operator to feel comfortable when driving. However, minor alterations are required prior to manufacture.

BATTERY BOX - The location and shape of the existing battery box is inappropriate for a production vehicle. The loss of the rear passenger seat has marketing drawbacks as it is unacceptable to most consumers.

The necessary correction is to relocate and redistribute the battery pack to a location that allows the rear seat to remain. This relocation could be accomplished by requesting that the battery manufacturer produce the cells in a horizontal configuration (this option was not available to the U of A design team) with the cell terminals relocated appropriately. This new cell configuration would allow the battery pack to be placed along the entire floorpan area of the passenger compartment - thus, the vehicle occupant seats would be situated over the battery pack. The containment system for the cells could be incorporated into the vehicle subframe itself with the cells on a rack that slides out of the side of the vehicle for repair or replacement.

ENGINE MOUNTS - The engine mounts on the existing U of A HEV are ready for manufacture in the sense that they are correctly located and have the strength required. However, these mounts must be optimized as to shape, number, location and size. This would provide an overall weight and material saving by allowing the mounts to be manufactured to specification using a casting process instead of a machining process. Aluminum is still recommended for the majority of the mounts.

DISCONNECT SWITCH - The existing electric power disconnect switch is an unattractive physical assembly located in the cargo area. The large size of the box is necessary because of the large "throw" required for a manual switch to safely disconnect the electrical power and prevent arcing at high loads.

In a production automobile, a solenoid would provide comparable safety, and could be located in a less visible location. This was not incorporated due to the original competition guidelines outlawing it, and the limited time available upon receiving the update.

DASHBOARD - The dashboard in the U of A HEV design is physically appealing and functionally practical however the hand working of a fiberglass dashboard on a production level is not feasible. This dashboard has been produced to fit well within the standard dashboard subframe and the manufacturing costs to implement it would be minimal.

POWER ELECTRONICS - The power electronics found in the U of A HEV are composed of off-the-shelf components which are readily available and inexpensive. The Central Processing Unit, located in the right side of the dashboard, would be simple to produce in mass quantities. Many of its components could be simplified or eliminated on a production level as a number of its features are not necessary in a consumer automobile. The mode switching process could easily be automated eliminating many of the manual controls found in this vehicle and relieving the driver of additional operational distractions. This automation could also be arranged to enhance the vehicle's efficiency by strategically switching modes at predetermined, optimum times.

BODY STYLING & ERGONOMICS

Body styling and ergonomics played a large role on the overall design of the U of A HEV. Wherever possible, consideration was given to whether a component or assembly was aesthetically and practically located. Some areas were fundamentally unchangeable like the exterior styling of the Escort itself and the electric power disconnect switch. Other areas received a great deal of attention and detail like the vehicle dashboard, and the exhaust venting of the battery box.

DASHBOARD - A great deal of instrumentation and control mechanisms unique to an electric vehicle had to be incorporated into the U of A HEV. These include: a current meter, regeneration controls, mode select switch, and a driver information system.

The decision to be made early in the project was to either attach each of these instruments and controls to the existing dashboard or to successfully incorporate each of them into an entirely new dashboard. The resources and expertise were available at the University of Alberta to pursue the second and more desirable option, and the construction of a original dashboard was initiated.

The new dashboard, which has been integrated into the U of A's modified Escort, is an aesthetically pleasing and ergonomically practical design with sweeping lines and flowing contours. An instrument array with a complete set of combustion and electric vehicle displays is included. Strategic placement of the additional instrumentation lets the driver concentrate on the operation of the vehicle instead of searching for an instrument.

The current meter is situated just above the standard instrument cluster. This meter uses a series of colored LEDs similar to those used to indicate the level on a stereo. As the level of current being drawn from the batteries increases, the number of LEDs are lit proportionally. This will allow the operator to have a better understanding of how hard the electric motors are working, thereby reducing the risk that they will overheat. With maximum output only available for one minute out of three, it is important that real time information is easily monitored.

A special system which has applications in the consumer market but was primarily implemented for use in the

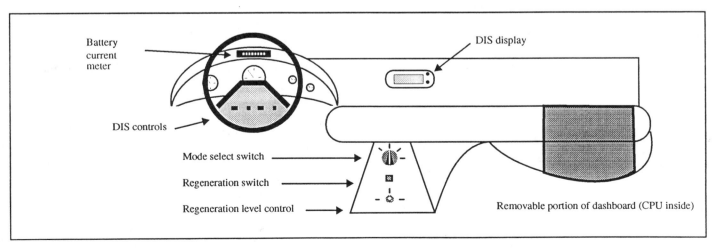

Figure 8: Schematic of Prototype Dashboard

competition is the Driver Information System (DIS). This system monitors and displays real time information on a variety of critical vehicle subsystems including battery temperature, current demand, electric motor and controller temperature, electric motor speed, and combustion engine speed. The information is displayed on an LCD screen located where the original vehicle clock was located. The DIS updates and displays this information to the LCD once per second. Since the volume of information is too large to be output in one screen, the driver has the option of scrolling through a variety of screens in order to obtain the desired information. The controls for the DIS are located on the vehicle steering column utilizing standard cruise control buttons. Additionally, the DIS is equipped with warning lights which will flash and automatically interrupt the current screen in order to display information which must be acted upon quickly. Examples of these interruptions include the battery or a motor overheating, or a terminal of the battery system shorting to chassis.

To change the operation mode (i.e. electric or hybrid), the driver will use the Select Switch which is conveniently located on the center console directly below the vehicle climate controls. This selector switch is ergonomically placed and designed to be very easy to operate. It is a rotary position switch with four distinct positions; OFF, ELECTRIC, HYBRID, and GASOLINE.

Also found on this center console is a push button control and an accompanying potentiometer. These controls are used to override regenerative braking and control the level of regeneration in gasoline mode. This regeneration is engaged by depressing a red button which subsequently lights up to indicate its operation. The accompanying potentiometer uses a continuous rotary motion to select the desired level of regeneration.

An additional feature which increases the functionality of the dashboard is a removable portion directly in front of the passenger seat. This portion is directly above the glove compartment and is used to hold the master CPU. This allows access to the computer allowing for easier modifications and repairs.

EXHAUST VENTING OF THE BATTERY BOX - The intake vents for the battery thermal management system are located in the floor of the vehicle underneath the battery box and are therefore hidden from view. The exhaust vent and its related ducting is attached to the top of this box. To provide access to the outside air for the exhaust to escape, a small rectangular hole is cut into the bottom of each of the rear passenger doors. From the exterior of the vehicle, none of this venting is obvious, and the vehicle aesthetics have not been compromised.

CONCLUSION

Eighteen months of imagination, design, creation, fabrication, and testing have resulted in a vehicle which is practical and marketable. The University of Alberta HEV design is producible on a mass production scale and satisfies a market that wants an environmentally friendly form of transportation but is unwilling to sacrifice the comfort and freedom offered by today's automobiles.

The U of A HEV runs on electricity - its primary mode, gasoline - its auxiliary mode, or a combination of the two (hybrid) - its performance mode. Electric power is supplied by a Nickel Cadmium battery which can be charged daily from a readily available 220 Volt plug (a dryer outlet). The combustion engine uses high octane unleaded gasoline which unlike fuels like M85 and E100 is commonly available across most of the world.

The vehicle has a range of approximately 72 km (45 mi) on electric power alone and an estimated total range of over 500 km (311 mi). The electric only range satisfies the needs of 75% of daily North American automobile travel. If this range needs to be exceeded, the use of gasoline is available. When added performance is required for passing or hill climbing, hybrid mode can be engaged.

The U of A vehicle, EMISSION IMPOSSIBLE, drives very much like the standard Escort. All of the common controls, instrumentation, and features of conventional automobiles are found in its design. Because of the variety of driving modes available, there are additional controls and instruments unique to the powerplant(s) being currently utilized by the operator. Additionally, this vehicle has maintained all of the standard occupant safety features; none of the important or safety critical frame members have been altered. Therefore, the vehicle is as structurally secure in the event of a collision as the stock Escort. The engine bay has undergone significant alteration with respect to the type of components contained, however, the weight, volume, and distribution have remained very close to the Escort's original engine bay. The battery system is the single largest weight addition to the vehicle and contains 135 NiCad cells. A battery box has been designed to house these cells and remain structurally intact and firmly attached to the vehicle floorpan in the event of a collision. The cells are not designed to survive such an impact and may spill a portion of their electrolyte into the box. The box has been designed to prevent any battery fluid from entering the passenger compartment.

The emissions of this vehicle when in combustion only or hybrid mode are expected to be quite low as the chosen Suzuki engine features "state of the art" emissions control and utilizes an engine management. The cost to the consumer in terms of fuel and electricity are predicted to be significantly less than those incurred by conventional automobile owners since this vehicle operates primarily in electric mode and electricity is relatively inexpensive when compared with gasoline.

Some unique features have been incorporated into the U of A design. The most notable is the design and manufacture of an aesthetically pleasing and ergonomic dashboard. For the competition in Dearborn, the vehicle has been equipped with a CPU to continuously monitor and display operating system status. This system also alerts the driver to potential safety hazards specifically those related to the electric motor/battery system.

Another important feature of this car is the ability to utilize the benefits of regenerative braking. The inertial energy of the vehicle is used to "top up" the battery pack whenever the vehicle is brought to a halt and is available in each of the three modes of operation. Electrical energy savings of greater than 8% can be achieved using this feature.

From an manufacturing perspective, this design

s very producible. All of the components chosen are readily available. The Escort chassis is very workable and adaptable for conversion to a hybrid vehicle. The rear passenger seats, eliminated in this prototype, could be re-incorporated by a relatively straight forward re-configuration and relocation of the battery. To increase the consumer appeal of the concept, the controller strategy could be easily automated.

Within the guidelines of the competition, the body styling and ergonomic aspects of the original Escort have been maintained or improved upon. All of the interior refinements such as carpeting and padded interior panels have been retained. New instrumentation has been incorporated into the dashboard to provide a functional driving environment. The minor changes necessitated by the battery system have been stylishly integrated into the vehicle exterior.

The electric technology of the future has been successfully integrated with the combustion engine of the past to provide a vehicle for today. The U.S. Department of Energy, SAE, and Ford motor company have tapped into the resources and potential available within the North American College and University system to find a solution to a pressing environmental problem, air pollution caused by automobiles. The hybrid concept may not be the final solution to this problem but it is a necessary step in the right direction and will help ease the public into an emissions free automotive future.

Hybrid Electric Vehicle Development at the University of California, Davis: The Design of Ground *FX*

R. Riley, R. Cobene, M. Duvall, A.A. Frank
Deparment of Mechanical Engineering, UC Davis

Abstract

The last few years have been an exciting time for alternative vehicle development. New concerns about the environmental impact of personal transportation and about the United States' dependence on imported oil have pushed energy efficient, ultra-low, and zero emissions vehicles to the forefront of automotive design. California's own mandate for Zero Emissions Vehicles (ZEV) takes effect in 1998, creating a tremendous push towards the difficult goal of producing a commercially viable, practical electric vehicle for sale in 1998. Beyond California, most of the world's automakers are simultaneously committing tremendous research and development resources towards the technology necessary for a viable electric vehicle.

The University of California at Davis is one of seven California universities participating in the 1993 Ford Hybrid Electric Vehicle Challenge. The Vehicle Design Team in our College of Engineering is one of thirty in the United States and Canada, each developing its own brand of viable two passenger hybrid electric automobile for this competition. The sponsors of this competition, Ford Motor Co., the Department of Energy, and the Society of Automotive Engineers, have established common guidelines and performance goals for the schools to attain.

UC Davis Hybrid Vehicle Design Concept

Among the benchmarks for the HEV Challenge are a range of 40 miles at 40 mph on electric power alone (ZEV Mode), a range of 200 miles using both electric and internal combustion (IC) power (HEV Mode) and Transitional Low Emission Vehicle (TLEV) rating. Our design team combined these goals with our own performance guidelines. This allows us to establish a set of standards for our vehicle that are appropriate for the Challenge *and* reflect the anticipated needs of drivers of the area we live in. We arrived at the following objectives.

HEV Design Goals

1. 60 mile range at 60 mph in ZEV mode.
2. 100 mpg fuel economy at 60 mph with IC engine *only*.
3. 0-60 mph acceleration in under 10 seconds in both ZEV and HEV modes.
4. Unlimited range in HEV mode.
5. TLEV emissions rating with IC engine.
6. Safety and driveability comparable to a conventional auto.

These goals are very demanding, but it is our desire to use this vehicle to prove to the consumer and to our own state government that the hybrid electric vehicle concept can produce not only a superior electric-powered vehicle, but also a superior automobile. To the best of our knowledge no single car, prototype or otherwise, offers this combination of performance, zero-emissions capability, and fuel economy. That fact alone makes these goals worth realizing. It is our hope at the university that this car can serve as the stepping stone from the conventional automobile to the electric, hybrid electric, or other alternative cars of the future.

But first, we must prove to the country's drivers that we can provide a car with superior emissions and energy efficiency without sacrificing the convenience and performance to which they are accustomed.

The Vehicle Design Team's goals helped to form the concept. To attain these objectives, the vehicle's design must concentrate on aerodynamic body design, light weight, and an innovative powertrain capable of meeting the performance criteria.

The design and construction process began in June, 1992 and will be finished for the HEV Challenge scheduled for June 1, 1993 in Dearborn, Michigan. The UC Davis hybrid electric vehicle is a two passenger commuter sports car. The finished vehicle weighs approximately 1800 lbs. The fiberglass body weighs under 160 lbs. including gull-wing doors and windows. The chassis is an aluminum space-frame with four-wheel independent suspension and a mid-engine, rear drive powertrain. Final weight for the rolling chassis is only 400 lbs., including tires, suspension, seats, and safety equipment.

The vehicle's powertrain features a similar level of creativity as the body/chassis. The integrated parallel hybrid electric drivetrain couples a 32 kW UNIQ brushless DC motor with a 570 cc, four-cycle Briggs & Stratton OHV motor with modern engine management and emission controls. These two powerplants mate through a common input shaft to a 5-speed transaxle. The battery pack is a 170 volt, 7.1 kWh, flooded Nickel/Cadmium array of 260 individual cells (two parallel strings of 130 each). The powertrain develops almost 95% of its peak HEV input torque of over 130 ft-lbs from 1500 - 4500 rpm.

The body of this paper explains both the Body/Chassis and Powertrain development for the UC Davis Hybrid Electric Vehicle. The HEV Challenge in June, 1993 will determine whether the vehicle meets its objectives.

Body and Chassis Platform Development

Vehicle Platform Design

The first step in the design process is an energy balance of the vehicle's power requirements. We commonly identify aerodynamic drag and rolling resistance as the two primary design dependent variables in efficient vehicle design. The limited electrical energy available in the battery pack mandates that the vehicle's design emphasize efficiency. The force equation is

$$Force_{drag} = 1/2 \, \rho \, A_f C_d \, V^2 + C_{rr} * W$$

$$\underset{\textit{Aero Drag}}{\uparrow} \qquad \underset{\textit{Rolling Drag}}{\uparrow}$$

ρ : *air density*
A_f : *Maximum Vehicle Frontal Area*
C_d : *Vehicle Drag Coefficient*
V : *Vehicle Velocity*

C_{rr} : *Coefficient of Rolling Resistance*
W : *Total Vehicle Weight*

Bearing drag, which is usually minimal, is neglected here for simplicity.

Before lengthy simulations take place on a computer, hand calculations are useful to determine the capabilities of the vehicle design. We used several varieties of a best case/worst case design scenario. We estimated various vehicle parameters that affect drag and powertrain efficiency, and then came up with a low and high value. From these parameters, possible fuel economy and electric range figures were obtained. For the powertrain, estimates of electric motor and powertrain efficiency were developed. Also, the minimum average brake specific fuel consumption (lbs.fuel/horsepower*hour) for the APU can be used to generate a fuel economy prediction. The calculations are done for a steady-state speed of 60 mph. Later on, simulations will be used based on the Hot 505 cycle Ford has proposed for emissions testing.

As is evident from Table 1, the vehicle's drag can roughly double from the best case situation if the vehicle fails to meet design criteria. Most of the parameters used are less than 25% apart, yet the sum of the "overruns" could cause an increase in total power consumption of almost 100%. We must also remember that numbers and simulations are just that, and that the real world vehicle could possibly exceed the "worst case".

Table 1 : Vehicle Design Parameters

Vehicle Parameter	Best Case	Worst Case
Frontal Area	16 ft^2	18 ft^2
Drag Coefficient	0.15	0.24
Loaded Weight	1900 lbs	2200 lbs
C_{rr}	0.006	0.008
Elec Motor Eff.	85%	75%
Drivetrain Eff.	95%	85%
BSFC minimum	0.50 lb/hphr	0.70 lb/hphr
Drag Forces		
F_{aero} at 60 mph	23.32 lbf	41.98 lbf
F_{roll} at 60 mph	11.4 lbf	22.0 lbf
Power Required		
P_{aero} at 60 mph	3.73 hp	6.72 hp
P_{roll} at 60 mph	1.82 hp	3.52 hp
P_{total} at 60 mph	5.55 hp	10.24 hp
ZEV Mode		
$P_{rear\ wheel}$	6.87 hp (5.12 kW)	12.68 hp (9.46 kW)
Watt-hours/mile	85.3	157.6
Range at 7.1 kWh	83.8 miles	45.3 miles
HEV Mode		
$P_{rear\ wheel}$	6.34 hp	11.28 hp
Fuel Economy at minimum BSFC	113.6 mpg	45.6 mpg

Table 2 : Body Design Considerations

1. Minimum Drag Coefficient (C_D)
2. Small Frontal Area
3. Enclosed Wheels
4. Enclosed Powertrain

Aerodynamics

To achieve an extremely low drag coefficient the body should be shaped to maintain laminar flow as far aft as possible and have the smallest region of separated flow possible. We accomplished this by basing the initial streamlined body design on a NACA 66-025 airfoil.

The 6-series airfoil sections were designed to maintain laminar flow over more of the airfoil than older designs. Within this family, we chose a minimum pressure point location at 60% of the chord length (66-series). The airflow sees decreasing pressure over 60% of the airfoil, reaches a minimum, then recovers pressure. The large initial favorable pressure gradient increases the transition Reynolds number and permits laminar flow to exist at higher velocity and/or greater body length.[1]

Laminar flow is highly desirable because it results in much lower skin-friction drag than turbulent flow. Traveling at 60 mph, our car has a Reynolds number of 7.6 million. For smooth-surface laminar flow the skin-friction coefficient is 0.0005; turbulent flow has a skin-friction coefficient of 0.0032. Even with pockets of turbulence, maximizing laminar flow dramatically decreases drag. [2]

Aerodynamically, a 67-series airfoil would perform even better with 10% more laminar flow. Practically, however, the different thickness distribution would not allow enough passenger and engine compartment space. Also, the NACA 67-series airfoil tends to have more flow separation in the aft region of the body at lower Reynolds numbers.

The airfoil shape was altered slightly from the original symmetric NACA form to perform better in the ground effect and package our whole our design more effectively. Five percent camber was introduced by using a NACA mean camber line of 0.7. This helps eliminate the negative lift due to close proximity to the ground plane. Cambering slightly raises the lower surface farther off the ground, reducing the pressure gradients beneath the vehicle. This assists in delaying turbulent flow and airflow separation.[3] This shape also allows us to enclose the wheels more completely.

Body Design

Our project objective of building an extremely efficient commuter vehicle required that we minimize the aerodynamic losses of our vehicle. There was no reason to waste power overcoming large amounts of drag when we were able to design an innovative body based primarily on aerodynamic efficiency.

Many factors, influencing everything from turn radius to engine cooling, had to be considered when designing the body. The main concepts behind our design are shown in Table 2.

Additional camber, however, would cause problems enclosing the rear wheels and powertrain components. It was also important not to introduce too much camber because we did not want to generate positive lift. Maintaining zero lift is important for several reasons:

- Lift causes induced drag
- Positive lift will reduce traction, reducing vehicle stability.
- Negative lift increases the force on the road, increasing rolling drag.

Sizing

Aerodynamic analysis of streamlined vehicle shapes shows that for a given thickness aerodynamic drag is minimized by using a vertical thickness equal to approximately 25% of the length. For a fixed thickness, ratios much larger than this will result in the flow separating further forward on the body increasing form drag. If the ratio is much smaller, the increase in length will cause a larger gain in skin friction drag than drop in form drag.

We determined the dimensions of the car based on two needs:

- Minimum frontal area
- Passenger compartment space adequate for two people and regulation cargo space.

For fixed conditions, minimizing frontal area minimizes aerodynamic drag and, thus reduces vehicle power requirements. A maximum body thickness of 41 inches was chosen because it allows just enough passenger head room. Using the 25% thickness-to-length ratio led to a design length of 164 inches. A maximum width of 70 inches was reached based on the track width requirements fitting within a tapering body shape and interior compartment needs including side impact crush zones. The frontal area is 17.5 ft^2.

Other body styling choices were based on literature with data on streamline shapes and existing aerodynamically designed experimental vehicles. Books such as *Fluid Dynamic Drag* by S.F. Hoerner and *Impact of Aerodynamics on Vehicle Design* ed. M.A. Dorgham contain drag coefficients and aerodynamic characteristics of many bluff and streamline body shapes.

[4,5] Recent examples of experimental vehicles, including GM's Sunraycer and Ultralite, and our own Supermileage vehicles are excellent examples of aerodynamic efficiency. The Sunraycer is an extreme example of design for aerodynamics, showing that a 6-series airfoil body can be used effectively for a vehicle in the ground effect. It ended up with a drag coefficient of 0.095 to 0.108. [6] The Ultralite's design shows that a practical car can be designed around aerodynamic efficiency. It is a four passenger vehicle with a drag coefficient of only 0.192. [7]

From these resources we determined that tapering the planform shape from front to back and curving the sides of the vehicle would minimize drag. We kept the same airfoil throughout the width of the body, varying thickness (and, consequently, length) to taper body height and length. The amount and rate of variation was determined by the size of the passenger compartment and the wheel track width requirements. This shaping resulted in a gradual decrease in maximum width from 70 inches at the lower surface to 42.5 inches near the upper body surface, which should reduce the adverse drag and stability characteristics in crosswinds. From front to back the body tapers from 70 to 53 inches. See Figures 1 & 2 for our original and final body designs.

We did not have access to either large-scale wind tunnels or sophisticated computational aerodynamics codes such as VSAERO to analyze and optimize our design. Local CFD experts told us that codes cannot accurately perform a three-dimensional, viscous flow analysis over a complex body accounting for the ground effect and parasitic elements such as door handles and seams between body panels.

We did perform some two-dimensional analysis to estimate that the zero-lift line for our airfoil section was -2.5°. Thus, the body should be angled slightly nose-down to maintain zero lift. This was only an order-of-magnitude estimate to use as a starting point. For the real three-dimensional case the true zero-lift angle must be determined experimentally.

To satisfy the need to reduce aerodynamic drag caused by wheels, the tires are enclosed within the body as much as possible. Fairings below the level of the body are not used because they would require a large addition in frontal area to allow room for the wheels to turn, increasing aerodynamic drag. Full fairings also have the potential to prevent cross flow under the car causing a reduction in the downward lift force.[6] This would cause problems due to an effective increase in upward lift.

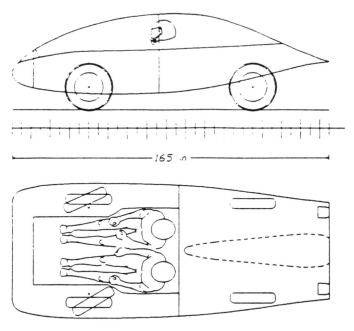

Fig 1. Original Body Design

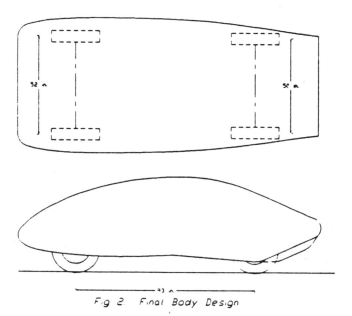

Fig 2. Final Body Design

Internal Airflow

Both the passenger and engine compartments need ventilation to supply airflow for cooling. Engine cooling systems cause drag which can increase the overall drag coefficient by 2% to 10% depending on how carefully the system is designed. The passenger cooling system does not have as large an effect on drag due its comparatively low air flow rate. [5]

In designing the cooling systems we placed intakes in high pressure areas and outlets in low pressure regions (relative to interior pressure). For 6-series airfoils pressure decreases as the air flows aft, so passenger and battery ventilation inlets are near the nose of the car where the pressure is highest.

Engine cooling inlets are placed on the underside of the body just before the engine compartment. Flow is diffused through the mechanical engine fan and exhausted at the location on the body underside with maximum curvature, as this is where minimum pressure occurs.

Redesign

Only one large-scale redesign was done to the body. The powertrain configuration and placement was not completed exactly as foreseen at the start of the project. Because of the long time needed to manufacture the body the shape was determined based on guesses of sizes and placement of all other components. Late in the manufacturing process we found that some powertrain components and frame members would not be concealed within the airfoil shaped bodywork.

From both an aerodynamics and an aesthetic point of view we didn't want to simply cut holes in the body and leave parts exposed in the airflow. At 60 mph the drag on the rough drivetrain and frame components could require an additional 1.5 hp based on a reference drag area of 1.4 ft^2. When the aerodynamic drag of the whole vehicle is overcome by only 4.64 hp, that is a significant requirement.

To remedy this situation we redesigned the underside and back end of the body. To create the additional space needed we changed the region of the airfoil which sloped upward beneath the engine compartment. Instead, we kept the lower surface closer to the ground 40 inches further aft. Slightly behind the rear wheels we curved the lower surface up a smoothly as possible around the transmission to meet the existing upper body surface.

17

For ease of manufacture and to minimize flow separation caused by a sharp curvature, the panel still did not enclose the transaxle completely. For aesthetics and aerodynamics we designed a small additional housing.

This underbody redesign provided several benefits, including:

- a reduction in aerodynamic losses due to form drag on transaxle, etc.
- additional space for cargo and other vehicle components.
- increased stability in crosswinds
- a convenient surface for taillights and license plate.

Manufacturing and Materials

The full-scale body plug was first carved out of Styrofoam using masonite stations every five inches to guarantee the correct shape. A layer of fiberglass and body filler was added and sanded completely smooth. Part lines were scribed onto the plug, dividing it into panels for wheel covers, doors, engine compartment access, etc.

Next, a fiberglass female mold was made for each panel. The final body panels were made using these molds to ensure that the outer surface of the car was smooth.

The body is made of a composite sandwich structure comprised of 6 oz./sq. yd. woven pre-impregnated fiberglass as faces on each side of Nomex honeycomb core. A typical body panel is 2 layers of fiberglass on each side of 0.250 in. Nomex honeycomb. Door panels required 6 layers of glass due to the large window areas. Wheel housings were stiffened by foam strips instead of honeycomb so that turn radius could be improved. For strength, additional plies of fiberglass were added in mounting locations.

One reason for choosing Fiberglass/Nomex was that we could easily form it to our unusual, nonlinear body shape. The primary reason, however, was the material system's high specific strength and stiffness. The sandwich averages 0.52 lb/ft^2 , yielding a body shell with of 68 lbs, excluding doors and windshields. The thicker doors with hinges, locking mechanisms, etc. add 20 lbs. The front and rear windshields, made of 0.250 in. Lexan, add 60 lbs, bring the total body weight to 148 lbs.

The body panels are attached to one another using nut plates. The panels overlap slightly with the outer panel bolting to a nut plate riveted to the inner panel. The body panels are secured to the frame by bolting the panels to frame members.

Ergonomics

The goal of the interior design was to ensure that the human factors involved in vehicle design and use were not neglected. The passenger compartment must be safe, comfortable, and attractive. The driver must have good visibility of the gauges and landscape, and all controls must be within easy reach.

We wanted the interior to also reflect the style of the exterior body. Thus, the main interior element, the dashboard, is formed of a series of curves with few linear edges or flat surfaces. This style also allowed us to design a wrap-around instrument panel that created more space for gauges than a typical panel. Our instrument panel covers 105 sq in, 130% larger than the panel of a Ford Escort. This large size is necessary because we need additional gauges to monitor both the electric powertrain and the alternative power unit (APU). Even with the extended instrument panel, all gauges fall within a space that is easy for the driver to scan quickly.[8]

The upper surface of the dashboard starts just behind the front bumper and extends 40 in. back. The occupants sit an additional 30 in. back. Both seats are mounted at a 12° angle to provide additional headroom so that the helmeted passengers will meet the HEV Challenge eye-height and 2 in. rollbar clearance requirements. The seats recline as well, allowing occupants of different heights to adjust their position for best visibility and comfort. Additionally, the driver's seat slides 28 in. along the length of the body to allow drivers from 5'0" to 6'3" in height to easily reach the pedals and other controls.

Visibility

To maintain good visibility with our low-slung body design, we maximized window area and positioned rear and side view mirrors carefully. The front windshield extends from the top of the car to the bumper, and wraps around the sides of the body, covering 24 ft^2. The rear windshield covers 14 ft^2. This is ample, especially when the driver uses the rear view mirror to see behind the vehicle. The doors each contain 4 ft^2 of window, divided into side and roof windows. The upper windows allow the occupants to see objects above and in front of the car as well as lessening the feeling of being in a enclosed space. The side windows provide excellent visibility to both sides of the car.

When trying to minimize the body's parasitic drag, we experimented with interior mounted side mirrors. We found that for our design, mounting the mirrors near the A-pillars within the body does not reduce visibility when compared to conventional exterior mounted mirrors.

Passenger Comfort

Passenger cooling is accomplished by fresh air ventilation. Heating is provided by a resistance heater powered by the main battery and regulated by the vehicles computer controller to prevent excessive battery drain. The airflow is concentrated at the occupants' heads. Military studies have found that if the head is kept at a comfortable temperature, the rest of the body will typically feel more comfortable as well. Ducting is used to route air to the windshield for defrosting.

Another aspect of passenger comfort we considered is long-term exposure to noise. The overall noise level in the passenger compartment is the sum of the noises generated by the power plant, tires, and airflow. At 60 mph, wind noise above 1000 Hz can reach 68 dB(A). Our electric motor drive belt specifications say that it may reach 110 dB(A) at 3700 Hz. Because these worst-case levels are at high frequencies we looked for a material that would be effective in this range, yet not add much additional weight to the car or reduce space in the passenger compartment. We chose 0.50 in thick sheets of embossed polyurethane foam with a density of 2 lb/cu ft. It will absorb up to 95% of airborne sound in high frequency ranges.

Chassis Development

Frame

In the formulations of our vehicle, several ideas were considered for the structural chassis. A light weight chassis was a necessary facet of our vehicle design. We studied three basic chassis concept: composite monocoque (GM Ultralite), ladder frame, and tubular spaceframe. The idea of a composite monocoque similar to the GM Ultralite had been considered but rejected on the basis of cost and complexity. In addition, this is not current method of mass producing a vehicle. A separate frame and body shell has an additional development

advantage, as the chassis can be finished and tested independently of the body. The more independent nature of the structure and the shell allows us to concentrate on weight reduction in the body without the vast structural concerns of the monocoque. The real-world result is that for a prototype of this nature, a frame and shell design is often lighter than a first-run composite monocoque.

Initially, hand modeling and Finite Element Analysis (FEA) were used to create frame concepts. The roll hoop and side bolster requirements of the HEV Challenge seemed to favor a tubular spaceframe constructed around these structural points. Repeated FEA simulations indicated that a frame constructed primarily of large diameter tubing would yield a light, rigid structure, while incorporating the roll and side protection features specified by Ford.

Several scenarios were considered for collision and as a result the frame was designed around a roll cage. Due to the light weight structure necessary for a low rolling resistance vehicle, the frame is constructed of an aluminum alloy. The aluminum tubes are welded together by the TIG welding process which produces pronounced strength reduction in the areas surrounding the welded joints, the Heat Affected Zone (HAZ). Unfortunately, the weight savings (aluminum is about 1/3 the weight of steel) of the aluminum over the steel is diminished by its lower fatigue resistance.

In design, one way to eliminate this fatigue problem is to thermally treat, solution heat treat and artificially age the whole frame. However, there was not a heat treating facility nearby that could heat treat our whole frame. Another solution to the fatigue problem is more fundamental and still solved our weight problem. We over-designed the structures to minimize deflections and, hence, stresses imparted on the aluminum joints in the frame. This approach provided a somewhat heavy frame but still a lower weight structure than steel.

A combination of past experience and the FEA results prompted the selection of large diameter aluminum alloy tubing as the primary frame material. We used 2.5 in. diameter, 0.065 in wall aluminum alloy tubing (6061 T6 alloy). Rectangular tubing of the same alloy was incorporated in specific engine mounting point. Alloy sheet metal serves for the floor pan and exterior battery enclosures. The final bare frame weighs only 150 lbs., contributing to an extremely light rolling chassis of 400 lbs.

Suspension and Brakes

We were well aware from the beginning that vehicle suspension systems, with associated handling characteristics, are very difficult to "design right" the first time. With this in mind we decided to use existing suspension technology that satisfied safety, strength, and light weight criterion. A steel frame prototype, or "mule", was used to develop the vehicle handling. The mule simulated the track, wheelbase, and weight of the final vehicle.

A MacPherson suspension system was chosen due to its simplicity and ease of modification. We decided to use the existing suspension from a Chevrolet Sprint passenger car for our rear system because it fit this criterion and is a driven system. The front system uses a Datsun 1200 because it is easily modified. These suspension components have proven to be very satisfactory on our prototype chassis. In fact, the handling characteristics of both systems on our prototype chassis out-performed most sports cars in a slalom course.

The development of the prototype chassis taught us that for our vehicle, the low center of gravity, lower weight, and mid-engine design would provide inherently better handling than the average conventional commuter vehicle. This enabled us to concentrate our energy on frame and drivetrain development, as we were very confident that our modified suspension components would work well. With our handling data from the prototype, we lengthened the wheelbase from 85 in. to 93 in. to improve front/rear weight distribution, increase passenger space, and smooth the vehicle's ride.

Again in the interest of a light weight structure, the brakes selected for our chassis are aluminum alloy disk brake components. These were purchased from a manufacturer of racing and specialty disk brake systems.

Tires and wheels

The initial calculations shown in Table 1 indicate that rolling resistance is about one-third of the total drag on the vehicle at 60 mph. This is a significant source of power loss. Aerodynamic vehicles always have a disproportionate amount of rolling drag due the dramatic reduction in aerodynamic drag. (P_{drag} for a Ford Festiva at 60 mph is over 12 hp vs our HEV estimate of about 6 hp.)

Tire selection is of utmost importance in a high efficiency vehicle. With this in mind our team researched tires available on the market as well as those not available on the market. Our first selection for our vehicle tires are the Firestone Tempa P195/90R14 space saver tires, a compact spare from a Ford Thunderbird. The engineers at Firestone quoted numbers up to 30% lower in rolling drag than tires that are commercially available. The Ford HEV rules and regulations panel disallowed the use of these tires in the competition on the grounds of the temporary nature of the tires, even after documentation diplaying the safety of prolonged use was submitted to them.

Further research revealed that the tires used on the Ford Ecostar produced equivalent rolling resistance to the unuseable space saver tires. These Firestone P 195/70R14 EVT (Electric Vehicle Tire) have a C_{rr} of only 0.006, meeting our best case estimate for rolling drag. Unfortunately, these tires demanded more space and our chassis and body design were modified accordingly. However, due to the fact that these electric vehicle tires are not DOT approved, the Ford HEV regulations board once again disallowed the use of these tires on our vehicle. This forced our team to select an alternate tire and decrease the efficiency of our vehicle.

With these two setbacks, we decided to use the Goodyear Invicta P195/70R14 tires which are also being used by our competition. These tires are still excellent low rolling resistance tires and with the help of Goodyear engineers we selected adequate tires and inflation pressures for our vehicles size and weight distribution. Figure 3 illustrates the importance of low rolling resistance in a comparison of these designs with a standard tire [9]

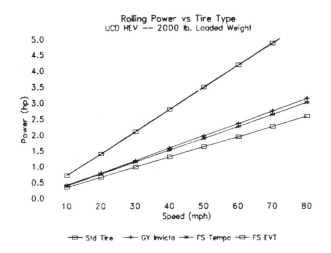

Fig. 3

Rolling Power vs Tire Type
UCD HEV –– 2000 lb. Loaded Weight

─▫─ Std Tire   ─+─ GY Invicta   ─*─ FS Tempo   ─▫─ FS EVT

Battery Enclosure Safety

Our vehicle uses a 7.1 kWh battery pack weighing 525 lbs and occupying over 4 ft³ of volume. It is difficult to safely place this much volume and mass, as the shape of our aerodynamic body and the enclosed nature of the vehicles wheels created unusual space enclosures within the vehicle. We ruled out the center packaging used in the GM Impact due to an unacceptable addition of width (12") and the corresponding increase in frontal area. The center tunnel will also be difficult to access. Another option, front packaging, places too much weight outside the confines of the wheel base, and leads to extended battery cables.

The enclosed space between the front and rear wheel on each side presented an ideal place to locate the battery enclosures. The HEV Challenge regulations already mandate a side bolster to protect each passenger. The frame design was modified to include an integral battery box on the right and left sides of the vehicle, between the front and rear tires. Each box is protect by four aluminum alloy 6061 T6 side impact members, two 2.5 in. OD 0.065 wall tubes, and two 1" x 2" 0.125 wall rectangular members.

To further protect the batteries, the individual cells are enclosed in rigid composite boxes and separated by nylon insulators. The interior of each aluminum box frame is electrically insulated with a combination of 0.125" nylon sheet and 0.125" neoprene. Each box is accessible through the top and side of the frame. The enclosures are tightly sealed from the passenger

compartment by a firewall. Ventilation is provided by one 41 cfm brushless DC fan on each box.

Battery safety is obviously a prime concern in the development of an electric-powered vehicle. The very nature of our cells improves their safety. The individual polyurethane casings are extremely rigid. In the event of a side impact, the batteries are protected by four side members, the composite boxes, and their own rigid cases. Also the electrolyte, potassium hydroxide, does not present a caustic burn danger.

Manufacturability and Recyclability

Vehicle manufacturability was an influential factor in our decision to use a spaceframe and body shell construction. Our fiberglass body panels could be duplicated easily in production by plastic pieces. An optimized form of the aluminum spaceframe could take advantage of custom extrusions and possibly bonded joints. These are not new concepts to the automotive world: the Ford Contour features a bonded aluminum frame.

Light weight construction will require new manufacturing techniques. Our finished vehicle, in its first iteration, weighs only 1800 lbs, less than a Ford Festiva. This includes our 525 lb. battery array.

Our powertrain uses almost entirely stock components. Our engine modification are purely design differences. An optimized, mass-produced drivetrain, including an 8-valve, liquid-cooled v-twin APU could weigh almost 100 lbs. less and feature more APU power and better efficiency.

Recyclability is inherently strong in a vehicle that contains over 300 lbs. of aluminum alloy. The NiCad batteries, as well, are now completely recyclable at the new SAFT-NIFE Nickel/Cadmium reclamation plant in Europe (SAFT covers shipping costs).

Powertrain Development

Our powertrain design is the second part of our hybrid electric design concept. The vehicle platform we have developed will determine the energy and performance requirements of the powertrain. The powertrain must balance efficiency and power in order to meet our vehicle's performance goals.

To repeat, these goals are:

1. 60 mile range at 60 mph in ZEV mode.
2. 100 mpg fuel economy at 60 mph with IC engine *only*.
3. 0-60 mph acceleration in under 10 seconds in both ZEV and HEV modes.
4. Unlimited Range in HEV mode.
5. TLEV emissions rating with IC engine.

To meet these goals, we chose a rarely used HEV powertrain platform: the small APU/large electric motor parallel hybrid. The two powerplants are packaged into an integrated mid-engine, rear drive drivetrain. We selected this configuration for its simplicity and high level of versatility. At UC Davis our primary goal is to use the hybrid electric concept to create a vehicle with not only superior electric performance, but also with fuel economy surpassing the capabilities of conventional automobiles.

The powertrain consists of a single UNIQ SR180P 32kW, brushless, permanent magnet DC motor paired with a modified 20 hp (15 kW), 570 cc, four-cycle, air-cooled Briggs&Stratton overhead valve engine. We designed an innovative single shaft arrangement to mate both units to a Subaru 5-speed longitudinal transaxle driving the rear wheels. This results in a slender, long package well suited to our narrow track width and abundant length in the rear of the airfoil-shaped body.

Parallel vs Series Hybrid Powertrains

One of the critical decisions affecting the HEV design process is the decision to go with a series or hybrid configuration. The series hybrid uses the Alternative Power Unit (APU) as a generator, while a parallel hybrid directly transfer the torque of the APU to the drive wheels.

We decided on the parallel drivetrain in the earliest design stages. We carefully reviewed the advantages and disadvantages of each concept and compared them with our overall performance goals for the vehicle. The results are shown in Table 3.

Notice that on-board battery charging is listed as both an advantage and disadvantage. We do not consider this type of operation feasible, especially in California. The California Air Resources Board's reaction to hybrids is lukewarm at this time. They believe that owners of hybrids will not use them in their intended ZEV capacity, due to limited range and diminished performance.

Table 3

Series Hybrid

Advantages	1. Convenient on-board battery charging.
	2. APU can operate at best efficiency more easily.
	3. APU can cycle on/off easily.
	4. Transmission is not required for APU
	5. Lower peak power batteries can be used in vehicle.
	6. Ease of powertrain integration.
Disadvantages	1. Convenient on-board battery charging.
	2. Electric motor is the only powerplant contributing to vehicle acceleration.
	3. Fuel economy is not maximized because drive efficiency is poor.

A pure electric vehicle presents the owner with no other option but to religiously maintain and charge the battery pack at home. Our main publicity efforts will be targeted at changing this perception. Therefore, we try to avoid on-board charging the battery with the IC engine, except in unusual circumstances.

To illustrate a benefit of this point, consider the 7.1 kWh battery pack in the UC Davis HEV. Tests show that a full charge requires about 9 kWh of DC power from a charging system over six hours. The Solectria charger we use is over 93% efficient, requiring a total of 9.6 kWh of line voltage. Using the nighttime charging rate of $0.08/kWh (Sacramento Municipal Utilities District, off-peak rate), a full charge costs approximately $0.77. Charging with an APU at even 90% total efficiency would consume at least 1.12 gallons of gasoline, even at minimum specific fuel consumption, which is not feasible at a six hour charging rate. Thus, the same charge, done with the APU, is likely to cost at least $1.40 ($1.25 per gallon).

Setting aside the APU charging controversy, series hybrids do have many advantages, which why they are so common among automaker concept cars. The APU can easily operate at preferred speeds and loads, lowering average specific fuel consumption and avoiding some emissions problems. The powertrain is mechanically simpler and typically lighter than a parallel powertrain, if the same APU and electric motor are used.

A series powertrain requires no mechanical interaction between the electric motor and APU, so there is no need to address the problems of integrating the output shafts of the two. An effective series design will typically be lighter, simpler, and, therefore, more reliable than the equivalent parallel powertrain. The series drive vehicle allows for more flexibility in selecting batteries. The designers can specify batteries with a lower peak power rating than the peak power consumption of the electric motor. Nickel-Cadmium batteries have an inverse relation between peak power capacity and total energy storage. If the designers choose to forego maximum acceleration in ZEV mode, they can use an electric motor whose capacity is only attained with both the APU and the battery pack together supplying full power. This can enable the vehicle to extract slightly more range with the same battery weight.

The new Volvo ECC diesel hybrid concept car is a good example of series design. The NiCad batteries have an extremely high energy density of 48 Whr/kg, but a peak output of only about 114 W/kg for a 770 lb pack [10]. The diesel turbine genset supplies the additional 30 kW for acceleration. In comparison, the NiCads used in the UC Davis hybrid rated at a nominal energy density of 30 Whr/kg, but the usable peak power output is over 200 W/kg. The Volvo's acceleration times are markedly different as well: 0-62 mph in HEV mode takes 13 seconds, as opposed to 23 seconds in ZEV mode. The Volvo design, while a proven ULEV vehicle, offers very little hope of increasing the ZEV credits awarded to HEV's in California because its hybrid scheme does not allow full acceleration in ZEV mode.

It became apparent at the early stages of our calculations and simulations that limitations in the series design concept were steering us away from our goal of maximum fuel economy. The parallel hybrid, although more challenging in its execution, offers certain advantages that fit our requirements. Table 3.1 lists these tradeoffs.

The parallel hybrid concept, when properly executed, maximizes the versatility of the vehicle in question. The vehicle in hybrid mode drives like a conventional car, with the throttle pedal directly controlling the IC engine. Also, the APU can add its power to the electric motor during full HEV acceleration. Our vehicle must appeal to the consumer as well as our own California Air Resources Board. Therefore, we chose a parallel hybrid powertrain design as the best method to appeal to both groups. Our research and development efforts were aimed at solving the integration problems between the APU and electric motor. This should create a smooth power flow through the transmission, improving driveability. Careful engine management and powertrain control can reduce emissions problems, while the vehicle's extremely high fuel economy lowers the total grams/mile produced.

Table 3.1

Parallel Hybrid

Advantages	1. APU power transmitted directly to drive wheels. 2. Improved acceleration. 3. Range and driveability similar to a conventional car. 4. APU recharging possible, *when needed.*
Disadvantages	1. Increased drivetrain complexity. 2. Multi-speed transmission needed for IC engine to be effective. 3. Emissions control of APU is more difficult, especially for NO_x.

Parallel Hybrid Electric Powertrain Development

Our efforts in powertrain development resulted in a lightweight, innovative parallel hybrid design capable of driving our energy efficient hybrid vehicle to its EV range goal of 60/60 and APU fuel economy of 100 mpg at 60 mph. The entire package, including IC engine, transmission, and electric motor/controller weighs only 380 lbs. and has a peak output of 134 ft-lbs of torque and 100 hp at the input shaft of the transaxle. The modified Briggs & Stratton engine is mated to the input shaft with an electromagnetic clutch adapted from a Nissan Continuously Variable Transmission (CVT). The Uniq Electric motor mounts outboard and transfers power through a 1.55:1 Gates™ cog drive belt. The transmission is a Subaru 5-speed longitudinal transaxle. The entire assembly mounts behind the passenger compartment driving the rear wheels.

Electric Motor Selection

The electric powertrain consists of the electric motor(s), any necessary converters or controllers, the battery pack, the battery charger, and any necessary safety equipment. We made an early decision to commit our research and development efforts to other sections of the vehicle. There are many excellent electric drive components available, prompting the decision to use available prototype or mass produced components. We attempted to find the best equipment currently available. This search resulted in a drivetrain that, while too expensive to be commercially viable at this time, represents what we feel 1998 model year electric vehicles will feature as standard equipment.

The electric motor used is Unique Mobility's UNIQ SR180P. This DC brushless motor main strengths are a sophisticated controller and extremely high peak specific torque. Due to the low power requirements of our vehicle in steady-state cruising (less than 5 kW at 60 mph), peak torque for acceleration is far more important than steady-state power. The motor uses the UNIQ CR20-300 controller. This 200 Volt solid-state controller has a peak output of 300 Amps. Thus, the system has an intermittent capability of 60 kW. We selected the UNIQ over its nearest competitor, the Solectria DC brushless. Solectria and Unique were chosen for their race experience and reputation for custom building dependable, high specific power electric DC motors. We summarized the performance of the UNIQ SR180P/CR20-300 system against two Solectria BRLS11/BRLS240H systems in Table 4. The Solectria motor/controller is much smaller, so a system of two are used for comparison.

Table 4

	UNIQ	Solectria (2)
Motor Weight	52 lbs	64 lbs
Controller Wt.	48 lbs	30 lbs
Cont. Power	32 kW	16.4 kW
Cont. Torque	34 ft-lb	22.1 ft-lbs
	at 6,600 rpm	at 6,000 rpm
Intermittent Stall Torque	66.7 ft-lbs	47.2 ft-lbs
Peak Power	~ 60 kW	29.8 kW
Max Speed	7,500 rpm	7,000 rpm
Peak Efficiency	93%	94%

Although the UNIQ motor is more than 25% more expensive, its peak torque characteristics make it a very attractive component for our system. It was important to remember when designing our electric drivetrain that this vehicle uses a relatively small IC engine, so acceleration depends primarily upon the electric motor. The CR20-300 also adds an integral, speed-sensing regeneration function. A two-motor system like the Solectria adds the capability of running only one motor during steady speed cruising. This can improve the efficiency of the motor/controller, but adds packaging and mounting complexity.

Main Battery Pack

Battery selection rates as possibly the toughest challenge facing any electric vehicle design. The viability of any electric or electric hybrid vehicles depends upon the emergence of a high power, high energy density, long life, affordable battery. Hybrid vehicles in particular require a higher power density due to the typically reduced size of their battery packs. Our own stringent weight goals also mandated a high energy density. Extensive testing by Argonne National Laboratory eased the task of selecting the appropriate battery. Some very promising prototypes exist, including Sodium/Sulfur, Zinc/Bromine, and the Ovonic Nickel/Metal Hydride battery. Unfortunately, none of these batteries are even commercially available, let alone affordable. This leaves us with a simple decision between Lead-Acid and Nickel/Cadmium batteries.

Flooded Nickel/Cadmium batteries and sealed Lead-Acid cells have markedly different characteristics. Flooded NiCads have extremely high power density, but are costly and require periodic maintenance (watering). Sealed Lead-Acid are less expensive, maintenance free, but have problems with power density and lifespan. The ANL tests reveal this relationship between SAFT STM5-200 Nickel/Cadmium batteries and Sonnenschein 6V160 sealed Lead-Acid [11].

Table 5

	Lead-Acid	NiCad
Energy Density	36 Whr/kg	55 Whr/kg
Power Density	91 W/kg	175 W/kg
Testing Lifespan	370 cycles	>900 cycles

Due to the exceptionally good lifespan and high specific power, we chose Nickel/Cadmium cells from SAFT. These small, 40 Ahr cells have a reduced real-world energy density of 30 Whr/kg. This reflects the difficulty of combining 140 individual cells in series. Following the Argonne tests, which are based a driving cycle, the NiCad batteries in our HEV should last for at least 50,000 miles. The tolerance of the NiCad cell for high current draw and repeated deep discharging fits our need. In fact SAFT recommends and endorses full 100% DOD runs without worrying about shortening their lifespan.

The battery charger is a 2000 watt Solectria BC2000. The high voltage DC charger is over 93% efficient, and regulated by a 0-5 volt signal. At a charging rate of 10A, our batteries will reach full voltage in only four hours. Adding a two hour trickle charge at 4A enables a commuter to completely recharge the pack during working hours.

Alternative Power Unit

Our APU is based on a Briggs & Stratton overhead valve Vanguard four-cycle engine. This powerplant is subsequently modified to include overhead camshafts, new combustion chamber, electronic fuel injection and ignition, and modern emissions control.

We redesigned of the "top end" of the motor in an effort to reduce fuel consumption and extend the usable RPM range of the motor from 3600 rpm to about 5000 rpm. Our electric motor is reduced by 1.55:1 to the input shaft, so motor and the APU operated in approximately the same range. The smaller, high swirl, two-valve combustion chamber is based on a well-tested, successful Supermileage vehicle design. This design, in a 100 cc Briggs&Stratton engine, achieved minimum specific fuel consumption of 0.4, and real-world fuel economy of 3,313 mpg in our one-person vehicle, Side FX.

Preliminary testing of our modified motor is depicted in Figure 4, with some allowances for the inaccuracies introduced by our 175 hp dynamometer.

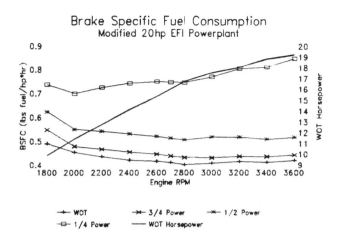

Brake Specific Fuel Consumption
Modified 20hp EFI Powerplant

WOT — 3/4 Power — 1/2 Power — 1/4 Power — WOT Horsepower

The stock 18 hp Briggs & Stratton Vanguard engine that we based our design upon features a relatively flat torque curve. This results in an engine with a broad efficiency range. Considering the engine's power curve, it is clear that the engine will operate at a very low specific fuel consumption due to its size. With the electric motor providing up to 100 ft-lbs of torque at the input shaft, we can concentrate on high efficiency, rather than high specific power for our APU design. This is really the only way to meet the lofty 100 mpg fuel economy goal.

The APU will also provide enough excess power to drive our lightweight vehicle in most circumstances. In fact, the vehicle can almost meet the Hot 505 cycle in APU-Only Mode as seen in Figure 5, below. The motor can meet all except the sharpest acceleration peaks.

Engine Management and Emissions

With the low-power IC engine, careful fuel management is critical. Our student-designed fuel injection system incorporates a hot-wire mass airflow sensor in conjunction with one heated oxygen sensor at each cylinder's exhaust port. Our own fuel-injection programming operates the multi-port, Bosch fuel injection system through an eight bit, C-programmable microcontroller. This custom building of the system allows us to tailor its operation to our specific engine management strategies.

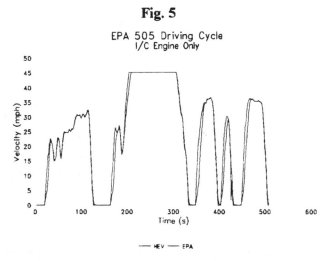

Fig. 5

EPA 505 Driving Cycle
I/C Engine Only

— HEV — EPA

Exhaust emissions are regulated by a combination of active Exhaust Gas Recirculation (EGR) valves for each intake port and a custom three-way exhaust catalyst. With the small engine average cylinder pressures will be higher, forcing utmost care to be taken to control NO_x. Therefore, each cylinder has an independent HEGO sensor and pulse-width modulated egr solenoid. The catalyst is constructed to maintain a high average temperature with the lower displacement of our engine.

A standard evaporative vacuum cannister will reduce emissions from the fuel tank and the intake manifold. Low levels of fuel evaporation are expected as the engine management controller will usually choose not to run the APU below 1000 rpm.

Powertrain Control Strategy

Our parallel configuration allows us tremendous flexibility in exploring the various driving strategies and emissions controls ideas. For example, our APU will run off a high-speed start from the electric drive motor. Our electromagnetic clutch can engage smoothly to quickly start the IC engine. The fuel management system, sensing engine speed above 1500 rpm, can delay fuel injection turn-on until the IC motor is up to speed, avoiding startup emissions. Thus, we can quickly bring the IC engine up to the drivetrain speed, extracting power much more quickly than with a conventional start.

We plan two primary driving configurations, electric-only and HEV mode with the APU providing most of the power. In ZEV mode, the electric motor drives the car until the powertrain microcontroller's battery monitoring routine detects a 80% DOD. HEV mode can be immediately and passively triggered by the controller. Then the APU will high-speed start off the electric motor. In HEV mode, the APU provides almost all the power. The electric motor begins to provide power only for acceleration, not steady-state. The engine controller will always reserve 20% of the battery capacity for this type of acceleration. This allows the car to attain almost unlimited range, while maintaining high acceleration capability in each mode.

Although the Hot 505 driving cycle will be run in APU-only mode, Figure 6 offers an initial insight on the interaction of the two powerplants.

Figure 6

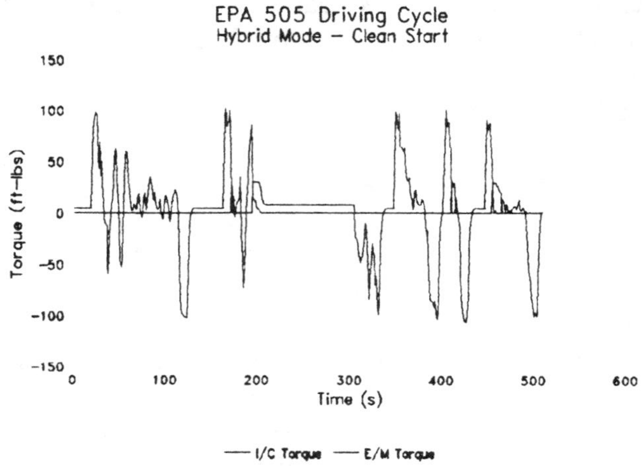

EPA 505 Driving Cycle
Hybrid Mode — Clean Start

— I/C Torque — E/M Torque

The electric motor's high torque peaks (remember the 1.55:1 reduction to the drivetrain) cover most of the acceleration while the APU supplies steady-state power. This illustrates the advantage the HEV has in city driving. Stop-and-go acceleration and regeneration are supplied by the electric motor/controller. Longer trip highway speeds will bias the power supply towards the APU, as evidenced by the extended time at 45 mph on the Hot 505.

26

Conclusion

The intensive twelve month design and development process at UC Davis has yielded a versatile, promising hybrid electric vehicle. The low curb weight of 1800 lbs, aerodynamic efficiency, and parallel drivetrain have enabled this vehicle to reach its performance goals. [12] This can shed new light on the entire hybrid electric vehicle concept. After meeting its goals and performing in the HEV Challenge, we may have a vehicle capable of driving from our state capital in Sacramento to Los Angeles at 100 mpg, and then switching to ZEV mode and crossing the 60 mile LA. Basin on pure electric power.

Epilogue

Design Successes and Failures

The UC Davis HEV, thankfully, had more vehicle design successes than failures. The body, chassis, and powertrain design successes and failures are discussed in the following section.

Body

As a whole, the body design was a success. The vehicle achieved a drag coefficient of approximately 0.2 and contributed significantly to the vehicle's performance. There were, however, many production pitfalls and design trade-offs. The body required more time than any other vehicle component. The body design also effected the car's ergonomics. Passenger comfort, egress, regress, and vision were sacrificed for an aerodynamic shape. Lastly, the body lacked practicality. Ground *FX* failed to have an easily accessible, on-board battery charger and fuel tank as well as conventional door handles.

Chassis

Like the body, the chassis was a success. The frame, after three months of on-road testing, shows no sign of failure or fatigue. Problems encountered with the chassis were due to poor component selection. Both the brakes and suspension performed poorly. Although, an unforeseen increase in vehicle weight was the major reason for the problems, a larger margin of error could have prevented these problems.

Powertrain

The powertrain, like the body and chassis, was a success but created significant problems for the UC Davis HEV Team. Problems did not emanate from the parallel configuration but from poor powertrain compartment configuration and poor material and component selection. The powertrain compartment configuration does not allow for sufficient cooling. Thus, the air cooled APU runs hot, limiting the performance. Components, clutch plates for example, in the powertrain failed due to poor material choices while other components like the electric motor drive belt could have been optimized for best performance. These problems and those related to the body and chassis will be addressed and improved upon in future vehicles.

Vehicle Improvements

For the 1994 HEV Challenge the UC Davis HEV Team has scheduled numerous vehicle improvements to solve the problems stated in the previous section. To implement these improvements a new vehicle is necessary.

Body

Improvements to the body will focus on manufacturbility, weight reduction, enhanced aerodynamics and practicality. Increased manufacturability reduces production and assembly time. Weight reduction and improved aerodynamics enhance overall vehicle performance. Adding access panels for the on-board battery charger and APU fuel tank as well as conventional door handles to the body increase the car's practicality.

Chassis

Similar changes are planned for the chassis. Weight reduction, increased manufacturability, user friendly battery enclosures, ergonomics, and intelligent component selection are the major chassis improvements. Like the body, weight reduction helps vehicle performance and increased manufacturbility should shorten production time. Larger, easily accessible battery enclosures allow fast battery maintenance and the ability to test different batteries in the future. Lastly, improved ergonomics, aiding passenger egress, regress, and vision enhance the vehicle's appeal. Proper component selection increase vehicle reliability.

Powertrain

The powertrain, too, will be revamped utilizing a parallel configuration. Scheduled improvements include powertrain size, weight, and noise reduction as well as increased component reliability, powertrain compartment reconfiguration with special attention to compartment cooling. Reduced size helps a currently crowded powertrain compartment but also reduces weight and increases rearward aerodynamics which, as mentioned above, enhances overall vehicle performance. Decreasing noise, emanating from the electric motor drive belt, adds to the car's appeal and careful powertrain configuration creates a user friendly compartment with proper cooling.

Lessons Learned

The UC Davis HEV Team members learned many lessons while building Ground *FX*. Two lessons, above all, deserve discussion. Lesson number one: Never assume the component specification sheet reflects actual performance data. Lesson number two: Proper project management is paramount for success.

Ground *FX* uses Nickel/Cadmium batteries for its main battery pack. After gathering information from a number of manufactures, a battery was chosen and the entire battery pack purchased. Without testing a single cell, the manufacture's data was used to determine the battery pack size. Upon receiving and testing the batteries, team members discovered Ground *FX* failed to meet the 40 miles at 40 MPH requirement. Consequently, more batteries were necessary. The additional 250 lbs. of batteries required to meet the rules created many problems.

The increased vehicle weight was a major reason why the car was plagued with brake problems. Brake pads were sized for a lower vehicle weight. The extra batteries also created a crowded powertrain compartment making maintenance difficult and contributing to cooling problems. The suspension, too required adjustment. Hence, specification sheets should be validated before design continues.

The second lesson learned dealt with project organization. The UC Davis HEV Team initially employed an amorphous blob organizational strategy in which no one person was the project leader and all the group leaders shared equal status. In theory, this style might appear attractive, but in practice, as the UC Davis HEV Team learned, the strategy failed. Without a managerial ladder, deadlines were missed and paperwork forgotten. To solve these problems an unofficial managerial ladder materialized ensuring tasks were completed. This unofficial managerial ladder, however, was far from optimal and fostered new, unnecessary problems. With a project of this magnitude, a detailed organizational strategy is paramount for success. A lesson learned by the UC Davis HEV Team.

Contributing Authors:

Rebecca Riley
Mark Duvall
Robert Cobene II
Paul Cassanego
Gregory Eng
Shula Fischer
Keith Kruetzfeldt
Greg Reimers

Advisor: Professor Andrew A. Frank
Department of Mechanical Engineering
University of California, Davis

References

[1] Abbott and von Doenhoff, *Theory of Wing Sections*, Dover Publicatins Inc.: New York, 1959, 119-122.

[2] Shevell, Richard, *Fundamentals of Flight*, Prentice Hall: New Jersey, 1989, 168-169.

[3] Waters, D.M., "Thickness and Camber Effects on Bodies in Ground Proximity", *Advances in Road Vehicle Aerodynamics*, 1973.

[4] Hoerner, S.F., *Fluid-Dynamic Drag*, pub. by author, 1965, 12.1-12.8.

[5] Dorgham, M.A., *Impact of Aerodynamics on Vehicle Design*, SP3 1983, 17-43.

[6] Hibbs, Bart, *GM Sunraycer Case History*, Lecture 2-2, SAE 1988, 18-43.

[7] Ashley, Steven, "GM's Ultralight is Racing Toward Greater Fuel Efficiency", *Mechanical Engineering*, May 1992, 64-67.

[8] Hartemann, Francois and Bernard Favre, "Human Factors for Display and Control", SAE 901149.

[9] Bosch Automotive Handbook, Ed. 2, 1986, 257

[10] Simanaitis, Dennis, "Volvo ECC", *Road & Track*, June 1993, 120-124

[11] DeLuca, WH, "Results of Advanced Battery Technology Evaluations for Electric Vehicle Applications", SAE 921572

[12] Winkelman, JR and Frank, AA, "Computer Simulation of the University of Wisconsin Hybrid Electric Vehicle Concept", SAE 730511

ELANT III Hybrid Electric Vehicle

Don Campbell Jr.

HEV Project
University of California , Irvine

ABSTRACT

The ELANT III Hybrid Electric Vehicle is a 1992 Ford Escort wagon that has been retrofitted with a combined electric motor and a gasoline powered internal combustion engine propulsion system. The vehicle is designed as an environmentally friendly two passenger commuter vehicle capable of operating in three modes. The first mode enables the ELANT III to operate electrically as a Zero Emissions Vehicle (ZEV) for short-range commuter travel. The second mode, the "Hybrid" (HEV) mode, where the car operates an Ultra Low Emissions Vehicle (ULEV), powered by the gasoline engine tuned for highway speeds, providing long distance travel capability. An auxiliary (AUX) mode enables the gasoline engine, also referred as the Auxiliary Power Unit (APU) to provide should the electric propulsion system be inoperable.

The ELANT III's performance design criteria were centered on efficiency rather than speed or mobility. The vehicle's 0-45 mi/hr (0-74 km/hr) time is less than 15 seconds and the top speed is greater than 70 mi/hr (113 km/hr). ZEV mode range is over 20 miles, and HEV range is over 400 miles.

The ELANT III is currently a conversion class entry in the Ford Hybrid Electric Vehicle Challenge, which is primarily sponsored by the Ford Motor Company, the Society of Automotive Engineers, and the U.S. Department of Energy. The design and construction for the project was provided by students of the University of California at Irvine.

INTRODUCTION

Taking its name from the University mascot, the "ELectric ANTeater" or ELANT III was designated to become a hybrid electric vehicle before the Ford HEV Challenge was announced. The ELANT I electric vehicle was completed by University students two years ago by their Electrical Engineering Electric Vehicle Project. As a standard DC motor powered vehicle, its performance and range were determined to be substandard. An AC motor powered vehicle was to be the next ELANT, but even its projected performance range were determined substandard. A hybrid electric vehicle was determined to solve the range problem suffered by current pure electrics. Since the vehicle would have a gasoline powered engine, reduced exhaust emissions would be a design requirement.

The ELANT III HEV power train would be the design focus, since all vehicles in the UC Irvine EV Project were conversions from existing automobiles. There are two basic configurations for hybrid electric power trains: series and parallel. A series power train has the fuel powered engine or APU drive a generator which is used for battery charging or as an electric motor power supply. The electric motor is the only prime mover driving the wheels. In a parallel configuration, either the electric motor and/or the APU drives the vehicle. Each system has benefits and disadvantages. It was UC Irvine team's decision to use a parallel configuration for reasons based on efficiency and simplicity. In a series HEV, battery charging is less than 25% energy efficient, indicating that less than 25% of the APU's power output goes towards useful work. Even if the APU's power output was transferred from the electric generator directly to an electric motor (which can be 90% efficient), a complex controller would be needed to regulate power output. One series configuration advantage is a greater amount of control over APU speed and exhaust emissions. In a parallel configuration, the APU can efficiently direct power to the wheels through a standard automotive transmission. A control system for a parallel configuration can be simplified to point that it requires no microprocessor control. For an equivalent power output, harmful exhaust emissions (such as carbon monoxide) from a parallel configuration should be slightly higher than a series configuration, but the carbon dioxide emissions for a parallel is significantly lower than what a series system emits due to higher fuel consumption.

DESIGN VARIABLES

The Ford HEV Challenge rules and regulations set the vehicle performance design criteria which the ELANT III team was to adhere to.

PERFORMANCE - Vehicles within the HEV challenge should be capable of a 0 to 45 mi/hr acceleration in 15 seconds or less. This rule set the minimum power output for the power train power plants.

RANGE - Zero emission range should be 20 miles or more. Hybrid range should be 400 miles or more. The ZEV range would be mostly influenced by type and size.

CURB WEIGHT - Ford Escort wagon chassis have a maximum weight capacity of 3800 pounds. When carrying 400 pounds of passengers and cargo, the maximum curb weight of the unloaded vehicle should not exceed 3400 pounds.

FUEL ECONOMY - Teams within the Ford HEV Challenge will be judged heavily on fuel economy. Lower fuel usage can also provide fewer total emissions.

EXHAUST EMISSIONS - Harmful exhaust emissions such as reactive organic gases (ROG or HC), carbon monoxide (CO), or oxides of nitrogen (NOx) are targeted to be much lower than current automotive emission standards. Ultra Low Emission standards (ULEV, as defined by the California Air Resources Board) are the targeted emission levels.

Such levels are:
0.04 g/mi HC
1.7 g/mi CO
0.2 g/mi NOx

BATTERIES - Current battery choices are limited by cost and thus restrict performance, but acceptable power and energy is attainable with lead acid batteries. Aviation batteries, and batteries containing precious metals, were not allowed in the HEV Challenge. 400 volts is the maximum battery system voltage.

CHARGING - Battery charging time should be eight hours or less. This is a typical overnight recharging time. Recharging power would come from a 230 VAC 30 AMP outlet.

COMMUTER CAPABILITY - The vehicle must have a battery capable of storing enough energy for busy highway traffic purposes. The controls of the car must not induce driver fatigue and should allow operation as a normal automobile would.

SAFETY - Safety rules for the HEV Challenge are of a race quality nature. Requirements include safety roll cages, 5 point racing harnesses (racing seat belts), and a 5 pound fire extinguishing system. Electrical safety is also notable. Proper insulation and circuit protection are required. Braking (both parking and dynamic), must conform to reasonable levels. Emergency handling must also be acceptable in order to prevent accidents.

POWER TRAIN DESIGN CRITERIA

POWER TRAIN - A replacement power train for a Ford Escort wagon chassis would be the focus for the ELANT III mechanical engineering students. Further design requirements for the power train were:

1. Electric energy efficiency of 85%.
2. High fuel economy, greater than 50 mpg.
3. Mechanical transmission efficiency, greater than 90%

4. Similarity of driving control operation, regardless of power train operation mode (ZEV, HEV, APU mode).
5. Power train mass or 450 lbs or less
6. Component size, total power train width less than 36 inches
7. High availability of components
8. Simplified assembly
9. Low cost of components

The replacement power train would also share the transverse mounted orientation and front wheel drive of the standard Ford Escort power train. After calculating power requirements, and review almost every electric motor and gasoline powered internal combustion engine, the following components were chosen for the replacement power train:

Electric Motor: 3 phase AC induction motor, 230 VAC, 15 hp continuous, 40 hp peak, 60 ft-lbs torque
APU: Geo Metro Lsi, Suzuki G-10 engine, 55 hp peak, 58 ft-lbs torque
Transmission: Ford Escort LX FWD 5-speed manual transmission with Hybrid Merging Unit transaxle

This parallel power train would require either an electric motor or the APU to deliver power to the standard Ford Escort transmission. To accomplish this, a "Merge Unit" would be used to mechanically connect either APU/electric motor with the transmission.

BATTERY - The battery system requirements would have to allow at least 292 VDC to enter the electric motor controller. Since battery voltages decrease with usage, a nominal battery output rating of 312 VDC was determined to be acceptable. If using 12 volt lead acid batteries, 26 batteries would be needed to fulfill this requirement. Maximum battery weight was restricted to 850 pounds. The following battery was chosen for the propulsion battery system: Trojan DC-22NF, 12 Volts, 30 lbs., 56 Ampere hour rating at a 20 Amp current draw.

VEHICLE COMPONENT SELECTION

ELECTRIC MOTOR - The ELANT III uses a 15 horsepower, 230V, class B, two-pole AC induction motor, donated by Electra-Gear of Anaheim, CA. The motor has Y/2Y parallel winding, NEMA 215M size frame and R type insulation capable of withstanding up to 360°F (200°C). Though our motor frame is rated at 15 horsepower, the R type insulation allows us to run the motor at higher than rated power for short periods of time. Thus we can draw up to 30 horsepower from the electric motor for up to two minutes, and more for shorter periods of time. The motor is air cooled.

ELECTRIC MOTOR CONTROLLER - In electric mode the ELANT III is driven by a 3 phase induction motor and controlled by a pulse-width modulated inverter acting as a variable frequency source. Figure 10 shows a general schematic for the motor controller.

Our Emerson Industrial Controls Eclipse II inverter/controller, donated by the manufacturer, is a high performance, general purpose, digital, adjustable frequency unit, usually operating on three phase 50/60 Hz input power. The inverter produces an adjustable frequency, adjustable voltage, three phase output. This is usually achieved in the following manner.

Three phase 60Hz 230VAC rectified and filtered to 324VDC. The DC voltage is pulse-width modulated by the inverter to generate a variable voltage, variable frequency wave form.

Since the HEV will not be connected to an AC source except during battery changing, we remove the rectifier portion of the controller, supplying instead 312 VDC battery power to the controller.

A voltage/frequency curve, as shown in figure 1, is programmed into the Eclipse's onboard microprocessor. This allows the voltage to vary with frequency, thus maintaining good magnetic flux density in the motor. The maximum voltage, where the V/Hz curve "levels off", is determined by the voltage characteristics of the batteries. As the electric vehicle is driven, the voltage available from the batteries will decrease. The V/Hz curve is required to have a maximum voltage which allows good motor performance even after the car has been driven for 30 minutes or more and significant charge has been drained from the batteries. Thus the V/Hz curve is set with a maximum voltage equal to that of the batteries after operation for half an hour.

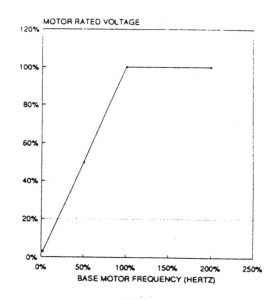

FIGURE 1
INVERTER/CONTROLLER V/Hz CHARACTERISTICS

AUXILIARY POWER UNIT - The APU is a 1991 Geo Metro LSi 3 cylinder engine. This engine has a weight of about 140 pounds, and a length of 15 inches from crankshaft pulley to the flywheel. The APU will be described in an "energy transfer" order, starting with the fuel tank and ending with the exhaust gas emissions.

Beginning with the fuel source, the standard Ford Escort 12 gallon fuel tank is used. Since the APU has a mileage greater than 40 mpg, less than six gallons of 87 octane unleaded gasoline fulfills HEV challenge range requirements. The Geo metro fuel pump is used to pump fuel to the engine. The standard Ford Escort fuel lines are used to transfer the fuel.

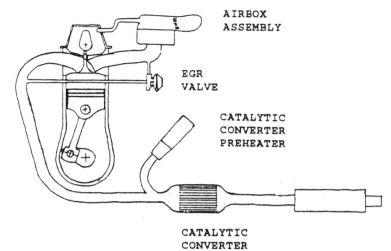

FIGURE 2
ADDITIONAL EXHAUST
EMISSION CONTROL
DEVICES

AIRBOX
ASSEMBLY

EGR
VALVE

CATALYTIC
CONVERTER
PREHEATER

CATALYTIC
CONVERTER

The Geo metro intake manifold and throttle body assembly are used, as is the Geo metro throttle body fuel injection/controller computer. However, many of the exhaust emission related features are modified to reduce the amounts of pollutant gases in the engine exhaust. These features are described in the exhaust emissions section. The air cleaner assembly is a custom made assembly using a K&N air filter which has a high air flow rate capability. This high flow rate air filter assembly will allow better engine "breathing", which should reduce HC and CO emissions.

Almost no engine mechanical features were modified on the APU, however the engine head and block were partially disassembled/rebuilt for cleaning. The standard camshaft on the Geo Metro engine was used since it controls proper valve timing and lift. The standard Geo exhaust manifold is used. Custom made exhaust pipes are used to attach the exhaust manifold to the catalytic converter. The standard Ford Escort muffler is also used.

Engine cooling is almost identical to the Geo Metro cooling system. An after market copper and brass radiator was used instead of an aluminum/plastic radiator.

The output from the Geo metro engine will enter the Merge Unit through a lightened flywheel.

The emissions system on the APU employs features found on the Geo Metro, and the Ford Escort, and an item not found on current production automobiles. Figure 2 locates the non-standard smog reducing devices. Evaporative emissions are controlled by the Geo Metro charcoal canister and Ford Escort fuel lines. The fuel filling nozzle employs a conically shaped receptacle as a seal which minimizes the amount of fuel vapors leaving the refueling nozzle during a refueling operation.

Most exhaust emissions related components or smog parts on the Geo Metro engine were retained and adjusted. Such items are the Positive Crankcase Ventilation (PCV) valve as well as the exhaust recirculation (EGR) valve. Since exhaust back pressure is expected to be reduced, additional exhaust gas recirculation was required. The Geo Metro EGR valve is adjusted to permit more "burned" exhaust gas to be recirculated into the combustion chamber. Recirculating exhaust gases reduces NOx emissions and burns most unburned fuel vapor fumes present in the exhaust gas.

The Ford Escort catalytic converter is used since it is larger than the Geo Metro catalytic converter. A larger catalytic converter has more catalyst surfaces exposed to the exhaust gases than a smaller one, thus exposing a higher percentage of the exhaust gas volume to be converted in to more environmentally friendly gases such as water vapor and nitrogen. All automotive catalytic converters are designed to operate at high temperatures. To ensure the effectiveness at cold starts, an electric heat gun is used to act as a catalytic converter "pre-heating" device. The heat gun exhaust is attached to the engine exhaust piping. A modified Escort EGR valve acts as gate between the exhaust system and the heat gun so that exhaust gases do not leak out through the heat gun air inlet.

ENGINE

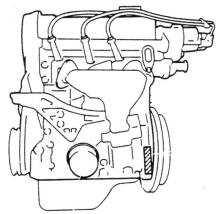

1991 Geo METRO
SERVICE MANUAL

ENGINE ELECTRICAL MODIFICATION – The engine electrical items for the HEV will mostly come from the Geo Metro. Beginning from the "system" battery, one 12 volt lead acid battery with the capability of sustaining 10 amps for one hour will be required. A 56 amp-hour propulsion type battery was determined to be cable of this requirement. Items that will rely on this battery are the engine starter, engine ignition system, the braking system, the general controller, the head lights, and any other general body electrical items. Battery charging will come from a Geo Metro alternator which is rated at 60 amps.

The ignition system will come from the Geo Metro. Items such as

the distributor and induction coil will be retained, but ignition timing is adjusted to improve exhaust emissions. The spark plugs used are "Splitfire" spark plugs since both are known for improving engine performance and efficiency.

Wiring relays and harnesses will be a hybrid setup. Both wires and connections from the Ford and Geo will be used. Geo Metro wiring harnesses will be used for mostly engine electrical items whereas Ford wiring harnesses will be used for body electrical items.

As part of the ignition system, an automatic or push button APU starting feature will be employed for enabling the APU to start up by a command signal from the HEV controller or the driver. This feature exists due to the APU's period of non-use during electric operation at low vehicle speeds. At "mid-range" vehicle speeds the APU must be engaged. An automatic starting system would make driving more convenient should it be found necessary.

TRANSMISSION/TRANSAXLE - The power from the electric motor and the APU is sent through a mechanical transmission device consisting of two separate components. These components are the standard five speed manual transmission from the Ford Escort wagon, and the "Merge Unit" which merges or selects power from the electric motor and/or gasoline engine to be directed to the transmission. Further requirements of the transmission and Merge Unit combination were mechanical simplicity, the ability of utilizing a low speed power plant at high vehicle speeds, and low power consumption. To fulfill these requirements, a 5 speed manual gear box is needed in conjunction with two electromagnetic clutch devices (EM clutch). The merge unit houses the clutches whereas as the transmission houses the 5 speed gear box. Control of the transmission is through the gear speed shifter. Control of the clutches is described in the general controller section.

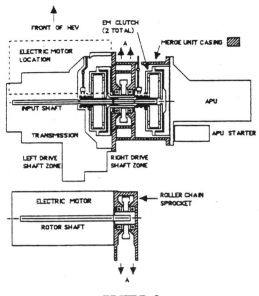

FIGURE 3
MERGE UNIT
CROSS SECTION

Advantages of using the Ford five speed transmission are direct mounting capability with the Escort chassis, use of existing gear shifting linkages, and utilization of the Ford Escort half shafts. The electric motor location is above and towards the front of the transmission (see figure 3). The location of the APU is towards the passenger side of the transmission , as is the Merge Unit.

The Merge Unit consists of two Mitsubishi Electric Electromagnetic (EM) clutches, one solid chrome-moly steel shaft, two hollow high strength steel shaft, four ball bearings, three shaft seals, two steel sprockets, one silent chain, and an aluminum casing. The silent chain and sprocket used with the electric motor is located in a sealed compartment filled with gear oil for lubrication purposes. A Morse HV Silent chain was chosen for noise and strength reasons.

The clutch attached to the APU flywheel is used to transmit torque to the transmission input shaft. This is used in hybrid (HEV) and auxiliary (AUX) modes of operation. The clutch located in the bell housing is used to transmit electric motor torque in electric (ZEV) and HEV modes of operation. Both clutches will operate as a dry disc clutch would operate. The nominal power consumption of each clutch is about 36 watts. Power is supplied by two sets of slip rings located at the forward par of each clutch. A rheostat switch from the general controller is connected to a brush which runs along the EM clutch slip rings. The rheostat enables a dry disc type of operation which permits clutch "slippage", which in turn places less stress on the Merge Unit shafts and gives the driver more control.

GENERAL CONTROLLER - In ZEV mode the general controller energizes the electric motor controller and the electric motor EM clutch. In APU mode, APU ignition is permitted and the APU clutch is used. Each of these modes is enabled by the mode switch. In hybrid mode, the general controller uses a simple drive strategy. Switches are placed at the base of the gear shift selector in the passenger compartment. The purpose of the switches is to sense which gear the car is in, and to activate which clutch is to be used. For slow speeds where the electric motor is required for propulsion, the first, second, or reverse gears are used. When the gear shift selector is in this position, only the electric motor clutch is activated, thus only allowing the electric motor to propel the car. The APU clutch will remain open. When the transmission is at medium to higher cruising speeds, the APU is used, thus when the gear selector is in third, fourth, or fifth gear, only the APU clutch will be activated and the electric motor clutch will remain open. At any operation, the clutch pedal will act as clutch operation control. The neutral position of the gear shifter places the APU and electric motor in a standby mode. See Figure 9 for the schematic design of the general controller.

THE BATTERY AND CHARGER SYSTEM - The battery selected was the Trojan DC-22NF Deep Cycle 12 Volt Pacer. It was necessary to use a wet battery to provide enough energy storage capacity. Dry cell batteries in the same price and weight range as the 22NF did not have nearly as much energy capacity. The 22NF is a lead acid battery and weighs 30 pounds. It has an Ampere hour rating of 56 at a 20 Amp current draw. It is 9.5 inches long, 5.5 inches wide, and 8.8 inches high.

The DC voltage required by the controller is approximately 324 volts. Using 26 12-volt batteries connected in series gives a nominal voltage of 312 volts. Actual tests of the batteries being used show a voltage of 12.6 per battery when fully charged, and eventually a voltage of 11.8 volts when "discharged". Therefore the controller will have 327.6 volts DC with fully charged batteries and a voltage of 307 when the batteries are nearly exhausted. The controller can operate at a range of 10% above and below the 324 volts needed, which is between 292 and 356 volts.

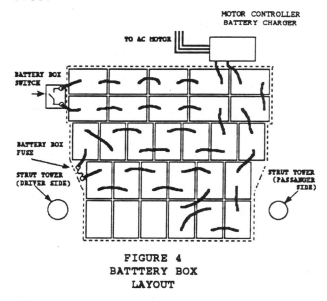

FIGURE 4
BATTTERY BOX
LAYOUT

At an average current draw of 10 amps, the battery has the capacity to last 5 hours as can be seen from figure 5 which presents the results of a test on one of the Trojan 22NF batteries. With 26 batteries in series and a nominal voltage of 312 volts, this gives us 3.12 kW of power and 15.6 kW/hr of battery energy storage which is less than the upper limit of 20 kWh specified in the HEV Challenge requirements. Normal driving draws more than 10 amps and produces less effective power and energy delivery. The 26 drive batteries are connected in the manner shown below. Note that the box has a 29 battery capacity.

The two empty slots shown in the above configuration represent a possible storage space for two extra batteries. They will help maintain an even weight distribution between the front and rear ends of the car, and will serve as replacements should any of the 26 batteries fail due to defects. The battery on the left end in the row contains the system battery.

To localize problems arriving from shorts between batteries, fuses are located between the first thirteen batteries and the second thirteen batteries and at the extreme ends of the pack within the motor controller casing. An AC circuit breaker is located between the line from the controller to the electric motor. A manual switch between the third and fourth batteries has been placed to act as an emergency battery power disruption switch. The manual switch is placed near the door so that a passenger can shut it off from both inside and outside of the car without difficulty. The batteries are enclosed in a rubberized stainless steel box. The top of the box will be removable so that the batteries may be serviced when needed.

For charging the batteries, a charger built with components from the rectifier section of the factory supplied electric motor controller. To fully charge each 12 volt battery, supplying at least 14 volts to each battery terminal is required. Therefore at least 363 volts DC is required to charge 26 batteries in series, which would required at least 269 volts AC. A step up isolation transformer with the proper tap setting will provide the required voltage.

Due to the large number of batteries being used in the vehicle, attention has been given to safety procedures. Lead acid batteries produce hydrogen gas. The hydrogen gas that escapes from the batteries can easily build up in the immediate vicinity, and ignite resulting in an explosion. Therefore an exhaust fan driven by a brushless motor is mounted in the lid on the battery box. Another danger involved with lead acid batteries is the acid spillage. In the event an acid spillage, the battery box contains baking soda which serves as an acid neutralizing agent. The metal box also has an acid resistant lining.

A Trojan DC-22NF battery was discharged at an average rate of 10 amperes to determine its capability. The results of this test are shown is figure 5.

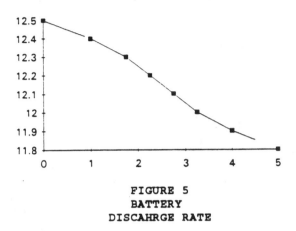

FIGURE 5
BATTERY
DISCAHRGE RATE

COMPONENT INSTALLATION

POWER TRAIN MOUNTING - Four mounts will fasten the HEV power train to the Ford Escort chassis. For simplicity's sake, the Ford five speed transmission is used. The advantage of using the transmission is the use of three existing mounts. The Ford Escort transmission is designed to hold a 316 pound engine. The weight of the replacement APU, electric motor, and Merge Unit add up to about 290 lbs. The fourth power train mount is located on the front passenger side of Escort chassis. This mount will be modified so that is can be fastened on to the Ford Escort passenger side frame rail an for supporting the APU. In terms of vibration damping resistance, small vibration levels are produced at an APU slow idle, but are not large enough to be considered as unpleasant. The electric motor is mounted on the merge unit by its C face flange. The electric motor is placed on the driver's side of the Ford Escort, slightly above the transmission.

The battery box is designed as a light, collision worthy, and air tight casing. The battery box is located above the rear seating area

(see figure 6). The battery boxe is attached to the Escort chassis by the roll cage, rear seat belt anchors, and at selected "hard" points on the floor panel. The battery box is made of 20 gauge stainless steel sheet metal. This material is resistant battery acid corrosion. The top panel is attached to the box by quick release pin fasteners. Plywood beams act as structural reinforcement for the front and rear sections of the battery box. Located beneath the battery box, the reinforcement beams provide a flat surface for the battery box floor. The inside of the battery box is coated with a rubberized undercoating as a form of electrical insulation. A caulking compound is used to seal any gaps in the sheet metal seams to prevent hydrogen gas from entering the passenger compartment. The weight of the 24 batteries within the box is about 750 pounds. The box is designed to carry 1300 pounds of static load. The box is also designed to remained attached to the frame in the event of a 30 mph frontal collision.

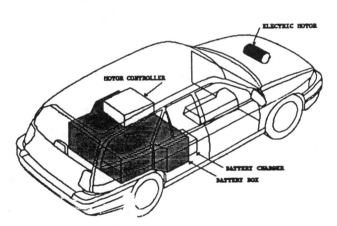

FIGURE 6
ELECTRIC PROPULSION
SYSTEM LOCATIONS

The electric motor controller is housed in a combination polyproplene/steel case to protect controller components from mechanical damage. This case also provides additional insulation from the high voltage components within the box. Steel casing componets are located next to high temperature components. An electromagnetic barrier coating isolates the controller from possible electro-magnetic interference. The electric motor controller is located above the battery box.

The braking system of the ELANT HEV used combination of Escort wagon & GT components. The standard front disc brakes from the Escort wagon were retained. To increase braking effectiveness, an Escort GT rear disc brake assembly replaced the Escort wagon rear drum brake assembly. The brake master cylinder and brake booster from the Escort wagon was retained. The proportioning valve or brake bias valve has been set to permit more brake fluid pressure to act on the rear disc brake calipers. The brake booster receives vacuum assist from a small electric motor powered vacuum pump-tank assembly.

The suspension was modified to handle the additional weight from the electric propulsion system. Suspension modifications include the replacement of all four coil springs and struts. All coil springs are stiffer than the current Escort coil springs in order to cope with ther additional weight as well as reduce brake "dive" and body roll. Tokico twin tube struts have replaced the stock struts. The standard front and rear sway bars are retained.

The manual steering system of the Ford Escort was not modified. Although a power assist feature would be preferable, the additional weight from a power steering system was a drawback that prevented implementation.

The current tires on the Escort wagon have been replaced by 185/70/R13 Goodyear Invicta radial tires since they are of a low rolling resistance, and capable of handling addition weight. The wheels are replaced by American Eagle Series 240 wheels in a 13" x 5.5" size. These wheels were determined to be one of the lightest aftermarket wheels available.

Safety systems for the ELANT III HEV are specified by the HEV challenge rules and regulations. For roll over protection, a six pillar roll cage is constructed of mild steel tubing. All standard Ford Escort seat belts have been removed, and the front belts replaced by Deist Safety racing

quality five point harnesses. The replacement harnesses are fastened to the standard front seat belt anchors and to the roll cage. A racing 5-pound 1301-halon fire extinguisher will be kept on board for fire protection (see figure 7). The discharge valves are located in the passenger compartment near the driver and passenger seats, near the APU, and in the battery compartment. For cargo restraint, an elastic net is fastened to the cargo compartment side walls and floor.

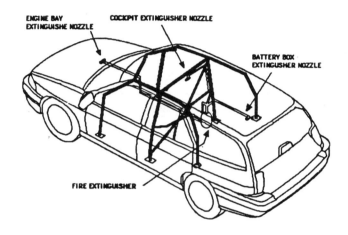

FIGURE 7
ROLLCAGE AND FIRE SYSTEM LOCATIONS

INSTRUMENTATION / CONTROLS LAYOUT

ELANT III uses the instrument panel provided with the Ford Escort. None of the existing components will be removed or changed, but new components will be added to the existing dashboard. These components include: a tachometer, temperature indication unit, and battery meters. Figure 8 shows the new layout with the following instrument and controls:

1. Present Instrument Cluster
2. Ventilation Control System
3. Temperature Indicator Unit
4. Tachometer
5. Battery Meters
6. Operation Mode Switch (Not Shown)

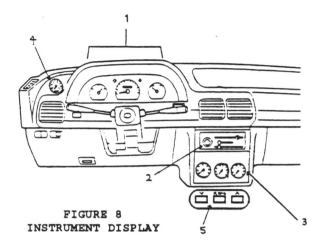

**FIGURE 8
INSTRUMENT DISPLAY**

1. Present Instrument Cluster
2. Ventilation Control System
3. Temperature Indicator Unit
4. Tachometer
5. Battery Meters
6. Operation Mode Switch (Not Shown)

TACHOMETER - This is a standard tachometer which operates on pulses generated by the main drive shaft in all modes of operation.

TEMPERATURE INDICATOR UNIT - This unit includes temperature indicators for the electric motor, main controller, and the battery array. The ICE temperature indicator remains unchanged.

BATTERY METERS - These units provide current, voltage, and kilowatt-hour readings of the DC battery power supply. The ampere meter uses a current shunt and a 50 mv movement.

ACCELERATOR PEDAL - The accelerator position is translated into a proportional voltage for input to the motor controller in the ZEV mode propulsion and serves in the traditional manner for propulsion.

VEHICLE MANUFACTURABILITY

Conventional materials and parts were chosen for the vehicle modifications. Most components in the vehicle are "off the shelf" type components. Specially built items such as Merge Unit were designed to be simple, inexpensive to build, yet strong enough to with stand the designed loads. Power train components such as the Ford transmission or Geo Metro engine have been produced in large quantities in the last two years and have been proved reliable.

SUMMARY

The vehicle has not been completely tested at the time this report was written. One positive result which stands out even now is the knowledge and experience gained about inventiveness, design methodology, project management, and cooperation among members of the team.

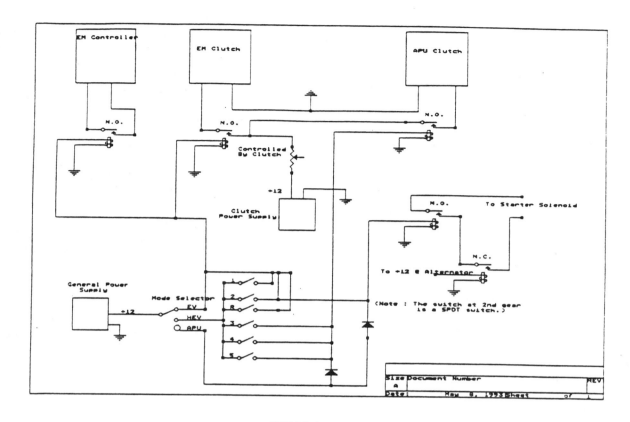

FIGURE 9
GENERAL CONTOLLER
SCHEMATIC

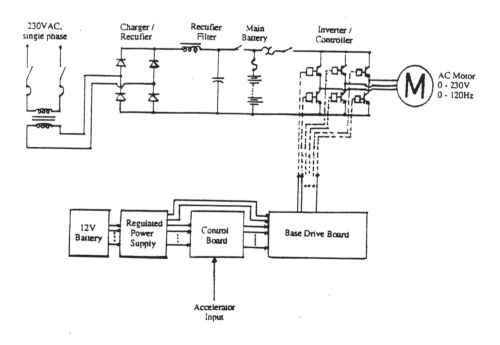

FIGURE 10
ELECTRIC MOTOR
CONTOLLER SCHEMATIC

ACKNOWLEDGMENTS

The author would like to thank the following team members for their contributions in writing to this report:
Mica Parks
Dave Decarion
Omar Hussein
Neel Patel
Fred Hsieh
Jeff Yoon.

For efforts in helping the students put the project and the car together we thank:

Larry Marquiss of Tuttle-Click Ford
Jim Cook of Electra-Gear
Dave Eisenberg of UC Irvine
Bharat Patel of Ford
Kyle Petrich of Ford

Special Thanks to Professor Roland Schinzinger for his assistance throughout the entire project.

The team would also like to thank the following sponsors for supporting the UC Irvine ELANT III HEV project financially and in kind:

Los Angeles Department of Water & Power
Emerson Industrial Controls
Electra-Gear Electric Motors
Tuttle Click Ford
Johnson Controls
Siemens
American Eagle Wheel Corporation
Goodyear Tire
Saddleback Radiator
Robert Bosch Corporation

as well as companies not mentioned here but listed elsewhere in this volume as supporters of HEV Challenge.

SOURCES

1. California Air Resources Board, Mobile Source Emission Standards Summary, Staff Report, June 30, 1992.

2. Motor Vehicle Manufacturers Association, Manufacturers Motor Vehicle Specifications, 1992 Ford Escort, November 15, 1991.

3. Emerson Industrial Controls, Eclipse 2A Motor Controller Manual, Grand Island, NY, 1992.

4. Helm Automotive Literature, 1991 Geo Metro Shop Manual, 1991.

5. North American Subaru, 1991 Subaru Justy Mechanical Manual, 1991.

6. Morse Industrial Corporation, Morse Chain & Sprockets Catalog RCS-83, 1983.

TABLE 1

VEHICLE SPECIFICATIONS

VEHICLE TYPE : Front engine, front wheel drive, 2 passenger, experimental hybrid electric vehicle

MOTOR

Type _____ 3 phase AC induction motor
Dimensions _____9 in outer diameter x 14.5 length
Controller___ Emerson Eclipse 2A controller with PWM inverter
Power _____15 hp rated 40 bhp @ 5,000 RPM
Torque_____60 lb-ft @ 0 RPM
Redline_____ 6,000 RPM
Weight _____70 lbs

ENGINE

Type_____Suzuki G-10, Inline-3, aluminum block and head
Bore x stroke_____75 (2.92) x
Displacement _____ 997 cc
Compression ratio _____8.5:1
Emissions controls_____catalytic converter with automatic preheater, feedback fuel-air-ratio control
Fuel Delivery system _____ Nippon Denso throttle body fuel injection
Valve gear_____OHC, hydraulic lifters
Power_____50 hp @ 5700 RPM
Torque_____ 58 ft lb @ 3300 RPM
Redline _____ 6000 RPM
Weight _____140 lbs

DRIVETRAIN

Transmission/Transaxle_____ Ford Escort 5-speed manual with powertrain Merge Unit
Clutch _____Dual Electromagnetic Powder
Final-drive ratio_____ 3.62:1

Gear	Ratio
I	3.42
II	1.84
III	1.29
IV	0.97
V	0.73

Weight, transmission _____70 lbs
Weight, Merge Unit _____70 lbs

DIMENSIONS AND CAPACITIES

Wheelbase_____98.4 in
Track,F/R _____56.5/56.5 in
Length _____171.3 in
Width _____66.7 in
Height_____53.6 in
Ground clearance _____10.5 in
Curb weight_____3200 lb
Weight distribution _____ F/R 48/52
Fuel capacity _____12.0 gal
Oil capacity_____ 3.7 qt
Water capacity_____ 4.2 qt

CHASSIS/BODY

Type_____unit construction
Body material _____welded steel stampings

INTERIOR

SAE volume, front seat_____52.2 cu ft
Luggage space_____21.0 cu ft
Seat adjustments_____fore and aft, seatback angle
Restraint systems_____5-point harness

SUSPENSION

F_____Strut type, independent front drive with upper strut mounted coil springs
R _____strut type, independent twin trapezoidal links with trailing links and upper strut mounted coil springs

STEERING

Type_____rack and pinion
Turns lock-to-lock _____4.3
Turning circle curb-to-curb _____ 31.5 ft

BRAKES

F _____9.25x 0.87-in vented disc
R _____9.88x 0.35-in non-vented disc
Power assist_____electric vacuum pump

WHEELS AND TIRES

Wheel size_____5.5 x 13 in
Wheel type_____cast aluminum
Tires _____Goodyear Invicta, P185/70/R13
Inflation pressure_____ F/R32/32

ESTIMATED PERFORMANCE

Zero to 45 mph 14.0 sec
Top speed 75+ mph

ESTIMATED FUEL ECONOMY

HEV mode city driving 45 mpg
Auxiliary mode city driving 35 mpg
HEV mode highway driving 55 mpg
Auxiliary mode highway driving 45 mpg

RANGE

ZEV mode 20+ miles
HEV mode 200+ miles
Auxiliary mode 450+ miles

University of California, Santa Barbara

Keith T. Kedward, Nick DiNapoli, Marc L. Syvertsen,
David Gross, Hyonny Kim, and Michael Wilson
University of California, Santa Barbara

ABSTRACT

A parallel configuration hybrid electric vehicle (HEV) has been designed and built for competition in the *Ford HEV Challenge*. The vehicle is powered by an ethanol (E100) powered internal combustion engine and two battery powered AC induction motors. Power to the road is managed by a central processing unit that interprets driver demand and controls the two propulsion systems based on a firmware stored algorithm and energy storage conditions. The vehicle features efficient, clean use of a renewable fuel, efficient, high voltage AC propulsion; regenerative braking; recyclable lead-acid batteries; recyclable steel frame and Acrylonitrile-Butadiene-Styrene (ABS) plastic body.

INTRODUCTION

Decreasing the automotive contribution to air pollution without compromising vehicle performance necessitates the development of hybrid electric vehicles. The student design team in the College of Engineering at the University of California, Santa Barbara earned participation in the *Ford Hybrid Electric Vehicle Challenge* sponsored by Ford Motor Company, the United States Department of Energy and the Society of Automotive Engineers. The project consists of the design, development and construction of a hybrid electric vehicle for competition in June of 1993. A cut away of the vehicle is shown in Figure 1. The project is a demonstration of sound, disciplined engineering through the effective integration of two energy conversion devices under one hood. The objective is to produce a practical, efficient, safe, environmentally sound prototype from the ground up, powered by a combination of electricity and ethanol. The combination of the two power units results in a clean, efficient vehicle without the severe power and range limitations associated with purely electric vehicles. Energy efficiency, low emissions, and adequate performance distinguish hybrids as the vehicle choice for the future.

VEHICLE CONCEPT - The initial vehicle concept was developed in response to the HEV challenge RFP. It has survived with only minor changes through to competition. The vehicle is designed around the premise that the transition to cars having ultra low and/or zero pollutant emissions should not be accompanied by a decrease in vehicle performance. Due to the current state and unpredictable future of electrochemical energy storage research and development, the transition cannot be made on batteries alone. The use of a moderately powered internal combustion engine in conjunction with an electric drive system provides adequate vehicle performance.

POWERTRAIN CONFIGURATION

The vehicle is a parallel configuration hybrid featuring 4-wheel drive and optional electric-only operation. The configuration is shown in Figure 2. The parallel configuration was chosen because it serves to reduce component sizes since only a fraction of the total vehicle power is transmitted to the road by each propulsion system. In a series hybrid, all of the power flows through each component. Therefore, for the same vehicle power, systems are smaller and lighter in a parallel hybrid. The independent-axle parallel configuration eliminates the need to modulate between two propulsion systems with some sort of differential. In addition, the losses of converting mechanical energy to electricity and back again are eliminated. The two power trains are mechanically independent, but can be coupled through the road if necessary. This powertrain configuration also allows for easy design of a computer controlled, 4-wheel traction control system.

ALTERNATIVE POWER UNIT (APU) - The APU is composed of an engine from a 1992 Geo Metro, linked to a Subaru Electronic Continuously Variable Transmission (ECVT) from a 1990 Subaru Justy. The engine and ECVT are mounted in the front of the vehicle and directly drive the front wheels. Ethanol fuel was chosen for the APU, as noted in the introduction, due to

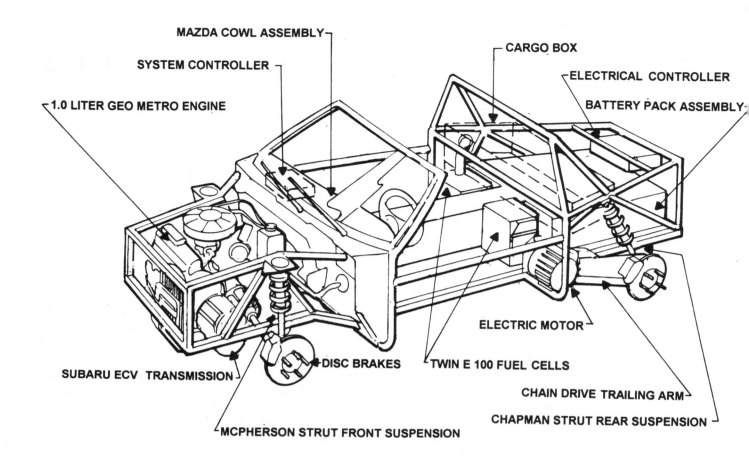

Figure 1: Cut-away view

its renewability, possibilities as a lower-emissions fuel, and to promote more development of its potential. Many challenges were imposed by these choices for an APU, including the conversion of the engine to ethanol fuel, the connection of the Geo engine to the Subaru ECVT, and the connection of the Subaru ECVT output shafts to the Mazda 323 front hubs.

The Geo Metro engine displaces 1.0 liter (61 cu.in.) and has three cylinders. Running on gasoline, it is rated at 36.5 kW (49 hp). The engine size was chosen to give adequate power, but still provide high efficiency and low emissions. The two major concerns in converting the engine to ethanol fuel were the necessary changes in fuel volume and ignition timing, and the compatibility of materials with ethanol.

For use of ethanol fuel, it is necessary to deliver approximately 30% more volume of fuel to the engine, and to advance the ignition timing. The stock throttle body injector was capable of delivering the required fuel volume, but the stock engine control unit was replaced with a programmable engine control system from Motec Systems USA in Huntington Beach, CA. This system allowed complete control and real-time adjustment of the injection and ignition parameters. Dynamometer testing allowed the parameters to be adjusted for ethanol fuel. After tuning, the engine ran well on ethanol, and

delivered a slightly larger maximum power output of 39 kW (52 hp).

Materials Compatibility - Many sources were consulted to determine the compatibility of the materials in the Geo engine with ethanol, and many answers were received. Ultimately, it was necessary to test materials directly for compatibility. The flexible fuel tubing, and a sample of aluminum, among other items, were tested by immersion in ethanol for extended periods of time. No changes were noticed in these materials. Due to the apparent compatibility of these materials, and the difficulty of finding other materials available to substitute in the engine in prototype quantities, a decision was made to retain the current materials. At the completion of dynamometer testing of the engine, no decay or other adverse effects of the ethanol fuel were noted on the engine components.

ECVT Adaptation - A set of adapter plates was made to allow the engine and ECVT to be bolted together. A roller clutch was installed in each drive axle to allow the electric motors to drive the vehicle without back driving the transmission and engine.

Emissions Control Strategy - The emissions control strategy for the UCSB HEV is similar to that used in most current small cars. Actively controlled fuel injection, including oxygen sensor feedback, exhaust

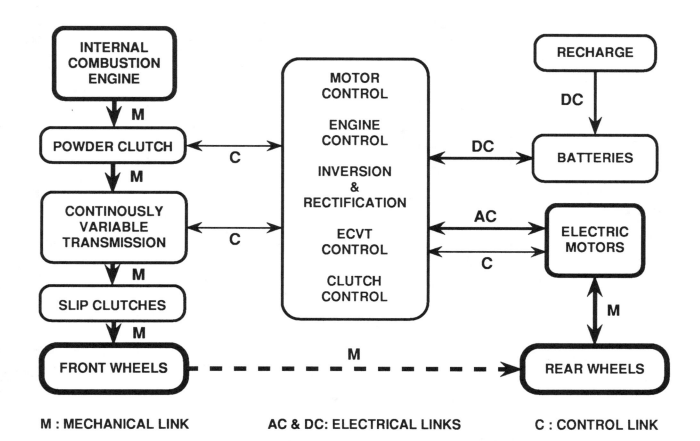

M : MECHANICAL LINK   AC & DC: ELECTRICAL LINKS   C : CONTROL LINK

Figure 2: Parallel Hybrid Configuration

gas recirculation, and a catalytic converter are used to control tailpipe emissions, and a standard charcoal canister system is used to control evaporative emissions. Besides these common controls, however, the choice of a small engine reduces overall emissions volume, and the use of ethanol fuel potentially could result in lower emissions. Unfortunately, emissions testing equipment was not available during dynamometer testing of the engine, but future chassis dynamometer testing may help to determine actual emissions levels.

The catalyst substrate was manufactured and donated by Allied Signal Corporation, is formulated for use with ethanol, and was canned by Car Sound Exhaust of Rancho Cucamunga, CA. The stock exhaust gas recirculation and positive crankcase ventilation systems was retained from the Metro engine.

The stock Geo Metro evaporative emissions control system is used. It stores fuel vapors from the fuel tanks in a charcoal canister while the engine is not running. These vapors are then released to be burned in the engine when it is running under normal conditions. This prevents venting of such vapors to the atmosphere.

Fuel Consumption - The overall strategy for controlling energy consumption on the UCSB HEV was to connect both power sources to the road in as direct

and efficient a manner as possible. Each system was then made as efficient as this design allowed. Fuel consumption was controlled on the UCSB HEV by many factors. The car was designed to be small, so that a small engine would be acceptable, and the aerodynamic drag and the rolling resistance were limited to some extent. Efficiency was a driving factor in the choice of the Electronic Continuously Variable Transmission (ECVT). The ECVT is more efficient than a standard automatic transmission, and it allows the engine to operate more often in ranges where it is more efficient. In addition, the control strategy may use the ethanol engine under driving conditions where it is more efficient, and use the electric motors in other conditions.

ELECTRIC MOTOR DRIVETRAIN - The electric drive train consists of 12 deep-cycle lead-acid batteries; two 16.5 N•m AC induction motors and controller; and a double reduction, constant ratio chain drive system. The system was designed to provide low speed (<45 mph) operation, adequate electric-only acceleration, additional power for hybrid mode acceleration, and power compensation at speed in hybrid mode.

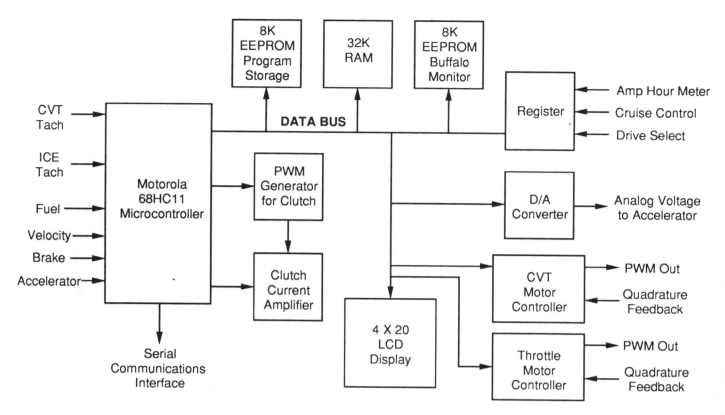

Figure 3: Central Processing Unit

AC Induction Motors - High voltage AC induction motors are used for superior efficiency, superior reliability, and low weight. The motors and controller provide regenerative braking and automatic differential action for the rear wheels. The controller converts the 144 VDC input from the battery pack in to three-phase AC to drive the motors, and determines the speed and torque output of the motors.

Chain Drive - A fixed 9.9 to 1 gear ratio was chosen due to the exceptional torque characteristics of AC induction motors and the available 12,000 rpm of the particular motors used. This ratio is achieved through a double reduction of ANSI 40 Roller chain passes. A double reduction was chosen for two reasons: the high ratio necessitates the use of two passes, and the use of an intermediate shaft located along the line of trailing arm rotation provides motor placement flexibility and zero chain stretch as the suspension moves. .

Energy Storage - After many months of investigation, research and deliberation, deep-cycle lead-acid batteries were chosen as the electrochemical storage means for the UCSB HEV. Although lead-acid batteries are "old-technology", no superior alternative emerged after looking at performance, price and recyclability. The battery pack is designed to be easily upgradable when, and if, a higher performance, cost effective alternative is developed.

Electric Power Consumption - The general strategy for creating an efficient vehicle explained above, in the

APU section, also applies to the electric systems. In addition, the electric motors and motor controller were chosen for their high efficiency. Regenerative braking also helps to conserve energy which would otherwise be wasted.

OPERATING STRATEGY

The purpose of the control strategy is to balance the use of the two resources (ethanol and electricity) to maximize efficiency, minimize emissions, and produce adequate power for acceleration. The operating strategy, and the vehicle in general, are designed around a freeway driving cycles (LA-4) with limited top speed. The control system consists of a central processing unit that controls an array of other processing units and actuators. This system is presented in Figure 3.

CPU DESIGN - The CPU forms the electronic link between the "gas" or power demand pedal, and the engine and motors. It is responsible for signaling the two power sources to generate certain levels of torque based on driver demand, the predetermined algorithm, and the relative amounts of energy available to each conversion device. For example, if there is much more ethanol than battery energy available, a proportional amount of increased demand will be shifted to the ICE. A filtering system is used on the input from the accelerator pedal to channel high frequency demands to

48

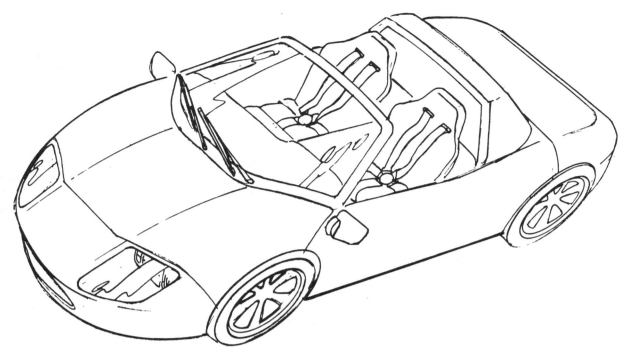

Figure 4: Styling Concept

the electric motors which can change torque rapidly with zero emissions and very high efficiency. The ICE will then slowly change its torque output in response to low frequency changes in driving cycle.

In addition to the hybrid mode, a "Zero Emissions Vehicle (ZEV) Mode" is available, which uses only electric power, and an ethanol only mode which uses only the engine.

The most difficult challenge in design of the CPU was to integrate the control of the electric motors and APU to allow smooth transition of power from one source to the other. Besides the task of programming this transition, it was necessary to develop interfaces between the inputs, outputs, and CPU. The "gas" pedal drives a potentiometer, the output of which is converted into digital form for processing by the controller. In order to control the engine, the digital signals are processed and sent to a servo motor which controls the throttle valve. Similar data conversion was necessary to drive the electronic powder clutch and the electric motors.

STRUCTURE AND CHASSIS

The vehicle is built on a steel space frame, using existing front suspension components and a rear trailing arm suspension of original design.

FRAME - The tubular space frame has been designed of mild steel to allow for easy integration of the many systems of the hybrid electric vehicle. Frame stiffness was the primary design driver. The primary structural group is a rectangular ladder frame base. This base has been designed to provide high stiffness while carrying most of the loads directly. Extending up from the ladder frame are triangular shock towers designed to hold the upper ends of the shocks and coils. These towers have been designed to carry the full weight of the vehicle with the aid of struts and cross-bars extending between the towers. The front and rear roll structures define the remaining overall shape of the vehicle. Two side impact members on each side of the passenger compartment protect the passengers in the event of a side collision. Members extending around the rear of the frame protect the batteries in the event of a collision. The frame was analyzed using both conventional and finite element methods to ensure adequate stiffness without excess weight.

Materials - All frame members are constructed of seamless mild steel tubing. The base of the frame uses rectangular tubing, and roll bars and extensions use round tubes. The total frame weight is estimated to be 198 lbs. Steel was chosen for its low cost, easy machinability, and recyclability.

CHASSIS - The vehicle utilizes brakes, steering, and front suspension systems from production vehicles. The hydraulic brake system uses Mazda 323 components, with the rear disc brakes from an Izusu Impulse. The steering is a Mazda 323 rack and pinion unit. The front suspension is also a Mazda stock strut system. The rear suspension is an original trailing arm with coil-over strut design. The windshield and firewall assembly was used as a whole from the Mazda. The adaptation of existing components saved time and cost in the prototype development.

BODY AND ERGONOMICS

The vehicle is a two passenger, open top roadster. The styling concept is shown in Figure 4. Plastic body panels were created for the exterior. The interior and driver controls were designed for ease of driving, familiarity, and comfort.

BODY STYLING - Contemporary sport styling is used in simplistic form with aerodynamics in mind. The intent of the styling is to present a fun alternative to the stereotypical conception of the 'electric vehicle'. The body is accented by five spoke alloy wheels, composite ellipsoid halogen head lamps, Corvette tail lights, and a removable top with snap closures. The entire front and rear sections are each one piece, hinged to open away from the vehicle for ease of access to all vehicle systems. A soft cover is provided for inclement weather.

BODY MATERIALS - The vehicle body is constructed of vacuum formed ABS plastic panels for recyclability; superior dent, corrosion, and abrasion resistance; and ease of manufacture. The vehicle bulkheads are constructed of Nomex honeycomb for strength, rigidity, light weight, and non-flammability.

ERGONOMICS - The driver controls are familiar and have been carefully placed to allow operation by any driver. Most of the stock Mazda 323 controls have been retained including the steering wheel and pedals. Cockpit displays have been modified or changed to reflect the hybrid nature of the vehicle and to provide the necessary information to the driver. The shifter has three positions: reverse, neutral, and forward, and a mode switch on the dashboards selects Zero Emissions Mode, Hybrid Mode, or Ethanol Mode.

VEHICLE SAFETY

Safety was a major driving factor in the design and construction of the UCSB HEV vehicle. Care was taken not only to meet the minimum safety requirements specified by Ford, but to exceed those requirements when possible. This philosophy influenced many parts of the car, from the ground up. The chassis was designed to be as strong as possible, to insure the passenger compartment would not be damaged severely in the case of a collision. The battery box was made from Lexan, which is light weight, resistant to potential acid leaks, relatively high strength and tougher than other plastics. The battery box also has a safety belt system which loops around the main group of batteries to help prevent them from entering the passenger compartment in the event of a frontal impact. The crush volume is also designed to help in this event. Though not required, a high density foam was inserted into the crush area to absorb and dissipate as much energy as possible.

Placement and construction of the two 5 gallon fuel cells was also done with safety in mind. Not only does the placement of the fuel cells inside the body, and within the frame rails of the vehicle reduce the possibility

of puncture, but the low density foam baffles inside reduce the risk of explosion even in that event. Finally, the roll cage is reinforced with two extra members between the front roll hoop and rear roll bar. These tubes are designed to help maintain the integrity of the passenger compartment in the event of roll over, and to greatly reduce the chance of the front roll hoop folding into the passenger compartment.

MANUFACTURABILITY

The use of mild steel for the frame provided an easily machinable and formable medium of which to construct the frame. All machining and welding operations were performed by students at the UCSB Mechanical Engineering Department student machine shop. Components purchased and integrated into the vehicle were all common, off-the-shelf components.

Some changes would be made if the vehicle were to be put into production. The space frame design would be modified for compatibility with automated manufacturing processes, the rear trailing arms would be constructed of steel stampings rather than welded and machined tubes, and an original windshield and interface would be designed. For the body panels, injection molding would be better suited to large quantity production than vacuum forming, and would allow the use of different plastics and a more lightweight product. For the APU, an engine and transmission package designed to go together would be designed, and the fuel injection algorithm developed with the programmable system would be programmed into a less expensive production system.

CONCLUSION

The design and construction of this HEV has been an educational experience for all involved. Some parts of the project were successful, and some could be improved.

Some changes which might be made in a future vehicle would be to use front end components (engine, transmission, suspension, steering) all from one vehicle, to design the frame with the knowledge of the exact dimensions of components to be added to it, and to design a new windshield interface. However, the project is considered successful as a first prototype construction.

The UCSB HEV has been designed to demonstrate the practicality of hybrid vehicles in general, and specifically a parallel hybrid. In addition to providing a transition to lower- and zero-emissions vehicles of the future, this hybrid shows that such vehicles need not compromise styling, drivability, performance, or practicality.

The UCSB HEV team would like to acknowledge the invaluable assistance of our sponsors, advisors, and the University, without which this project would not be possible.

TRANSITIONAL ZERO EMISSION VEHICLE TECHNOLOGY: THE CSUN HYBRID ELECTRICAL VEHICLE

Phyllis Russell, David Borden, Maria Williams, and Salvador Gracia
California State University Northridge

ABSTRACT

California State University Northridge School of Engineering converted a Ford Escort Wagon into a Hybrid Electric Vehicle for the 1993 HEV competition. The purpose was to implement a design according to the criteria dictated by the event. The HEV, named the Voltswagon, was designed for optimum performance at the competition. System modeling was performed as a guide in component selection to enhance performance. Five lead-acid batteries were used in a series configuration to supply electrical energy to a traction motor. Energy needs of the batteries, auxiliary systems, and traction motor were monitored by a system controller designed specifically for the HEV. The original IC engine was replaced with a smaller engine (auxiliary power unit or APU.) This APU was fueled by M85 to enhance the low emission characteristics of the HEV. The total design also encompassed safety and ergonomic considerations.

INTRODUCTION

Air pollution is a global concern. In the state of California, there is pending legislation for mandating 2% of manufactured vehicles to be emissions free by 1998. The criteria for a ZEVs (Zero Emissions Vehicles) is currently satisfied only by electric powered vehicles, however, present electric vehicle technology is restricted in performance and ergonomics. The ZEV performance is limited by excessive battery mass, limited range, speed, and acceleration. HEVs (Hybrid electric vehicles), are an alternative to the ZEV. The HEV consists of an electric drive powered by batteries and an APU (auxiliary power unit). The APU provides energy to the drive system with the ultimate goal of keeping emissions to a minimum. Various fuels can be used with the APU.

The FORD HEV Challenge allows preselected universities across the United States to participate in a movement toward the design of low emission vehicles. The competition will manifest many design philosophies and research for application to future vehicle design. This event also serves as a valuable educational experience for a senior design project. The nature of the project lets students realize the importance of teamwork for the pursuit of technical success.

The School of Engineering at California State University, Northridge (CSUN) has long demonstrated interest in vehicle competition. Our vehicle design experience dates back to 1985; the opportunity to develop and manufacture a HEV will provide technical insight to an emission free future. The CSUN HEV, known as the Voltswagon, represents a two year, senior design effort. The success of the project was made possible by the sponsorship of FORD, the US Department of Energy, and the Society of Automotive Engineers.

The design philosophy behind the Voltswagon was dictated by the nature of the FORD HEV Challenge. Critical design decisions were governed by event point allocation, vehicle performance, fuel economy, cost, safety, and reliability. The purpose of this technical report is to convey our design in terms of the aforementioned criteria.

DESIGN PHILOSOPHY

The CSUN Voltswagon design was dependent on ultimate performance in the Ford HEV Challenge. An evaluation of the points allocated per event gave indication of critical design areas. Component selection was biased by cost, weight, and performance parameters; however, the Voltswagon design decisions were geared toward winning the competition.

Sixty percent of the competition points are allocated to dynamic events. The design strategy for the vehicle began with an optimization analysis of dynamic event scoring. The dynamic events include Emissions (15%), Commuter Challenge (15%), Efficiency (12.5%), Acceleration (10%), and Range (7.5%). Evaluation of the point criteria yielded a correlation between events. Performance in the Range event has an impact on point allocation for emissions and efficiency and almost half of the dynamic points rely on the range performance. The vehicle design focused on Range criteria of travelling forty miles at forty miles per hour. This minimum performance criteria was the basis of our design philosophy.

Prior to the design of the electric drive system for the Voltswagon, a force balance on the vehicle was considered, as shown in Figure 1. Our objective was to determine the motive force required to maintain the desired performance of forty miles per hour.

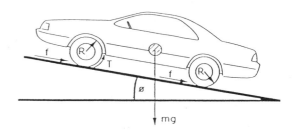

Figure 1
Vehicle forces

Applying Newton's Second Law to balance the vehicle forces:

$$\sum F = \frac{T}{R} - C_d \left(\frac{\rho V^2}{2} \right) A_{ref} - \mu mg \cos\theta - mg \sin\theta = ma \qquad (1)$$

Simplifying this equation for cruise conditions, meaning constant velocity on level ground, the torque requirement at the wheels becomes a function of aerodynamic drag and rolling resistance.

$$T = \left(\frac{1}{2} C_d A_{ref} \rho V^2 + \mu mg \right) R \qquad (2)$$

Both relationships served as governing equations for component selection, parametric analysis, energy consumption, and performance fine-tuning. The torque at the wheels can be optimized by parameter adjustment. Variables within design control are the drag coefficient, the vehicle frontal area, the vehicle mass, the rolling radius, and the rolling friction. The Voltswagon frame and body remained stock in terms of the reference frontal area, but the drag coefficient was reduced by a belly-pan implementation. The strive for mass reduction remained constant throughout the development process. The wheel radius was increased to improve our speed performance, and an alternative tire selection allowed for a decrease in rolling resistance. Now, let us introduce the specifics or our design.

Figure 2 below shows the components that were placed in the engine compartment. The decision to place these items in the engine compartment were based on competition restrictions and decisions to use the existing drivetrain. Each of the components shown will be discussed in the report.

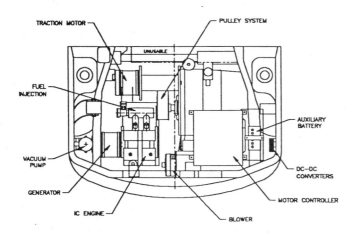

Figure 2: Component Layout

ELECTRIC MOTOR

An electric motor had to be chosen that would deliver the requirements for the EV mode of the competition. In order to determine a motor size for the Ford Escort HEV conversion, many variables had to be considered. These variables include torque curves, efficiencies, transmission ratios, vehicle weight, wheel radius, and coefficient of drag. Motor inertias, gear inertias and gear efficiencies were also taken into consideration. Ease of installation, cost and weight were also important.

Initially, a system of three motors were considered: one in back for cruising, and two in front for acceleration. However, the cost was found to be exorbitant, the system would be heavy, and the controller for this system would be quite complex.

Many motors appropriate for HEV use were considered including relatively inexpensive brushed DC motors. The high cost of maintenance due to speed limitations imposed by the design, worn brush riggings, rotation windings, and commutators would translate into frequent brush replacements. The high maintenance costs coupled with low efficiencies, made this selection unattractive. Therefore a DC brushless motor was chosen.

A motor was chosen that would minimize energy required for the EV mode in the competition, and yet provide acceptable acceleration performance. This decision was based on cost penalties incurred by a larger engine, which would not be offset by the potential points gained from an increased performance. Our drive motor is a Unique Mobility DR 156 SW coupled to a CR 130-200 controller with regeneration.

INTERNAL COMBUSTION ENGINE

An internal combustion engine was required that would supply the power to a generator to produce the drive power required in the HEV cruise mode. In choosing an IC engine, cost was the major consideration. A 250 cc four stroke water cooled IC engine was located that fulfilled the severe cost restraints, while at the same time being capable of supplying the power necessary. This IC engine was easily placed in the engine compartment because of its compact size. An engine speed was selected based on its efficiency as shown in Figure 3. A number of 250 cc engines are available; we chose a Kawasaki Ninja 250. This unit produces up to 30 hp base power at 10,500 RPM.

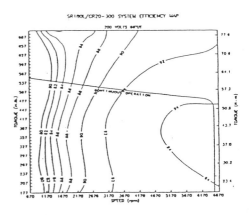

fig.3

POWERTRAIN DESIGN

The power train design consisted of coupling a 20 hp traction motor to the vehicles stock transmission. Due to the traction motor's high rpm operation, a step down ratio of 2:1 was implemented. The basic design consisted of efficiently coupling the traction motor to the transmission by means of a synchronous belt (timing tooth belt). The design of the power train incorporated the flexibility of going with or without the stock clutch/flywheel assembly with minimal modifications. The design was optimized for compactness due to space limitations in the existing engine compartment. The decision of using synchronous belts was obvious in that they are more efficient than V-belts and are also lighter in weight. An aluminum flywheel was used for the clutch surface, in order to save weight, compared to the original Escort flywheel.

TRANSMISSION AND IC ENGINE SHAFT CONFIGURATION

Analysis and design of the IC engine drive shaft and the transmission shaft was a challenging problem (see Figure 4).

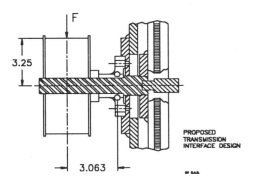

Figure 4: Transmission Shaft

In both designs, the existing shafts needed to be extended to incorporate a proposed pulley system for gearing. Due to space and weight considerations, both designs called for their respective shafts to be cantilevered. Adding extension to the existing shafts created complications in the analysis. To simplify the process, a best case scenario was used.

In the transmission shaft, a stepped shaft was to be welded to the clutch assembly and supported outside the transmission face plate by a flanged bearing unit . The longest unsupported distance was from the bearing to the center of the pulley. The stresses at this bearing were deemed to be the most significant for analysis purposes.

For the IC engine shaft, the design was much more complex. Since (before modification) the existing shaft only extended for 0.5 inches (12.7 mm) and was splined, it was decided to couple the extension shaft with a pin. The shape of the engine case required the pulley to be located at distance from the supporting engine bearing and from the pin that was located out on the shaft. Again, the longest unsupported distance was from the bearing to the pulley. The stresses at that bearing and also the shear stress on the pin would be analyzed.

To analyze the stresses on the shafts, the loading had to be considered. Both shafts were delivering power and therefore seeing a torque. The force, at the center of the pulley was also creating a bending moment. Looking at fatigue for rotating shafts, a differential element located on a shaft would undergo an equal amount of compression and tension within one cycle which exemplifies to a case of fully reversed bending. On first examination, since the competition would only last a week, the impulse was to only be concerned with the static case. However, a quick calculation shows that at 3500 rpm, a shaft reaches a million cycles in 4.75 hours. Therefore, both shafts were analyzed statically and dynamically in cases of uniaxial, combined loading involving bending and shear stress.

The passing or failing of the designs would be dependent on their factor of safety. For this analysis, the safety factor was solved for, since the design data was known. The factor of safety equation used is known as Goodman's linear relationship (Ref. 1), and is based on a modified Goodman Diagram. For an optimal passing condition, a safety factor of four would be required. This value was arrived at by using a recommended factor of safety of two (for well-known materials operating under reasonably constant environmental conditions, subjected to loads and stresses that can be determined readily (Ref. 2), and then doubling the safety factor to four to allow for impact loading (Ref. 3). If absolutely necessary, this total factor of safety could be modified to three since the designs are based on stringent space and weight requirements.

The transmission shaft design passed the factor of safety criteria. Originally this design had included another bearing at the end of the shaft, but due to the space limitations, the original design had to be modified. It was important that the new design passed safety and function requirements.

The IC engine shaft design failed the factor of safety requirement in fatigue by a substantial margin. The shaft could not be left cantilevered. The pin shear stress was well within the limits of the materials based on the given simplified assumptions. If this design were to be used, it would have had to be looked at in much closer detail.

The transmission shaft design could be implemented. The actual horsepower delivered would be less than that used in the analysis. The pulley would not be 100% efficient, so the force on the shaft would be less than the figure used in the analysis. Even with the very conservative analysis, the design passed the factor of safety requirements. By utilizing this design, space was conserved.

The IC engine shaft design could not be implemented without adding another support to the end of the shaft. The space considerations did not allow for that. It was also questionable whether the design utilizing the pin would be able to function for the length of the competition. If it did not, it would be impossible to replace the pin and shaft without machining operations. It was decided to pursue an alternative design employing a small gear set using the IC engine crank shaft. This would fit in the given space, and be more practical to implement. It appears that with the new configuration, there will be no problem passing the safety factor considerations.

The generator was driven directly off the IC engine crankshaft through the use of a gear set. The existing clutch assembly within the IC engine was removed, along with the shifting mechanism, shifting lever, and the entire transmission. The clutch crankcase cover was replaced by a flat 3/8" aluminum plate, upon which the generator was mounted. A pair of spur gears were selected from the discarded transmission. The generator maximum power output occurs at 6500 RPM. An engine speed of approximately 8500 rpm is the minimum speed at which the IC engine will produce the power required by the generator at a speed of 6500 rpm. A speed ratio of 1.27 was needed to accomplish the desired speeds for the IC engine and the generator. A gear set that matched this requirement was then selected.

Since the gearing system solved the IC engine - generator interface, a compact, efficient transfer of energy between the IC engine and the generator was possible. The CSUN Voltswagon incorporated a series electrical design rather than parallel, meaning that the electrical energy from the generator goes directly to the 120 V electrical buss.

BATTERIES

The main source of energy used in this vehicle is provided by five on board batteries. The battery selection was a crucial decision that ultimately affected the vehicle's acceleration and range. Several types of batteries considered. Among them were Lead-acid, Nickel-Cadmium (Ni-Cad) and Nickel-Iron. Other candidates, such as Sodium Sulfur, were rejected from consideration based on cost and commercial availability.

Lead-acid batteries appear to have the best combination of desirable attributes. Lead-acid batteries have a high watt hour to dollar ratio and a dependable charge/discharge cycle life. They are commercially viable at an affordable cost. There is also the possibility of recycling lead-acid batteries that adds to their appeal. Unlike Ni-Cad batteries, these batteries do not require special charging schemes. However, there are a few disadvantages to lead-acid batteries. They consist of a low specific energy density, increased weight and larger size. Additionally, lead-acid batteries require periodic maintenance to prolong their cycle life.

Nickel-iron batteries maintain a higher energy density when compared with lead-acid batteries. Specifically, 50 Whr/kg to 30 Whr/Kg, a 20 Whr/kg margin in favor of these Nickel Iron batteries. They also offered a 40% reduction in battery weight for approximately the same amount of energy density. An added plus is that the Nickel -iron batteries have more charge/discharge cycles than the conventional lead acid batteries. Unfortunately, their price is very high since they just recently entered the consumer market.

In third place were the Nickel-Cadmium batteries. One of the most notable characteristics of the Ni Cad is their low internal resistance which yields a high current. It should also be noted that the Ni Cad batteries known as "Flat Discharge Curve" which occurs at low to medium current drains. Other primary benefits of Nickel-Cadmium batteries include low maintenance, excellent long-term storage, rapid charge, good charge retention and a higher energy density than lead-acid. The downfall for these Nickel-Cadmium batteries is that they must be discharged fully before attempting to recharge them.

Therefore, the design of their charging system will have to overcome the thermal runaway effect (aka "Viscous Cycling"). Adding to their downfall was their significant cost which averaged twelve times that of the lead acid type.

After extensively researching the various types of batteries that were commercially available, a Gill #6381 battery was selected. The battery is a 24 volt, lead acid battery that weighs approximately 80 pounds. It was selected for its excellent energy density, capacity vs. discharge rate, high watt hour to dollar ratio, dependable charge/discharge cycle life, weight and cost.

BATTERY TESTING - The actual battery testing began with a fully charged battery, which had a specific gravity of 1.285 to 1.290 and a terminal voltage of 25 to 26 volts. After each battery had its specific gravity and initial voltage from each cell measured, a current flow was selected (i.e. 30 amps) to flow from the battery. A load cell simulated a loading condition by providing a significant amount of resistance. The necessary resistance was modeled by filling a 55 gallon drum with water. To commence the current flow in the loop, four electrode plates were lowered into the drum. The DAS recorded the voltage and current levels within the testing arrangement. Battery efficiency was then calculated.

During testing, when the voltage began to drop at a high rate, the circuit was disconnected by lifting the electrode plates from the load cell. Shortly thereafter, the specific gravity of each battery cell was measured. After disconnecting the circuit, the battery had the opportunity to recharge itself as an open circuit. Roughly two hours were used for recharging the battery. Then, the same load was applied so that the recovery performance of the battery could be examined. This testing procedure was conducted repeatedly. Thus, various amperages were drawn from the battery. Drawing different levels of current from the battery created a range of speed and depths of discharge.

The method of charging the batteries may be constant current charging or constant voltage charging (or a combination of both). However, to obtain maximum service life and capacity, along with acceptable recharge time, an economical constant-voltage current-limited charging method was used. This method applies constant voltage to the battery and limits the initial charge current. As the terminal voltage of the discharged battery increases, its current acceptance decreases. The battery is fully charged once the current stabilizes at a low level.

Aside from the charging method, the charging configuration was determined. Two configurations were considered; parallel and series. It was concluded that series charging is preferable to parallel charging. The series configuration does not require extra wiring and/or switches (that add to the cost and use high currents) to convert the already existing series of batteries into parallel. This transformation from series to parallel would also increase the amount of power loss. The series configuration saves time, money and reduces the possibility of creating shorts and explosions at the competition site. For the series configuration, all that is required is one main switch to disconnect the battery pack from the rest of the system.

The energy required by the vehicle to maintain a speed of

40 mph for one hour was calculated to be 5.7KW. This calculation assumed that the vehicle minimum target weight would be met, and that auxiliary systems (headlights, wipers, heating system, etc.) would not be used.

Battery tests were conducted to determine how many batteries would supply the required 5.7 KWH. Minimum and maximum limits of possible current draws were determined to be 30 and 66 amps, respectively. When 30 amps were drawn, the battery output of 710 watts was maintained for 1.61 hours. This resulted in an energy output of 1.14KWH. A second test drained 66 amps from the battery. This test showed that battery output averaged 1499 watts for 0.53 hours. This is equivalent to 0.794 KWH. Using these tests it was determined that five 24 volt lead acid batteries were needed to achieve the required power output of 5.7 KWH.

BATTERY HEATING - Battery performance is also temperature dependent. A thermal model of the lead acid batteries predicted a temperature rise for the charging and discharging of each battery to be 11.7°F and 6.1°F, respectively. These amounts are not enough to significantly impact battery performance. It would have been advantageous to incorporate a battery heating system to increase the energy output of the batteries. Experimentation, however, revealed that the energy and time requirements for any significant performance increase were too great. Although investigated, battery heating was not practical to incorporate into the CSUN Voltswagon design.

BATTERY HOUSING - The batteries are housed in a box which has several functions. It restrains battery movement, separates the batteries from passengers in case of explosion or fire, and keeps hydrogen fumes confined until they are exhausted to the outside. The material selection for the housing had to be strong, lightweight, and fire resistant. Several materials were considered. Sheet metal or aluminum were too conductive and could become untouchable with an electrical malfunction. Polyethylene would become soft with any kind of battery heating and would not hold its shape. Fiberglass honeycomb composite is stiff, lightweight, fire resistant, and easy to manufacture, however, it will not hold up well structurally. Therefore it was decided to build a frame of aluminum and to place composite panels in between.

Although it would have been ideal to heat the batteries, other electrical components required cooling. The two systems that required cooling were the traction motor and the generator. Each of these components required separate blowers (fans). The blowers were selected based on calculated required flow rates (40 cfm) and pressures.

A ventilation system was required for the battery box. A 24 VDC axial brushless fan was chosen because it fulfilled the requirements for battery box ventilation; power consumptions is 6 Watts.

GENERATOR - Cost was the major factor used in choosing a generator. A generator was available from a previous project. Tests were conducted on this generator investigating if it would fulfill the HEV system requirements. Knowing the generators maximum output power at a specific speed, all that was needed was an IC engine that could supply the

required energy to the generator. Since generator output was 3 phase AC, a rectifier was necessary to convert AC power to DC power. It was decided to purchase a rectifier. Purchasing the rectifier reduced time for implementation. We incorporated a Unique Mobility DR 127 SW CD brushless motor/generator.

DC DC Converter

A DC to DC converter was required to convert the main bus voltage (120 VDC) to 24 VDC and 12 VDC to operate auxiliary loads. The 12 VDC system supplies power to the horn, turn signals, brake lights, vacuum booster pump for the brake system, windshield wipers, headlights and gages. Cooling fans required by the traction motor and generator as well as a recirculating fan for the battery box required a 24 VDC system.

Two DC-DC converters provided a convenient method for converting voltages. One converter transformed 120 volts to 24 volts (200 watts) and supplied the 24 volt system, while the 12 volt system (400 watts) was supplied by another converter. The 12 V system is parallel with a 12 V starter battery for the APU.

Two DC-DC converters were selected that were capable of supplying high power requirements. These power requirements were based on calculated service loads. The maximum power consumption for the vehicle would be 689 watts. The DC-DC converter paralleled with the 12 V battery, will have no problem supplying this peak power.

SYSTEM CONTROLLER

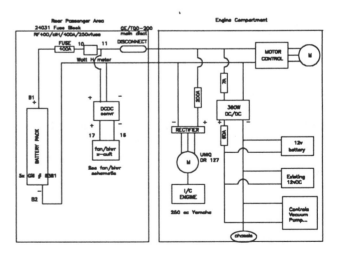

Figure 5: System Controller Configuration

Early on it was decided that a controller would be needed to throttle and dual inject the APU. Once an I.C. engine had been selected as the APU unit, it became apparent that the time that this controller had available to perform the duties of throttle control and fuel injection would be limited due to the high speeds at which the engine had to operate. Thus, any attempts to monitor other system areas, such as voltages and currents, could be hampered by this limited time span. A system controller as shown in Figure 5, offered the benefits of being able to monitor any desired area, perform some simple controls, output data for operator information, and generate a signal for APU speed control, all without burdening the EFI/Throttle controller with these tasks. Since it was not to perform any time dependent functions, its speed of operation was not so critical, and it was eventually decided to implement this type of control strategy into the HEV.

The controller's primary task is to communicate with the EFI/Throttle controller (hereafter referred to as the 'slave') via a three-line parallel interface. One line carries the APU enable signal, which tells the slave controller to initiate its engine start-up sequence. A second line is an input from the slave which tells the system controller that the APU has warmed up and is ready to begin throttle control. The third line is an output which, when low, tells the slave to decrease engine speed; a high signal is sent to raise the speed. (See Speed Control below)

The controller continuously monitors six analog input voltages: bus voltage, battery current, generator current, electric motor speed, electric motor temperature, and generator temperature. A voltage divider circuit had to be built for the bus voltage and motor speed voltage, and an RC filter had to be designed for monitoring currents, which was done by measuring the voltage drop across a shunt. A microcontroller on-board temperature sensor is used as the reference for the temperature measurements, which are achieved with K-type thermocouples. These six signals are read 50 times, averaged, multiplied by a gain, and given an offset in less than three tenths of a second. Signals were additionally conditioned with a combination gain-filter circuit which consists of op-amps and capacitors built into the hardware.

The controller also controls several devices via relays. One relay enables the electric motor controller by connecting two low powerlines available from the motor controller. Another relay enables a speed limiting circuit, which is essentially a resistor put in series with the speed signal sent from the acceleration pedal to the motor controller. The remaining two pairs of relays are controls for the centrifugal blowers used to cool the electric motor and generator respectively. One relay on the pair turns on the blower to a 'low ' setting, the other to a high setting. The motor blower is always on low when the vehicle is operating, and will switch to high if the temperature calculated from above reaches a pre-set limit set in the software. The generator blower will turn on low once the APU is started, and will also switch to high if some pre-set temperature is reached. Note that if the system controller fails, all relays return to the open position, turning off the electric motor, and the start signal the slave controller goes low, which signals the slave to disable the APU.

Finally, a 4 X 40 LCD screen is configured to show all the analog inputs, plus some calculated values such as the battery state of charge (estimated) and the current going to the electric motor. A pushbutton changes the screen to display the status of the APU, the blowers, and the selected mode (HEV, APU, EV). If the temperature in either the generator or motor reaches some pre-set limit, or if the battery state of charge goes below some limit, or if the APU has been signalled to start and is not yet ready, alarm messages will flash on the screen to inform the operator.

SPEED CONTROL - Generator voltage is related to the speed of rotation of the generator. Current is related to the torque supplied. There are several potential drains on the generated power: the electric motor to supply motive force, the batteries in a charging state, and the DC-DC converters which are used to operate the 12V system requirements and the cooling blowers. The batteries discharge when the supplied voltage (the bus voltage) dips below their combined cell EMF, and they charge when the voltage is above that level. Since power is a function of voltage and current, the I.C. engine driving the generator has limited torque, and since the generator must operate at a significant rate of speed to produce adequate voltage (130V at 6500 rpm), it was decided that the batteries should not become severely discharged if possible in order to prevent them from current limiting the system at high operating voltages. This led to the strategy of only using the batteries for acceleration while in HEV or APU modes, allowing the APU to produce the power for steady state cruise while the batteries either charge or remain idle.

Of course, the competition calls for a minimum electric-only distance for a high points score, so this vehicle will be capable of travelling until the batteries are severely drained. The limitation at the battery-drained point is that the APU would have to supply the acceleration power, which would be low since the APU was designed to be small in order to decrease fuel consumption and thus emissions.

Therefore, the following strategy will be applied to control the APU speed. If the vehicle is in the EV mode, no APU action will be taken: the system controller will monitor the analog signals and control the electric motor blower. In HEV or APU mode, however, the APU will be started, allowed to warm, and then be signalled to 1) increase speed if the generated power is below some pre-set maximum AND the batteries are not charging beyond some set limit, 2) decrease speed if the generator is producing power above some pre-set maximum OR the batteries are charging beyond some limit. This will set the voltage level, which in turn will enable the batteries to either charge or discharge depending on the conditions. If accelerating, the APU will become quickly overloaded, slow down, and allow the batteries to start discharging. At cruise, the speed will again increase so that the batteries are at either a charge state or neutral state. Additionally, if the APU speed hits some lower limit and it is still overloaded (indicating depleted batteries) the motor speed limiter relay is enabled, which will lower the top speed of the vehicle and thus decrease the load on the APU.

The emissions control strategy involved several systems including the fuel injection microcontroller, fuel selection, fuel delivery to the ICE (carburetion versus fuel injection), and exhaust gas treatment. The fuel injection microcontroller performs three operations. One is to regulate the flow of fuel into the manifold via the injectors, another to operate a start/stop procedure for the combustion engine, and finally to control the incoming air flow by throttling the internal combustion engine using a stepper motor.

All of the processes will be performed by the continuous monitoring of the vital signs of the engine. The microcontroller gets input from sensors as to the change of the operation of the internal combustion engine and then corrects either the fuel flow or the position of the throttle depending on the need of the system for proper operation. The sensors that are monitored are the manifold temperature and pressure, coolant temperature, exhaust (O2-sensor), and engine speed.

FUEL CONTROL - The electronic fuel injection system (EFI) is a vital part of the engine operation and emissions control. A carburetion system will not suffice to meet the emissions standards expected for the competition using the M85 fuel. The injectors will have to be controlled as to the need of the engine. The microcontroller reads the signals from the sensors and then adjusts the injectors for an exact quantity of fuel to be released into the manifold. This will keep the engine running properly and keep emissions down to a minimum. There are many advantages of utilizing a fuel injection system over a carburetor design. The fuel injection method of fuel management can deliver fuel more efficiently near the inlet valve within the intake manifold which would produce a much more even distribution of the fuel/air mixture. With the fuel being injected into or very close to the intake valve, which operates at very high temperatures, vaporization occurs more readily. The vaporized fuel combines with the incoming air, thus creating a thorough mixture of fuel and air. This is beneficial for an even flame propagation within the cylinder, which is necessary for an increased power stroke during combustion. Starting, idling, and warm-up are improved as a result of the even fuel vaporization, whereas use of a carburetor during these situations would stall the engine at or near idling speeds. Finally, the fuel is directed under high pressure throughout the system which avoids vapor loss that occurs in carburetors in hot weather, specifically in the float bowl, which must be maintained at atmospheric pressure (Ref. 5). Another expectation from the microcontroller is the start/stop operation of the combustion engine. The main electrical controller sends an ignition sequence signal to the fuel injection controller. The signal tells the EFI controller the proper times to start and stop the operation of the internal combustion engine. It then replies to the electrical controller that the engine is APU ready.

The third operation of the controller is the throttling of the internal combustion engine. A speed control signal is sent from the main controller to inform the EFI controller whether to throttle the engine or not. When more or less electrical power is required out of the generator, which is driven by the internal combustion engine, the electrical controller informs the fuel injector controller to increase or decrease the throttle on the engine, respectively. The EFI controller then sends four signals to the stepper motor as to the direction to turn for the desired throttling position. The throttle will open or close giving the combustion engine more or less power, hence the desired output from the generator. The stepper motor will be throttled at its lowest around three quarter throttle and its maximum near full throttle. This is done to supply the required power and to keep the hydrocarbons and NOX low in the exhaust. The less the throttle varies the less pollution comes out of the tail pipe.

The fuel chosen to power the internal combustion engine in the Hybrid electric vehicle was M85 because of its low emission characteristics, as shown in Table 1 .

Fuel	ROG	CO (g/mile)	NOx
Gasoline	35	1.4	.66
M85	.25	1.0	.45
E95	.95	1.9	.50
CNG	.19	0.10	.44
Electric	.006	0.008	.07

*ROG (Reactive Organic Gases)

Table **1**: Fuel Emission Data

M85 is more corrosive than gasoline, therefore, careful selection of all components in contact with the fuel was required. All fuel system components were researched and/or tested for M85 compatibility. Any questionable materials were changed. The largest component in the fuel system was the fuel tank.Fuel tank compatibility was a major concern. After much research, the fuel tank was found to be fabricated of polyethylene, an M85 compatible material.

Since the CSUN Voltswagon was to be operated using M85 as a fuel, a greater concern of emissions was necessary because of the increase in aldehydes from combustion of M85. It was therefore necessary to find the best catalytic converter formulation to reduce NOX, CO, HC, and aldehydes. It was decided that a three way catalyst was the best choice because there is no need for an air pump. An air pump would add unwanted mass to the HEV. Since a catalytic converter had to be chosen, it also had to be sized for the IC engine that was being installed in the HEV.

Catalytic converter size is dependent on exhaust gas flow rate and engine volumetric efficiency. After using these parameters to calculate a catalyst volume, the ideal volume obtained was 93 cubic inches (1.5 liters). From the available M85 specific catalytic converters available, the most efficient was a formulation containing 5 grams Platinum to every 1 gram Rhodium at a concentration of 40 grams per cubic foot of catalyst volume. This specific formulation has conversion efficiencies in excess of 90% for HC, CO, NOX, and aldehydes (Ref. 6). Decreasing the time required for catalyst light-off was also necessary to reduce cold start emissions. A light off catalyst or 'pup' catalyst was considered, but past experience has shown that engine performance can decrease by as much as 20% due to increased back pressure. The decision was not to use a 'pup' catalyst, but to insulate the exhaust system up to the underfloor 3-way catalyst. This decreases the time necessary before the catalyst becomes operational, thereby reducing cold start emissions.

VEHICLE STRUCTURE

TIRE SELECTION - Alternate tires were selected in order to minimize rolling resistance. The tires that were original equipment on the Ford Escort wagon were Goodyear Invictas, size 175 70/13. Their overall diameter was 22.65 in. The weight of each tire and wheel was measured to be 32 lbs., and the rolling resistance coefficient of friction of the tire was 0.0087. The maximum inflation pressure of the Goodyear

Invicta was 35 psi.

The following factors were considered for the improvement of the tire performance: weight, rolling resistance, cost, maximum inflation pressure, and overall diameter of the tire. Because of the positioning of the shock mounts in the front of the vehicle, it was decided to keep the same overall diameter of tires as the original equipment tires.

After choosing new tires, the reduction in weight for each tire and wheel went from 34 lbs. to 32 lbs., a difference of 5.9%. The allowed inflation pressure increased from 35 psi to 44 psi, a difference of 20.5%. The rolling resistance also decreased, going from 0.0087 to 0.007, a reduction of 19.5%.

These improvements in the performance of the tires should increase the overall performance of the VoltsWagon while reducing the overall energy requirements.

AERODYNAMIC DRAG - Aerodynamic drag is another source of friction that was reduced. Panels made of ABS plastic were fabricated and attached to the underside of the car. Complete panelling of the underside of a test vehicle reduced the drag coefficient by an estimated 0.04 (Ref. 4).

BRAKES - Reducing aerodynamic drag and rolling friction were beneficial, however, some systems depend on friction to operate effectively. The braking system shown in Figure 6 is one crucial system that depends on friction.

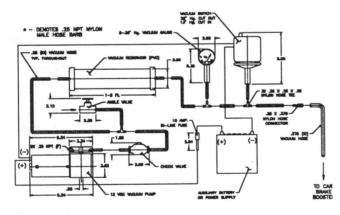

BRAKE VACUUM RESTORATION SYSTEM

Figure 6: Braking System

Restoring vacuum to the power brake booster with the original engine removed from the vehicle became a problem. The source of the vacuum was lost. The APU cannot be used to supply vacuum from its intake manifold; this was mainly due to two reasons: first, the smallish APU would not be able to supply a sufficient vacuum for the stock booster (which was designed to operate at 19.7 in. Hg), and second, the vehicle will not be operated solely in the HEV mode. During the competition the vehicle must be run in the ZEV mode (batteries only) as well as the HEV mode, especially in the range event, which taxes the entire energy reservoirs (liquid and electrical) of the car. The braking performance must remain consistent throughout the competition, regardless of the power mode used by the driver. Therefore, a system based on

another source of vacuum had to be utilized. It was decided that a system using a 12 VDC vacuum pump as the prime mover would be utilized at the competition, but other systems could be explored for production vehicles. In the interest of noise and vibration reduction, as well as energy consumption, a differential vacuum switch was used; this cut the duty cycle of the pump to approximately 50-75% (without the switch, the pump would run constantly). The system as a whole will be fail-safe because the standard hydraulic braking system was left intact; if vacuum to the power brake booster failed or was lost, the brakes may still be applied, albeit with much increased pedal effort.

While the original braking system was left intact, many other systems had to be changed or modified. Some systems that did not exist on the original car had to be created to fulfill competition rules. One such system was the fire suppression system required for occupant safety.

FIRE SUPPRESSION SYSTEM

The requirements and implementation of the fire suppression system were analyzed for the best compromise in cost, weight, effectiveness in task, and availability of components. Various methods were studied, and a final decision was made based on the above mentioned parameters. The specifications of the competition rules were the principal guidelines in assessing the optimum system to be used. Since the rules required a remote operated five pound 1211 or 1301 halon fire extinguishing system, a halon 1211 system was modified for use in the HEV (see Figure 7).

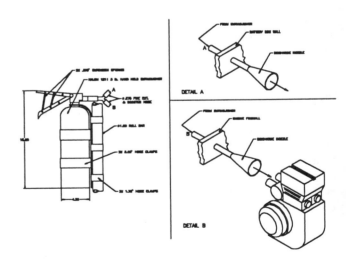

Figure 7: Fire Extinguisher System

Although the driver and passenger will have personal fire protection in the form of fire-resistant suits, gloves, shoes, and helmets, the Halon 1211 system chosen for the competition will be needed in case a mishap occurs during operation of the APU or recharging of the batteries. The system design was based on a standard hand held Halon 1211 extinguisher containing 5.0 lb. of agent, and modified to a point where semi-automatic operation was possible.

ERGONOMICS

The HVAC system is a very important part of the vehicle because it provides comfort and safety for the driver and the passengers. It is also important from a marketing point of view because customers demand these systems in their vehicles in order to control the environment within the vehicle.

The heating system is not an option but a requirement for production line vehicles manufactured in the United States per NHTSA. This requirement is based on the fact that the vehicle operator must have an unobstructed view of the road ahead. Therefore, any condensation or ice formed on the windshield must be effectively removed for safe operation of the vehicle.

Air conditioning is a requested add-on item on a majority of the vehicles sold. The heating system selection for hybrid electric vehicles is a difficult matter because there is not any single system that could provide a good solution without having adverse effect on some other system of the vehicle. The research found that there were three possible ways to heat the passenger compartment by using electricity and one way to use waste heat from the internal combustion engine.

Electrical heaters can easily be used to heat the passenger compartment, but that would have an adverse effect on the vehicle operating range due to the heavy electricity demand by the electric heaters from the batteries. Three typical electric heater solutions exist:

    a) hair dryer
    b) controlled electric heater system
    c) heat pump system.

The hair dryer approach is favored by people who do Electric Vehicle (EV) conversions by themselves. They favor it because it is cheap and relatively easy to do. However, the problems with such approach are high energy consumption of 1200-1500 watts and unsafe operation due to the lack of control or close monitoring of the system.

The controlled electric heater system is a big improvement from the first choice. Such a system is specifically designed and manufactured for electric vehicles. The system is monitored by a controller that will prevent overheating and thus reduces the possibility of accidental fire. The third choice is a heat pump system. This kind of system can function both as a heater and an air conditioner, thus one system serves two different functions. Such systems will be available in the near future. Neither the total system cost nor the system weight are available at this time. The decision was to maintain existing heater system to provide heating during HEV mode due to the low cost and to satisfy NHTSA requirement. The ventilation system must provide fresh air into the passenger compartment in order to provide maximum comfort for the driver and the passengers. The existing ventilation system for the incoming air is maintained in order to reach this goal.

Although numerous air conditioning systems exist, they are mainly manufactured for vehicles with large internal combustion engines with excess power available. Some lower power consumption air conditioning systems exist that are mainly directed toward the EV market. They have reasonable power consumption of 1000 to 1100 watts. It was decided not to install the air conditioning system into the vehicle. This decision was reached since added costs would and the added weight would decrease vehicle performance during various competition events.

MANUFACTURABILITY

To simplify the manufacture of a Voltswagon for consumer appeal, several modifications would be required. For example, the batteries would have to be relocated to allow for adequate passenger seating and safety requirements. To further enhance consumer appeal, air conditioning should be installed. During the course of production, safety guidelines would be necessary to ensure the proper use of methanol. Other modifications would also be needed in order to transfer the technology of a competition vehicle to a commercially viable automobile. Converting the Voltswagon into a mass produced consumer vehicle would require minimal adjustments for an assembly line process.

NOMENCLATURE

T   .... Torque at wheels
R   .... Wheel radius
Cd ...... Drag coefficient
ρ ..... Air density
v   ..... Relative vehicle velocity
Aref .... Frontal reference area
μ ..... Coefficient of rolling friction
m ...... Vehicle mass
g ...... Local gravity acceleration
θ .... Road angle

REFERENCES

1. Collins, J.A., FAILURE OF MATERIALS IN MECHANICAL DESIGN. New York: Wiley, 1981, pp. 214 - 222.

2. Shigley, J.E., MACHINE DESIGN. New York: Mcgraw Hill, 1956, pp. 158 - 161.

3. Shigley, J.E., MECHANICAL ENGINEERING DESIGN: SECOND EDITION. New York: Mcgraw Hill, 1972a, pp.254-263

4. Gillespie, T.D., FUNDAMENTALS OF VEHICLE DYNAMICS. SAE: 1992, pp.72 - 122.

5. Ford Corporation, 1992 FORD ESCORT SERVICE MANUAL, Mcgraw Hill, 1991, New York, pp. 03/04A/4-03/04B/11

6. Paper 872052, CATALYSTS FOR METHANOL VEHICLES, International Fuels and Lubricants Meeting and Exposition, Gregory K. Piotrowski & J. Dillard Murrell, 1987.

California State Polytechnic, Pomona - The APEx

Niles K. MacDonald and Brian D. Metz
California State Polytechnic, Pomona

ABSTRACT

In response to the Hybrid Electric Vehicle Challenge issued by Ford Motor Company, California State Polytechnic University, Pomona has designed and built a hybrid electric vehicle, APEx. This report addresses the vehicle design and operational strategy of APEx. The report is divided into four sections of principle design concerns. The first section describes vehicle structural design. Included are descriptions of the preliminary placement study of internal systems, safety considerations, and finite element analysis for normal and inverted static loading. The second section summarizes the vehicle's power-train into the different categories of mechanical, electrical, and APU subsystems. The third section addresses body design and the influence of ergonomics on the overall design strategy. The fourth section will define material selection rational and vehicle manufacturability.

VEHICLE STRUCTURE

STRUCTURAL FRAME DESIGN- The base structural element of the frame is a horizontal plane, as seem from the left or right side, containing the two primary rails running the major length of the vehicle. Reinforced by cross bracing, other secondary structural elements are seen as elevations from the main-rail datum. The roll cage appears to rest upon this horizontal plane when actually it straddles the main rails and widens the main passenger compartment by connecting to out-rigger extensions of the frames cross-members. The battery containment box is a projection downward from the horizontal plane. It utilizes angled-steel straps to support the weight of the battery pack and takes advantage of being between the two mail rails for additional side-impact protection. Where the two main rails end in the rear at the suspension, a projection upward occurs leading to a rear platform. This platform is positioned above the rear suspension, providing a mounting site for the electric motor, motor controller, transmission, and APU systems. Preceding the forward termination point of the main rails, mounting towers for the front suspension rise up from the horizontal plane. Forward of the towers, projections angle up from the ends of the main rails. The forward end rails are short projections used to define the forward compartment of the vehicle and provide a structural element for the front bumper attachment. Figures 1 and 2 show plan and elevation views of the frame.

Front Suspension - A double A-arm suspension was purchased from TCI industries and is used for the front suspension of the APEx vehicle. The TCI A-arms have the geometry of the Ford Mustang II/Pinto A-arms and are typically used for after-market applications. The A-arms are of unequal length to allow steering offset and the control arm lengths and the mounting positions are designed to minimize change in track and to utilize favorable camber change. This type of suspension has a compact arrangement of components and also has a geometry that allows good tire contact when the car rolls.

Coil-over shocks are used for their simplicity and compactness. All suspension bushings are ball joints of polyurethane for long quiet life and minimum maintenance. The A-arm pivots are Tungsten Inert Gas (TIG) welded to the vehicle and are constructed of tubular 1020 mild steel with a 1.5 inch outer diameter and a .095 inch wall thickness. The upper A-arms have a length of 7 inches while the lower A arms have a length of 10.5 inches. The coil-over shocks are 9 inches long, uncompressed.

The disk brakes used in the front of the vehicle have an outside diameter of 10.25 inches and a thickness of .375 inches. The hubs and dual-piston calipers are constructed of aluminum.

Rear Suspension - The APEx vehicle takes advantage of the positive characteristics of the semi-trailing arm type rear suspension.. The trailing arms and other components were taken from a salvaged BMW 2002. The semi-trailing arm design provides slight negative camber during roll for good cornering characteristics. It is light, simple and inexpensive, and also provides desirable characteristics such as a good camber curve .

The front and rear suspensions are independent, allowing control of the roll centers and sensitivity (i.e. avoiding the effect of a bump on both the front and rear suspensions at the same time). The rear suspension also

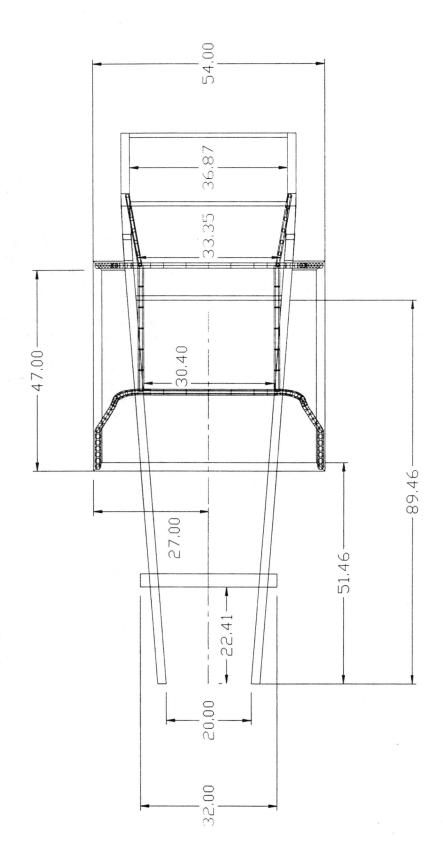

Figure 1. Plan view of vehicle frame structure with dimensions.

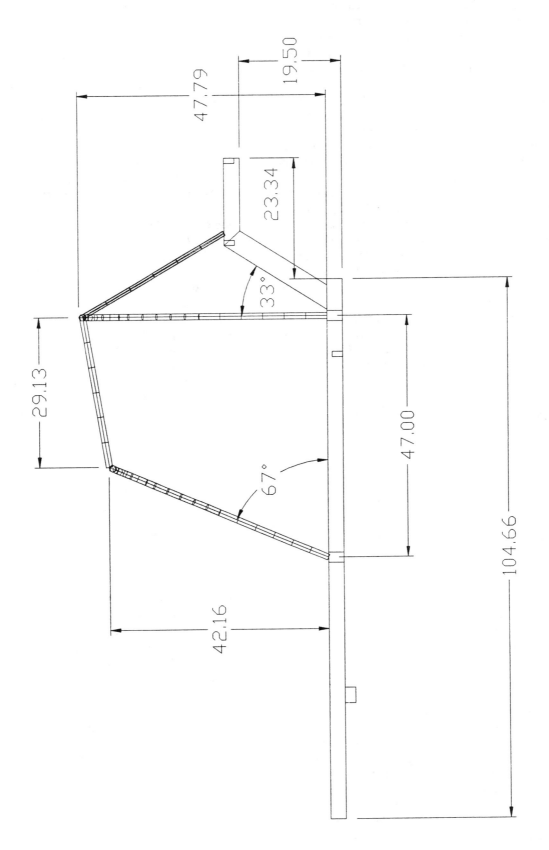

Figure 2. Elevation view of vehicle frame structure with dimensions.

makes use of coil-over shocks for space savings and simplicity. The semi-trailing arm has a shorter branch of 10.5 inches and the other branch of 15 inches. The arm is made of formed and welded 1020 mild steel. The coil spring is about 10 inches long and the bushings are ball-type or polyurethane. TIG welding is used to join the semi-trailing arm suspension to the rear section of the APEx frame. Drum brakes were chosen for the rear of the vehicle for simplicity and low cost.

FINITE ELEMENT ANALYSIS - The first part of the HEV structure design deals with static loading of the vehicle frame. The first analysis consisted of an anticipated normal static loading of the vehicle resting on its four wheels. The second analysis was an inverted static loading of the vehicle resting on the top of its roll cage.

Normal Static Loading - The maximum displacement of the vehicle due to internal loading is 0.158 inches toward the ground. Table 1 gives the forces exerted onto the frame by the various internal loads. The location of this displacement is where the front hoop of the roll cage is attached to the frame. The reason why maximum displacement occurred here is because the batteries as whole are grouped in this area and the batteries are located in the middle of the frame. This is something similar to a simply supported beam with maximum deflection occurring at mid-span with a load applied at the mid-span. Vehicle loading assumed for the normal static case is shown in the table below.

Vehicle Loading-Normal Static Case

Component	Load (lbs)
Chain	10
APU	125
Batteries (10)	825
Cargo	45
Controller	50
Dashboard	15
DC motor	110
Doors	50
Wiring	70
Firewall	10
Fuel and Tank	50
Occupants and seats	235
Shafts and transmission	35
Coupler	10

Stresses Under Normal Static Loading- Low to moderate levels of stress were found on the chassis. The maximum stress found on the chassis was 2,628 psi where the batteries are located. This translates into a factor of safety of 12.18 using 32,000 psi as the yield point of SAE 1018 cold rolled steel. SAE 1018 cold rolled steel is the material used for construction of the chassis.

The maximum principal stress experienced by the frame is in the roll cage. It occurs where the front hoop of the roll cage connects to the outrigger extensions and its maximum value was found to be 4,599 psi. Another high stress area is at the top of the roll cage on the driver's side. A possible reason for this is that the roll cage, in particular the lower front hoop, must resist bending of the chassis due to the loading caused by the main batteries. The small area of high stress on the driver's side could be attributed to the asymmetric loading due to the uneven weights of the DC controller and the transmission. The factor of safety based on the 100,000 psi yield strength of SAE 4130 (the roll cage material) gives a factor of safety of 21.74.

Inverted Static Loading - The maximum bending displacement was 0.840 inches due to internal loading. This displacement occurred at the front end of the vehicle on the driver's side. The front end experienced maximum displacement due to the long moment arm generated by the APU and the fuel tank. Stresses Under Inverted Static Loading- The inverted static analysis of the HEV vehicle is as follows. The maximum principal stress computed was 19,842 psi. As in the normal static analysis, the high areas of high stress occurred on the front hoop of the roll cage and in top of the roll cage on the driver's side. These stresses were greater than the stresses found in normal static analysis since only the roll cage is supporting the entire weight of the vehicle and the area of the roll cage is much smaller than the area covered by the four wheels of the vehicle in the normal static analysis. A factor of safety based on stress experienced and the yield point of SAE 4130 chromoly is 5.04. The chassis experienced negligible stress since the entire weight of the frame was being supported by the roll cage.

PLACEMENT STUDY - This part of the APEx structural design deals with the preliminary placement study of its major internal components. A diagram showing all components and their approximate placements with respect to the interior of the car can be found in Figure 3. The Auxiliary Power Unit (APU) has been placed at the front of the vehicle frame, behind the front axle. Immediately forward of the APU is the five US. gallon fuel tank (racing "fuel cell"). The fuel tank separates the APU system from the electrical system, thereby reducing the chance of a fire in the event of a collision. The driver and passenger of the car have been placed in the center of the roll cage in order for the frame, roll cage, and internal components to provide maximum occupant protection. Underneath the passenger and driver is the battery tray containing 10 main power system batteries. Placing them underneath the main frame and at its geometric center lowers the car's center of gravity, thereby improving the vehicle's cornering abilities. Finally, a cargo bay occupies the remainder of the front section internal space of the HEV as defined from the front end of the accessory battery group to the nose of the vehicle.

SAFETY CONSIDERATIONS - The APEx shall have several considerations in its design to accommodate the relative safety for passengers. The major components can be summarized into several categories.

Front Impact - Vehicle occupants are protected from frontal impact by a 300 mm crush zone as specified by the Ford HEV Challenge Rules and Regulations. This area consists of an energy-absorbing bumper and shock absorbers.

A bumper and shock absorbing assembly from a Honda CRX is used on the APEx since the CRX is approximately the same weight as the APEx and should provide adequate frontal impact protection.

The cargo box has been placed in the forward

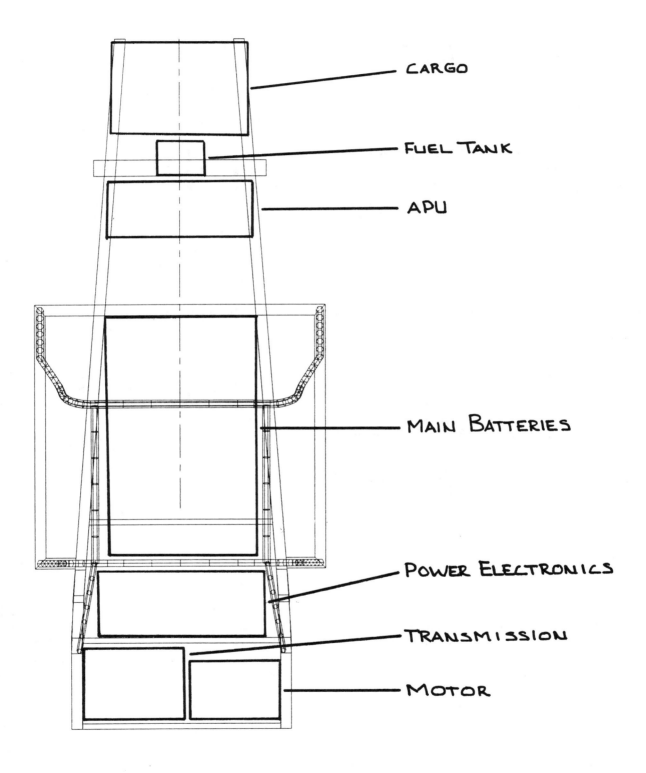

Figure 3. Approximate placement of vehicle systems relative to frame structure.

section of the vehicle and is an integral part of the front crush zone.

Side Impact - Occupant side impact protection is provided by the passenger and driver side doors. The doors are constructed of 16 gage 1020 steel in the form of rectangular sections and the door frame is also constructed of this material. The upper section of the door consists of only a window and a channel and is not structural. A side protection beam located inside each door provides additional protection against side impact. The beam is about 36 inches long and is made of 4130 alloy steel tubing with an outside diameter of one inch and a wall thickness of .065 inches. The beam extends from the front hinge to the rear latch and is located at a height of about 15 inches above the frame rail which places it above the laps of the occupants. In addition to the door and the beam, the frame outriggers also provide side impact protection below lap level.

Roll Cage - In order to protect the occupants from contact with the ground in any rollover attitude, a roll cage has been incorporated into the design of the APEx. With the surface referred to in regulation 11.4.1 of the Ford HEV Challenge Rules and Regulations defined as the uppermost surfaces of the roll bar and roll hoop, drivers as tall as 6' 3" and wearing a helmet can be accommodated.

The roll cage structure consists of a front roll hoop and rear roll bar, two aft braces and two joining members near the roof. The front roll hoop is slanted toward the back of the vehicle at an angle of 23 degrees from vertical. The braces are located at angles of about 31 degrees from the vertical roll bar and are attached to the top of the roll bar structure.

4130 chromoly steel was selected for roll cage construction because it offers the best balance of cost, strength, weight and weldability compared to the other mild steels and alloy steels considered. The occupants are protected from the roll bar by 2.5 cm of foam padding which covers all roll cage tube sections where driver contact with the roll bar could be made in the event of a collision.

The roll cage is securely attached to the frame by means of outriggers which are welded to the frame structure and extend from both the driver side and the passenger side from the center section of the vehicle.

Seat Belts - Occupant restraint is accomplished with a five point, quick release racing-type harness system as required by section 11.44 of the Ford HEV Challenge Rules and Regulations. The primary torso attachments are mounted to the rear-platform cross-beam which is positioned directly behind the occupant seats and above the trailing arm suspension mounts. An attachment plates have been welded to the frame adjacent to the doors, as well as to a 1" x 1.5" x 0.063" bar located between the two seats. These attachments are locations for the pelvic mounts of the restraints. The pelvic restraint, which passes around the cushion's forward outside edge, has a mount welded to the base plate on which the seats are welded to. This plate in turn is bolted directly to the frame. As the floor board below the occupants' seat is composed of Lexan and is the top housing for the battery container, this mounting configuration was deemed appropriate.

Battery Containment - To insure safety, the APEx car uses two levels of battery containment. The first level consists of outriggers which provide connections for the battery containment tray. This should greatly restrict the movement of the batteries in the case of a collision. The second level of battery containment is the battery container itself. The battery compartment is made of corrugated Lexan panels supported with steel angles. This design offers an excellent secondary level of structural strength to contain the batteries in the event of collision while minimizing weight. Finally, each battery is bolted to the battery access tray to maximize battery restraint.

POWERTRAIN CONFIGURATION

SYSTEM DEFINITION - The power train selected for the Cal Poly APEx is a series hybrid type configuration and is based on a series wound DC motor drive source, as shown in Figure 4. The motor drives a continuously variable transmission (CVT) which in turn drives the differential of the car. Reverse drive is accomplished by reversing motor direction of rotation.

The battery pack is made of 10 deep cycle, marine type, lead-acid batteries connected in a series configuration for a nominal voltage of 120 volts. Power from the battery pack is fed to the DC bus which carries power to the controller where it is conditioned for delivery to the motor.

A series drive train was chosen for its flexibility and simplicity. This configuration allows other types of APUs to be installed and tested as they are developed. Furthermore, the vehicle can eventually be converted to pure electric, as new battery technology emerges, without altering the main drive train mechanism.

Motor Selection - A series DC motor was chosen because its torque-speed characteristics, simplicity, and high availability. The DC motor performance closely matches the requirements of the electric vehicle. The motor selected is manufactured by Advanced DC Motors. It is a series wound, brush type motor operating from 0 to 120 volts, with a specified rating of 72 - 120 volts. The motor is rated at 19 HP with a peak power level of 60 HP. This ratings were chosen to match vehicle parameters such as drag coefficient and weight, and to satisfy competition acceleration and speed requirements.

Battery Selection - The selected batteries are Johnson Controls, marine/rv DieHard batteries model no. 9658. These are liquid electrolyte, deep cycle lead-acid batteries with a high power to weight ratio. The prime considerations for battery selection was based as follows: batteries must be readily available, "off the shelf" technology that could be obtained from distributors around the country; they must be affordable to the point that replacement at the end of their useful life would not be too much of a cost burden to the consumer. (The promise of "exotic" batteries was enticing; however, it is felt that until large scale production has been achieved with thorough testing, the average user would not be capable of replacing these batteries at a reasonable expense. Thus, exotic batteries not readily available or experimental were not considered.) batteries must be fully recyclable so as not to defeat a prime purpose of the Hybrid Electric Vehicle

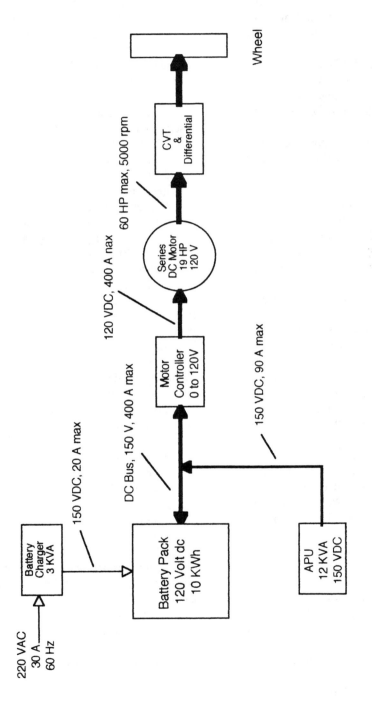

Figure 4. Series hybrid power train block diagram.

Challenge.

APU Selection - The selection of the APU was based on the vehicle power requirements while cruising at speeds of approximately 45 to 50 mph. This allows minimum APU size and weight while still providing adequate power to cruise and charge the batteries. The generator selected is a 12 kVA, 150 V, 3 phase generator manufactured by Fisher Electric. The Fisher generator is compact and light weight and is designed to be turned at approximately 3500 rpm. The APU is direct coupled to a 16 hp Briggs & Stratton Vanguard, selected with the generator's input requirements as main criteria.

SYSTEM OPERATION - The APEx vehicle may be operated and driven like ordinary passenger vehicles. The driver operated controls are similar to those of existing production vehicles barring the addition of several extra operational switches and monitoring gages.

The battery pack is the vehicle's main source of energy. It provides the controller with a fixed source of power. An accelerator pedal coupled to a slide variable resistor signals the motor controller to regulate the flow of power to the electric motor and provide for speed and torque control. Dashboard switches provide control ZEV, APU or HEV mode selection. During HEV mode, a digital controller monitors the battery-pack charge status. When the status of charge is down to approximately 30%, the digital controller signals the driver to start the APU. APU is then manually started by the driver and becomes the primary source of energy.

Since the APU provides more power than it is required for cruising at 40 mph, the excess power can be used up to charge the batteries. If this condition is maintained for a sufficient length of time, battery charge will increase to a point at which APU operation is no longer required. At approximately 85% of charge, the APU will be shut down automatically and driving can continue with battery power only.

While not in use, the battery pack in the APEx car can be charged overnight from an electrical outlet. A choice of 220 VAC, 30 A or 120 VAC, 20 A outlet can be made, however, to reduce charging time the 220 VAC outlet must be used. This should provide for the 6 hour limit recharging time during competition.

ELECTRICAL POWER CONSUMPTION- Power usage is determined by such parameters as vehicle size, weight and other dynamic parameters. For a relatively low system voltage of 120 volts, high currents will be flowing in the system. Currents of up to 90 amps can flow in the battery-controller loop, and currents of up to 170 amps flow within the motor-controller loop while cruising at speeds of about 45 mph. The power usage at this time will be of the order of 8 kW out of the battery pack.

Due high loads the experienced during acceleration and hill climbing, high current levels are present in the system. Currents of up to 400 amps flow out of the battery pack and into the motor. During these periods of peak loading, the intermittent power level may reach 48 kW.

The electrical power system for the APEx car is floating with respect to chassis ground, therefore no currents are conducted through chassis. This ensures that no voltages are developed at the chassis due to these currents. Thus, occupants of the vehicle are safe from shock hazards.

EMISSION CONTROL STRATEGY - The principle goal of the APEx is to reduce the emissions of passenger vehicles while retaining a comparable performance platform. The analysis of the emissions produced by the APEx while operating in hybrid mode are analyzed at several points During the systems operation.

Crankcase Emission Control System - The engine is equipped with a closed crankcase system to prevent discharging crankcase emissions into the atmosphere. Blow-by gasses escape the crankcase through a vent tube. The tube exhausts into the air cleaner. There, the gasses are returned to the combustion chamber through the carburetor.

Evaporative Emission Control System - The engine is equipped with an original equipment evaporative emissions system that complies with California Air Resources Board (CARB) requirements. Fuel-vapor is routed into a canister. When the engine is not running, the vapor is absorbed and stored in the canister by charcoal. When the engine is running, manifold vacuum holds the purge control valve (PCV) open. When the valve is open, the engine draws the stored fuel-vapor into the engine through the air cleaner.

Exhaust Emission Control System - The air to fuel ratio has a direct effect on the exhaust emission levels. The diameter of the carburetor's main jet controls the air fuel ratio delivered to the engine; the other carburetor circuits are not a factor since the engine runs continuously at wide open throttle. Main jets are available in various sizes. The main jet size is decreased incrementally and emissions data are tabulated until the engine begins to run poorly. Emissions data are also recorded for increasingly larger main jets. Exhaust emission curves are formed by plotting the tailpipe emissions against the main jet size. The curves are used as a guide to select the correct main jet size. The selected jet delivers a lean air to fuel ratio. The lean ratio results in a reduction in carbon monoxide (CO) and hydrocarbons (HC) and an increase in oxides of nitrogen (NO_X).

Exhaust gas re-circulation (EGR) counter acts the increase in NO_X by reducing the combustion temperature. NO_X production is directly proportional to combustion temperature. Exhaust gas is directed into the intake manifold to dilute the intake charge. The diluted charge results in a lower combustion rate, and therefore, reduced peak combustion temperatures. The combustion temperatures are also reduced by the fact that the specific heat of the exhaust gas (high in CO_2) is greater than air. The higher heat capacity of the exhaust gas leads to an increase in the amount of combustion heat absorbed by the working fluid, resulting in lower temperatures. Calculations of the associated adiabatic flame temperatures verify this fact.

Ignition timing has an effect on combustion temperature and therefore NO_X formation. Peak combustion pressure occurs farther passed top dead center (TDC) when timing is retarded from the maximum break torque (MBT) setting. The larger volume (past TDC) at the peak pressure thermodynamically results in lower temperatures and therefore lower NO_X production.

The emissions control strategy does not include many common emissions control devices. Catalysts (including preheated catalysts), air injection, and closed loop fuel injection offer significant improvement in emissions quality. The development time, cost, and complexity of these devices are not justified.

BODY DESIGN AND ERGONOMICS

The ergonomics of the APEx is focused on providing a safe and comfortable car for a wide variety of drivers. Research began by determining the limits of the passenger compartment, dash configurations, and visibility requirements. Much of the APEx body design is modeled after the aesthetics of the Honda CRX hatchback.

MATERIALS SELECTION & MANUFACTURABILITY

MATERIAL SELECTION - The material selection for the APEx was based on weight, manufacturability, recyclability, and cost. Weight was the most important factor in determining which material was to be used. Chromoly or mild steels were used for the frame structure of the APEx for their simplicity in fabrication techniques, low cost and availability. The primary material selection challenge came about in the design for the body of the APEx. Two general categories of materials were selected.

Composites - The APEx's front fenders are constructed from fiberglass. The rigidity of fiberglass made it a logical choice for areas of high wind loading, such as the front fenders.

Plastics - There are two different categories under plastics: thermoplastics and thermoset plastics. Of the two, the APEx utilizes thermoplastics. Thermoplastics are polymers which behave in a plastic, ductile manner when heated. These polymers can be formed at elevated temperatures, cooled, and then reheated and reformed into different shapes, all without changing the basic structure of property of the polymer. Thermoplastics are recyclable. Because of the on-recyclability of thermoset plastics, the APEx body is principally composed of thermoplastics.

Acrylonitrile-Butadiene-Styrene (ABS) plastic is one of the most versatile members of the thermoplastics family. ABS polymers offer a unique combination of light weight, toughness, rigidity, corrosion resistance, and excellent surface appearance. Polycarbonates offer the same characteristics as ABS plastics, except they have higher impact strength and lower corrosion resistance. ABS does not produce harmful fumes or dust and does not pose any kind of health threat during fabrication. ABS can be easily worked and the final product will have an excellent surface finishing. ABS is lightweight, inexpensive, and strong.

The vehicle's side body panels; roof, doors, and rear section are all composed of vacuum-formed thermoplastics. The front fenders of the vehicle are formed of fiberglass for rigidity needed to withstand high wind loading experienced in that area.

California Polytechnic State University, San Luis Obispo

Safwat Moustafa, Faculty Advisor,
Eric Cusick, and Eric Boettcher
California Polytechnic State University

ABSTRACT

The Hybrid Electic Vehicle Team at Califonia Poly-technic State University, San Luis Obispo has worked hard to completely design and build a ground-up vehicle for the 1993 Ford HEV Challenge. The impressive student effort has resulted in the development of many custom vehicle features. Original designs include a parallel powertrain, high voltage vehicle & charging systems, computer control, tubular frame, front & rear suspensions, and an aluminum body. This innovation is a direct result of student volunteers working toward a common goal.

POWER CONFIGURATION

The coupling of two powerplants for the HEV Challenge was heavily investigated, examining the advantages between the prominent configurations of series and parallel. Parallel, although more complicated than a given series layout, was chosen for the powertrain. The comparative efficiencies between the two made the decision obvious. Additionally, the entire concept of designing and building a ground-up vehicle was used to encourage everyone to build the best and most efficient HEV possible, allowing the acceptance of added complexity.

A comparison between a series and a parallel powertrain layout began with a general conception of how each system appears. Research into past efforts helped to illustrate the simplicity and desirability of a series system. However, these perceptual benefits were taken at the price of efficiency, when viewing the entire power scheme. The parallel configuration allowed for each powerplant to directly move the vehicle where efficiency is saved because of fewer energy conversions. In a series powertrain an engine drives a generator, which then feeds batteries, which than eventually feed the motor, driving a powertrain. Assuming optimistic efficiencies still places the series layout at nearly a 10% deficit to the parallel, in full HEV operation.

The components for the powertrain were chosen for efficiency and estimated power requirements that the vehicle would require. Assumptions about average velocity and potential energy capacity led to the selection of the 71

Solectria motor and controller units. The motor/controller combination enables the motor to develop 18.75kW of power. This purchase, along with rules at that point in the competition, made the APU selection favor the Geo Metro 1 liter engine. This 36.75 kW engine is more than able to move the car during average driving or in the acceleration event.

ELECTRIC MOTOR/CONTROLLER - The 28 HP , 9 KW AC induction motor (AC GTx20) and matching AC300 controller from Solectria rounded out our system. What we needed to get from our motor and controller was roughly 30 HP for acceleration, operation from a relatively low voltage - so that the battery weight was kept down, and a motor that could operate continually at high cruising speeds without needing excessive cooling. This system was the closest match we could find from any company and it was far cheaper (over $10,000) from the most desirable solution from Unique. Unique manufactures a line of much more powerful motors, but they also require much higher operating voltages which mean more weight and so on. With our AC300 controller we achieve a 98% efficiency in the conversion of the DC voltage to AC while getting a myriad of features that add safety and convenience as well. These include high temperature current limiting to prevent motor damage while allowing us to still drive with some limited amount of power, several emergency interrupt capabilities, and the ability to change on the fly from a highly efficient delta winding to a wye winding which allows us to double our torque at low speeds. This last feature allows our HEV to cruise with the highest efficiency while using the high torque mode to help us accelerate up a hill or onto a freeway. This switching is performed in a very similar way to that used for entering the four wheel drive mode on a truck. A lever in the cockpit is pulled which disables power from getting to the motor while a three pole switch is turned that re-taps the motor connections. By the time the handle has reached its final position, the motor controller has been switched into the proper operating mode and then the motor interrupt is released. If higher efficiency operation is desired, the handle should be left in the delta position. There is no absolute need to use the wye mode and the use of that mode is opaque to the operation of the rest of the vehicle.

AUXILLARY POWER UNIT - In trying to decide what alternative power plant we would use we felt that 15hp was our minimum need. From this figure we then tried, through group brainstorming, to come up with alternatives. The engine had to be:

- lightweight
- fuel efficient
- have low emissions
- be either easily available or manufacturable.

In our discussions we noted that the available power plants that fit our design best were those for use in automobiles. These already had extensive design in the areas of emissions and fuel economy. Their negatives were mostly due to size; a car engine that makes only 15hp is hard to come by. Three different possibilities presented themselves in the discussion:

- 15hp industrial-use engine
- 600cc automobile engine imported from Japan
- 1000cc engine from a Geo Metro.

In comparison, the industrial-use engine in theory emmited close to if not more than the 600cc engine because of designs inherent to an auto engine and not to an industrial-use engine, such as fuel injection, electronic ignition and catalytic converters. If the necessary time, equipment and experienced personnel were available, an existing industrial-use engine could have been modified to fit our needs. The final choice became the Geo Metro 1000cc engine. This engine, unlike the 600cc engine, was available locally and as an entire system (all wiring ,electronics and supporting structure included). Once this decision was made it became our goal to optimize its efficiency.

The areas we looked at were intake flow, exhaust backpressure, lubrication and a few modifications found on race engines. One of the most exciting new technologies in auto engines is the use of ceramic thermal coatings. We used this type of coating to coat the tops of the pistons, the combustion chamber and the valve faces. This reduces the amount of heat lost to the cooling system during the power stroke thereby increasing the amount of push on the piston. The coating also acts to raise the knock limit and cushion the piston if knocking occurs, allowing higher compression ratios. Initial estimates were in the order of a 10% power gain. We've also tried to reduce to a minimum all intake and exhaust restriction. In the area of emissions we fabricated an electric catalytic converter preheater in order to cut down the cold start emissions by causing the catalytic convertor to fire off much sooner than it presently does. This is coupled with as much insulation as is possible between the engine and catalytic converter. Finally we are using all synthetic lubricants in order to cut down on internal friction.

BATTERIES

When we first started the process of selecting the batteries and the electric motor, there were an overwhelming number of considerations to be weighed against each other. Our first step consisted of measuring the relative impact of each of these considerations against how many points were being awarded in the specific events. Though the format of the competition changed slightly over the past 14 months, what were the primary considerations and their priorities haven't changed much. The main factors for our team specifically included:

- finding a battery technology that would provide the voltage and current we needed without being too bulky or too heavy
- finding a motor and controller capable of our acceleration requirements
- matching these two systems together such that they would make a coherent system.

Our design team set baseline performance requirements including:

- the maximum weight
- the minimum ZEV range desired
- the expected cruising power requirements.

From these we focused our attention on components capable of meeting these goals. We looked for batteries that could provide a minimum of 120 volts and over 30 horsepower in energy when at a low state of charge. We needed a battery life that would meet the 300 life cycle limit specified by Ford while meeting a high enough level of safety and recyclability to be in tune with the broader goals of the competition.

We ultimately decided upon a sealed, recombinant lead acid battery manufactured in the U.S. by the Concorde Battery Corporation. The batteries have a small footprint (approx. 10" x 7.6") which saves on space and a 24 volt nominal potential. We choose to place two groups of five series connected batteries in parallel on opposing sides of the car. This combination provides us with about 6.7 Kwhr of energy at the three hour rate. This was originally intended to be 10 Kwhr with slight modifications by Concorde that they did not ultimately commit to. That modification would have greatly increased our ZEV range as well as the weight of the batteries, but at this time we feel confident we can still expect a 40 mile ZEV range and have better acceleration due to the lower weight of just over 600 pounds.

Since we are designing an electric vehicle, there were several reasons this approach seemed desirable. This configuration of the batteries provides an even weight distribution on the chassis, it lowers the currents flowing through the wires and batteries reducing electrical power losses, it provides twice the available power to accelerate the vehicle at low states of charge, it extends the life of the batteries by cutting the charging rates and discharge rates to much lower levels, and it means high rate discharges will have a smaller effect on battery voltage variations. It is true that we could have avoided some of these troublesome effects by using a different type of battery; however, the only other battery technology that seems to be fully developed today is nickel-cadmium which costs twice as much, requires many more interconnections, is not recyclable, and uses cadmium which is highly toxic, non-recyclable and harmful to the environment. Thus, we concluded that nickel-cadmium batteries are not very desirable for high volume production. Using sealed batteries means that the batteries produce no gasses during their operation, they are 100 % maintenance free for life, they will not corrode the environment they are in and they will not spill if tipped (they can operate perfectly upside-down)! Once the batteries are considered to be at the end of their expected life, they can be brought back to the manufacturer and completely recycled. From a mass production standpoint, a consumer should be able to return their batteries for a refurbished set making an initial investment only once.

Two companies stand out as being superior choices for supplying electric vehicle motors and controllers, Unique Mobility (Englewood, CO) and Solectria (Arlington, MA). Both offer motors with very high efficiencies and power to weight ratios as well as solid state controllers with interfacing already designed with electric vehicles in mind. Considering the electric motor and controller are the heart of any EV, this is no place to skimp. Both Unique and Solectria oblige by providing very expensive systems that are truly state of the art, but these units are custom made to best suit the needs of the vehicle in hand. There is no way I can over emphasize the importance of having a "well balanced" system and these two companies can help make everything work better together. If the batteries are not matched to the controller or the controller isn't well matched to the motor, not one of the three components will perform to half of their highest ability. The biggest battle in choosing these three components is compiling a number of "complete systems" that are weighed against each other as independent solutions.

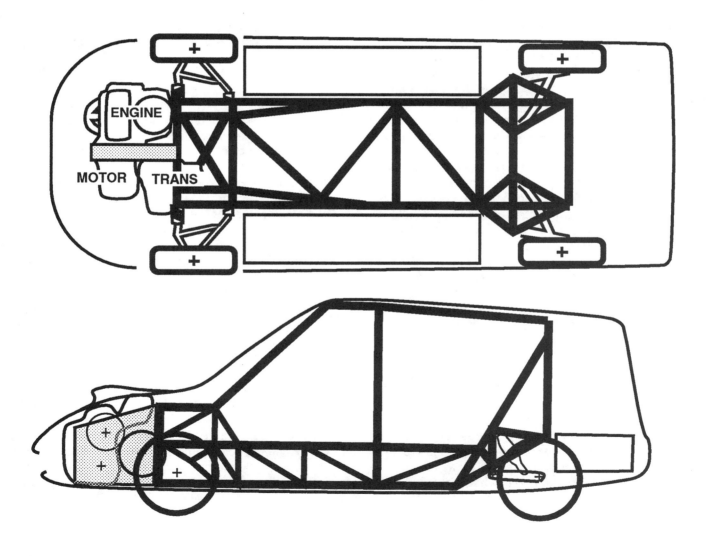

HEV LAYOUT

CONTROL STATAGY

CONTROL STRATAGY MODES - The operation of the HEV will be controlled through the mode switch of the vehicle. The mode switch allows the operator to choose between ZEV, HEV, and APU modes. Further detail has been developed for the HEV mode, consisting of efficiency, range, and power sub-modes. These modes work to allow the driver versatility in HEV operation.

Zero Emission Vehicle Mode - The ZEV mode simulates the operation of an electric vehicle. Here, the battery packs are the sole energy source for the locomotion, made possible by an electric motor directly coupled with the powertrain. The input from the driver, through the throttle, is directly relayed to the motor controller, which then commands the motor in its function. Added features to the electrical operation include regenerative braking and low speed torque capabilities. These two options are available anytime the electric motor is activated, with the regenerative braking also functional during APU operation. These features will be discussed in more detail later.

Hybrid Electric Vehicle Mode - HEV mode enables both powerplants to directly drive the vehicle, supplying mechanical power to a common powertrain. As mentioned previously, this mode has been divided into three parts. Each sub-mode allows the driver to effectively favor one or both of the powerplants, depending on the driving environment. The efficiency sub-mode has the electric motor operating, similar to ZEV. However, when the operator demands more power, which is conveyed through pedal position, the APU activates. The same applies to the range sub-mode, which begins with the gas engine. For these sub-modes, when the high power demand ends, the powerplant that is considered secondary shuts down. This system response of placing both units into the system is effectively jumping the control up to the power sub-mode, consisting of both powerplants always on line and ready to perform.

Auxillary Power Unit Mode - The alternative power unit has been designed to power the vehicle through the APU mode. This operation is very characteristic of a conventional vehicle, combusting fossil fuel for mechanical power. Points of operation for this mode would be after the battery supply had been depleted or when the performance of a single, more powerful drive unit is desired.

The regenerative breaking and low speed torque are product features of our motor/controller. The regenerative braking, which can be used virtually any time, allows for some of the dynamic energy of the vehicle to be converted into electrical energy rather than been lost to friction in a braking situation. The signal for this feature is taken directly from the brake pedal, when displaced. Regenerative braking and conventional braking work in tandem to slow or stop the vehicle. The low speed torque enable the motor to double its torque output through a wiring change. However, this torque is only available at low motor speeds and is very inefficient to develop. This feature is activated by a second shifter, with only two positions.

CONTROL STATEGY IMPLEMENTATION - The HEV

is controlled by a 386SX-16MHz industrial computer system with a math coprocessor. The computer system has:

- 32 analog input ports
- 4 analog output ports
- 50 bi-directional digital lines
- a dual axis servo controller card
- a floppy disk
- a monitor/keyboard interface card
- a LCD display mounted in the dash.

A computer was chosen due to its versatility. Because we are not experienced engineers on vehicle dynamics, we needed the ability to change the assumptions we made when building this vehicle. With the computer we can change any parameter during testing. The computer also gives us the ability to control and monitor other systems on the car. The computer system could also record the response of the vehicle to different driving conditions. This information could then be taken via a floppy disk to a desktop computer and analyzed.

All of the software will be read from this floppy disk. The control strategy can be easily changed by swapping floppy disks. This provides an attractive option: a customer could chose different modes of operation depending on their needs.

The driver of the car has 4 inputs to the CPU:

- power
- accelerator pedal position
- brake pedal position
- mode selection.

The computer is powered up when the driver turns the key like in a regular car. Then, the driver selects the mode of operation for the car based on the driving conditions. The ZEV (zero emissions vehicle) mode will be selected when the electric motor is to be used by itself. The HEV (hybrid electric vehicle) mode will be selected when a greater power output is needed. The APU (alternate power unit) mode will be used when the battery capacity is very low. The APU mode is used primarily to extend the range of the vehicle.

The CPU will distribute the load between the electric motor and internal combustion engine based on the mode selected, the position of the accelerator pedal, and the position of the brake pedal. The computer will turn the power on to each power plant based on the mode selection. The accelerator pedal and brake pedal will send a voltage to the computer. If ZEV or HEV is selected, the computer will then turn a potentiometer, via a servo motor, to control the motor. The motor controller's output is based on the resistance of the 10 kohm pot; 5k = idle, < 5k = regenerative braking, and > 5k = drive. If HEV or APU is selected, the internal combustion engine is controlled by a servo connected to the throttle linkage. When the driver switches from ZEV to HEV mode, the CPU will be required to start the engine and bring it to the drive train RPM before the driver can take advantage of the additional torque.

The RPM of the electric motor, engine, and drive train

will be monitored in order to engage the engine, determine the velocity of the car, and determine the gear. In order to determine the RPM of the engine and motor, magnetic pickups are placed close to the teeth on the flywheel; one flywheel is on the engine, the other is on the input to the transmission. These pickups will generate a 4 Vp-p sine which will be converted to a voltage by LM2917 frequency to voltage converters. The drive train RPM is determined by converting the pulse from the speedometer cable output that is used for the speedometer on a GEO Metro. The voltages from these sensors are input through the analog input card and interpreted by the computer. The three RPM's and the velocity of the car will be displayed on the dash. These RPM's will also be used to optimize the load distribution.

For safety reasons the CPU also monitors the temperature of all ten batteries as well as the motor, engine, motor controller and computer. The temperature is sensed by LM 335 temperature sensors who's output is 10mV/K. This voltage is amplified 2.5 times in order to reduce the effects of noise. These temperatures are displayed on the dash at all times. If any temperature approaches the maximum temperature for that component, the computer will display a warning sign on the display with instructions on how to proceed.

In order to operate efficiently, the CPU must know the energy storage on the HEV. The RS232 output of the Watt-Hour meter supplied by Ford Motor Company is connected to the RS232 port of the computer. This meter gives us current and voltage readings which can be translated into power. The fuel capacity monitored by using the standard fuel sender on GEO Metro; this sender varies its resistance based on fuel level.

This controller system consumes 100 w. The power for this system comes from a 13.2Vdc battery. This battery is charged by one of two means: 120Vdc to 13.4Vdc DC to DC converter or alternator on the engine.

In order to combat the problem of "drive by wire", the control for the motor and engine is readily switchable. The power and ignition for the engine can be changed back to the key switch as in conventional cars by the flip of a switch. The mechanical linkage for the fuel injection can then be attached to the accelerator pedal. The electric motor will be switched by switching a plug. This will convert the potentiometer at the accelerator pedal from a voltage source going to the computer to a resistance going to the motor controller. The power for the motor will come from a switch located on the dash. In the event of an emergency, the two power plants can be turned off by an emergency shutoff switch located on the dash.

CHARGER

Having an electric vehicle without an on-board charger is like having a hang-glider without any mountains to launch from, a great idea but practically useless after your first run. We did however feel that we could not build a practical on-board charger while meeting the requirement of having an isolation transformer on the vehicle itself. The best solution would be to use a pulse width modulated, high frequency battery charger that takes advantage of high switching speeds to reduce the size of the transformer to something suitably sized for the application. This solution is also very expensive. To reduce cost and complexity we choose to build a simple battery charger based on a full wave bridge rectification scheme that is highly efficient and extremely reliable. In the development of our charger, we started by scavenging the power transformers and rectifiers of a prototype Chloride Spegel charger on loan to us from PG&E. The Chloride charger was originally intended for a 250 Volt 50 amp input with a maximum output of over 40 amps at 230 volts, intended for the G-van electric vehicles currently being used by utility companies.

With the specifications provided to us by Chloride we were able to design our new charging electronics around what we already had without needing to acquire a lot of expensive components. In the first stages of testing we manually changed the taps of the primary isolation / step down transformer during the charge cycle to match the requirements of our batteries. We could not use the control electronics provided on the existing charger since the sealed batteries are not designed for the over voltage charging method used with vented wet cells. Instead, we must use what is known as a constant potential charge method; however, we had to implement our own control electronics to perform the transformer tapping we initially did by hand to prevent the charger from drawing excessively high currents at the beginning of the charge. We also had to add a second transformer to step 220 volts down to 110 volts. This was required because even with a near unity power factor we could not get a full 6.7 Kwhr's worth of energy out of a 15 amp 120 volt outlet in the six hours we have to charge. Though we came very close, we decided that it was necessary to use the 30 amp 220 volt option for charging but at only a slightly higher rate than before. We are in no hurry to charge the batteries since the battery life and charging efficiency will be higher at slower rates. We are aiming instead to charge in about five and a half hours as opposed to three or four hours which we are now capable of. The addition of the second transformer modestly drops the power factor of our charger but not to to the extent that it will cause us any problems at slow charge rates. This whole exercise brings up the point that a commercial charging station for the broad range of EV's that will eventually come to the market must be designed to accommodate a variety of charging methods, voltage ranges, electrical adaptors and probably incorporate its own power factor correction.

Another primary cause for concern was in obtaining suitable components to complete the high voltage system. The requirement stating we needed a switch rated to disrupt full load battery current proved to be quite costly. In fact, care must be taken to work with the manufactures on every part of the high voltage system to compensate for the differences between high voltage DC systems from the AC ratings these devices are specified with. Since in a DC system no phase lag exists between the voltage and current, disrupting a high current DC signal under load without arc welding the contacts in place becomes quite a challenge. Electroswitch Inc. was the only company we could find who had a switch rated to disrupt 200 amps at 200 volts under load in a package suitably sized for vehicular use. Keep in mind that this type of switch is a $500 investment that comes with all kinds of problems of its own. Questions about the required fuse types and ratings of high current DC systems should be referred to the manufacturer. We were told to use the JTD fuses from LittelFuse for the main fuses of our battery pack. We also found the need for a number of isolated DC-DC converters which are high frequency electronics that provide the power for our 12 volt electronics without electrically connecting the two systems together. These components are expensive as well, but necessary for safety reasons.

CHASSIS

Among the considerations used in the layout of the chassis were the Rules & Regulation set by Ford Motor Company and the basic layout that our team initially conceptualized. The major criteria that affected the chassis design were:

- a tandem seating arrangement for better aerodynamics
- twin battery packs to be mounted on each side of the passenger compartment
- a 94 inch wheelbase to get a 30 foot turning radius
- a modular powertrain system for the engine, motor, transmission and related accessories
- a single gull wing door for on the left side of the car.

To determine weight distribution and total weight of the car, the locations and weights of individual components were entered into a spreadsheet with moment equations to find the center of gravity and total weight of the vehicle. The front to rear weight bias is 57/43 and the side-to-side bias is only 0.4% off center.

The forces used to analyze the frame are:

Roll-Over	1.5g load on top of A-pillar
Front Impact	29g load on front of frame
Side Impact	23g load on side of frame
Bump	3.2g load through suspension
Braking	0.9g load through suspension
Cornering	0.9g load through suspension
Twisting	1500 lbf*ft torque on front

The roll-over case came from NHTSA for passenger vehicle testing. To pass the test, a maximum of 5 inches of deflection is allowed. The front impact case was derived from assuming an impact with a solid object at 30 MPH and stopping in the length of the crush zone (12 inches). The side impact test was derived from a solid object hitting the side of the car at 30 MPH and stopping in 18 inches (the width of the battery boxes).

Harsh driving conditions were also considered. The worst conditions were determined by the front suspension designer to be a 3.2g bump which is hitting a 4 inch bump at 60 MPH, a 0.9g braking acceleration, and a 0.9g cornering acceleration. The accelerations that the chassis will absorb from the road will be substantially less than those listed above due to the shocks absorbing a certain percentage of the forces involved. The twist case was done with the rear of the frame restrained solidly.

Computer simulation of the frame was done on CAEDS finite element analysis software. The initial simulation of the frame was done with no cross bracing in the chassis. The cross bracing seen in the final design was added as needed to reduce deflections and forces on individual members and to reduce twisting.

MATERIALS - There were two steps to making the decision on frame materials. The first was choosing what kind of frame to build: a space frame of tubing or monocoque system using aluminum honeycomb. Since cost was a major component in the competition, the cheaper and easier to obtain tubing needed for the space frame was the deciding factor. Then, the decision between carbon steel, alloy steel, or aluminum was made based on three criteria:

- cost
- manufacturability
- weight.

Aluminum was removed because it is substantially more difficult to weld than steel, and early Ford rules would not allow the use of aluminum roll hoops. Carbon steel was chosen over alloy steel for two reasons. The first is cost. Since carbon steel is much cheaper than alloy steel, it would be much easier to get the material donated. The other reason is that to get the most out of alloy steel, it must be heat treated and no facilities nearby was large enough to fit our frame.

MANUFACTURABILITY - Once the decision to use carbon steel was made, manufacturability became a big plus. The frame can easily be built on a production line with MIG welders and simple jigs. The jig only needs to consist of pipe clamps and a flat surface to mount them. The only possible problem area would be in the rear portion of the frame. The fish mouthing is relatively complex, but the design could be changed slightly and jigs to facilitate the cutting of the tubes could be built.

BATTERY BOXES - The battery boxes for the HEV were to be a deviation of a past project that employed aluminum honeycomb structures as the main support. This would also appear on this vehicle, due to reduced frame requirements, lightweight, and availability. This material was also used in the rear structure, taking advantage of the materials energy absorption characteristics in a rear collision situation.

SUSPENSION DESIGN & HANDLING

FRONT SUSPENSION - The front suspension of our vehicle is composed of Geo Metro components modified to function as a double A-arm suspension system. Key modifications to the Metro components include replacing the steering knuckle's upper shock mount to accommodate a ball joint for the upper A-arm. The shock absorber and spring were then attached to a custom lower A-arm. The stock Geo Metro steering system was altered, but the stock steering ratio was maintained.

The geometry of the suspension linkages was designed with considerations to caster, camber, roll center, ackerman steer, bump steer, and how these vary with vehicle ride height and roll angle. Stock Geo Metro caster angle and steering angles were maintained in the design, and the roll center was designed to be slightly above ground level.

The material chosen for the A-arms is chromoly steel tube, due to its high strength, toughness, weldability, and ease of fabrication. For the suspension arm bushings, graphite-impregnated urethane bushings are used to maintain suspension geometry while still providing for high frequency vibration isolation.

The A-arms and coil over shocks are the only non-standard Geo Metro components that merit manufacturability concerns. The A-arms would likely be aluminum forgings or stamped steel structures, and the coil overs may be better integrated into the design of the frame and A-arm structures.

REAR SUSPENSION - From the very beginning, packaging was a major concern in the design of the vehicle. The shape of the vehicle called for the luggage container to e located below and behind the rear seat. As a result, a trailing arm design, instead of an A-arm design, was chosen for the rear suspension. The suspension also had to have a geometry to enable a proper attachment of a coil-over shock to an already designed chassis. The suspension had to withstand a 5-g vertical load and two 1.5-g loads in the horizontal plane, all at the center of the contact patch of the tire. 4130 steel was chosen from the beginning due its high strength to cost ratio.

The first step taken was to choose a geometry that would meet the packaging criteria and allow for adjustment in camber, toe-in, and toe-out. Another issue that was very important was manufacturability. It was felt that due to time constraints, the suspension should be easy to build and the amount of welding and machining should be kept to a minimum. Financially, there was not much of a concern because the difference in the cost of materials between the trailing arm designs was minimal. The geometry was rather simple. The needed points of the chassis were drawn in 3-D on a CAD system together with other known points such as the tire center. After the rear portion of the chassis was recreated, different geometries were drawn. The present HEV rear suspension configuration was chosen due to its simple yet effective design. Other designs considerations were much heavier, more difficult to design, and much more time consuming to build.

Adjustments to the system also had to be rather simple and quick. This was accomplished by analyzing each direction of adjustment on their own. Toe-in and toe-out simply required plates or "shims" of proper thickness between the interface of the suspension brackets and the chassis to achieve the desired angle. The camber adjustment however needed more attention. High loads at the chassis/suspension bracket interface was a concern for obvious safety reasons. It was decided, after looking at

many designs, to pivot the trailing arms about a vertical axis traveling through the center of the outside brackets. The actual axis would be a steel sleeve placed through and welded to the chassis with a 0.5 inch grade 8 bolt through the sleeve attaching the bracket to the chassis. The inside brackets would be attached to the chassis with two 3/8 inch grade 8 bolts. Careful scrutiny of the statics of the system using high loads and safety factors showed that the bolts were well within safety standards.

BODY

The HEV would often operate as a typical electric vehicle. The power available for such operation is very limited and not to be wasted. For this reason, many steps were taking to reduce the power requirements of the vehicle. The first and most obvious is the passenger layout. Tandem seating has been used to reduce the frontal area of the vehicle. Secondly, the body has been aerodynamically refined to reduce drag. The basic vehicle layout is a combination of two aerodynamics shapes, the lower body and the occupant canopy. However, the team felt that a certain statement could be made with the vehicle, in an attempt to break away from the stereotypical electric vehicle appearance. As a result, and hood scope has been placed over the engine. This added feature does increase the drag on one side of the vehicle, but it also helps to bring in a familiar shape to the entire vehicle.

The occupants will gain access to the vehicle through a single gull-wing door located on the left side of the vehicle. This side selection allowed the gear shifter not to interfere with the ingress and egress of the driver. Once inside the passengers would be seated just like in any other vehicle. The driver would have an instrument cluster to observe, standard controls to manipulate, and a mirror on each side for rear vision.

MATERIALS - The body for the HEV was a major design undertaking, that would ultimately consist of complex curves and flat planes. The easiest material choice for a quick, 'one off' body would be fiber glass. However, this material has several disadvantages to it beyond fabrication properties. The first shortcoming is the lack of recyclability. The challenge rules imply a theme of recyclability, and this material would not fall into such a category. Secondly, the amount of time necessary to produce a quality product potentially involved many hours of labor, through possible mold making and a lot of sanding. The final item that struck down a fiberglass body was the involvement of resin in the construction process. Resins require that many precautions be taken when used. These reasons helped the group accept the challenge of building an aluminum body panel system. Projections were that an aluminum body would require an equal amount of time as would a fiberglass body, would weigh the same, and fell into the category of being recyclable.

The windows for the vehicle were allowed to be safety glass or 1/4" plastic. Plastic was chosen as the desired material based on past experiences in fabrication and availability. Optical integrity was insured by carefully creating precise and extremely smooth molds.

MANUFACTURABILITY - The body, being made from aluminum, would require the knowledge of forming and joining techniques. Fortunately, the group was able to possess sufficient background in both these areas to construct a fine product. Other areas such as the electronics and computer system provided little in the way of choices.

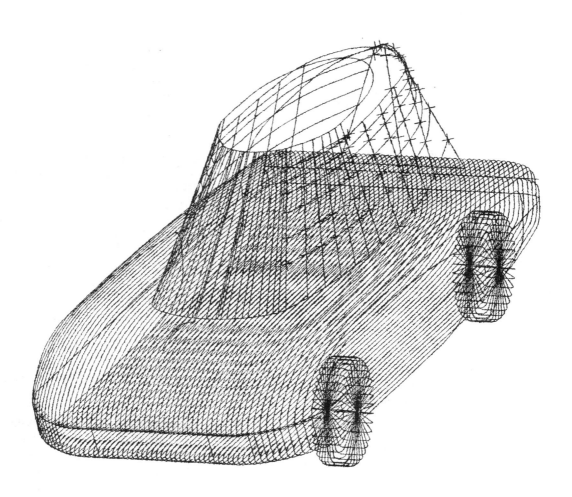

COMPUTER BODY DESIGN

Colorado School of Mines - Blaster #10

**CSM/HEV Team, Christopher G. Braun, Faculty Advisor
and David R. Munoz, Faculty Advisor**
Colorado School of Mines

ABSTRACT

The Colorado School of Mines Hybrid Electric vehicle is a converted 1992 Ford Escort LX station wagon with a gross vehicle weight (GVW) of 1565 kg. A series configuration was adopted because its ease of implementation. The major components are: a 32 MJ (8.7 kW-hr) battery bank made up of NiCd cells; a 22 kW (continuous) series wound, brush commutated DC electric motor; a pulsed width modulated (PWM) electric motor controller; a custom built, permanent magnet 16 kW alternator; and a 620 cm^3, 14.5 kW Kawasaki V-twin alternate power unit (APU) modified to burn neat ethanol.

The car is designed to operate in two modes; zero emission vehicle (ZEV), batteries only, and hybrid electric vehicle (HEV), a combination APU/alternator and batteries. Safety features include a four-point roll cage, a single point ground, an electrical kill switch and an on-board halon fire suppression system with smoke detectors located in the engine compartment and battery box exhaust.

INTRODUCTION

This paper describes the Colorado School of Mines (CSM) entry into the 1993 Ford Hybrid Electric Vehicle (HEV) Challenge. The experience provided a unique educational opportunity in engineering design and development for undergraduate students and faculty. The CSM team submitted a proposal in December of 1991 and was selected as one of thirty schools in the U.S. and Canada to compete.

The goal of the Colorado School of Mines Hybrid Electric Vehicle (CSM/HEV) team was to design, construct and test a working vehicle powered by an electric motor and a small internal combustion engine/alternator combination as a range extender.

An organizational structure, shown in Figure 1, was developed as part of the proposal and then later implemented during the design and construction phases of the project. The students working on the vehicle were a mix of seniors enrolled in their final capstone design course and

CSM/HEV Organizational Chart

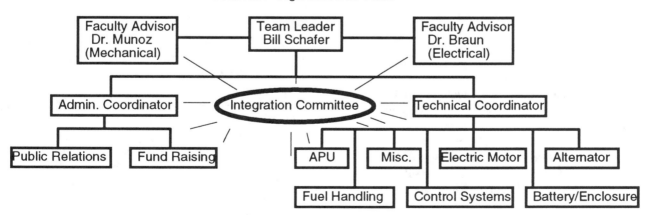

Figure 1. The organization chart of the CSM/HEV team. The integration committee is composed of the team/ sub-team leaders and advisors.

various lower division undergraduates who volunteered. Each semester several sub-teams were established to design and build coherent sub-systems within the car (Figure 1). Formal communication between the sub-teams was conducted in the weekly integration meeting which brought all student sub-team leaders and faculty advisors together. Generally, the weekdays were used to design, organize and prepare for construction; most construction took place on weekends.

Each sub-team, while working with their faculty advisor, developed the design specifications for their sub-systems. Individual components were selected and purchased after exhaustive searches of commercial manufacturers. Decisions were made by the sub-teams after considering tradeoffs in performance, cost, ease of implementation and manufacturer support. The sub-team brought their decisions and analysis to the weekly integration committee meeting for coordination and information sharing.

OVERALL DESIGN APPROACH

The operation of a hybrid electric vehicle (HEV) requires coordination of many different sub-systems and competing design strategies to achieve an operating vehicle. A system was developed which included electric motor control, power conditioning electronics, alternate power unit (APU) speed control and instrumentation.

The first and most substantial design decision involved the overall configuration of the power system. Each characteristic of the car design i.e. performance, reliability, efficiency, safety, ease of implementation, etc. was listed. After considering the HEV Challenge Rules and our view of the desired vehicle performance characteristics, a number of designs were generated and assessed to determine the optimal configuration. This process led to the selection of a series configuration with the APU/alternator electrically coupled to the drivetrain.

Figure 2 shows a general physical layout of the CSM/HEV. The major subsystems include an electric motor/controller, an ethanol-fueled APU with an alternator, a high-capacity battery bank, the driver control panel and computer/data acquisition system. A number of design decisions led to this layout. For example, the APU, power electronics platform and electric motor and controller were placed at the front of the vehicle for co-location of related systems. Additionally, this provided sufficient mass forward of the car's center of gravity to balance the battery bank and allowed good airflow for cooling the electronics and APU.

The battery bank, with a mass of 290 kg, was placed in the rear of the vehicle in a large aluminum enclosure. By placing the battery enclosure just aft of the front seats, eliminating the

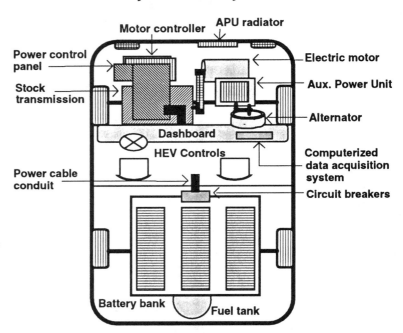

C.S.M. Hybrid Electric Vehicle Physical Block Layout

Motor controller · APU radiator · Power control panel · Electric motor · Stock transmission · Aux. Power Unit · Alternator · Dashboard · HEV Controls · Computerized data acquisition system · Power cable conduit · Circuit breakers · Battery bank · Fuel tank

Figure 2. Shown is the physical layout of the CSM/HEV. The front of the vehicle is at the top of the drawing.

rear passenger seating, and keeping the height low we were able to achieve a front/rear weight bias of 41%/59% with an overall low center of mass which strongly contributed to excellent vehicle handling.

POWER SYSTEM

Shown on Figure 3 is a block diagram representing the key features of the CSM/HEV power system. The CSM/HEV design has two power sources: batteries and the APU. In the ZEV mode the batteries are the only source of power for the electric motor and car systems. In the HEV mode the APU can be used to power the vehicle as well as charge the batteries.

The driver can enable or disable the power sources through high amperage, DC circuit breakers (400 A for the batteries, 150 A for the APU, and 10 A for each of the two DC-DC converters). Not shown is a "pull switch" which is a series switch mounted on top of the battery bank enclosure used as a safety enable of battery power.

Operation of the CSM/HEV is similar to most HEVs. The driver first must connect the battery system by inserting the pull switch and then closing the battery circuit breakers. This powers the vehicle and instrument systems through two 12 V DC-DC converters. The main contactor control switch on the dashboard is set to pre-charge and then on -- allowing power to flow to the electric motor from the batteries. All other standard vehicle systems - lights, brakes, throttle, signals - operate as a standard Ford Escort. Power to the electric motor

C.S.M. HEV Power System Block Diagram

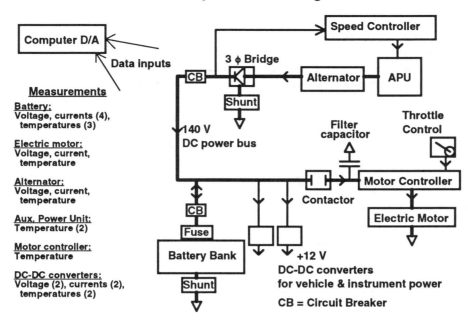

Figure 3. Shown is the CSM/HEV power system block diagram.

is controlled by a potentiometer connected to the driver's throttle pedal.

The APU is started by engaging the APU enable switch on the dash and toggling the APU choke switch to on. The standard Escort steering column 3-position keyswitch is used to start and operate the APU. The alternator is connected to the propulsion power bus by closing the alternator circuit breaker. The APU throttle is engaged, either manually or by the APU speed controller, to set the power flow from the APU/alternator. Shutting down is simply done in the reverse manner. An emergency "Kill Switch" may be used to shut down the propulsion system -- the vehicle and instrument systems will remain on line.

ALTERNATE POWER UNIT - The HEV Challenge rules required a minimum range of 333 km at the range event, including 67 km on battery power only, and 267 km at an average speed of 75 km per hour. It was estimated that the APU must generate a minimum of 14 kW to overcome the steady-state power losses of the vehicle while traveling at highway speeds and accommodating a variable terrain typical of that encountered in the northern midwestern U.S. The power magnitude was determined by the power required to overcome the wind, rolling resistance and propulsion system losses. A safety factor was incorporated, over and above that associated with steady-state vehicle losses, to account for accelerations and variations in terrain.

A 4-stroke, liquid cooled, electric start, carbureted, spark ignition engine (Kawasaki V-twin, model FD620cc) was selected as the APU. The engine weighs 41 kg (dry) and is sold as an APU for remote electric power generation or to provide shaft power for pumps. Viton carburetor seals replaced the

stock O-rings to allow the use of 100% ethanol. No other substantial engine modifications were necessary.

A small water-brake dynamometer stand was constructed to test both the electric motor and APU, allowing the APU sub-team to brake-in and measure the actual engine torque, power output and fuel consumption. The measured power (at nearly 1828 m elevation) was 12.2 kW at 3330 rpm. Estimated fuel consumption for the 267 km traverse was 30.2 liters ethanol with the car traveling at an average 75 km per hour on flat terrain.

FUEL SYSTEM - In the conversion of the CSM/HEV, the fuel system was redesigned to accommodate the use of denatured ethanol. The design of the fuel system included pre-combustion air/fuel and exhaust handling subsystems.

The pre-combustion network involved the transfer of ethanol from the fuel tank to the carburetor. Materials used for fuel lines and the fuel tank were compatible with ethanol, lightweight and relatively inexpensive. Ethanol was stored in a 30.3 liter, racing type, fuel cell made out of polyethylene. An additional 1.5 liters is stored in the fuel lines and filler neck. Baffles within the cell inhibit spillage and minimize the possibility of explosion. The fuel cell was installed in the opening of the spare tire cavity. A hole through the car body on the rear passenger side was cut for the installation of the fuel filler assembly. Materials used that proved compatible with the ethanol were polyvinyl chloride (PVC) pipe (transparent and opaque), a polyethylene radiator hose and Viton rubber for gasket material. We are still searching for acceptable, long-life sealants that are ethanol safe and can maintain a seal in the presence of vehicle vibrations. The fuel lines selected were polypropylene to withstand the corrosive properties of ethanol. The tubes were sheathed with braided stainless steel to prevent long term wear and fatigue. Before the fuel enters the fuel pump, it flows through a fuel filter.

The fuel pump selected was a positive displacement type capable of a maximum flow rate of 160 liters per hour. The pump draws a steady-state current of 3 amps at 12 volts. A fuel block was installed on the engine compartment fire wall. It has one incoming port and three outgoing ports. One of the extra outgoing ports was used to recirculate fuel back to the fuel cell. This recirculation could be used to cool the fuel to alleviate problems of vapor lock within the carburetor in the event of very warm weather during the competition. The second outgoing port transfers ethanol from the block to the carburetor. The third outgoing port was to be used for a cold starting subsystem if needed.

Ethanol has a high latent heat of vaporization and low vapor pressure as compared to gasoline. Early in the design process, this was perceived as a major concern because of anticipated problems with cold start of the APU. Therefore, numerous ways for alleviating the cold start problem were investigated. Fortunately, in testing the vehicle during the spring prior to the challenge, we found little or no difficulty in starting the engine, even on days where the temperature dropped to 7^0 C (45^0 F).

The stock Kawasaki choke, actuated by solenoid, was used with the carburetor to aid in cold starting the APU. During the competition, the APU speed was controlled using a hand actuated throttle and the stock flyweight governor because of difficulties in implementing our APU Speed Controller. The APU speed varied from 2900 to 3000 RPM depending upon the voltage of the battery bank and the electric motor power load.

The exhaust gases from the combustion of ethanol flowed through a 3-way catalytic converter and a muffler that was roughly half the volume of the stock components due to space limitations imposed by the required heavy electric cables carrying current between the batteries in the rear of the vehicle and the electric motor and alternator in the front of the car.

Since ethanol is an oxygenated fuel, fewer CO emissions should result when burning it as opposed to gasoline. However, the emission results from the competition indicate that for every vehicle burning ethanol, CO emissions were 10 times the 1994 standards for light-duty vehicles. Further work will be necessary to determine why the CO emissions were so high. It is possible that the engines used in the Challenge were small, largely unregulated and will require redesign for cleaner burn. Could these high CO results be related to the techniques utilized to measure ethanol emissions?

ALTERNATOR - The alternator provided a means of converting shaft power from the APU to electric power needed for the electric motor or batteries. Aside from choosing the alternator, the other factors addressed included testing, mounting, and mechanically coupling the alternator to the APU.

Based upon the power requirements to propel the vehicle at freeway speeds, an alternator power output of 16 kW was selected. A battery bus voltage of 120-140 V leads to a amperage rating of about 125 A DC from the alternator and diode bridge. A custom built alternator was the only choice to meet these requirements and keep the size/weight to a minimum.

Our alternator was designed and manufactured by Fisher Electric Motors, Inc. This alternator is an advanced permanent magnet design with 12 pole pairs. The shape of the alternator is cylindrical with a diameter of 0.267 m, a length of 0.102 m and a mass of 10 kg. The maximum power design specification was to output 120 VDC at 125 A when driven at 4000 RPM.

Because of space limitations, a belt drive system was selected to transmit power from the APU to the alternator. Its placement in the engine compartment was determined after the APU was mounted. It was connected to the APU with dual v-belts guided by the pulleys. The mounting of the alternator was designed to place it in the limited space of the engine compartment. The mounting consisted of a rigid pivot point member placed on the shock tower of the engine compartment on the passenger side of the vehicle. The other member consisted of a lever arm capable of applying the appropriate tension on the belts, which rotate about a radius of curvature of 0.53 m from the pivot point.

A strength analysis of the material used in the mounting of the alternator was performed after installation. Factors included the belt tensions of 583 N, the orientation of the tension forces, the alternator weight of 98 N, and the force of rigid impacts. A stress analysis was performed on ALGOR, a finite element engineering analysis program. The maximum stress on one member was 88 MPa with 59 MPa on the other. The stress concentration factor, located at the bolt holes, was below the yield strength of steel (207 MPa).

Testing showed that the alternator winding inductance was higher than specified. This forced us to adjust the alternator speed (RPM) for varying loading conditions over a much larger range than anticipated to compensate for the higher internal impedance voltage drop.

APU SPEED CONTROL - The APU Speed Control unit is a dedicated Motorola microprocessor 68HC11 board with a DC motor powered throttle actuator that implements a Proportional Integral-Derivative (PID) control loop to stabilized the bus voltage for propulsion while at the same time controlling the rate of battery charge. This speed controller dynamically adjusts the APU throttle such that the instantaneous propulsion power demand is met and the battery bank is returned to a full state of charge. If the electrical load increases, through increased electric motor loading or battery charging, the APU speed controller adjusts the throttle upwards to compensate and conversely as the load decreases.

Due to difficulties in integrating the speed controller within the Ford/DOE HEV Challenge deadline, initial operation of the HEV did not make use of the APU Speed Control unit. Rather, the throttle was routed to the driver control panel and could be hand actuated from idle to full-on and regulated by the stock APU governor. In operation, the driver sets the loading of the electric motor by the electric motor throttle control - the rest of the power is absorbed or supplied by the battery bank. The vehicle operated reasonably well in this manner but required the driver to continually monitor the battery state of charge to ensure that it was not overcharged. When the battery was fully charged, the operator would then set the APU throttle cable to idle and operate the vehicle from battery power.

USER INTERFACE AND DATA ACQUISITION - A critical design goal for our HEV was to provide the driver and/or the passenger with complete status and direct control of all the vehicle sub-systems. To this end we placed voltage, current and temperature indicators on a custom dash panel (Figure 4). Below the dashboard are a number of switches and LED indicators controlling the operational mode and showing the status of the vehicle systems, respectively. The central wiring point, the junction where all control and signal

cabling are brought together, is located behind and below the switch panel.

To gain a better understanding of the performance of our vehicle and to fully instrument the various sub-systems, one of our major goals was to integrate an on-board data acquisition system. This system was designed to acquire a number of voltages, currents and temperatures and update the driver/passenger on the vehicle operating conditions.

A laptop computer based data acquisition system is used to monitor several different system parameters. A C++ computer program was constructed to interface the computer to the sensors via an Analog Devices RTI-820 A/D converter and signal conditioners. This allows the driver and/or passenger to be easily updated on a computer screen. The program also supplies the user with a history of the entire trip for analysis purposes during and/or after the trip.

The computer chosen for the HEV was a Texas Instrument Win386 laptop because it could be interfaced to the data acquisition cards through a bus extender card. The RTI-820 board has a 12 bit resolution and a capability of multiplexing 64 channels with an acquisition rate of up to 19 kHz. The signal conditioners used included Analog Devices STB-HL02 for high level voltage measurements (0-10V) and an STB-TC for low level measurements (0-100mV). The 16 channels available in the STB-TC are ambient temperature compensated for thermocouples.

Status and control signal lines were routed through the car in 10 pair, shielded cables. Figure 3 lists the type and number of measurements for each sub-system. The various voltages, currents and

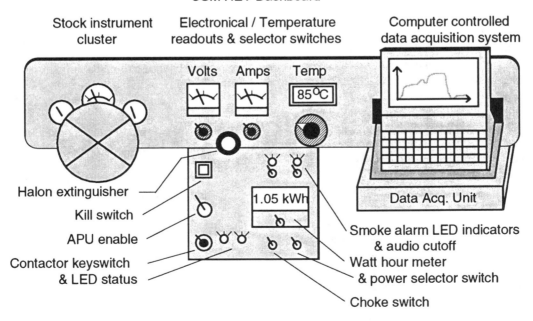

Figure 4. The CSM/HEV dashboard layout. The computer system controls and displays the measurements from the data acquisition system.

status indicators were wired to the dashboard gauges and the computer data acquisition system through the central wiring point. The thermocouple sensors were run directly from the various sub-systems to both the dashboard temperature readout and the computer data acquisition system.

POWER ELECTRONICS - From the circuit breakers on the battery bank, the power was brought forward to the engine compartment through a large electrical conduit run under the vehicle chassis. This conduit held the 4/0 main power cables as well as smaller power cables for the DC-DC converters. These cables were routed to the power electronics platform positioned just above the transmission in front of the driver.

Located on this power electronics platform (Figure 3) was the main power contactor (Albright SW200-22 rated for 1000 A opening) which enabled power to electric motor and the 3 phase bridge rectifier (PowerEx ME500810 100A, 800V 3ϕ bridges, two in parallel). This bridge with a 0.1 mΩ shunt to measure the alternator current and a 20 mF filter capacitor converted the alternator AC output to DC to power the motor or charge the batteries. Also located on this platform was the two DC-DC converter (Sevcon Generation II 128 V/12 V, 30 A) which converted the battery voltage level to 12 volts and various control relays and sensing lines. One DC-DC converter was used to power the car systems and other large loads, the other was used to power the instrumentation, control relays and the computer/data acquisition system.

These power electronics devices were fastened to a 9.5 mm aluminum plate on the driver side of the engine compartment and rested on the transmission. The plate is hinged at the rear, so that it can be lifted up to allow access to vehicle components underneath. Under the plate are several heat sinks for cooling. Another plate was made of 9.5 mm aluminum to mount the motor controller. This plate was attached to the transmission mount, directly under the main electronics platform. The motor controller was attached to the underside, while large heat sinks were attached to the front. The plate angles to ramp airflow over the heat sinks and up to the heat sinks of the main platform. This design provides adequate cooling for the for all of the power electronic components.

ELECTRIC MOTOR AND CONTROLLER - The electric motor and controller are the key drivetrain sub-system. Several different motors and controllers were considered and in end we went with a series-wound DC electric motor from Advanced DC Motors FB14001 with a MOSFET-based controller PMC-1221 from Curtis PMC. The motor is rated for about 30 kW continuous but we are limited to less than 22 kW due to the maximum average power capability of the controller. This motor controller is very compact, lightweight and

relatively inexpensive. However, it lacks the capability to regenerate energy from the motor to the power bus/batteries. The decision to acquire this motor and controller was made after considering the price/performance of various systems on the market. We would have preferred a high average power system, but the cost increased from $2,000 to over $20,000. This motor and controller has worked reliably over the entire project.

BATTERY SYSTEM - After a significant search for electric vehicle batteries, it was determined that only two practical and available choices existed, lead acid or Nickel-Cadmium (NiCd). NiCd batteries were selected since they have far better lifetime, power density and energy density than lead acid cells and we found a supplier of surplus aircraft cells making them affordable. The specifications of the batteries selected and battery system configuration are listed below:

- SAFT VP230KHB NiCd Sintered Plate Cells
   23 Amp-Hour, 1.26 VDC nominal
   36 W-hr/kg
   0.95 kg
- Battery Packs
   15 total battery packs
   20 cells connected in series
   26 VDC when fully charged
- Battery String
   5 battery packs in series (100 cells in series)
   110-155 VDC operating range
- Battery System
   3 battery strings in parallel
   32 MJ (8.7 kW-hr) energy storage

In designing the battery enclosure to meet our goals and the rules for the HEV competition, the following specifications were established:

- Design, build and installing a battery enclosure capable of holding the 300 NiCd battery cells in the event of an accident
- Minimize the affect the battery enclosure/bank has on vehicle handling by placement and sizing
- The enclosure should be economical to construct and easy to gain access into the battery bank
- It must be sealed to contain any leakage or explosions, yet ventilated to remove any buildup of hydrogen gas. Also, it must have a smoke detector and a Halon fire extinguisher.

The large aluminum enclosure was designed to contain the batteries during normal car operation and in case of a collision with a stationary object while the car was moving at 83 km per hr. The enclosure is a rectangular box made of 6.35 mm thick 5052 aluminum.

Using ALGOR, the bottom plate of the enclosure was modeled to determine the maximum stress and displacement. Different plate thicknesses were used in the calculations to find the minimum satisfactory plate thickness. The plate designed had a maximum deflection less than 2.5 mm and a maximum stress below the yield stress of the aluminum. The good corrosion resistance and weldability of the aluminum also lead to our decision to choose this material.

The container was also equipped with a forced air ventilation system which pulled air from beneath the vehicle, distributed it evenly across the batteries and pulled it outside of the vehicle to remove gases and vapors. The exhaust was mounted on the top of the battery enclosure and exited through a vent on the passenger side of the car. A brushless DC fan rated at 9.4×10^{-3} m^3/s (20 cfm) was used for ventilation. The fan draws its power from the main battery pack and operates at any time the battery system is electrically connected to the vehicle or during battery charging.

Additional space within the enclosure was also needed for the fuses, switches, and other connectors necessary for the operation of the batteries. The container was securely mounted to the inside of the HEV. The bottom and sides of the enclosure are welded together. The top plate of the enclosure is secured to the sides of the enclosure by four latches and aluminum angle. The piece of angle aluminum is mounted along the back edge of the enclosure to prevent forward movement of the enclosure top in the event of a frontal collision.

A refrigerator type seal was used between the top plate and sides of the enclosure. The bolt sizes used for fastening the enclosure to the chassis were calculated assuming a possible collision time of 40 milliseconds with the vehicle decelerating from 80 kmph.

Battery packs were constructed to effectively organize and contain the individual battery cells within the enclosure. They were interchangeable and made of 6.35 mm acrylic which is non-conductive and resistant to the corrosive attack of the battery electrolyte. The organization of the battery cells in the battery packs was compatible with the power required for the vehicle. Each battery pack was bolted into the enclosure to prevent movement during operation of the HEV. There will be a further design iteration on these packs because the 6.35 mm thick plastic bottom bolted to the base of the large aluminum enclosure is brittle and prone to breaking during normal battery installation and removal procedures.

The individual battery cells were electrically connected within the battery packs using 3.2 mm x 12.7 mm x 50.8 mm copper bars bolted to the top of the cells. The battery packs are connected together with a cable assembly consisting of an Anderson "PowerPole" connector, a length of 1/0 welding cable and a 2/0 compression lug.

A significant learning experience worth mention relates to a fire hazard that exists when the nuts that fasten the copper bars to the battery posts are **not** sufficiently tight. The resulting high electrical contact resistance causes local heating yielding battery post temperatures sufficient to melt the polyethylene cell wall. At the end of our test cycle the batteries were nearly discharged, resulting in increased venting of hydrogen gas. This, along with the lose connections and insufficient airflow led to a hazardous condition where several battery cells were feeding a hydrogen fire. We were fortunate that we ended our test cycle and detected the fire before substantial damage occurred. Twenty cells were replaced and an audible smoke alarm was added to the design of the battery ventilation system. We found that a 5.6 N-m (50 lb-in) torque was sufficient to minimize the problems of electrical contact resistance. In addition, petroleum jelly was smoothed onto each post to protect the copper from corrosion.

The three battery strings are connected in parallel prior to running into the circuit breaker box mounted on the front of the enclosure. The positive leads of all three strings are brought together at the 400 amp fuse placed at the passengers side of the enclosure. The positive wires are connected to the fuse and to an Anderson "SBX" connector and then to the circuit breakers. The Anderson connector is mounted on the drivers side of the enclosure and allows for the removal of a portion of the positive wire. This "pull switch" enables the users of the vehicle to disengage all battery power to the vehicle. A current measuring shunt is connected to each negative lead of the three battery strings. The other side of each of the three shunts are tied together and connected to another shunt. This enables us to measure each battery string current as well as two ways to measure the total current. Each shunt is 0.1 mΩ (500A / 50mV).

Strengths of the enclosure subsystem design include: 1) the ability to withstand a collision from 80 kmph, 2) a flexible battery connection system, the batteries can be connected in several different arrangements, 3) battery cells and battery packs are quickly replace, a bad cell or pack can be quickly removed and replaced, 4) low cost, simple materials and manufacturing methods.

Weaknesses in the design include: 1) poor battery cooling which has not been a problem even during hard usage during the competition, 2) limited amount of space within the enclosure, additional space would allow for the installation of more battery safety equipment within the enclosure, 3) loss of the vehicle rear seat and 4) inferior materials for battery packs.

BATTERY CHARGING - An off-board battery charger was acquired from Bycan Corporation. It is a microprocessor controlled charger, equipped with an isolation transformer and rated for 20 A at 160 V constant current charging. It requires a 208 V, 20 A single phase outlet and allows the user to select various voltage and current settings for a three step charging process. For our system the first step provides a constant current of 15 A until the battery voltage reaches 145 V, the second step provides a constant current of 5 A until the battery voltage reaches 150 V, the last step is a constant voltage trickle charge to 155 V limited to 5A. The charger takes about six hours to fully charge the battery bank. During this time the battery exhaust fan runs continuously.

The Bycan battery charger is connected to the vehicle through a polarized connector behind the original gas filler door. The charger wires are routed to a 25 A circuit breaker, located with all other circuit breakers between the driver and passenger, and then to the battery bank through the main power fuse. This configuration enables the fuse to always be in any circuit involving the batteries.

VEHICLE HANDLING

The suspension of the stock Escort was modified to accommodate the increased vehicle weight introduced by the batteries. In general, the goal was to use after market performance equipment for these modifications. Coil springs, stiffer than those on the stock Escort and fabricated by Suspension Techniques, were installed in the front and rear. These were designed to allow improved performance with the resulting weight distribution of the CSM/HEV. In addition, stiff anti-sway bars were installed to augment the stock anti-sway bars in the front and replace those in the rear. For added stiffness, less compliant, polyurethane bushings replaced the rubber stock bushings. High performance gas shocks, supplied by Tokico were used in place of the lighter-duty stock shocks.

American Racing supplied the 0.356 m (14 inch) aluminum racing wheels and Goodyear supplied the P185/60R14 tires. These tires were lower profile than those on the stock Escort [0.330 m (13 inch)] but were the same overall diameter and therefore provide improved handling of the heavy vehicle in a sharp turn.

In general, the our car had excellent handling capabilities, as demonstrated through the outstanding performance in the handling stages of the qualification tests during the 1993 challenge.

SUMMARY

In conclusion, the CSM/HEV was a successful team effort combining a low cost, good performance and efficiency in the overall design. We placed 7th overall during the competition (5th in the dynamic events), and took the prize for the most efficient ethanol APU in the conversion class. We achieved this by a team effort of students, faculty advisors and generous sponsors.

ACKNOWLEDGMENTS

We gratefully acknowledge the support of our sponsors. We thank the Public Service Company of Colorado, the Colorado Corn Administrative Committee, the Ohio Corn Growers Association, ARCO Coal and the Colorado School of Mines for their very generous monetary support. Also we would like to thank the many companies and individuals who donated money, in-kind support and advice. Last, but certainly not least, we thank all of the people who supported this HEV Challenge at Ford, the U.S. Department of Energy and SAE for their vision of the future and hard work to make this competition a reality.

Design of a Hybrid Electric Vehicle

William E. Kramer
Colorado State University

ABSTRACT

A parallel hybrid electric vehicle design is presented. The vehicle was designed to meet the requirements for the conversion class of the *1993 Hybrid Electric Vehicle Challenge*. This paper addresses the concept, design and fabrication of a hybrid electric vehicle (HEV).

INTRODUCTION

In these days of declining energy resources and increasing concern for the environment, there has come a need for personal transportation methods that combine efficiency and economy while minimizing environmental damage. During the "Energy Crisis" of the 1970s, electrically powered vehicles appeared to be a viable transportation alternative to internal combustion automobiles. However, battery technologies gave electric vehicles an unreasonable driving range, and low specific output (power per kilogram of battery) motors gave the electric vehicles (EVs) anemic acceleration performance. High initial costs, and poor range performance contributed to the lack of enthusiasm from the general public, who were accustomed to inexpensive vehicles and inexpensive fuel. However, the energy and environmental crises were still looming on the horizon, demanding solutions. A compromise had to be found that would meet public demand for inexpensive private transportation, and would exhibit acceptable range and power characteristics. Simultaneously, such a vehicle has to minimize environmental damage, and meet stringent safety standards. It is expected that a hybrid electric powered vehicle could meet this need. This paper describes the selection, design and implementation for the conversion of a 1992 Ford Escort Wagon to a parallel hybrid vehicle. The conversion utilizes an internal combustion engine and a water-cooled permanent magnet motor and water-cooled controller for the drivetrain.

COMPETITION STRATEGY

Designing a car with two different powertrains while leaving the standard controls intact poses major obstacles. The brake and clutch pedals remain the same but the throttle pedal must be an accelerator pedal for the gas engine and a speed pedal for the electric motor. The existing mechanical accelerator pedal was replaced with an electronic foot pedal. The pedal utilizes a potentiometer to generate a zero to ten volt signal required by the electric motor controller and engine systems. This allows direct integration into the electronic control of the motor controller and adapted control of the engine throttle using a servo circuit. Figure 1 shows the major components of the vehicle. These include the potentiometer pedal, mode switch, engine throttle control servo, motor and motor controller, batteries, computer, clutch actuator and internal combustion engine.

The mode switch is a three-position rotary switch which determines whether the vehicle operates in Auxiliary Power Unit(APU) Only, Zero Emissions Vehicle(ZEV), or Hybrid mode. Hybrid mode is an optimal combination of the other two modes. The mode switch also sends a digital signal to the control computer, indicating the tasks for the computer to perform.

In the APU ONLY mode all of the power to the wheels comes from the internal combustion engine. During this mode, the accelerator potentiometer exclusively energizes the throttle actuator circuitry and the electric motor and controller are disabled through the use of the low voltage enable/disable switch on the controller. This mode is required for emissions testing.

The ZEV mode is required during sections of the Urban Drive Event , the Range Event and the Acceleration Event. In this mode the accelerator potentiometer is redirected by the mode switch exclusively to the electric motor controller. The engine starter and engine control module are disabled, thus not allowing the engine to run.

To place the vehicle in hybrid mode the driver will place the mode switch in the third position. This position, unlike the other two, does not exclusively direct the potentiometer pedal output but rather gives this control to the computer to decide where to direct the signal. The vehicle will first run in hybrid/electric mode. While running in hybrid/electric mode the computer will redirect the potentiometer signal to the motor controller. The computer will monitor the battery voltage, the amount of battery energy remaining, and the distance traveled since transition to hybrid mode. If conditions such as overheating, low voltage, low charge, or mileage limit arise, the computer will switch the vehicle over to engine power.

To change to engine power, the computer first starts the engine. After the computer receives a signal that the gas engine is running, it then slews a voltage signal to the throttle actuator until the rpm of the engine matches the rpm of the electric motor. The computer engages the APU clutch, redirects the potentiometer signal, and disables the motor and controller.

While running in the hybrid/engine mode, the potentiometer signal is redirected to the acceleration control circuit and the motor and controller are disabled, as in APU only mode. The computer will monitor the engine coolant temperature, engine status and pedal position. If the pedal is fully depressed for a preset period of time, the computer will assume that the engine needs help. It will see if it can change back over to the more powerful electric motor. Also if the computer senses any major problem with the engine it will change back to electric power.

In changing back to electric power, the computer needs to first determine that the electric system is operational. This involves checking the battery voltage and the motor and controller temperature. If these conditions indicate that it is safe to change, then the computer enables the motor and controller. It then adjusts the speed setting of the motor equal to the rpm of the engine. The computer then sets the engine throttle to idle, reverts the potentiometer pedal signal to the electric motor controller and disengages the engine clutch.

The electric motor selected has very good power regenerative capabilities. It can be set to operate like a generator. If the brake pedal is pushed, then a signal is sent to the motor controller telling it to regenerate power to the batteries. This will assist the brakes and will recover some of the power which is generally lost as heat during braking. Also, while running on engine power at low speeds, when not all of the available power from the APU is being used to drive the car, the computer will decide how much power regeneration to request from the motor. Thus optimizing the efficiency of the gas engine and replenishing the battery power. This will help increase the range of the vehicle.

Running in the hybrid mode will allow zero emissions while running on electric power and will also have the long range

benefits of an internal combustion engine. The engine only needs to produce minimal power for highway driving as power for around town acceleration comes from the electric motor. A parallel hybrid design was chosen over a series configuration because it is expected that the concept will be more efficient than its series counterpart.

BATTERIES

SELECTION - The following criteria was used to compare battery types and technologies:

Cost. The team will be assessed a fixed cost multiplier depending on the type of battery technology the team chooses.

Energy Density. As energy increases, range of the vehicle increases.

Volume. The entire pack must fit in the car, and the battery packs should not intrude into the interior on the vehicle.

Weight. The weight of the pack is limited to 490 kg (1080 lbs). The pack must be able to fit into the weight distribution scheme.

Practicality. Is there manufacturer support, and information on the performance of the batteries?

Charge Acceptance. Can the batteries be effectively charged in less than 6 hours with standard house wiring? What level of charge can the batteries accept during power regeneration.

Battery Buss Voltage. The maximum voltage as seen by the motor controller must never exceed 211 volts.

Energy. The maximum energy for any battery pack must not exceed 20 kWh at the 3 hour discharge rate.

The criteria above were considered in a matrix format for lead acid, NiCd and NiMH and are given in Figure 2. After careful consideration of the performance characteristics and the existing budget, the team decided to design the system based on lead acid batteries. It was determined that a parallel pack of lead acid batteries would minimize the cost and increase the energy capacity compared to a single battery pack of NiCd batteries. Since the volume required for a parallel pack of lead acid batteries would be greater than any packs of NiMH or NiCd Batteries, the team decided to first use lead acid batteries in the design of the battery boxes and high power electronics. The battery boxes were designed so that different battery technologies could be used with minimal modifications.

PERFORMANCE - As a result of these decisions and the matrix, the team utilized two 180 volt battery packs of

Johnson Controls UPS12-95 12-volt lead acid batteries. The two battery packs are connected in parallel. Each pack consists of 15 batteries and are placed in the front and rear compartments of the vehicle. Each battery has a capacity of 27 Amp-Hr@ C3 discharge rate and both packs weigh 354 kg (780 lbs) with a total volume of 144 L (5.1 Ft³). Estimated range of the vehicle for electric only operation is approximately 77 to 88 km (48 to 55 miles).

VENTILATION - A battery box enclosure was designed for both the front and rear areas of the vehicle and were designed to allow each battery pack to be removed from the vehicle. Each battery box uses two ventilating fans located near the top of each box. One fan runs whenever the battery pack circuit is connected to the motor controller. Its sole purpose is to supply 10 cfm for ventilation purposes. The second fan runs whenever the temperature of the center battery in the pack exceeds a predetermined setpoint. Intake air enters the front area of the battery box, and is isolated from water through the use of a filtering system.

BATTERY CHARGING

180 Volt Batteries - An off-board battery charger is used to charge the battery system. The charger has an input rating of 220 VAC @ 15.2 Amp with an output rating of 240 VDC @ 12 Amps. The charger has a C90 isolation transformer and is manufactured by Good-All Electric of Ft. Collins, Colorado. The batteries are charged through the use of a specialized connector manufactured by Meltric of Cudahy, Wisconsin. The receptacle for this connector is located behind a hinged door on the rear quarter panel of the vehicle. The charger will recharge both of the vehicle's battery packs in 6 hours. There are plans to include an on-board charger.

DC/DC Converter- Since the 12 volt accessory battery supplies power during all three vehicle modes, the capability to recharge this battery must be available at all times. The engine alternator recharges the accessory battery whenever the engine is running at a speed greater than 1300 revolutions per minute. A DC/DC converter recharges the 12 volt battery from the 180 volt battery pack whenever the voltage is below 12.0 volts. This charger remains on until the battery voltage rises above 12.5 volts. This also allows the accessory battery to be recharged while the 180 volt battery pack is being recharged.

The DC/DC converter selected is manufactured by Vicor for industrial applications. Two 300-watt converters are wired in parallel to supply sufficient power for the 12 volt system, as well as recharge the accessory battery. They convert a voltage from a range of 75 - 375 volts down to 13.2 volts. They are well-built and are tested for an operating temperature range of -40°C to +85°C. Input-to-output isolation of 3,750 volts totally eliminates output interaction problems. The electrically-isolated baseplate allows mounting to the motor controller box as a large heatsink. This DC/DC converter selection effectively meets the power requirements while being reliable in severe conditions.

ELECTRIC MOTOR AND CONTROLLER

SELECTION - The design criteria for the selection of the motor and drivetrain were based on a combination of the competition requirements and on requirements that have been established by the DOE for regular passenger vehicles, which would enable the vehicle to outperform its competitors, while clearly meeting the minimum competition requirements.

Competition Expectations:
- Attain cruise speed of 65 km/h (40 mph)
- Maximum speed of 88 km/h (55 mph)
- maneuver up a 15% grade
- 0-73 km/h (45 mph) in 15 seconds
- maximum overall efficiency

Team Expectations:
- Maximum speed of 105 km/h (65 mph)
- Constant 48 km/h (30 mph) on 7% grade
- Constant 24 km/h (15 mph) on 10% grade
- 0-73 km/h (45 mph) in 13 seconds
- Minimum elapsed time for the Commuter Challenge
- Best Electric Efficiency

Based on dynamic computer simulations of the batteries, vehicle and electric motor, the team selected a water-cooled DC permanent magnet motor manufactured by Unique Mobility of Golden, Colorado. The UNIQ™ SR180 34-kW water-cooled motor was selected for the following reasons:

- Cost effective
  The manufacturer has offered to make the motor and controller package available at a discounted cost.
- Minimize complexity and spatial requirements
  The SR180 motor is extremely compact for the amount of power available, only taking up about one-fourth the volume of the stock 4-cylinder engine. The required motor controller is about the size of 4 shoe boxes set side by side.
- Low overall weight
  The total weight would be approximately 42 kg (92 lbs.), which is about a third of the weight of the stock 4-cylinder engine.
- Sufficient power
- High efficiency in drive and regenerative modes
  An expected efficiency range of 88-92% in drive mode, and 80% in the regenerative mode.
- High transaxle mechanical efficiency
  The actual gearing efficiency
- Compatible with the motor's power output
  Using the Escort's transaxle will allow a direct interface of the motor to the input shaft of the transaxle.
- Low weight
  A design concept that can meet the vehicle performance requirements and has less mass.
- Capable of handling high motor speeds
  The stock manual transaxle can safely handle up to 7,500 rpm. However, it is not anticipated that the

motor speed will be exceeding 6,500 rpm.

GEARING - The electric motor utilizes a 1 to 2 gear ratio, driver to driven, between the electric motor shaft and the shaft connected to the transmission. This ratio is used to match the engine speed with electric motor speeds which will result in efficient operation of both the motor and the engine.

BEARING LIFE - A simple analysis on the bearing of the electric motor was performed. The analysis takes into account the load on the bearing due to belt tension horsepower. The results of the analysis are given in Figure 3. Three different loads were considered. The analysis is a worst case scenario when the motor is run continuously at either intermittent, rated, or average power conditions. Based on these results, the bearing could fail after 20 months of continuous operation. Since the average drive time is not expected to be more than 8 hours a day 7 days a week, the analysis indicates that the bearing should be checked in about 60 months.

COOLING - Both the electric motor and controller are water-cooled. In order to cool these two components, a closed-loop cooling system was required. The primary components in the system include a water-to-air heat exchanger, pump, automatic air vent, and piping (see Figure 4 for piping schematic). The heat exchanger system was sized to remove a load of 4.2 kW (3,600 KCal/hr). This load is based on expected losses through the motor and controller during normal operation. Since the space is very limited at the front of the vehicle, two heat exchangers were piped in parallel. Using the pressure losses through all of the components, a circulating pump was sized and was installed under the hood of the vehicle. Most electric motor systems utilize air for cooling. Air cooled systems are very prone to debris and moisture damage. It is expected that a water cooled electronic drive system will enhance the vehicle's reliability and performance.

ENGINE

SELECTION - Due to time and budgetary constraints, only internal combustion engines have been the focus of Auxiliary Power Unit (APU) design for the 1993 HEV Challenge. Fuel cells would be more suitable for the design of a hybrid electric vehicle, and theoretically more efficient. However, current technology in that field is limited, and material costs are not justifiable for application on the vehicle.

The engine selected is a Kawasaki FD620D-AS01. It is a liquid-cooled, 90° V-Twin that displaces 617 cubic centimeters. The power output is rated at 16 kW (22 bhp) at 3600 rpm, and a torque output of 47 N•m (34.7 ft•lbs) at 2400 rpm. It has a dry mass of 41.5 kilograms. It features a throttle-body electronic fuel injection system, an electric fuel pump, an overhead valve combustion chamber, and an aluminum block with cast iron cylinder liners. This engine was designed by Kawasaki Heavy Industries (KHI) in conjunction with John Deere, and is available on the John Deere 445 Heavy-Duty Garden Tractor.

The selection of the engine was based on a list of requirements involving desired vehicle performance, engine performance, and engine design. A group of engines were compared in a weighted decision matrix (see Figure 5). Following is the list of requirements:

- Vehicle Propulsion
  - Steady-state 88 km/h (55 mph) on a 0% grade
  - Engine operating at its minimum brake specific fuel consumption (BSFC) rating

- Reserve Power at minimum BSFC for Emissions Control Strategy
  - Stoichiometric Air/Fuel Mixture
  - Catalytic Converter
  - Exhaust Gas Recirculation

- Built-in Emissions Control Potential
  - Electronic Fuel Injection
  - Small Combustion Chamber
  - Compression Ratio
  - Low BSFC
  - Liquid Cooling

- Minimal Packaging Volume

- List Cost

- Low Weight

The Federal Test Procedure (FTP) emissions testing process suggests that the vehicle be able to maintain a speed of 72 km/h (45 mph), and accelerate at 4.8 km/h per second (3 mph per second) on an inertial-weight chassis dynamometer. The engine was designed primarily for range extension and "limp-home" rather than high performance. Therefore the vehicle will not accelerate sufficiently to keep up with the driving trace, however this is not a requirement of the competition. The vehicle is capable of maintaining a cruising speed of 72 km/h (45 mph), and top speed to date on engine power alone is 80 km/h (50 mph) at 1,524 m (5,000 ft) altitude.

EXHAUST - The exhaust manifold that came with the engine was essentially a muffler connected to the cylinder head exhaust ports. This muffler/manifold configuration was unsuitable due to the packaging constraints within the Escort's engine compartment. In lieu of the muffler/manifold, a custom header was fabricated. The carbon-steel header pipes have a 25 mm (1.0 in) inside diameter. The header has a double layer of ceramic insulation wrap to not only keep the exhaust gas temperatures high and flowing with high velocity, it also helps to prevent increased underhood temperatures. The catalytic converter is located under the passenger compartment floorpan, directly behind the front sub-frame crossmember. An OEM-style muffler is located about 350 mm (14 in) downstream of the catalytic converter. It was attempted to follow the stock tailpipe routing as close as possible. Due to the rear battery box installation, the tailpipe could no longer be routed over the rear axle assembly. Instead the tailpipe is routed along the passenger side of the vehicle, and travels just underneath the right-rear control arm. This poses a clearance problem with the control arm only in situations where the right-rear wheel is fully suspended.

FUEL TANK - The OEM 45 L (11.9 gal) fuel tank was removed in order to fit the electric motor controller and APU fuel tank in the same space (see Figure 7). The replacement fuel tank is made of spun aluminum and has a capacity of 30 L (8 gal). The tank was modified to allow for over-fill plumbing and vapor expansion. The fuel pump/level sender assembly is mounted in the center of the tank. The level sender assembly used is from a John Deere 445 garden tractor, and was chosen due to its compatibility with holding the submersible fuel pump and its ease of installation. A cylindrical fuel tank was chosen so that implementation of a CNG storage tank could be easily made in the future.

EMISSIONS - The emissions target was the California Air Resources Board (CARB) Transitional Low Emission Vehicle (TLEV) standard:

- 0.125 g/mile NMOG (HC, aldehydes)
- 3.40 g/mile CO
- 0.40 g/mile NOx

In order to meet this goal, a few changes were made to the engine systems. First, the fuel system pressure was reduced in order to clean up the emissions on a "gross" level. Second, a catalytic converter was installed to determine an emissions basepoint for computer modifications. Third, an oxygen sensor feedback control was implemented to "fine tune" the fuel control to maximize catalyst effectiveness and to further reduce emissions.

Fuel Control - The engine control system that comes with the John Deere/Kawasaki engine is called Digital Fuel Injection (DFI). The DFI system is an open-loop control system that reads an engine speed, a manifold absolute pressure (MAP), and intake air temperature in order to calculate the mass flow rate of air entering the engine. Upon calculation of the air flow rate, the computer uses a look-up table to find the corresponding fuel injector pulsewidth that will open the injector and deliver the amount of fuel required to achieve a predetermined air/fuel ratio. The ECU also reads the engine coolant temperature, and adds an air/fuel ratio enrichment factor until the engine reaches operating temperature. In addition to fuel delivery, the ECU controls the ignition timing based on engine speed and MAP.

The amount of fuel injected is a function of the fuel injector pulsewidth and the fuel system pressure. Since the fuel injector pulsewidth tables could not be accessed, the system fuel pressure was modified. A baseline emissions test was performed with the engine, using the EPA proposed I/M 240 dynamometer test schedule (similar to the Phase III "Hot 505" FTP test used in the Challenge). Results showed that the engine was running with a rich air/fuel mixture; too rich, in fact, for a catalytic converter to be effective. It was decided to reduce the fuel system pressure until the effective air/fuel ratio approached stoichiometry. An adjustable, fuel pressure regulator was installed as well as an exhaust-gas oxygen (EGO) sensor. To find an air/fuel mixture close to stoichiometry, the output voltage of the EGO sensor was monitored as the fuel pressure was reduced in increments of 7 kPa (1 psi), with a steady-state load applied to the engine at 2800 rpm. The fuel system pressure was reduced from the original factory setting of 172 kPa (26 psi) to 138 kPa (20 psi). Steady state 4-gas analysis showed a 67 percent decrease in CO concentrations, and a 27 percent decrease in HC concentrations.

After obtaining an air/fuel mixture closer to stoichiometry, it was desired to implement more accurate fuel control over the entire load and RPM range. In order to maintain this tight control, a feedback control algorithm was necessary. Since the ECU tables could not be modified, it was decided to modify the MAP input signal. The concept is to modify the map signal as a function of the EGO sensor's voltage output. Thus if the EGO gives a lean signal, the MAP input to the ECU would be offset towards a higher pressure in order to increase the pulse-width and give a richer mixture. Since the MAP input is also used for ignition control, the modified MAP offsets must be minimal to keep the ignition tables stable.

Catalytic Converter - In order to optimize engine performance, fuel economy, and emissions, the engine should be run with a stoichiometric air/fuel mixture. A three-way catalytic converter (TWC) is best suited to stoichiometric conditions. In addition, a TWC gives optimized conversion efficiencies for HC and CO oxidation and NOx reduction. According to competition regulations, maximum converter volume is 4 liters. The Escort's OEM converter volume is 1.5 liters. According to Allied-Signal, the volume of a catalytic converter should correlate with the engine displacement. A substrate with 0.7 L volume was thus chosen to correlate with the 0.617 L engine. The substrate is a ceramic honeycomb with a cell density of 400 / cm^2. Heated catalysts were investigated, but the additional expense and complexity outweighed the benefits of faster light-off times. Also, because of the small catalyst volume being used, light-off times are not a major concern.

Exhaust Gas Recirculation - Exhaust gas recirculation (EGR) was investigated as a tool to reduce the NOx emissions of the engine. Although the engine has a high (10.3:1) compression ratio, it was projected that TLEV NOx levels could be met if the air/fuel ratio is precisely maintained at stoichiometry. Several EGR systems from smaller vehicles were investigated, and could be installed and retrofitted for NOx reduction pending final emissions test results.

Fuel Choice - The chosen fuel for the ICE Wagon is reformulated gasoline. The competition encourages the use of alternative fuels. It has been determined that using an alternative fuel such as M85 (85% methanol) or E100 (ethanol) rather than reformulated gasoline was beyond the scope for the 1993 competition. Before alternative fuels can be implemented, the engine must first be able to run clean and efficiently on gasoline.

The main challenges to overcome in using methanol or ethanol in engines designed for gasoline are the alcohols' corrosive properties and different burn rates. Each fuel requires different operating temperatures and has different cold-start characteristics. Alternative fuels are attractive due to potentially superior emissions performance and reduced reliance on imported petroleum, but are inferior in terms of the energy available per unit volume.

Interim Results - The second I/M 240 test was performed with a 1.5 L TWC, and the fuel pressure was set to 131 kPa (19 psi). The results showed drastic improvements in HC and CO emissions, but also showed a significant increase in NOx emissions (see Figure 6). The increase in NOx was caused by a slightly lean air/fuel mixture, which will be corrected by raising the fuel pressure to 138 kPa (20 psi) and implementing the EGO feedback control.

COOLING - The approximate size of the engine's radiator was determined by using heat transfer relations based upon the 1st Law of Thermodynamics. The model used was a single-core, cross flow heat exchanger. The surface area required to dissipate the heat generated by the engine was calculated to be about 900 cm^2 (140 in^2). The engine's cooling system was required to dissipate approximately 14 kW (12,000 kCal/hr). Due to size constraints, a radiator from a 500 cc motorcycle engine was chosen to accomplish this task. Based on horsepower , this radiator was a satisfactory selection to meet the required load. This radiator also met the requirement of easy replacement.

STRUCTURES

COMPONENT LAYOUT - Figure 7 shows the component placement for the main systems in the vehicle. The engine, electric motor, transmission and front battery box are located under the hood of the vehicle. The gas tank and electric motor controller are located under the rear seat. The second battery box is located in the spare tire area in the rear of the vehicle. Power is distributed through conduits which extend from the front and rear battery boxes to the electric motor controller box. Weight bias and interior integrity were the primary factors in the selection of the location of these components. The vehicle design allows the vehicle to be used as a five passenger vehicle. Interior changes in the car include a CRT display located in the center console. A roll bar and fire suppression unit are located behind the front seats.

The one intrusion into to the interior is the spare tire which is placed on the passenger side, behind the rear wheel well. Directly opposite the spare tire, there is space planned for an on-board charger. The rear cargo compartment floor is raised about two inches due to the battery box lid. The controller box, located under the rear seat, contains the motor controller, fuse, and shunt. This box is accessible by removing it from beneath the car. The gas tank is positioned in front of the controller box. Five high-voltage cables come out of the front of the controller box. Three of the cables provide power to the motor and the remaining two cables provide power to the motor controller from the front battery box.

Weight Bias - The original Ford Escort had a 60-40%

front-rear and 50-50% left-right weight bias. A design goal was to try to match the original bias specifications. The original weight of the vehicle was 1068 kg (2355 lb). After removing the 1.9 L engine, exhaust system, and fuel system, the weight of the vehicle was 825 kg (1819 lb). Since then, the following weights have been added:
1. Drive train (IC Engine, Electric Motor, Clutch, and cowling) = 100.7 kg (222 lb)
2. Fuel tank (Fully fueled) = 21.3 kg (47 lb)
3. Controller Box = 38.6 kg (85 lb)
4. Batteries (Pb-Acid) = 900 lb; (NiMH) = 272.2 kg (600 lb)

The weight distribution for three scenarios is given below. All values are expressed in kilograms:

	Original	Lead Acid	NiMH
Front	641	840	726
Rear	427	762	739
Total	1068	1601	1466
F/R Bias	60/40	52/48	50/50

It is also important to note that the competition has set the weight limit at 1729 kg. Of this amount, 180 kg is added for the driver, passenger, and ballasted cargo. This means the curb weight of the car can not exceed 1549 kg. This limits the total amount of weight added to the car to 724 kg. Undoubtedly, weight is a major factor in determining vehicle components as well as placement, in order to keep our weight bias as close to that of the original vehicle.

DRIVETRAIN - The hybrid electric vehicle drive train consists of 6 major components: engine, engine clutch, motor gears, electric motor, transmission clutch and transmission. A cross sectional view of the drivetrain is given as Figure 8. The major component parts are labeled on the drawing as follows:

Label	Description
1	Engine Output Shaft
2,6	Engine Clutch
7,8	Driven Electric Motor Gear
14	Transmission Flywheel
15	Transmission Clutch

During electric mode, the engine clutch is controlled by an electronic actuator to keep the shaft of the engine from turning with the transmission. Power is transmitted from the motor to the engine through the use of a Gates Polychain gearing system. The engine is directly coupled to the transmission through the use of a mechanical clutch. When engine power is required, the engine clutch is controlled to allow the engine shaft to turn through the transmission. The shaft connecting the engine to transmission clutch plate is supported by the bearings at the engine's output shaft and a bearing located on the electric motor support bracket which is attached directly the transmission housing.

SPRING SELECTION - The additional battery weight,

imposes an increased load to the front and rear springs, 199.6 kg (440 lb) and 335.7 kg (740 lb) respectively. For this reason different coil springs were needed to support the additional weight. The new springs are 60% over drawn and are made from tempered chrome silicone steel with a 14.27 mm wire diameter. This corresponds to a 26.3 kN/m (150 lb/in) of compression rating. These new springs will ensure that the car has at least 100 mm of wheel travel, as specified in the competition rules. In addition to different springs the rear bearings may need to be replaced with ones that can better accommodate the increased shear stress.

BRAKING SYSTEMS - The power brake system was replaced with an electric vacuum system. This system consists of a Gast-manufactured vacuum pump (#MOA-V111-JH), check valve, and a diaphragm vacuum switch. This system keeps the vacuum of 495.3-520.7 mm of mercury without continually running the vacuum pump. The vacuum assist is supplemented by regenerative braking from the electric motor. This is accomplished by a signal being sent to the motor controller whenever the pedal is pushed.

ROLL BAR - Although the unmodified Ford Escort meets the Federal Crash Standards, in the event that a rollover occurs, a roll bar is necessary in order to support the added weight. In the course of designing and placement of the roll bar, it was decided that for convenience, it would be advantageous to make the brace arms pivot in order to increase accessibility to the mid-section of the car. Therefore, the following was accomplished. The brace arms are welded to a steel collar that clasps onto the roll bar main hoop. The collar is held in place by two pins on each side of the hoop and are designed to be easily removable. The pivot ends of the braces are held with a bolt penetrating the brace and secured in the bracket that is bolted to the main frame of the vehicle. A list of the competition requirements follows:

- Securely attached to a structural member.
- Located directly behind the seat backs.
- Allow greatest distance possible between top of bar and occupants' helmet.
- Braced in fore or aft direction within 15 cm from top of roll bar.
- Braces at an angle of 30 degrees from vertical.

Materials used:

- 38.1 mm o.d. x 3.2 mm nominal wall thickness cold drawn over mandrel steel tubing for main hoop and collars.
- 3.2 mm steel plate metal for mounts.
- 38.1 mm x 6.4 mm thickness square tubing for pivot brackets.
- 4-grade, 9.8 mm bolts for securing mounts and brackets to the frame.

FIRE EXTINGUISHER - The fire extinguishing system consists of a 2.3 kg (5 lb) halon bottle with a piping distribution system. The halon bottle is attached to the vertical member of the roll bar, located behind the driver's seat. The extinguishing system is actuated manually by releasing a pin and pulling a cable which releases the chemical into a piping system. The halon is distributed from the bottle through a series of 1/4" tubes that are connected to the front and rear battery boxes, engine compartment, and the motor controller box.

CONTROLS

COMPUTER SELECTION - For best performance of the hybrid mode, a computer is required to optimize efficiency, minimize emissions, monitor major systems, and still make the car easily driveable. The computer hardware and software must be easily changed or upgraded. The computer must endure the harsh environment of a vehicle. The computer selected for this role is a rugged, miniature PC from Octagon Systems. The hardware and software is 100% compatible with other standard personal computers. This computer utilizes a 386SX processor at 25 MHz. Its uses a revised version of DOS 3.31 on a ROM chip. These qualities allow rapid software development and excellent hardware expansion potential. Additionally, the entire computer system is designed specifically for harsh environments, including an operating temperature range of -40°C to +85°C, and for the vibration and shock experienced in a car. The computer system which meets the control strategy requirements includes six cards: CPU, Analog I/O, Digital I/O, Reed Relay, VGA graphics, and a RAM disk card. Thus the entire computer system is very reliable, while easily allowing the additions needed to monitor and control the vehicle's many components.

PROGRAM ARCHITECTURE - The computer's flexibility allows any typical software compiler to be used. The C programming language has the best combination of processing speed, graphics libraries, versatility, portability, and rapid development for this embedded application. During software development, the program structure is simply one large, infinite loop. Although this method of real-time software doesn't have the fastest response, it is initially the simplest method to get the computer completing the necessary tasks. Depending on the vehicle mode and several dynamic variables, the time interval for one software cycle is between one half and one second. If a task needs to be called more frequently, it is selectively placed in the loop two or more times. After the software functions have been tested and proven, some portions of the software are put on interrupt control. Faster computer reaction times are expected from this change.

INPUTS AND OUTPUTS - Digital and analog sensors throughout the car are monitored so the best decisions can be made and any major problems detected. The sixteen analog inputs include the throttle pedal position, vehicle speed, two tachometers, several temperatures, motor coolant pressure, voltage, and current. The analog outputs are for the engine throttle, desired electric motor speed, and electric motor regeneration. The digital inputs include clutch and brake pedal positions, APU clutch position, joystick direction, mode switch position, and engine status lines. The reed relay card has 8 relays, which direct the hybrid mode throttle signal, and control several higher-power relays, such as the APU clutch, APU starter, and motor controller "logic enable". For most inputs, the sampling interval is sufficient to retain desired accuracy. However, a few variables, such as electric current and kWh, depend on a dedicated processor. The supplied DOE energy meter will be used as the primary sensor for these inputs.

USER INTERFACE - A computer graphics monitor in the dash displays only the critical values so the driver can quickly check the vehicle systems. The driver's concentration remains on the task of driving, rather than scanning many mechanical gauges on the dash. The graphics display selected is a 9" gray-scale VGA cathode ray tube (CRT). It is powered by the twelve volt accessory battery. Since day and night operation are desired, other types of graphics displays require lighting. The CRT used consumes less power than many back-lit liquid crystal displays (LCD) or electroluminescent (EL) displays. Additionally, the CRT is built to withstand vibration better and operate in a wider temperature range (-25 C to +60 C) than other displays, such as LCD, EL, vacuum fluorescent, and plasma. Finally the CRT is by far the least expensive of all these options.
Software variables and graphic displays can be changed through the use of a menu on the screen, controlled by a joystick. The joystick best suited for this application is the power mirror adjustment joystick. It is easily within the reach of the driver, allowing maximum safety while making a menu selection. A few screens of gauges are available for viewing, with the default screen showing the most critical gauges.

CONCLUSIONS

BATTERIES - At the writing of this report, a vendor is considering the build of a prototype NiMH battery for use by our team at a reduced cost. The only major change to the design of the battery boxes and high voltage wiring would be that only a single battery pack would be required, but the pack would have to be split up between the rear and front of the vehicle. Based on dimensions given by the vendor, the battery technology should fit into the existing battery box design without adversely affecting the front to rear and left to right weight bias of the vehicle. It is expected that this change will increase the range is ZEV mode to 175 km (110 miles).

VEHICLE PERFORMANCE - Dynamic vehicle testing has been performed utilizing a gear ratio of 2.38 to 1 between the transmission and the electric motor. Only the rear battery box was installed during the tests. Under these conditions, the vehicle can accelerate from 0 to 72 km/h (45 mph) in 14.8 seconds. Top end speeds in excess of 96 km/h (60 mph) were obtained over rolling hill terrain. The vehicle has demonstrated speeds in excess of 32 km/h (20 mph) over grades greater than 10%.

Chassis dynamometer testing utilizing only the engine has

demonstrated a top speed of 81 km/h (50 mph). Test results from an I/M 240 driving cycle tests have shown a significant improvement in emissions due to fuel pressure reduction and the addition of a three-way catalytic converter. Carbon balanced fuel economy is estimated at 17 km/liter (40 mpg) highway. As demonstrated by the data in Figure 6, modifications of the stock engine emissions system has resulted in a significant reduction in CO, HC, and NOx.

ELECTRIC SCHEMATIC BLOCK DIAGRAM

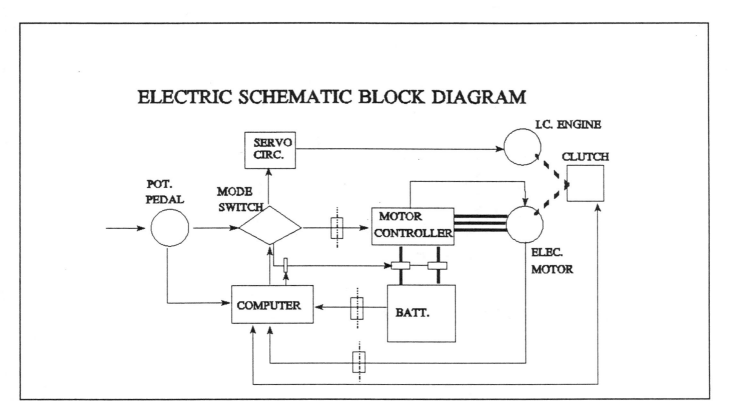

Figure 1 Electrical Block Diagram

Figure 2 Battery Selection Matrix

TABLE 1

Criteria	Pb Acid	Pb Acid sealed	NiCd	NiMH sealed	NiMH
Cost	Low	Low	High	Very High	Very High
Durability	300 cycles	300 cycles	2000 cycles	2000 cycles	2000 cycles
Maintenance	Watering	None	Watering	None	Watering
Environmental Impact	Contains Lead	Contains Lead	Contains Cd	Low	Low
Safety	Possible spill	No free acid	Possible spill	No free acid	Possible spill
Recyclability	Easy	Easy	Vendor buy back	Vendor buy back	Vendor buy back

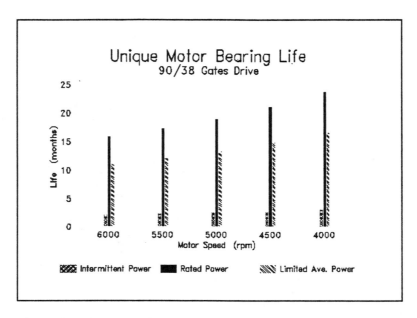

Figure 3 - Motor Bearing Analysis

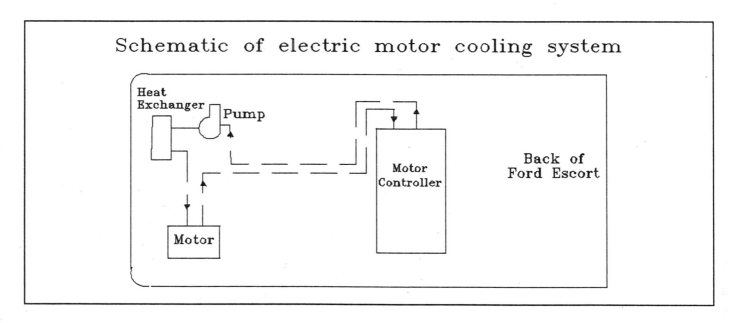

Figure 4 Closed Loop Motor Cooling Schematic

Figure 5 - Engine Selection Matrix

Engine Manufacturer/ Model	(*3) Meets Power Requirements	(*2) Exceeds Power Requirements	(*3) Low Emissions Potential	(*2) Packaging	(*1) Cost	(*1) Weight	(*1) Cooling System	(*1) Availability	(sum) Total Score
BMW K75	5	-4	4	4	-5	4	5	4	35
Briggs Vanguard 18	5	0	2	5	-1	5	3	5	43
Ford Escort 1.9	5	-5	5	1	-3	1	5	5	30
Geo Metro XFi 1.0	5	-2	5	3	-3	3	5	5	42
Honda NT650 (1988)	5	0	3	3	-3	4	5	2	38
Honda NX250 (1988)	5	0	3	4	-3	4	5	2	40
Honda XL600V (1989)	5	-2	3	3	-3	4	5	2	34
Honda XR650L (1992)	5	-1	2	3	-3	4	3	4	33
Kawasaki EN500 (1990)	5	-2	3	4	-3	4	5	3	37
Kawasaki FD620	3	0	3	5	-2	5	5	5	41
Kawasaki FD620 EFI	5	0	4	5	-3	5	5	5	49
Kohler CH18	4	0	2	5	-1	5	3	5	40
Kohler CH20	5	0	2	5	-1	5	3	5	43

Figure 6 - Interim Emissions Results

	ICE Wagon Baseline	ICE Wagon 131 kPa fuel, TWC	Current Standards	TLEV Goal
HC, grams/mile	1.45	0.329	0.39	0.125
CO, grams/mile	47.5	1.74	7.0	3.4
NO$_x$, grams/mile	1.7	3.2	0.4	0.4

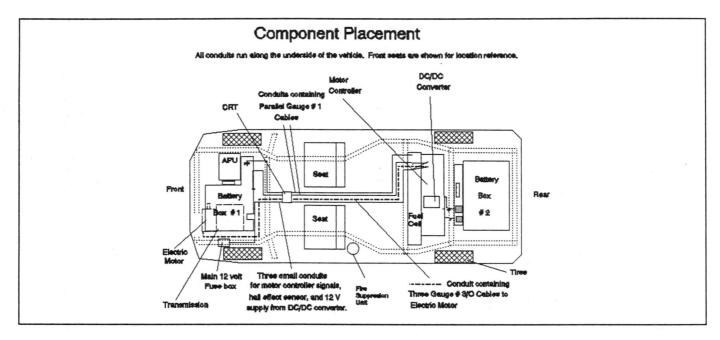

Figure 7 Vehicle Component Layout

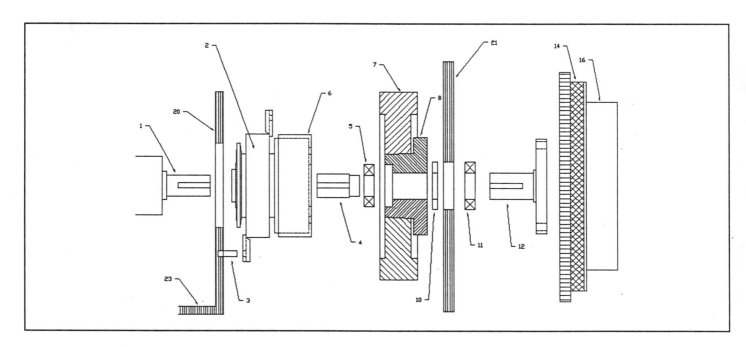

Figure 8 Drive Train Cross Sectional

The Concordia University Hybrid Electric Conversion Vehicle

Tadeusz Krepec, Faculty Advisor, Denis Dionatos, Petros Frantzeskakis, Harry Kekedjian, Achilles Nikopoulos, and John Theofanopoulos
Concordia University

ABSTRACT

A conversion of the donated Ford Escort Wagon was performed, emphasizing manufacturability, durability, driveability and safety. An important objective was to minimize the amount of major modifications that would be required for the mass production of such a vehicle. This vehicle's unique feature is that it incorporates both a series and parallel configuration. The gas-powered engine can either drive the vehicle at speed of 72 km/h or perform on board charging with the aid of a high powered alternator. A permanent magnet brushless DC motor is used as the main electric drive unit, while a series wound electric motor is incorporated and utilized only for acceleration purposes. Lead-acid batteries are used due to their low cost and adequate performance. Extensive battery testing is summarized for the following batteries: Delco Voyageur, Optima, Chloride, East-Penn RV31-210 and RV27-175. A mathematical model and simulation is outlined, followed by an optimization process which provided the final determining factors in our component selection and overall design.

INTRODUCTION

The primary purpose of designing an HEV is the need to be less dependent on fossil fuels. Vehicle safety is an essential aspect in the design and was a top priority before completing this vehicle. The following goals were also considered to be very important:

- lowered cost of conversion, allowing effort to be placed on durability and driveability,
- lowered cost of production, permitting the implementation of HEVs alongside gasoline vehicles
- consumer confidence, having the benefits and reliability of current technology.

The Concordia HEV Team (CHEV) employs two electric motors and an internal combustion engine (ICE) to meet the competition performance requirements. Complementing the electric motor drive system, the ICE supplies an energy source for a driving range extension. Both of these systems can be applied in any configuration (ie. series or parallel shown in Figure 1). A series setup uses a generator to convert mechanical energy into electrical while, a parallel drive configuration is established by directly coupling the ICE with the transaxle.

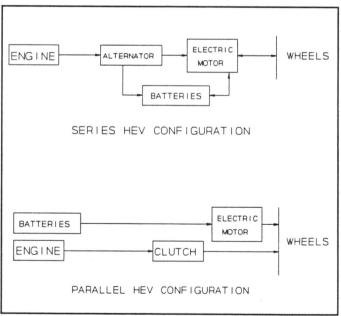

Fig. 1 Series and Parallel Configurations

The mounting scheme and brackets for all three power units were manufactured and placed in the engine compartment. All of the motors are connected to the drive shaft through a chain-driven extension shaft. Existing engine mounts were used to support the motors and to allow the transaxle, motors and attachments to move as one combined unit.

POWERTRAIN CONFIGURATION

This project's goal was to design and convert a vehicle at the lowest cost with high efficiency and optimal performance characteristics. The vehicle was converted and modified with commercially available, off the shelf accessories that are accessible by the average consumer.

Efficiency, simplicity and ease of assembly were the key determining parameters in the component choice and placement. Displayed in Figure 2, it can be seen that the component placement in the Ford was carefully thought out. In table 1 there is an explanation of this schematic.

Enclosed within the interior, the shielded battery packs are securely attached to the structure in the latitudinal direction, with the weight being evenly distributing over the rear axle.

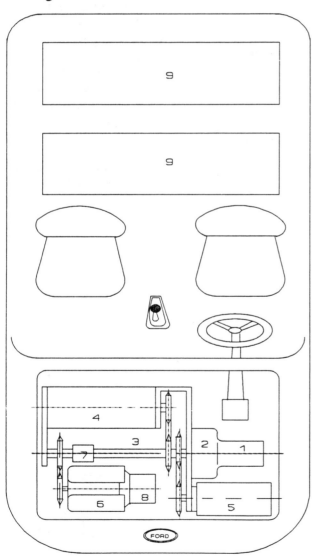

Fig. 2 Vehicle Layout

Table 1 Component Description

1. Five-Speed Transmission
2. Clutch/Flywheel Assembly
3. Drive Shaft
4. Electric Motor
5. Electric Motor
6. Internal Combustion Engine
7. Clutch for ICE
8. Alternator unit for ICE
9. Battery Enclosures

ELECTRIC MOTORS - Two electric motors are being used to drive the HEV, the first is a permanent magnet brushless DC motor (PMB/DC) and the second is a series-wound DC motor (SW/DC). The use of these two different type of motors provides high acceleration and efficiency. DC motors were chosen for their excellent performance and lower overall weight and cost. Compared to AC motors they do not require the costly DC-AC converters and a high supply voltage for a productive operation. Drivetrain efficiency required for an electric vehicle with a reasonable driving range can best be provided by a PM electric motor. Furthermore the acceleration requirements for normal vehicle operation and for those imposed by the competition stipulates the use of high power motors.

High power PMB/DC motors are just starting to become available, but are still in the early developmental stages and also quite costly. The unproven reliability of such a motor precludes its use. By choosing a smaller permanent magnet motor and sizing it to drive the vehicle in the range event provides for a very high efficiency. Under most circumstances a reasonably sized motor can drive a fully loaded vehicle therefore it is also reasonable to keep this motor working all the time and supplement it only when acceleration is required.

The electric motor that will always be working during any EV portion of the competition must be able to withstand considerable abuse. Varied driving conditions and many different drivers requires a reliable and efficient system. Weight and cost limitations are also very crucial factors in the selection.

Taking these requirements into consideration the Solectria BRLS16 was chosen as the primary electric motor. It offered the best efficiency, power, and price combination and has been successfully incorporated in other electric vehicles. The Solectria Corporation also provides a controller for their motor, which is capable of regenerative braking. This particular model was optimised for 144V rather than 120V thus increasing the vehicle range with the use of extra batteries.

"A permanent magnet motor provides more electromotive drag when no power is applied than any of the other types of DC motors. This is because the fields of the permanent magnet motors are active , whether an armature current is applied or not. This feature is a desirable characteristic since it brakes the motor in a manner similar to the existing internal combustion engine." [1]

The second motor was selected based on the following criteria. The acceleration motor needed to be powerful and small in size and weight. It also required electromotive drag so that it could freewheel when not in use. A SW/DC motor spins freely on its bearings when no field current is applied. Its use will be limited to small bursts of acceleration therefore its efficiency is not as critical. These criteria were accomplished by using the Advanced DC (A/DC) 203-06-401 SW/DC motor. A SW motor has its field coil connected in series with the armature, therefore the current in the armature is the same as the current that flows in the field windings. The torque in the armature will increase faster than the current applied and will effectively produce adequate torque to move the vehicle from rest. [1]

The A/DC motor was matched with a Curtis controller which does not provide for regenerative braking. This is an adequate setup since this motor is used periodically for accelerating and thus regeneration is not a main concern. The limits to the performance are due to the maximum amperage of 400A the controller can provide at the 120V DC it is connected to. Even though its rated output is 60 kW, the A/DC provides 48 kW of instantaneous power limited by the controller, not accounting for the controller efficiency.

A diagram of the electric motors torque vs. speed curves can be seen in Figure 3. The Solectria and the A/DC provide their maximum power at different speed conditions, therefore sprocket ratios were necessary to permit both motors to function at their optimum conditions. One can thus determine where to set the reference speed. The procedure is discussed further in the simulation section.

APU - The alternate power unit or ICE, chosen for the Concordia HEV is the Briggs and Stratton (B&S) 16 HP Vanguard Model Series, model type 0375. It was selected based on its low specific volume as well as its low fuel consumption. This gasoline powered ICE has been configured to run on either a series or a parallel configuration. The driver has the freedom of extended city driving in series mode as well as a greater efficiency for extended highway driving in parallel mode.

A series configuration requires a fuel driven generator to produce electricity for the electric motors,

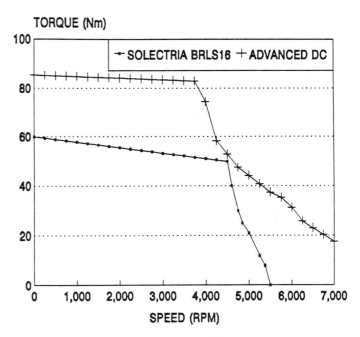

Fig. 3 Torque-Speed Curves [2][3]

whereas the parallel drive configuration is established by directly coupling the ICE with the transaxle. The greatest advantage of the series configuration is that the ICE is kept at a constant speed and therefore the exhaust emissions are easier to control.

For the implementation of the series configuration, a customized alternator was built and installed directly onto the ICE shaft by Fisher Electric Motor Technology Inc. A schematic of the alternator is shown in Figure 4.

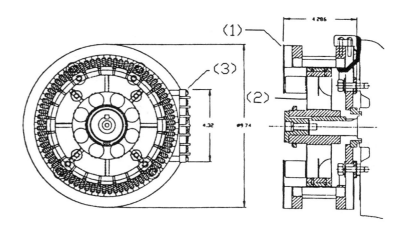

(1) Stator
(2) Rotor
(3) Three Phase AC Output

Fig. 4 Alternator Assembly Schematic [5]

101

The alternator was designed to produce a power output of 9 kW at 2700 rpm which corresponds to a full load condition for the ICE, (see Figure 5) where the fuel economy is roughly 2.84 litres/hr [4].

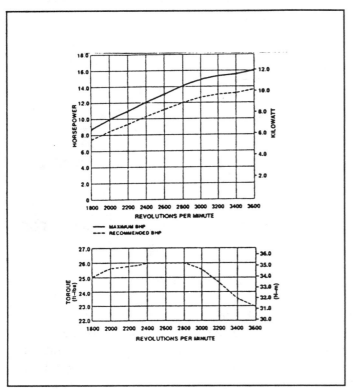

Fig. 5 Briggs & Stratton Curves [6]

The no-load voltage at this speed is 150V and can supply up to 60A rms when loaded. At these design conditions the APU can be used to supply power to the electric motors and partially charge the battery pack when the average power required for the particular driving condition is less than 9 kW. The battery pack is still required to supply high current peaks for accelerating the vehicle.

In parallel mode, the APU transmits torque directly to the stock transmission through a chain driven electro-magnetic clutching. A schematic of this configuration can be seen in Figure 6.

The sprockets numbered from one to three represent the APU and electric motor connections respectively. The driver can select this mode of driving by a switch in the driver's compartment when the suitable cruising speed is reached. This is quite similar to a cruise control unit found in many passenger vehicles today (see control strategy). When this mode is not selected, the clutch is disengaged and the engine can run independent of the transmission in series mode, or be turned off all together.

The APU-transmission speed reduction was selected such that a target speed of 72 km/h can be reached in 4th gear. Selected for this configuration were 33 and 29

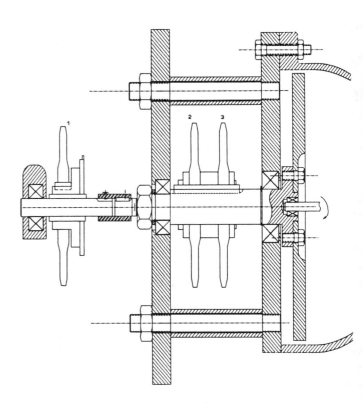

Fig. 6 Component Assembly and Parallel Configuration

tooth sprockets. The vehicle cruising speeds for 4th gear are thus calculated in equation 1. This cruising speed will be maintained provided that the APU can deliver the load required. On a flat grade at 73.12 km/h (20.31 m/s) the power required from the APU to maintain the speed is calculated in equation 2 knowing the total resistive forces (rolling resistance and aerodynamic forces shown in the simulation section) and assuming an overall drivetrain efficiency of 89%.

4th GEAR:

Final Drive Ratio = 3.619, 4th Gear = 0.972

$$Wheel\ Speed = \frac{2700 rpm}{\frac{33}{29} \times 3.619 \times 0.972} = 674.52 rpm \quad (1)$$

Vehicle Speed = 73.12 km/h.

$$P = \frac{F_{total} \times V}{0.89} = \frac{294.59\,N \times 20.31\,m/s}{0.89} = 6723\,W = 6.723\,kW. \quad (2)$$

Evidently the APU has been sized generously in order to accommodate variances in load such as grade changes and face winds and yet still maintain our design cruising speed. The fuel consumption at this ideal cruising condition without load changes is estimated at 2.84 litres/hr which translates to:

$$Fuel\ Consumption = \frac{73.12\frac{km}{hr}}{2.84\frac{liters}{hr}} = 25.75\ \frac{km}{\ell}. \quad (3)$$

TRANSMISSION MODIFICATIONS - It was considered that at certain times there will be up to three motors simultaneously driving the vehicle. These changes required a unique layout for the transmission system.

All components up to and including the flywheel were retained. The original five-speed transaxle, differential and driveshaft were not changed. Through simulations the use of the five-speed transmission was found to be necessary in order to meet the acceleration requirements. This strategy helped keep costs down but there was the disadvantage of working with the gearing designed for a different powerplant.

The driven shaft of the transaxle was extended to allow for the mounting of an external drive system. Coupling the motor directly to the driveshaft would be optimal in terms of manufacturability and efficiency. The power of the chosen motors did not allow for this option. Also their operating speed required a certain amount of gear reduction.

It was first proposed to use a set of manufactured gears to provide the transmission and the necessary gear reduction. Unfortunately their cost, weight and the additional equipment such as an oil enclosure for lubrication and cooling forced us to consider other options. The use of the Gates Polychain kevlar belts and pulleys was also deemed impractical. These offered high efficiency and low noise levels but they were heavy and required considerable width, which conflicted with our limited amount of space. The solution finally used for the external drive was a simple set of motorcycle chains and sprockets. A layout of this solution can be seen in Figure 7.

Motorcycle chains and sprockets are readily available and can be chosen in such a manner that different gear reductions can be obtained. The inter-changeability of chains and sprockets is also important especially when different tests are performed or if something breaks during an event. A change in the external drive system can be effected in a short period of time enabling the vehicle to reenter and qualify for as many points as possible. Chains and sprockets were the lightest drive combination necessitating the smallest work space among the proposed drive systems. The use of chains required a tensioning system. It was accomplished by allowing each motor to slide in bracket slots thus adequately tightening its respective chain. This method saved weight and money since chain idlers and the related

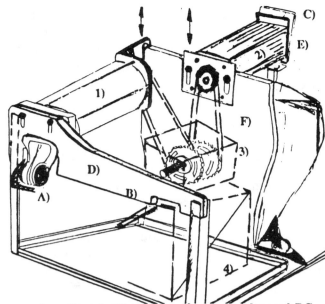

1.	Electric Motor, Manufacturer: Advanced DC
2.	Electric Motor, Manufacturer: Solectria Corp.
3.	Drive Shaft and Sprockets
4.	ICE Placement
A.	Mount #1
B.	Mount #2
C.	Mount #3
D.	Mounting Plate (Left)
E.	Mounting Bracket (Right)
F.	Trans-axle Coverplate

Fig. 7 Drive Compartment Schematic

mounts were not used. Furthermore chain installation is not hampered because motor movement within the slots is minimal and the motors could be initially set in one position before they are permanently mounted in their final locations.

Properly installed chains offers a very good driving efficiency. Approximately 1% of the efficiency is lost in heat buildup, friction and backlash. This was also a deciding factor in the selection of the chains as the driving system.

An inevitable problem with any external drive system including chains, is noise. This problem is taken care of by shrouding the chains with a custom-designed cover. The cover shields the chains and sprockets from any contaminants and protects them from any foreign objects that can get caught inside their path. Proper lubrication is also very important in the chain drive system. It will be ensured by regular precautionary maintenance consisting of oiling and an inspection of the chains and chain paths for cuts and debris.

The transmission modifications were integral in the fabrication of the CHEV and allowed for the possibility of a parallel drive. An extension to the electric motor drive-shaft was designed to drive the ICE with properly selected sprockets and chains. This setup was illustrated in the previous section, in Figure 6.

BATTERY OVERVIEW - The battery selection process for the CHEV involved a compromise based on the batteries that best balance performance, cycle life, capacity and weight. It is important that the battery system:

- withstands continuous charging and discharging on a daily basis,
- functions under extreme working conditions such as high and low ambient temperatures,
- withstands vehicle vibrations and
- also allows for fast recharging.

Despite a considerable amount of research effort into the development of advanced batteries for electric vehicles, the only practical battery systems commercially available are still lead-acid and nickel-cadmium (nicad). A direct comparison between similar lead-acid and nicad systems revealed that lead acid provides a comparable performance at a fraction of the nicad system's cost. [7] It is the simplicity in design of the lead-acid module that allows for low cost production on a local basis. This, in turn has resulted in the development of a solid industrial network of production, distribution and recycling in Canada and the United States. [8]

For the CHEV deep cycle open lead-acid type batteries were selected. They are relatively maintenance free, aside from periodic watering. The battery casings are designed to operate as a "check-valve" allowing excess pressure to escape.

The power and energy density requirements of a vehicle can be estimated through vehicle simulations (shown in the simulation section).

The CHEV possesses a 144V bus with a maximum battery weight restriction of 350 kg. The weight restriction translates into a module weight of no more than 29 kg. Batteries were first analyzed based on their capacity in the required weight range. There are several types of 12V modules commercially available, including the spiral-wound Optima 800, the tubular plate Chloride 6EF78, the flat plate Delco Voyageur and the RV27 and RV31 by East-Penn. Their characteristics are summarised in table 2. For a 12 module battery pack, the total weight of each analyzed battery is as follows:

- Delco   : 288 kg,
- Optima   : 216 kg,
- Chloride : 312 kg,
- RV27   : 295 kg, and
- RV31   : 342 kg.

A preliminary calculation revealed that the CHEV would require a continuous draw current of 45 amps to maintain a constant velocity of 72 km/h with a bus

Table 2 Battery Characteristics

	DELCO	OPTIMA 800	CHLORIDE	EP RV27	EP RV31
VOLTS	12	12	12	12	12
WEIGHT (KG)	24	18	26	25	28.5
CAPACITY (AHr) C/1	--	--	38.6	35.6	41.8
ENERGY DENSITY (AHr/KG)	--	--	1.48	1.42	1.47

voltage of 144V. Figure 8 depicts typical discharge curves for power vs. time. The East-Penn RV31, in terms of energy, outperformed the other batteries.

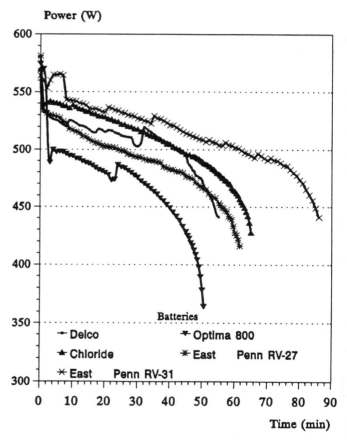

Fig. 8 Discharge curves with 45A continuous draw

Although a continuous draw of 45 amps is not realistic in terms of a true driving cycle, it offers a good indication of the duration of the charge available from the batteries when subjected to a fast discharge. The continuous discharge method for battery testing does not take into account other factors such variations in wind resistance, acceleration from rest, temperature and other factors which greatly affect battery performance and capacity. However, under heavy stop and go routines, regeneration can increase capacity by as much as 20% depending on the amount of stopping that takes place.

The nominal voltage of the CHEV is a 144V bus powering the electric drive system. The charger that will be used will be a 144V DC, 20.1A taper charger manufactured by Alltech Electronic Ltd. Most manufacturers recommend that the batteries be discharged to a depth of no more than 80%. Although it is possible to resuscitate batteries that are completely discharged, such a practice reduces their cycle life damaging them, with a possible risk of reversing their polarity. Fast charging is possible to a certain extent, however, it must be kept in mind that recharging is the reversal of the chemical process, therefore it should not be excessive.

CONTROL STRATEGY

The HEV has three modes of operation identified as Series, Parallel and Electric Vehicle (EV). Only one mode can be active at any instant, and the required mode is selected using two toggle switches located in the center of the dash.

MODES OF OPERATION - Series is the primary operating mode where the vehicle is driven solely by the two electric motors. The ICE is also running and is used to recharge the battery pack.

Parallel mode is equivalent to cruise control in a regular vehicle. The vehicle driven by the ICE is kept at a constant speed of 72 km/h. The electric motors are available to the driver and may assist the ICE in negotiating a steep slope or in passing other vehicles. The battery pack is not being charged in this mode.

In EV mode the vehicle is running solely on electric power. The ICE is turned off and is therefore not charging the batteries.

The control panel illustrated in Figure 9 contains all the toggle switches and indicator LEDs required for switching between operation modes.

CHANGING OPERATION MODES - To ensure proper vehicle operation when switching modes, several guidelines must be followed.

The series mode must be active when the car is started. To place the car in this mode, switch 1 is placed in the series position, and switch 2 is placed in the engine-on position. If the ICE is not running, turning the ignition key to the Start position, will activate it. If the vehicle has been running in EV mode, placing switch 2 in the engine-on position, and start the ICE, using the ignition key.

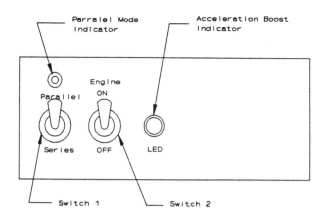

Fig. 9 Control Panel

Parallel mode used primarily for long distance driving will be engaged when the ICE is running (as in the series mode). Switch 1 will be placed in the parallel position and this mode will only operate if the vehicle is placed in 4th gear. It is necessary for the shaft RPM to be situated at 2700 $\pm$ 150. Exceeding these limits may cause damage to the engine and/or the clutch assembly. It must also be noted, that the ICE will disengage from the drive shaft, every time the brake pedal is pressed. If the shaft RPM drops below the specified levels, it is advised that the electric motors be used to help bring the ICE back to speed. This mode is accessible only when the vehicle is in Series mode. One cannot pass directly from EV mode to Parallel mode.

EV mode is the purely electrical mode of the vehicle with switch 1 set in the series mode and switch 2 in the engine-off position. The ICE cannot be reactivated as long as switch 2 remains in the engine-off position. A push-button on the manual shifter will activate the A/DC for better acceleration. This acceleration boost mode is indicated by a LED on the control panel.

ELECTRICAL CIRCUIT COMPONENTS - The main control unit is located in the dash, behind the toggle switches. All the controls, such as charger relays, clutch relay and engine kill relay are controlled from this unit.

The entire circuit, illustrated in the Appendix is composed of 6 mechanical relays, 4 solid state relays, 5 resistors, 2 NPN transistors and one logic gate chip. This low number of components increases the system reliability and ensures that all tasks are performed with a minimum amount of power consumption.

An external timing circuit, illustrated in Figure 10, placed near the ICE, and in series with the charger relays, ensures that the engine has achieved optimum speed before connecting the charging system to the battery pack. This effectively limits the current through the charging wires to 60A.

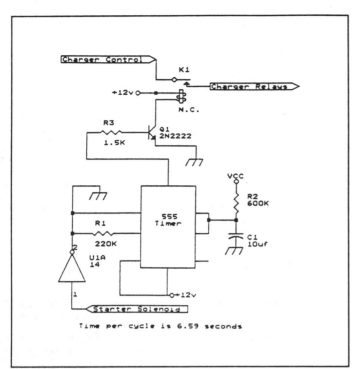

Fig. 10 Timer Circuit

WEIGHT DISTRIBUTION

In order to get a breakdown of the HEV weight, the original unladen vehicle weight of the Ford Escort Station Wagon (1100 Kg) and 59/41 front-to-rear bias was used as a starting point. Table 3 and Table 4 summarise the current rear and front weight distribution of the Concordia HEV.

The current vehicle weight at 1718 kg is slightly below the GVW+10% rating. Therefore, vehicle structural integrity and handling have not been compromised from the point of view of overall loading. Nevertheless, front/rear and left/right weight distributions have been calculated. The front/rear weight bias is calculated in equations 4 to 6. Calculation of the left/right weight bias is shown in equations 7 to 9.

$$FRONT\ WEIGHT\% = \frac{847}{847+871} *100 = 49.3\% \quad (4)$$

$$REAR\ WEIGHT\% = \frac{871}{847+871} *100 = 50.7\% \quad (5)$$

$$\frac{FRONT}{REAR}\%\ Weight\ Bias = \frac{49.3\%}{50.7\%} \quad (6)$$

$$LEFTSIDE\ WEIGHT\ BIAS\% = \frac{420+422}{1718} *100 = 49.0\% \quad (7)$$

$$RIGHTSIDE\ WEIGHT\ BIAS\% = \frac{427+449}{1718} *100 = 51.0\% \quad (8)$$

$$\frac{LEFTSIDE}{RIGHTSIDE}\%\ Weight\ Bias = \frac{49\%}{51\%} \quad (9)$$

Table 3 Rear Weight Distribution

ITEMS	REAR WEIGHT (Kg)	LEFT WEIGHT (Kg)	RIGHT WEIGHT (Kg)
Total Rear Weight of Standard Ford Escort Wagon	451	212	239
Weight of First Battery Tray	210	105	105
Weight of Second Battery Tray	154	77	77
Wiring	4	2	2
Cargo Ballast Box with 20 Kg	26	13	13
Rollbar	20	10	10
Exhaust System (rear)	6	3	3
TOTAL ANTICIPATED REAR WEIGHT	871	422	449

Table 4 Frontal Weight Distribution

ITEMS	FRONT WEIGHT (Kg)	LEFT WEIGHT (Kg)	RIGHT WEIGHT (Kg)
Total Frontal Weight of Standard Ford Escort Wagon	649	305	344
Removal of Engine and Cooling System	-143	-53	-90
Removal of Existing Exhaust System (Weight at Front)	-13	0	-13
Weight of Passenger and Driver	160	80	80
Solectria Electric Motor BRLS16	29	29	0
Solectria Controller BRLS240H	7	7	0
Advanced DC Electric Motor 203-06-4001	49	0	49
Curtis Controller 1221-B74	5	5	0
Briggs & Stratton ICE 3075	40	0	40
New Exhaust System (Weight at the Front)	4	2	2
Fisher Alternator	10	5	5
Mounting of Drive Systems	15	5	10
Transaxle Cover Plate	20	20	0
Outer Bearing Plate	15	15	0
TOTAL ANTICIPATED FRONTAL WEIGHT	847	420	427

SUSPENSION AND BRAKING MODIFICATIONS

With the significant weight contribution of batteries in the rear of the vehicle, minor modifications to the braking system and rear suspension were inevitable. The objective was to retain the original level, comfort, braking and handling of the stock vehicle. The overall weight increase to the front was not substantial thus modifications to the front suspension were not necessary.

SUSPENSION - To better estimate the suspension modifications required, the basic suspension model of Figure 11, has been used to simulate the behaviour of the system.

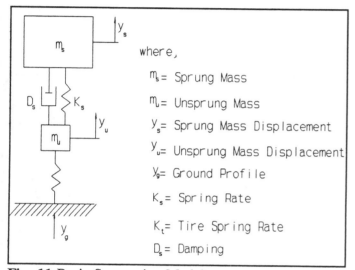

where,

m_s = Sprung Mass

m_u = Unsprung Mass

y_s = Sprung Mass Displacement

y_u = Unsprung Mass Displacement

y_g = Ground Profile

K_s = Spring Rate

K_t = Tire Spring Rate

D_s = Damping

Fig. 11 Basic Suspension Model

Using this model, a force balance can be written for each mass:

$$m_u \ddot{y}_u + D_s(\dot{y}_u - \dot{y}_s) + K_t(y_u - y_g) + K_s(y_u - y_s) = 0 \quad (10)$$
$$m_s \ddot{y}_s + D_s(\dot{y}_s - \dot{y}_u) + K_s(y_s - y_u) = 0$$

The dynamics of the rear suspension system was simulated in Figure 12 for a quarter car model subject to a radical change in road profile of 5 cm. Original stiffness and damping values were linearized and approximated from vehicle specifications. The simulation displays the displacement of the sprung mass from its original position. The response of the second curve indicates an increase in oscillations when the additional weight of the converted vehicle is introduced. The third response is almost identical to the original system. This was accomplished by increasing the damping and stiffness by 50%. From these results, a rough estimate was provided as to the extent of modifications required to restore the comfort and driveability of the vehicle.

Modification of the rear suspension involved

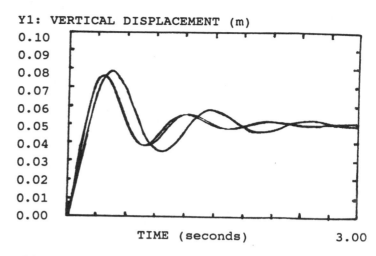

Fig. 12 Simulation of Suspension Dynamics

replacing the original springs with cargo springs and an addition of rubber spacers within the springs. Consequently, the level of the vehicle was raised by 5 cm, returning it to the approximate level before conversion. Road tests were performed with the modified suspension and good comfort levels and handling were noted. This compared favourably relative to similar tests that were performed on the original vehicle.

BRAKING - Upon initial testing of the braking system, the additional vehicle weight increase and the absence of engine vacuum, produced difficulties when trying to stop from speeds beyond 40 km/h. Imposed stopping distances (figure 13) were finally met after the installation of an electric vacuum pump which along with regular braking assisted in stopping the car.

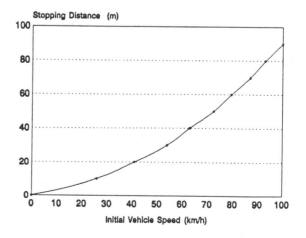

Fig. 13 Imposed Braking Distances

An illustration of the electric vacuum pump and its components, supplied by Solar Car Corporation is shown in Figure 14.

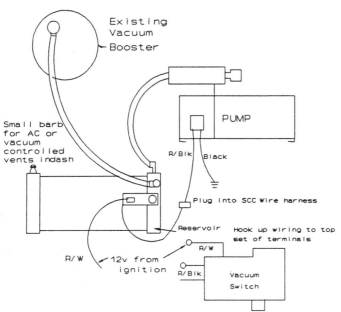

Fig. 14 Electric Vacuum Pump

FUEL DELIVERY AND EMISSION CONTROL STRATEGY

A simple, low cost and practical fuel delivery and emission control strategy was implemented in the CHEV. The B&S Vanguard ICE was united with the following fuel delivery system:

- a stock Ford Escort Wagon fuel tank,
- an in line fuel pump and
- a Nikki downdraft carburetor unit.

The high pressure stock fuel pump (hpf-pump) was replaced with an in-line solenoid activated fuel pump for the following reasons. This hpf-pump would have required a manifold enabling fuel to enter the carburetor and also allowing flow to return back into the fuel tank. In terms of current being drawn, the hpf-pump has a continuous draw of 3A whereas the solenoid activated pump requires only a nominal current of 0.1A. The substantial differences between these two pumps, precluded the use of the hpf-pump, especially for HEV applications. Thus it was replaced with the in-line pump.

The emission control strategy consists of a single bed three-way catalyst and optimal tuning of the carburetor unit. The catalyst volume of 347.4 cm³ was sized for the 480cc ICE. Johnson Matthey testing revealed the

following catalyst composition:

- Pt   1243.1 g/m³,
- Pd   0.0 g/m³,
- Rh   261.4 g/m³.

To ensure the catalyst reaches its optimal operating temperature of 400 °C the exhaust system was wrapped with fibreglass insulation starting from the tuned exhaust headers to the catalytic converter. The catalyst was placed at 56.5 cm from the ICE exhaust ports. This effectively limits the power lost due to back pressure and also minimizes any catalyst deterioration. In Figure 15 the fuel delivery and exhaust system is shown. The exhaust header was designed and fabricated by the CHEV team.

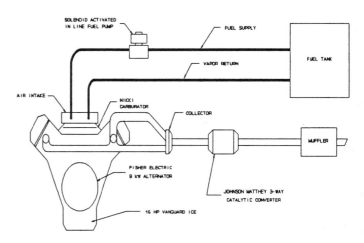

Fig. 15 Fuel Delivery System and CHEV Exhaust

The most efficient carburetor fuel delivery system is not capable of maintaining the stoichiometric air fuel ratio when exposed to varying speed and load conditions. To lessen this detrimental parameter and to obtain an effective emission control scheme the speed of the ICE was set at 2700 RPM via a mechanical governor for both the series and parallel modes. Testing is being currently performed (at the time of which this report was written) at the Environment Canada, Mobile Service Emissions Division (Ottawa, Canada). Based on these test results appropriate measures will be taken to meet the FTP emissions standards.

SIMULATION

MATHEMATICAL MODEL - A mathematical model is essential in order to analyze the performance characteristics of the HEV. The primary concerns are acceleration, capabilities to negotiate grades and range at various speeds. The two determinant factors in the HEV's potential performance lies in tractive effort and resistive forces. The tractive effort is the net force developed at the wheels which can be used to accelerate the vehicle. Tractive effort has two limiting factors:

- the drive and transmission unit characteristics and
- the coefficient of road adhesion and the normal load on the driven axis.

With reference to Figure 16 the maximum tractive effort limited by road adhesion can be calculated using the following equations. [9]

Front wheel drive:

$$W_f = \frac{l_2}{L} W - \frac{h}{L} \left(R_a + \frac{aW}{g} + R_d \pm W \sin\theta_s \right) \quad (11)$$

$$F_{maxf} = \mu W_f \quad (12)$$

The main resistance forces: aerodynamic force, rolling resistance force and climbing resistance force encountered by vehicles will be analyzed as per the following procedures.

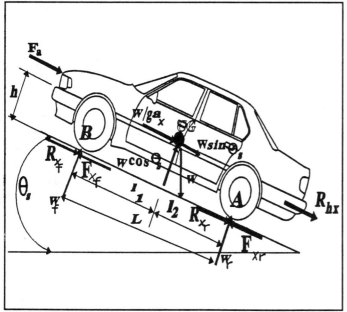

Fig. 16 Tractive Effort

The coefficient of drag and frontal area are parameters which have been pre-determined since the CHEV is a conversion. The general trend by which the frontal area and coefficient of drag should be varied is seen by the aerodynamic resistance, F_a, equation 13.

The rolling resistance, F_R, can be calculated by equations 14 and 15.

$$F_a = \frac{\rho}{2} C_d A_f \left(V_{HEV} \pm V_{wind} \right)^2 \quad (13)$$

$$F_R = \mu_r \cos\theta_s (mg) \quad (14)$$

$$\mu_r = \mu_{const} + \left(0.0015 * \frac{V_{HEV}}{27.77} \right) \quad (15)$$

Where the dynamic coefficient of rolling resistance (μ_R) is a function of tire pressure, contact surface, tire radius and vehicle speed (V_{HEV} in m/s) and μ_{const} is the static rolling coefficient.

Climbing resistance is the force created by the grade change of the road (F_{CR}), calculated using equation 16.

$$F_{cr} = \sin(\theta_s) mg \quad (16)$$

The total resistive force is calculated by summing the climbing, aerodynamic, and rolling resistances.

$$F_{resistive} = F_{cr} + F_r + F_a \quad (17)$$

The tractive effort is calculated by taking the difference between the force developed at the wheels, by the drive unit, and that of the total resistive forces.

$$F_{tractive} = F_{dw} - F_{resistive} \quad (18)$$

The acceleration of the vehicle can then be calculated as follows,

$$m_{eff} = mass_{HEV} + \frac{Jeff}{r^2} \quad (19)$$

where J_{eff} is the effective inertia and m_{eff} is the effective mass and r is the effective radius of the wheel.

The following effective mass (m_{eff}) can be simplified by multiplying the vehicle mass by the following factor γ_m (which is a function of the overall drive ratio ξ_0):

$$m_{eff} = mass_{HEV} \, \gamma_m \quad (20)$$

$$\gamma_m = 1.04 + 0.0025 \, \xi_o^2 \quad (21)$$

The time required to accelerate to a certain speed can be calculated by:

$$t = m_{eff} \int_{V1}^{V2} \frac{dv}{F_{tractive}} \quad (22)$$

which can easily be integrated by the use of a digital

computer.

SIMULATION PROCEDURE - Using the governing mathematical equations a simulation was developed in FORTRAN. When the program was completed, actual testing was performed in order to determine the validity of the simulation. The stock 1992 Ford Escort Wagon was loaded to 1550 kg and acceleration tests were performed. The time required to accelerate from (0 to 72 km/h) was obtained for several trials yielding a 10 second nominal value. The design parameters of the Ford Escort were used as inputs for the simulation. Results of the simulation revealed that the vehicle would accelerate from 0 to 72 km/h in 10.2 second. This ensured that the simulation was performing in a similar manner to the actual system objectives, hence validating the model. A second simulation was developed using a TUTSIM simulation package. The results of this simulation were closely related to those obtained from tests using the FORTRAN simulation.

OPTIMIZATION PROCESS - The optimization process involved varying several design parameters to see an impact on the vehicle's performance. These design parameters were as follows:

- vehicle weight
- sprocket drive ratio
- tire rolling resistance

Since the stock transmission was used in the CHEV the final drive ratio was modified via the sprocket assembly. By varying the design parameters within some determined limits, the impact on some chosen system objectives was investigated. This was achieved by a graphical method where some nominal values of the design parameters were assigned. The system objectives are:

- time required to accelerate from 0 to 72 km/h,
- range of the vehicle at 72 km/h cruising speed and
- the maximum obtainable grade.

Each objective function is obtained by varying one design parameter from left to right, while holding the remaining nominal values constant. To make the graphical representation compact the objective functions were placed on the vertical axis having one scale. The design parameters were drawn on three horizontal scales and placed one below the other. Figure 17 demonstrates the graphical optimization process which was used for the EV mode.

This figure, clearly indicates the direction each design parameter should be varied in order to obtain the

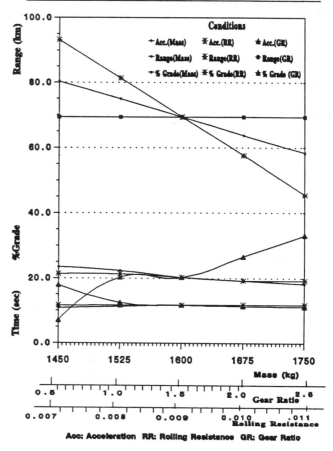

Fig. 17 Graphical EV Optimisation

optimal objective functions. As a next step, different weights were assigned to the objective functions and calculations were made to optimize the design parameters to achieve the required trade-offs. The imposed competition requirement to accelerate from 0 to 72 km/h within 15 seconds, requires an emphasis to be placed on the acceleration function.

The optimal constraint design parameters obtained from Figure 17 are as follows:

- vehicle weight: 1700 kg,
- sprocket drive ratio: 2.0,
- tire rolling resistance: 0.007.

By the simulation of these design parameters, the following objective functions were determined:

- 0-72 km/h in 11.79 seconds,
- 87 km range at a constant speed (64.4 km/h) and on a levelled surface,
- 25.5% obtainable grade.

110

The analysis also showed that the Solectria motor had a 92.5% efficiency running at constant speeds of 72 km/h. By deactivating the Advanced DC, the Solectria takes the full load thus producing this efficiency. A similar optimisation procedure was followed for the HEV and APU modes of operation.

MANUFACTURABILITY AND ERGONOMICS

The Concordia HEV was converted without sacrificing interior styling, comfort and the general aesthetic appeal. By reducing vehicle modifications and employing workable simple solutions the conversion process was quick and effective.

There are no visible protrusions thus preserving the original vehicle aerodynamics and styling. The mounting of the controllers and motors was performed in an orderly fashion, paying careful attention to the placement of brackets and wiring. The vehicle interior was significantly modified without compromising the driver and passenger comfort. A roll cage, five point seat belt harness and a fire extinguishing system was added for safety. The additional dash gages do not crowd the driver's vision. These gages provide ample information to the interested enthusiast without intimidating the average driver.

Each newly installed part in the vehicle was sized and manufactured accordingly. The use of steel is evident in the main drive assembly, but in many instances where moderate stress levels would be encountered, aluminum was chosen instead. Using aluminum substantially reduced weight, cost and the overall manufacturing time since it is easier to machine.

The major components in the automobile were purchased "off the shelf", except for the customised alternator. The additional components required to mount these parts to the car were all built in the student machine shop. In light of this, duplication of the CHEV would be quite simple once detailed drawings of all components are documented.

CONCLUSION

As demonstrated in this report, designing a practical, efficient hybrid electric vehicle which meets today's performance standards involves considerable time and preparation. The objective of the design was to maintain a low overall vehicle weight while capitalizing on storage space. This facilitated the task of placing the batteries without significantly compromising interior space, comfort and styling.

Development of a suitable drivetrain involved rigorous analysis of various electric drive systems as well as recognizing the advantages of both parallel and series configurations. The Solectria and the Advanced DC electric drive system combination was chosen based on overall cost, efficiency and power. A parallel configuration using two separate drive systems was seen to be the most practical in terms of overall efficiency at constant cruising speeds. The series configuration allows for range extension in city as well as highway driving. In both cases the speed is kept relatively constant therefore simplifying the emission control scheme.

A hybrid electric vehicle already makes note of the fact that today's battery technology still imposes a strict constraint on the range of an electric vehicle. The most logical battery choice would therefore come from the lead-acid family. Discharge tests showed that the East-Penn RV31 possessed the highest energy density in its class at a comparable price.

A control strategy was developed that would not compromise the integrity of each drive system's autonomy. Although the electronic motor controllers were purchased, the control scheme was imperative in granting the driver a means of controlling the various operation modes.

Final assessment of the weight distribution disclosed an excellent front/rear and left/right bias of approximately 49/51 for both. The total vehicle weight was just below the GVW+10%. The effects of the added weight were countered by minor suspension and braking system modifications.

The use of a valid mathematical model in conjunction with a computer simulation provided an overview of what is involved and where complications may arise. Together, they form a useful tool for projecting the performance of a particular system as well as the impact of varying certain design parameters. Although the mathematical model has its limitations in terms of accuracy, it is a helpful instrument for making comparisons and can guide the designer toward developing an optimal design. The computer simulation was used to optimize vehicle parameters in order to minimize the number of manufacturing iterations that would be required to reach a final design. A final simulation using optimized parameters revealed that the proposed vehicle design would meet the imposed vehicle performance requirements.

In fact it has been established the CHEV would be very competitive with today's hybrids in acceleration, range and gradability in each operating mode.

ACKNOWLEDGMENTS

The authors of this report, Petros Frantzeskakis, Achilles Nikopoulos, Harry Kekedjian, Denis Dionatos and John Theofanopoulos would like to thank the balance of the CHEV team members, George Metrakos, Chris

Psinas, Byung Son, Bruno Forcione, Luciano Martin, Manual Afonso for their hard work and dedication to this project. We appreciate the help and support extended by Deborah Harbec, our technical advisor Dr. R. Rajagopalan, our faculty advisor Dr. T. Krepec and our sponsors:

Energy Mines and Resources Canada,
The Quebec Provincial Government,
Environment Canada, Mobile Service Emissions Division,
International Rectifiers,
Briggs and Stratton,
Concordia University Department of Mechanical Engineering,
Robert Bosch Corporation,
Ford Motor Company,
NGK,
Siemens,
Advanced Lead-Acid Battery Consortium,
Goodyear,
ABB - Asea Brown Boveri,
Delta Transformers,
British Petroleum,
Detroit Edison,
Agip Motor Oils,
Alcan,
Dupont Automotive,
Johnson Controls,
Federal Mufflers,
Johnson Matthey and
Motorola /Telex.

REFERENCES

1. Ted Lucas and Fred Reiss, How To Convert To An Electric Car, Crown Publishers Inc., NY, New York, 1975.

2. Solectria Electronics Division, Pamphlet and Instruction Manual.

3. Advanced DC Motors Inc., Motor Technical Specifications.

4. Briggs & Stratton, Fuel Consumption Pamphlet.

5. Fisher Electric Motor Technology Inc., Alternator Technical Specifications.

6. Briggs & Stratton, Engine Specifications.

7. Karl V. Kordesch, Batteries, Marcel Dekker Inc., New York, 1977.

8. Robert Bosch, Automotive Handbook, Robert Bosch GmbH, 2nd Ed., 1986.

9. Thomas D. Gillespie, Fundamentals of Vehicles Dynamics, Society of Automotive Engineers, USA, 1992.

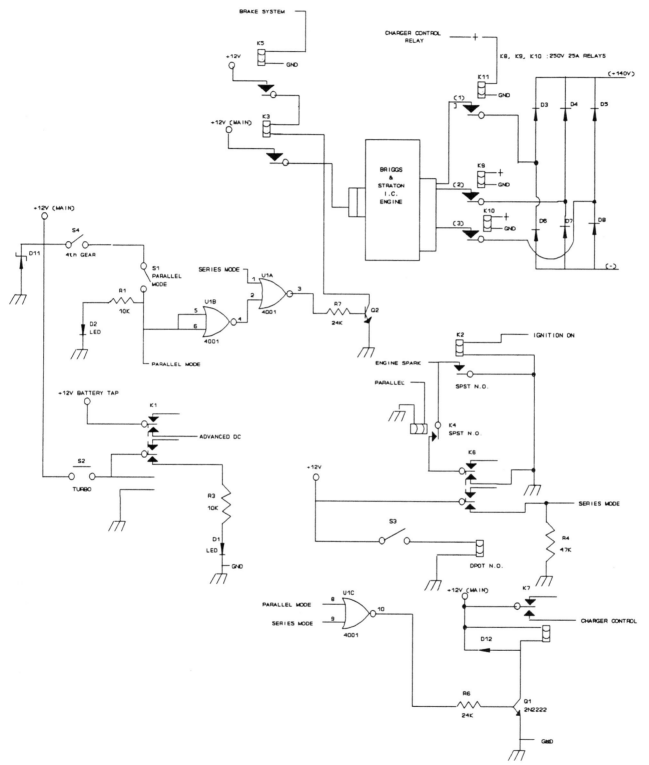

Fig. 18 Circuit Diagram

1993 BLIZZARD

The Cornell Hybrid Electric Vehicle

Richard Warkentin, Assistant Professor
Robert Thomas, Professor
Brian Magierski, Co-Project Manager
John Bilezikjian, Co-Project Manager
Cornell University, Ithaca, New York

ABSTRACT

The Cornell University Hybrid Electric Vehicle (HEV) Team designed and constructed a practical, two-passenger, series-configured HEV. This vehicle – The Blizzard – won the ground-up category of the 1993 HEV Challenge, sponsored by Ford Motor Company, the United States Department of Energy, and the Society of Automotive Engineers. The Cornell HEV was designed in accordance with all of the regulations specified by the 1993 HEV Challenge organizers and the New York State Registry of Motor Vehicles and has the performance, ride, and comfort characteristics of today's economy cars. Through the use of an electric motor configuration incorporating both an AC and a DC motor, we developed a highly efficient powertrain that, enhanced by a small, methanol-burning alternate power unit (APU), provides the acceleration and range demanded by today's consumers with a significant reduction in emissions.

INTRODUCTION

Across the United States, concern is growing over the hazardous effects of pollution on the environment. This concern is leading to major governmental policy changes affecting every household and industry. California, New York, and Massachusetts recently enacted legislation requiring that 2% of the vehicles sold in their states have zero emissions capability by 1998, and 10% by the year 2003. Several other states with major metropolitan areas, including New Jersey and Pennsylvania, and a number of European cities as well, are considering similar legislation in an effort to reduce hazardous emissions.

These positive efforts to improve the environment have led energy producing industries to intensify their search for safer, cleaner fuels and have led automobile manufacturers to step up the development of practical low- and zero-emissions vehicles. Electric-powered vehicles (EVs) are a promising solution to the pollution problem in the future. However, with the batteries currently available, EV buyers can choose between vehicles with medium-range/poor performance or low-range/higher performance characteristics. Current EVs have a maximum range of about 120 miles on a single 5 to 8 hour battery charge and those with the best acceleration take 8 seconds to reach 60 mph. Furthermore, the cost of EVs are expected to be two to three times higher than gasoline-powered vehicles with superior performance. An alternative is the HEV. HEVs bridge the gap between pure EVs and gasoline-powered vehicles by capitalizing on the advantages of both electric and combustion power. They can provide the range, performance, and safety characteristics that consumers expect from an automobile while offering a zero-emissions mode for driving situations where pollution is a problem.

The 1993 HEV Challenge was established to demonstrate that HEVs are a feasible alternative to today's gasoline-powered vehicles. The competition stressed practicality and safety. Thus restrictions were put in place to discourage impracticalities such as exotic batteries, high-priced composite frame materials, and very low-profile racing body styles. However, several performance requirements were established to pique consumer interest such as 0 to 45 mph acceleration in under 15 seconds and a minimum top speed requirement of 45 mph. In addition, to further demonstrate the HEVs practicality as a commuter vehicle for both rural and urban applications, the HEVs must have a minimum range of 200 miles under highway driving conditions and must be capable of covering at least 20 miles in purely electric mode under conditions much like the stop/start rush hour traffic in major cities.

CORNELL TEAM–To meet the time and design requirements of the HEV Challenge, we employed many of the newest concepts in Total Quality Management and made extensive use of concurrent engineering, advanced computer modeling and simulation, and design for manufacture and assembly. The result of this modern project management effort was the design, development and construction, from the ground up, of the low cost, highly efficient, and practical HEV that won the Ground-Up Category of the 1993 HEV Challenge. This vehicle known as The Blizzard by the Cornell HEV Team has a range of up to 60 miles in ZEV mode, an HEV range of 250 miles, and 0-45 mph acceleration time of 8.3 seconds.

VEHICLE STRUCTURE

The first step in designing the vehicle was the definition of a specific set of design goals. These vehicle design goals were translated into functional requirements for the major vehicle systems. Many of vehicle design goals were dependent on vehicle frame meeting all dimensional and safety requirements mandated by the competition, as well as the conventions for passenger vehicles in production today: it had to allow enough room to house and protect two occupants and all vehicle components; it had to be strong enough to withstand repeated dynamic loading under rigorous driving conditions; for passenger comfort and good vehicle handling characteristics, the frame also had to possess high bending and torsional stiffness; and, it had to be low-weight, low-cost, and aid the manufacturability of the overall vehicle. Due to the drastically shortened development cycle time (design, development, construction, and testing of The Blizzard would be completed in under 10 months) frame construction had to begin before designs of other components, particularly the body, were finalized. The frame design, therefore, had to be robust enough to minimize its sensitivity to potential changes in the rest of the vehicle.

We selected a tubular space frame design which, unlike the uni-body construction of today's production vehicles, does not use the body as a primary structure. In addition, use of a space frame allowed "hard points" and mounting points to be placed virtually anywhere on the structure. This added to the flexibility of the design, and provided construction, weight, and cost advantages, as well as high strength and stiffness.

The best of our preliminary designs were analyzed using two finite element analysis (FEA) packages, first PATRAN©, and then CAEDS©. The results of these FEA analyses (an example of an early frame design is shown in Figure 1) indicated that the frame's torsional stiffness would be a significant factor in optimizing vehicle performance. The equation of torsional stiffness per unit mass for thin wall tubing of radius r, and wall thickness t, as shown below,

$$\frac{GJ}{\text{kg}} = \frac{2\pi r^3 tG}{2\pi rt\rho} = r^2\frac{G}{\rho} \qquad (1)$$

suggested that the ideal frame should be a large mono-tube made from materials with high shear moduli G, and low density ρ. Equation (1) also indicates that stiffness and weight would be optimized by maximizing the mono-tube radius. However, care must be exercised as increasing the tube radius, for a given wall thickness, can result in a member that, while theoretically is torsionally rigid, is so weak that it cannot support light loads or even its own weight.

After performing a series of experiments on a variety of materials with high specific shear moduli (G/ρ), we found a unique way around the "minimum tube thickness" problem. First, an efficient space frame was constructed with 4130 Cr-Mo steel, a high strength low alloy steel. Then, a high stiffness composite structural shell was wrapped around the parts of the space frame requiring the most rigidity. The composite shell is composed of four layers of fiberglass separated by a layer of 1 in. thick polyethylene foam (Styrofoam). Epoxy resin was used because of its ability to bond to metal. Fiberglass

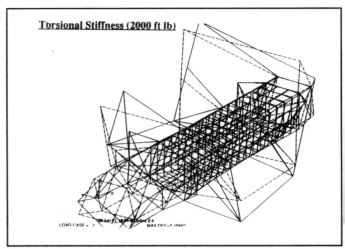

Figure 1

was used because of its moderate stiffness at relatively low cost, while polyethylene foam was chosen for its cost, weight, and manufacturability. Since fiberglass is flexible and epoxy is viscous, the composite shell could be wrapped around and bonded to the steel frame without using any fasteners. This construction method allows the frame to distribute concentrated loads throughout the shell and reinforces it against normal loading. Furthermore, the steel members enclosed by the composite shell provide convenient locations for the mounting of vehicle components, and the long composite shell provides a sealed and acid-proof environment for the battery pack. Figure 2 shows the composite shell from the rear of the vehicle.

We also considered the strength and fatigue behavior of

Figure 2

the chassis. Iterative FEA allowed us to simulate the worst static and dynamic loading conditions the frame would experience, and helped us size the tubing to minimize stresses and maximize longevity without compromising vehicle weight. The design load we used for analysis consisted of superimposing the effects of a 4g bump (i.e., a 1g vertical load at each wheel), 2g twist, 1g corner, and 1g braking on a fully loaded vehicle. This combination of loads is a balance of those typically used in the analysis of race cars and passenger

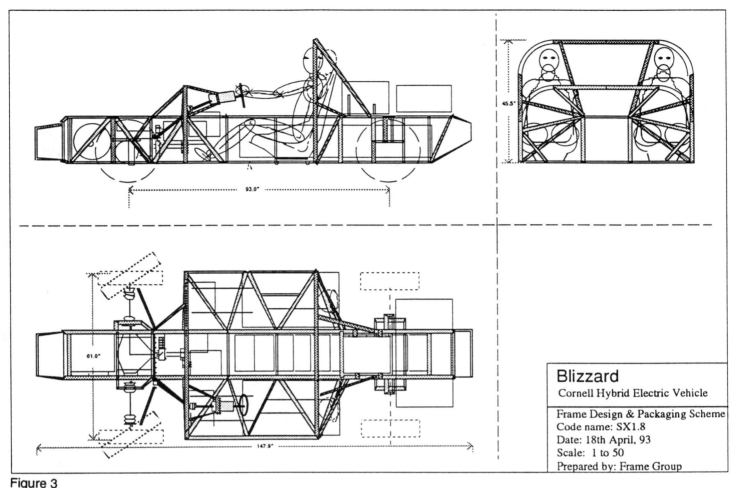

Figure 3

<table>
<tr><td>Blizzard</td></tr>
<tr><td>Cornell Hybrid Electric Vehicle</td></tr>
</table>

Frame Design & Packaging Scheme
Code name: SX1.8
Date: 18th April, 93
Scale: 1 to 50
Prepared by: Frame Group

vehicles. All loads were applied to the chassis model through the contact patches of the wheels or through the suspension attachment points to the frame. To lessen construction complexity, we limited the number of members meeting at a joint to a maximum of six and minimized the number of different tube sizes used. The optimized frame geometry is shown in Figure 3. The worst loading combination produced a maximum stress of about 9000 psi on the structure, well below the allowable stress and endurance (fatigue) limits of the materials used.

Our failure analysis also addressed the potential of buckling failure of the structure. For tubular columns of a space frame structure, the critical buckling load is governed by the equation:

$$P_{crit} = \pi^2 EI \frac{c}{l^2} \qquad (2)$$

where E is the stiffness, I is the cross-section moment of inertia, l is the member length and the joint coefficient, c, is 1.5 for a welded frame.

In The Blizzard's space frame the two longitudinal members, running along the top of the structural shell, absorb the largest compressive loads and have the greatest unbraced length and are therefore most likely to buckle (see Figure 3). The critical buckling load on these members is 8200 lbf. which is well above the maximum load these

members will experience. This result was further confirmed by FEA, which indicated that the critical buckling load of our design was five times the maximum design load combination.

The completed frame weighs only 175 lbf and provides over 5,000 ft lbf/deg of torsional resistance. Under a simulated 1500 lbf midspan load the corresponding maximum deflection was 0.125 cm. In addition, the final frame geometry allowed accessible mounting locations for all components and resulted in a weight distribution of 46% front/54% rear. Also, most of the vehicle components were packaged close to the center of the vehicle to improve vehicle handling. The center of mass of the fully loaded vehicle was calculated at 19 inches above the ground.

With the geometry, layout, and component packaging relating to the primary frame structure determined, other frame functions such as crash protection were addressed. The Blizzard is equipped with front and rear crumple, or energy absorption, zones. Both are primarily steel subframes that bolt on to the space frame, allowing for easy removal and repair or replacement. The tubing used on the subframes is sized such that they will begin to buckle in a 10g crash. In less severe impacts, the subframe members will deform elastically and act as springs to store impact energy. The front crumple zone geometry, visible in Figure 3, is designed such that it also acts as an engine cooling duct and a heat shield for the exhaust pipe. In addition to the subframes, layers of

Lomod™, high impact resistant plastic manufactured by G.E. Plastics, is also mounted behind both the front and the rear body panels to provide additional impact protection, and the Lexan® body panels/bumpers themselves offer substantial energy absorption.

Side impact protection was also designed into the vehicle. Competition rules specified that occupants be protected from a side impact by a frame member extending from the roll hoop to the roll bar at roughly lap height. To allow easy access to and egress from the vehicle cabin, we chose to locate these side impact protection members inside the doors, rather than weld them directly to the frame. These members overlap the roll hoop and roll bar and they are securely hinged at the roll hoop and latched at the roll bar. Placing the safety members in the door also improved door stiffness, resulting in doors capable of supporting more than 200 lbf at the latched ends without noticeable deflection.

SUSPENSION

Independent, unequal–length double A-arm suspensions were designed for all four wheels. This design was chosen to take advantage of the strength of our space frame for inboard shock mounting points and for its design flexibility. The frame's torsional box is only 40 cm tall, making impractical the McPherson strut design typically found on most front wheel drive cars. Additional frame members would have been needed to create upper strut mounting points that could both withstand the localized shock loads and could position the strut angle for acceptable handling characteristics. The wheel motions of a vehicle equipped with a double A–arm system, however, are constrained by the upper and lower suspension links. The shocks and springs can be angled to meet packaging needs (up to 45° from vertical for our racing shocks) and fewer mounting brackets are necessary.

A notable complication we had to overcome was the packaging of the front constant velocity joint near the bottom of the front shock/spring assembly. For a conventional front wheel drive McPherson strut system, the bottom of the strut is attached on top of the hub, above the constant velocity joint. For our double A–arm system we needed to locate the bottom of the shock on the lower A-arm, as close as possible to the outboard spherical bearing and therefore under the constant velocity joint. This location was required to direct most of the suspension load through the shock thereby minimizing the loads transmitted through the a-arms. To accomplish this, we brought the lower shock mounting point inboard 4 in. and reinforced the lower A-arm to withstand the increased bending loads.

The objective of the suspension design was the creation of a suspension system offering the ride and handling behavior of a modern small car. The behavior of a variety of A–arm geometries were simulated on computer to determine body roll and camber changes at the wheel in roll, bump, and droop. Ideally, the roll center will not migrate horizontally and will be located between 1 in. and 4 in. above the ground. A low roll center is necessary to prevent excessive lateral weight transfer during cornering maneuvers. Our simulated roll center migration in the horizontal direction for 5° of body roll was minimal at 3 in., and the roll center height remained

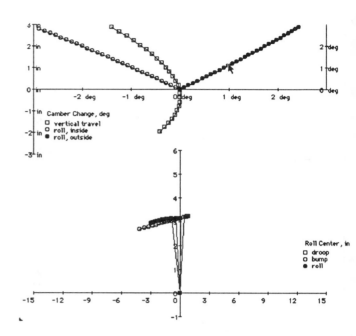

constant at 3 in. above the ground (see Figure 4).

The suspension arms were constructed of welded 4130 Cr-Mo steel tubing. Threaded plugs and bearing cups welded at the ends of the A-arms allowed for attachment of rod ends and spherical bearings. We used rod ends and spherical bearings in place of standard automotive ball joints because they are smaller and because the rod ends can be screwed in or out, allowing us to easily adjust caster, camber, and toe.

The two important criteria for "good ride" are that the front ride rate be about 30% less than that in the rear, and that the ratio of frequency in pitch to frequency in bounce be less than 1.20. Our vehicle has a 46%/54% front/rear weight bias, necessitating stiffer springs in the rear. Coil springs were custom made with a stiffness of 240 lbf/in each for the rear and 200 lbf/in each for the front. The lower natural frequency of the front springs is conducive to 'flat ride', where an automobile minimizes pitching motions when traveling over a road bump. A proven condition for good ride requires that the frequencies in pitch and bounce be nearly equal. The vehicle ride equations are:

$$f_p = \frac{(k_f + k_r)g}{2\pi W} \qquad (3)$$

$$f_b = \frac{(k_r b - k_f a)g}{2\pi W} \qquad (4)$$

Where f_p and f_b are pitch and bounce frequencies, k_f and k_r are the front and rear spring rates, a and b are the distances from the be vehicle's center of gravity to the front and rear wheels, and W is the vehicle weight. For The Blizzard:

$$\frac{f_p}{f_b} = 1.07 < 1.20 \qquad (5)$$

Pitching motions are caused not only by road inputs but also by front–rear weight transfer due to acceleration and deceleration. These pitching motions may be reduced by incorporating anti–geometry into the suspension design. The upper and lower suspension arms may be angled relative to each other to give anti–squat properties in the rear under acceleration and anti–dive properties in the front under hard braking. The Blizzard was designed with intermediate values of 70% anti–squat and 30% anti–dive to best balance ride harshness and pitching moments.

The Blizzard's wheel base of 93 in. is only 6 in. over the minimum specified by the competition rules to help us achieve a turning radius of 5 m. We designed a steering geometry with 75% Ackerman steering. Because we use a non–power–assisted steering rack to reduce power usage, we kept the scrub radius small at 1 in. This scrub radius was achieved by using rims with a large negative offset which allowed the packaging of suspension components closer to the center of the wheel. An anti–roll bar was used in the front to supplement the roll stiffness of the softer front springs. It also served to counter the oversteer tendency of our vehicle due to the rear weight bias. Tire sizing and inflation pressures further assisted in ultimately giving our car a controllable understeer character.

BRAKES

We used ventilated disk brakes mounted at all four wheels, with the front caliper being of a fixed double action design and the rear being of a floating single action design.

The 10 in. front and 8 in. rear rotors are capable of making a full stop from 60 mph every two minutes, while maintaining rotor temperature below 200°C. The model of rear calipers was chosen for their integral mechanical parking brake. To hold The Blizzard on a 20% incline the rear calipers have a nominal rating of 2.88 lbf/psi. This rating is twice that of the front calipers and would cause the rear brakes to lock before the front under heavy braking. To correct this, the braking effect was purposely reduced in the rear through the selection of smaller rear rotors. In order to further control the braking bias, the two independent master cylinders were split front to rear, rather than diagonally, and to provide stable braking under all conditions an adjustable bias rod connecting the master cylinders was built and set to split braking load 58% front and 42% rear.

TRACTION DRIVE

Most electric traction motor systems available today offer higher power at the expense of efficiency, or higher efficiency at the expense of power. Thus, to date most EVs have offered either performance or range: one at the expense of the other. The Blizzard's unique dual drive power transmission system enables the optimal combination of two motors with complementary characteristics. The primary motor is highly efficient in a cruising regime and provides adequate torque and power for moderate acceleration. The secondary motor is

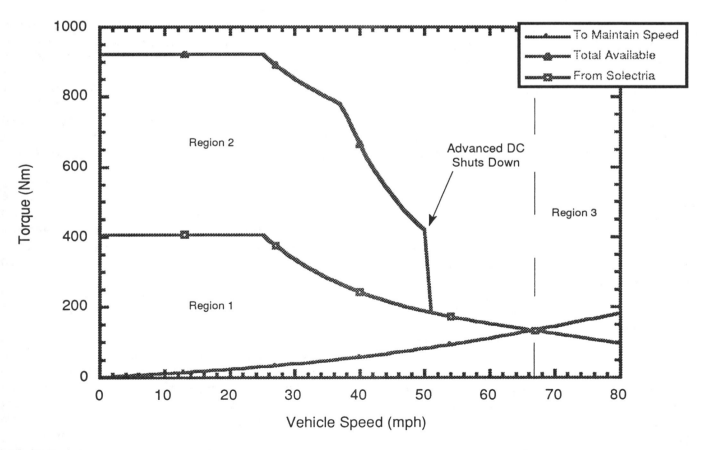

Torque at Vehicle Drive Wheels

Figure 5

less efficient, but it provides substantial additional torque and power for acceleration and/or ascending steep grades. Weight and cost penalties of the two motor system are small. Further, our power transmission system allows both motors to drive the front wheels, eliminating the mechanical complexity, weight, and packaging space needed for an all-wheel drive system. The alternate power unit (APU) is an eighteen horsepower internal combustion engine converted to burn M85 to minimize emissions. The APU drives a generator which is connected in a series configuration, to recharge the batteries and power the electric traction motors. A digital control system coordinates the motor and APU operation.

MOTOR CHARACTERISTICS—Since during cruising only one motor and controller are in use, it is essential that the motor and controller be highly efficient to maximize range. We chose the Solectria ACgt20 AC induction motor and AC300 controller system primarily for its ninety-three percent peak efficiency. The Solectria motor provides eight horsepower nominal and twenty-eight horsepower maximum. The AC300 controller also provides regenerative braking, many safety features including overheat protection and high pedal disable, cruise control, and speedometer and odometer outputs.

Our second electric motor is only used for situations requiring higher power, such as acceleration and climbing moderate to extreme grade. Although this motor is not operated continuously, efficiency was still a consideration in the motor selection. The Advanced DC L91-4003 DC motor we chose provides a maximum forty-two horsepower and, with the Curtis PMC 1441B controller, is approximately eighty percent efficient in the higher power range.

OPERATING STRATEGY—Both motors drive through synchronous belt systems that are connected to a single input shaft driving a hypoid differential. The driven pulley of the Advanced DC's belt system is connected to an overrun clutch mounted on the input shaft. When the desired torque, as indicated by the accelerator pedal position, is less than the maximum the Solectria can provide, power to the Advanced DC is cut (i.e., only the Solectria will drive the wheels) and the input shaft overruns the driven pulley of the Advanced DC system. This accomplishes two goals: the Advanced DC is not dragged along by the Solectria so energy consumption is reduced and the Advanced DC could be geared for optimal acceleration and not be over-revved during high speed cruising. This operating situation is represented by "Region 1" in Figure 5. When the desired torque is greater than the maximum the Solectria can provide, the micro-controller signals the Advanced DC to provide torque equal to the difference between the desired torque and that which the Solectria alone can provide. When the angular velocity of the driven pulley of the Advanced DC system reaches that of the input shaft, the overrun clutch engages, allowing both motors to drive the shaft simultaneously. This operating situation is represented by "Region 2" in Figure 5. "Region 3" is beyond the vehicle's performance envelope, as top speed is given by the intersection of the torque required "To Maintain Speed" curve and the maximum "Total Available" torque curve.

Both synchronous belt drive systems provide some gear reduction, with the differential further reducing the output speed and increasing the output torque. The differential splits the torque and transmits it to the wheels through constant velocity joints and halfshafts.

DESIGN AND COMPONENTS—The primary design parameters for power transmission system components were the torque and speed characteristics of the motors. The differential, provided by Dana Corporation, met not only these requirements, but also allowed for an independent suspension, had minimal mass due to its cast aluminum carrier, and provided a 5.17:1 gear reduction to minimize the additional gearing to achieve the roughly 10:1 overall reductions needed. We chose the gear ratio for the Advanced DC to maximize acceleration for the low end speeds encountered in an urban or suburban commuter situation. We chose the Solectria ratio to provide adequate acceleration at low speeds, but primarily to provide efficient highway cruising.

The major parameters for the two belt drive systems were packaging, gear ratio, and belt torque capacity, all of which have interrelated trade-offs. For a given gear ratio, the smallest pulleys that can provide that ratio for the belt pitch are desirable, both for packaging and rotational inertia reasons. However, the smaller the pulley diameter, the higher the belt forces, and therefore the larger the belt width for a given load and the higher the reaction forces imparted on the motor and drive shafts. Furthermore, rotational inertia increases as the square of diameter, but only linearly with mass. Therefore, a smaller, wider pulley is preferable to a larger, thinner one from a purely inertial standpoint, but viscous drag losses due to accelerating air in the pulley teeth, albeit relatively small, becomes an issue as well.

We selected a synchronous belt drive over a v-belt drive because synchronous belts provide positive drive contact through the belt teeth, reducing the belt tension required to transmit a given torque, and thus the sizes of the shafts and motor bearings. This also reduces shaft vibration and fatigue, and bearing wear. We chose polyurethane belts with a curvilinear profile and aramid tensile cords over alternatives such as rubber curvilinear profile belts and rubber reinforced parabolic profile belts. The polyurethane belts had the highest torque capacity per belt width, which allowed the use of narrower belts and smaller radius pulleys, resulting in better packaging and lower pulley mass and rotational inertia.

We designed and manufactured the input shaft to the differential ourselves. The shaft design accounted for stress created by both the torsional and transverse loads, as well as stress concentrations produced by keyways. The shaft is mounted to the differential input at one end and supported by a pillow block and bearing at the other end. The overrun clutch is a Zern unit, selected based on its overrunning speed and torque capabilities. Finally, we constructed the halfshafts from both GKN and Dana Universal Joint Division constant velocity joints and corresponding shafts.

CONFIGURATION ADVANTAGES—Our power transmission system provides the optimal combination of the different motors' characteristics because it allows transmission of the high power motor's torque when desired, while causing minimal losses when only the high efficiency motor is required. Further, the separate belt drive systems enable separate gearing of the two motors, in this case maximizing torque from the high power motor at low rpm and maximizing the speed band of the high efficiency motor. Driving through a mechanical differential provides simple and reliable transmission to the wheels. From a handling viewpoint, the independent carrier differential and halfshaft configuration reduce unsprung mass and provide a fully independent front suspension. Finally, although this dual drive power transmission system is unique in its combination of two different motors, we have used proven production components in its construction, thus assuring reliability and enhancing manufacturability for near future production.

BATTERIES

BATTERY SELECTION—Many design considerations factored into the selection of the Blizzard's batteries including cost, energy density, energy capacity, power density, voltage, current capacity, durability, maintenance, environmental impact, safety, and recyclability. The batteries must be able to supply enough current to match the acceleration capabilities of the electric motors, and also have a high ratio of energy supplied to weight. To maximize the range of the vehicle, the batteries should store the maximum energy allowed by the competition technical specifications. The voltage of the battery pack was chosen to be 120 volts, primarily due to the available motors and other system components. After extensive examination of available batteries, Trojan 27TMH batteries best fulfilled the powertrain requirements and were selected for The Blizzard.

BATTERY SPECIFICATIONS—The Trojan 27TMH is a 12V battery consisting of six 2V cells in series. It weighs 60 lbf and has a claimed energy capacity of 83 Amp-hrs at a 3 hour discharge rate. In The Blizzard ten of these batteries are connected in series to provide a pack with 120V and 9.97kW-hrs at 3 hour discharge rate. The energy which can be extracted from the pack drops by approximately 0.4 kW-hrs per 5 degrees below 30°C (1). The energy available also increases above 30°C peaking at about 60°C after which it declines slowly. Ohmic losses will heat the batteries so the battery compartment is ventilated to control temperature and prevent hydrogen gas accumulation during periods of hard and frequent acceleration. It should be noted that the motors are capable of drawing 60 kW during acceleration. In supplying this power, the batteries are required to supply a specific power of 220 W/kg, safely within their capability.

The Trojan 27TMH batteries were purchased from a distributor for $70 each. This price is significantly less than the cost of many other types of batteries. The batteries will last for a minimum of 300 cycles to 80% depth of discharge. If a typical daily commute is 20 miles (2), and the projected range of our vehicle is, for the purposes of this sample calculation, 60 miles, then the projected life of the batteries is about 3 years. A figure which might be used to compare the expense of various battery types is the cost per cycle. For the Trojan 27TMH batteries, the cost per cycle is $2.26. This compares favorably with other battery technologies and if electricity is costed at $0.10/kW-hr and regular unleaded gasoline at $1.20/gal the operating cost is quite competitive with today's passenger cars. The only maintenance required for these batteries is the addition of water and completion of an equalizing approximately once or twice each month.

ENVIRONMENTAL IMPACT—The infrastructure is already in place for recovering the materials from lead-acid batteries and over 90% of all lead-acid batteries are currently being recycled (3). Manufacturing and recycling processes exist which produce a minimum of environmentally harmful products. During their useful life, the concentration of sulfuric acid in the electrolyte is, at most, 30% by weight when the battery is fully charged (4), so even contact with skin is not an immediate hazard. This is further improved by the fiberglass-wrapped torsional box structure, which contains and protects the batteries.

ALTERNATE POWER UNIT

We chose a series configuration for the Blizzard's alternate power unit (APU), an engine/alternator combination that generates electricity, for a few reasons. Incorporation of another drive system into our "hybrid" electric powertrain would have been complicated, would have required additional powertrain components and packaging space, and would have reduced our powertrain efficiency. Furthermore, with the APU not mechanically connected to the drive wheels, the APU could be optimized for power and emissions at one speed. Finally, recognizing the APU conceptually as a power storage device, which could in the future be replaced with a zero emissions device, or become unnecessary with improvements in batteries, separating the APU from the powertrain offered design evolution flexibility.

Electrical power from the APU can either be used to drive the motors or recharge the batteries. Our generator set is comprised of a Briggs and Stratton 18hp engine with a Fisher Permanent Magnet Alternator connected directly to its crankshaft. A rectifier converts the three-phase AC current to DC for use by the power electronics. We converted our engine to burn M85 for low emissions and high power output. The Fisher Alternator was chosen because it is lightweight (21 lbf) and highly efficient (≥92%). Our engine/alternator combination weighs only 100 lbs, yet delivers as much power as a commercial 250 lbf generator set.

The acoustic emissions of the APU are significantly reduced by a muffler that was specially designed for our system by the Nelson company, a Briggs and Stratton affiliate. The muffler is smaller and lighter than ordinary mufflers and reduces the sound level, of the APU operating at maximum RPM and under maximum load, to 73 dB. The engine's mechanical noise was also reduced using sound absorbent foam.

EMISSIONS—To minimize emissions, an experimental catalytic converter was used. This convertor was developed by Allied Signal Automotive Catalyst Company for use with methanol fuels and was sized for use with our small (540 cc) engine. A charcoal canister was also installed to collect fuel vapors that escape from the carburetor when the APU is turned off. Emissions were evaluated by sampling them from the exhaust, both before and after the catalytic converter, using real time emissions analyzers that measure the concentrations of CO, CO_2, NO_x, and total hydrocarbons.

FUEL CONSUMPTION—The fuel consumption rate of the APU was determined during extensive dynamometer testing. In designed experiments the carburetor jet size, compression ratio, and engine speed were varied and the effects on power and fuel consumption were monitored. From this data, it was determined that using an 0.055 inch carburetor jet, a compression ratio of 10.75:1, and an engine speed of 3150 rpm minimized fuel consumption without significantly affecting our maximum power. These settings give us a specific fuel consumption of 0.125 cc/(hp*sec). while generating 16.75 HP. To achieve our target range of 250 miles it was determined that 8 gallons of methonal would be required. Aero Tec Laboratories supplied an 8 gallon fuel cell which provides excellent crash protection and is equipped with a flapper valve to prevent fuel spillage during a rollover.

VEHICLE CONTROL SYSTEM

SYSTEM OVERVIEW–The Vehicle Control System (VCS) interprets data from the accelerator pedal and the speed sensor of the Solectria controller. Based on this data and driver input from the dashboard, the VCS issues torque commands to the Solectria and Curtis controllers.

DRIVER INTERFACE-The driver is provided with the standard brake and accelerator pedals. A switch replaces the "gear-shift" of a transmission and allows forward, reverse, or neutral. Another switch defines the use of the electric motors. Three modes are available: "HI" allows only the use of the Solectria motor; "LO" is used for acceleration, where the high power Advanced DC motor and the Solectria are both on, and "AUTO" blends in the Advanced DC whenever additional power is needed (hill climbing, acceleration). In AUTO a high-level algorithm attempts to maximize power output while minimizing power consumption.

Currently, cruise control is handled by the Solectria controller. However, if the Solectria is unable to maintain speed on a reasonable slope, then the Advanced DC will be needed. With the Advanced DC, cruise control may be replaced with torque control. While different from today's automobiles, in which cruise control holds speed constant, there is an advantage to torque control. There will be no wasteful accelerations, like those caused by small movements of the driver's foot or a speed control algorithm.

HARDWARE–The VCS is implemented with the Intel EV80C196KB Evaluation Board. The microcontroller supplied on this board features standard digital lines, an analog to digital converter, Pulse Width Modulated (PWM) outputs, and an RS232 serial port. The CPU clock frequency is 12MHz, which is high enough to allow real-time control. The 64kb address space provides ample room for control algorithms.

EVALUATION BOARD–The Evaluation Board retains all of the important features of an independent EV80C196KB and may execute code without a host. For debugging purposes, the evaluation board supports an Embedded Control Monitor (ECM) when hosted by a PC-compatible. The ECM and the target system (i.e., the code running on the microcontroller) are run concurrently. This arrangement allows interrogation and modification of the state of the target system during execution. Moreover, the packaging of the Evaluation Board provides I/O connectors, sockets for off-chip RAM and ROM, and a convenient interface to the A/D converter. The most significant feature of this system is the ability to debug and enhance the code, with a PC laptop, while driving the car.

INTERFACE CIRCUITS–Torque commands to the Solectria and Curtis motor controllers take the form of two PWM signals from the microcontroller. Each PWM signal is applied to an RC network which provides a DC voltage proportional to the integral of the input. The integrated signal is supplied to an Op-Amp level shifter through a unity-gain buffer. The Op-Amp shifts the DC voltage into the range required by a particular motor controller. The shifted signals are used in place of potentiometers at the pedal inputs of the motor controllers.

The other interfaces are much less complicated. Relays are used to allow the microcontroller to manipulate the switching aspects of the Solectria and Curtis controllers. The Evaluation Board provides all necessary support circuitry for the A/D converter.

EMERGENCY SHUTDOWN–Independent of the microcontroller's interface circuitry, an overspeed sensor circuit was installed that will perform an "emergency shutdown" of the motor if the motor's rotation exceeds a desired rpm. This would be important were a drive belt to break during normal operation, where the rapid change from a loaded to a no-load situation could cause a motor to exceed its maximum RPM rating. Motor rotation is sensed by a magnetically actuated switch which closes once per motor shaft revolution. This produces a square wave of variable frequency, whose pulses are counted over a small time interval. If more than three pulses are counted during this interval, then an error is signaled and the motor controller is deactivated. The length of the time interval determines the rpm at which the motor controller is shutdown.

SOFTWARE–Assembly language code runs a finite state machine, interleaved with interrupt service routines. The finite state machine guides the vehicle into a proper mode of execution based on the status of the driver's switch inputs and the speed of the vehicle. Once in a moving state, the bulk of the work is transferred to the interrupt service routines. These routines perform analog to digital conversions on the vehicle's speed and the accelerator pedal's position. These routines also monitor the cruise control and neutral switches. Based on this information and the current state of the state machine, the appropriate torque control algorithm constructs new PWMs.

TORQUE CONTROL ALGORITHMS–There are three torque control algorithms, one for each of the motor modes previously defined. One of the algorithms simply creates a PWM for the Solectria with a duty cycle proportional to the accelerator pedal position. Another uses the same approach to create a PWM for the Advanced DC, in addition to the PWM for the Solectria. The third control algorithm, which employs closed-loop feedback control, is the most complicated. A state observer algorithm will use the speed sensor feedback from the Solectria controller to estimate the velocity and acceleration of the vehicle. This observer will track the dynamic state of the car. The algorithm will also monitor the accelerator pedal reference signal. This reference input is associated with a requested velocity by a linear relationship. Then, by comparing the reference and observer velocities, the Solectria PWM is adjusted to regulate the desired speed. If the Solectria is unable to meet the requested velocity after a fixed number of iterations, then greater torque is required to meet the driver's command. Hence, the Advanced DC is activated and its PWM is controlled in the same fashion, until adequate velocity is attained. This sort of algorithm is needed due to the use of two motors with different characteristics. This control scheme will be used in normal driving, where the reference input is changing, and possibly in cruise control mode. The algorithm is particularly suited to implementing cruise control, because if changes to the reference signal are ignored, the algorithm will regulate a constant speed output under varying loads.

BODY STYLING

The body was designed as a nonstructural shell that protects vehicle subsystems and occupants. Thus main dimensions, such as width and height, were predetermined. The body was styled with manufacturability and aerodynamics as the primary design criteria. After examining several body material/processing alternatives vacuum forming of thermoplastic body panels was selected. With the guidance of GE Plastics, it was determined that Lexan® would be the most suitable thermoplastic for vehicle applications. The body design was completed using the solid modeling module of CAEDS. With this system it was possible to make accurately dimensioned templates which were used in manufacturing our molds. By using CAEDS we were also able to quickly make design alterations to accomodate the processing requirements of Lexan®. Finally, the 3-D body created in CAEDS gave us a good feel for the body's overall complexity and thus its manufacturability.

ASPECTS OF DESIGN—Aerodynamic drag of bluff bodies, such as cars, is due mainly to pressure drag resulting from flow separation. Thus, our goal was to design a body that limited flow separation yet met the constraints of the existing frame and was manufacturable. The resulting design, produced by trying to satisfy these conflicting requirements, is pictured in Figure 6.

The "roundness" of the front end establishes the area over which the dynamic pressure can act to induce drag. The location of the front edge of the vehicle determines the location of the stagnation point. Minimum drag is obtained when the stagnation point is kept low on the frontal profile of the vehicle. Thus, the nose of the car is kept low to the ground and well rounded. A front spoiler was added that while slightly increasing pressure drag, significantly reduced underbody drag. The front fenders flare out towards the wheel wells creating a smooth transition of flow along the side of the car. The hood is steeply sloped allowing air flow to remain attached as it approaches the windshield.

The windshield establishes the flow direction as it approaches the horizontal roof and thus has a direct influence on drag. Shallow angles reduce drag, but complicate vehicle design in terms of solar heating of the passenger compartment and optical distortion. Due to cost considerations, we used a windshield from a current production car which added a dimensional constraint. A 1993 Buick Park Avenue windshield, the closest match to our design specifications, is mounted into a steel frame at a 45° inclination. The window frame also serves as a support for the side windows and the solar panel roof.

Except to keep flow attached, the roof and doors contribute relatively little to the vehicle drag. Thus, these components were designed with manufacturability as the primary concern. For example, the doors were designed to be symmetric, so that only one mold was needed to produce both door panels. The side windows were made separately and shaped to fit the cavity between roof, door panel, front windshield, and rear quarter window.

The shape of the rear end of the car has a direct impact on aerodynamic forces through control of the separation point. Another considerations is the potential for dirt deposition on the backlight and the tail lights. And of course the shape of the frame had to be kept in mind. Taking these factors into account, we decided to make the rear of the car a semi-fastback with sides that tapered in toward the rear.

DRAG ESTIMATION—Effort was made to analytically determine the frontal area, A, and the coefficient of drag, C_d, for use in performance calculations. The projected frontal area of The Blizzard is 2.44 m^2. The drag coefficient was estimated using a method introduced by R.G.S. White (SAE paper no. 690189). This method assigns a drag rating, D, to nine categories related to body design and the overall drag coefficient is calculated as

$$C_d = 0.16 + 0.0095 \sum_{i=1}^{9} D_i \qquad (6)$$

Following this procedure The Blizzard's estimated coefficient of drag is 0.3025.

MATERIALS—The material used in the production of our body panels was Lexan 9030, produced by General Electric Plastics. It is advertised as one of the toughest, most versatile of all engineering plastics. Lexan 9030 offers high impact strength (Tensile Impact, type "s", 275 ft-lb/sq. in.), reasonable heat resistance ($\approx$ 250°F), and excellent mechanical properties over a wide temperature range. Lexan 9030 panels can be repaired with standard body filler, but require special polycarbonate based paints.

MOLD PRODUCTION—One of the significant advantages of vacuum forming is the need to produce only a male mold. With the limited development time the ability to avoid producing female molds was crucial.

The vacuum forming process exposes molds to extremely high temperatures (400°F), and high compressive forces (14.7 psi vacuum), so the material selection for the molds is very important. We chose to use a synthetic wood produced by Ciba Geigy with the industry name Renshape 450®. This material, a compressed urethane, contains no grain within its structure, and thus allows for easy shaping and meets the requirements for strength and thermal stability. Using standard shop tools, primarily circular saws, planers, and hand sanders, the Renshape 450® was easily shaped to the profiles and cross-sections produced using CAEDS. By properly supporting the underside of our molds, the vacuum pressure did not pose a problem. To supplement our limited supply of Renshape 450® hardwoods such as poplar and mahogany were used. Cracks and defects on our molds were filled with common polyester resin-based body fillers to prepare them for panel production. Most inspection was done by sight and touch. The last step in mold production was drilling 0.040 in. holes along critical areas of the mold to allow the vacuum to pull the Lexan onto the molds and remove any entrapped air.

Using combinations of materials on individual molds was found to be detrimental as differring material behavior under the vacuum forming conditions resulted in discontinuities on our panel surfaces. Still, this was a satisfactory process for our limited production. For mass production, our molds would have been made from aluminum blocks milled to the desired shape of the body panels. For shapes which could not be milled, the aluminum would be carved or sanded by hand. The aluminum molds would be able to withstand the thousands of cycles required for mass production.

VACUUM FORMING–Lexan® sheets were vacuum formed at the General Electric Plastics facility in Pittsfield, MA using molds designed and fabricated at Cornell. The Lexan® sheets (5 ft by 6 ft by 1/8 in.) were pre-processed by heating at 400°F for approximately 2 minutes. The softened sheets were then placed over the male molds and a vacuum was formed to draw the sheets onto the molds. Processing took approximately 15 seconds after which the Lexan® body panels were removed from the molds and allowed to cool for several minutes. The entire process is very quick and simple—the set up time for each mold was approximately 10 minutes while the forming process for individual pieces, including cooling, took under 5 minutes.

COSMETICS AND MOUNTING–Once the formed body panels returned from Pittsfield, they were trimmed of excess material and any defects resulting from the forming process were sanded or touched up with body filler. Using 1/4 turn fasteners, the panels were mounted to light steel members extending from the frame to critical high pressure stabilizing points. The 1/4 turn fasteners allow for quick and easy removal of the body panels when repairs to vehicle components are necessary, as is often the case with experimental vehicles. Figure 7 shows The Blizzard after having endured a 20 mph impact to the right front fender sustained during the 1993 HEV Challenge.

ERGONOMICS

PASSENGER COMPARTMENT LAYOUT–The cockpit layout for The Blizzard was designed around the torsional box that runs through the center of the vehicle and provides separation between the driver and passenger. Many of the Blizzard's controls and instruments are housed on an exten-

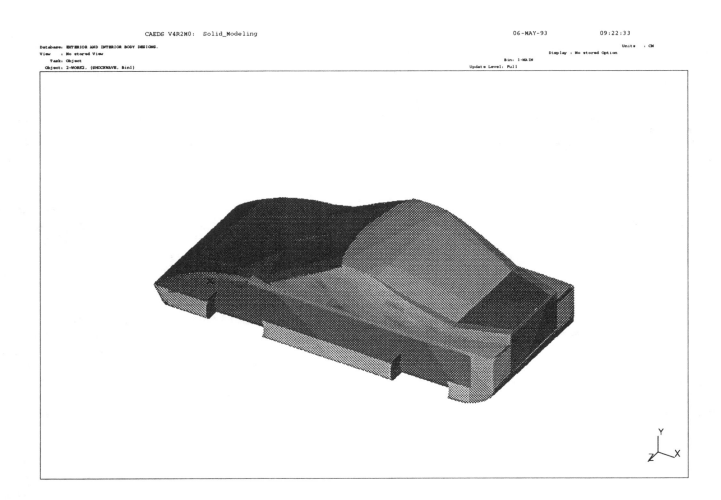

Figure 6

Figure 7

sion of the dashboard which lies on top of the torsional box. Important controls, such as the battery disconnect switch and the fire extinguisher discharge handle, are within easy reach of both driver and passenger. There is also an access panel to the main power electronics that permits easy replacement of fuses, disconnect of battery pack, or other maintenance needs.

DASHBOARD AND INSTRUMENTATION- The dashboard was constructed of fiberglass coated Dupont Styrofoam. Individual foam sheets were glued together to form a large block of material that was then formed into the desired shape using a variety of hand and power tools. The foam was covered with fiberglass to create the finished shape and texture. The fiberglass gives the dashboard strength and durability, while the underlying foam can absorb energy and reduce the risk of injury to the vehicle occupants in case of a collision.

The Blizzard's instrumentation is divided into two sections on the dashboard. The main instrument panel is directly in front of the driver and contains analog voltmeter, ammeter and fuel guage, and digital speedometer and trip computer. There are also indicators for the turn signals and hazard lights, as well as a high-beam-on indicator. The center console, located above the torsional box between the driver and passenger, contains the main power switch, APU controls, light switches, digital kilowatt-hour meter, fire suppression system control, emergency battery disconnect, and operating mode switch. To make the driving experience more enjoyable, The Blizzard is equipped with a seven-disc CD stereo, tilt steering wheel, adjustable seats, and a solar powered ventilation system.

All the lighting requirements of the New York State Department of Transportation have been met by using lights found on production cars. Lightweight (6 oz. each) plastic headlights were recessed under the hood to reduce drag.

SUMMARY

In a little over ten months a team of 38 Cornell Engineers engineered and constructed a practical hybrid electric vehicle. Their completed vehicle, The Blizzard weighed 2100 lbf including over 600 lbf of batteries, and is powered by two electric motors generating a total of 60 kW. The battery pack contains 10 kW-hrs of energy and is supplemented by a methanal fueled internal combustion engine that can produce 16.75 HP. The Blizzard features four wheel disc brakes and four wheel independent suspension. It can carry two people and luggage over 250 miles and is capable of reaching 45 mph in 8.3 seconds. This vehicle, when its components are valued at retail levels, has a cost of just over $32,000. With The Blizzard the Cornell Hybrid Electric Vehicle Team won first place overall in the ground-up category at the 1993 Ford/SAE/DOE HEV Challenge

The Blizzard was dedicated to Terrence Quinn, a valued team member and friend, who died in January 1993.

REFERENCES

[1] Hackleman, Michael. "Making Electric Vehicles Work: The Myth of the Better Battery," NESEA Solar and Electric Vehicle Conference Proceedings, 1992.

[2] Meyer, George E. "Batteries: Environmental Impact in Production, Use and Disposal," NESEA Solar and Electric Vehicle Conference Proceedings, 1992.

[3] Thomas Roy Crompton, Battery Reference Manual, London: Butterworths.

University of Idaho and Washington State University

Traci Anne Hudson and Dean Edwards
University of Idaho and Washington State University

ABSTRACT

The University of Idaho and Washington State University have joined forces to design and build a hybrid electric vehicle for the Ford Hybrid Electric Vehicle competition. Located only 8 miles apart, the two schools have utilized equipment and facilities from both sides of the Washington/Idaho border. This team is competing in the ground up competition.

The design presented by the University of Idaho/Washington State University team is a series hybrid vehicle. The powertrain begins with a 20 hp Kohler DC Engine that runs on unleaded gasoline. A 400 volt Fisher alternator powered by the engine charges a lead-acid battery pack that consists of 28 GNB UPSolyte batteries. This battery pack produces a 336 volt DC current that is sent through a frequency controlled invertor. The invertor powers a 100 kW AC motor, which was designed and built by AC Propulsion Inc. A first gear transaxle, taken from a Chevrolet Citation, provides gear reduction of the AC motor output. A rear sub assembly from a Cougar XR7 transmits power to the wheels, completing the powertrain. The vehicle consists of a 5086 Aluminum space frame, shelled in a foam-core, fiberglass body.

INTRODUCTION

The purpose of entering this competition was to gain experience in designing and building a ground-up vehicle in hopes of improving on this design for future competitions. The vehicle has also been used to generate interest among high school students in engineering at both universities. The powertrain will be used in the electrical engineering power electronics classes.

Hybrid electric vehicles are categorized as either series hybrids, or parallel hybrids. Generally a series hybrid consists of a generator charging an electrical storage system, which in turn drives an electrical motor. The parallel configuration consists of an electrical storage unit powering an electrical motor which will drive one set of wheels, and an alternate power unit, usually a conventional power train, driving the other set of wheels. The parallel system is difficult to integrate smoothly, and often more difficult to control in extreme driving conditions than the series systems. For these reasons a series configuration was chosen for this vehicle. The series system used consists of a 20 hp gasoline motor driving a 400 volt alternat or, which charges a 336 volt lead-acid battery pack. The DC supply from the battery pack is converted to 336 volts AC, using a frequency controlled invertor. The invertor drives a 100 kW AC induction drive motor. The output from this motor is then put through a gear reduction into the final drive. Each of these subcomponents is discussed in detail below.

POWERTRAIN CONFIGURATION

The fuel system

A twelve gallon, foam filled, fuel cell was chosen to hold the unleaded gasoline for the internal combustion engine. It is of one-piece, seamless, polyethylene construction and has a ball check valve that prevents fuel from spilling in case of a rollover. It has two 8 AN outlet and one 6 AN vent fittings. The tank is located directly behind the driver seat on top of the battery box. It is enclosed by an aluminum and fire retardant, fiber matt firewall that also encloses the invertor and AC drive motor. The filler hose exits the vehicle behind the driver door. Covering the filler hose end is a screw on cap and an external door. Two fuel lines exit the tank. One provides fuel to the gasoline heater that is part of the battery thermal management system. The other sends fuel to the IC engine. A mechanical pump on the engine pumps the fuel. Because this is not a high-pressure fuel system requiring steel fuel lines, flexible rubber lines are used exclusively.

The internal combustion engine

The engine selected to power the alternator was the Kohler Command C20. This twin cylinder, 4-cycle, 20 hp engine has several desirable features. The engine uses unleaded gasoline and meets 1994 CARB emissions standards and industrial noise regulations. Both features are improved over Kohler's standard design by design changes in the exhaust system. The engine features overhead valves that improve volumetric efficiency and raise the compression ratio. This contributes to more complete fuel combustion, better efficiency and little carbon buildup. Hydraulic valve lifters, a feature exclusive to Kohler in this power range, eliminate valve adjustment and reduce valve-train noise. Another feature that is seldom seen on engines in this power range is the high-pressure oil pump and full-flow oil filter. This system delivers lubrication at 30 p.s.i. to the camshaft, crankshaft, connecting rods and rocker arms.

The cylinders are in a V-configuration with an aluminum head and crankcase and cast iron liners. Other engine features are as follows:

Dimensions (lxwxh):
16.99 in. x 16.58 in. x 18.17 in
Displacement
38 cu. in. (624
Bore:
3.03 in. (77 mm)
Stroke:
2.64 in. (67 mm)
Torque
32 lbs. ft @ 2500 rpm (44 N*m)
Compression ratio:
8.5:1
Dry weight:
90 lbs. (41 kg)
Oil capacity (w/filter):
2 U.S. qts. (1.9 L)

The engine uses a 12 volt electric starter and dual wire controls. Its fuel system has an in-line fuel filter and a fixed jet carburetor. The engine will run at 3600 rpm, where it produces its maximum horsepower and uses fuel at a rate of 1.9 gallons per hour.

The alternator

Fisher Electric Motor Technology, Inc. designed and built the alternator to match space limitations in the vehicle and the engine operating speed of 3600 rpm. Fisher Electric Motor Technology, Inc. has a line of brushless DC alternators of the same rated output and was therefor chosen to build the system. The alternator is built with super magnets and robust modern components. The alternator is directly mounted to the engine shaft so that no pulleys, bearings, or maintenance is required. It was built to the following specifications:

Output:	15 kW
Voltage:	400 Volts DC
Current:	40 Amps
Operating Speed:	3600 rpm
Phases:	3
(WYE connected)	
Resistance:	0.2 Ohms
(phase-phase)	
Diameter:	8.375 inches
Length:	4.0 inches
Estimated Weight:	25.5 pounds

Power is fed from the alternator by a 2/0 wire to avoid an overload or generation of excess heat from transient peaks during startup. The same size will be used to ground the alternator to the batteries and electric drive motor.

The lead-acid battery pack

The vehicle has 28 GNB UPSolyte batteries at 12 V each. This produces a total of 336 volts and an energy capacity rated at 9.4 Kwh. The battery pack is heated to increase the capacity and improve the life. Therefor, 1 inch thick polystyrene insulation coats the inside of the battery box. Also, a complete seal of 1/8 inch thick PVC dielectric insulation lines the box to ensure that the car is insulated from any electric current that the batteries hold.

From the battery box, the wiring will be routed to a 400 A, 500 V fuse, then to the contactor, to the invertor, and then back to the battery box. The contactor is used to break the current in case of an emergency, according to Ford HEV regulations. It has a manual switch located on the outside of the car and a remote switch near the driver's seat. The battery pack is attached to the invertor using a welding cable and connectors. Four feet of extra cable length is added to the battery pack since the battery pack is loaded in one piece from underneath.

We chose to use 2 AWG cable with THHN insulation because this size cable will be large enough for the steady state current that the car will be using. This cable size was also recommended by AC Propulsion Inc., who designed and manufactured the invertor. The batteries are connected using flat copper battery terminals, and a terminal cover over the battery terminals to help stop accidental contact with the battery terminals.
The batteries are held down at each corner with a lattice made out of wood. It is self supporting inside the battery box, so that there won't be any contact with the frame or the outside the battery box. The lattice will be structured so it will only touch the insides of the PVC insulation, thus preventing a route for a current to follow.

The invertor and AC motor

The invertor and AC drive system was designed and built by AC Propulsion Inc. This drive first appeared in GM's Impact prototype. This system also appeared in Road and Trade magazine after being used to convert a Honda Civic CRX. The system is currently being sold for use in prototype vehicles and is not used in any production vehicles.

The system consists of 2 major components and some control circuitry. Power from the battery pack is converted from 336 volts DC to 336 volts AC. The speed of the motor is controlled by varying the frequency of the input signal. By maintaining a constant voltage to the motor, the torque output of the motor is essentially constant. This invertor is state of the art equipment and operates at 97% efficiency. It also acts as a battery charger, saving the weight of carrying a separate system.

The AC Drive is a frequency controlled, AC, induction, motor . Its output is an almost constant torque curve of 109 ft/lbs. The flat torque response means that a transmission is not needed, but with a top speed of 12,000 rpm, a gear reduction is needed.

The gear reduction

The AC motor used to propel the car has an output that ranges from 0 rpm to 12000 rpm. The useful power range of a standard drive motor is approximately 600 rpm to 3500 rpm or a useful range of 2900 rpm. To gain a desired speed the use of gear advantages must be incorporated. The HEV has a useful rpm range that can obtain a wide speed range but, it does not have the power to give desirable accelerations. The excess rpm range can be converted to an increase in torque by the incorporation of a gear reduction. The gear reduction needs to bring the motor output to the wheels of the car at such a speed that the car will travel in the desired speed range of 0 MPH to 75 MPH.

A gearbox was selected after looking at many transmissions, transfer cases, and transaxles and speaking to most of the wrecking yards and transmission shops in the area. Possibilities were limited due to the space requirements. A four-speed transaxle used in GM cars was selected because of its shape, gear combinations, simplicity, and size of car it was designed for. Modifications include the removal of all gears except first gear, the clutch fork, and shifting mechanism. These items were removed to reduce friction, increase oil capacity for cooling, and to reduce unnecessary weight. This transaxle has its own differential so the original Ford differential in the rear subframe was eliminated. The combination brings with it a large reduction in the weight of the car, but a great deal of modification to the rear portion of the frame. Some modifications include changing the mounting system for the upper control arm and the front of the lower control arm. Axles were custom made

with Ford CV joints on one end and GM CV joints on the other end.

CONTROLLER STRATEGIES

The IC engine control

The IC engine control unit was donated by Murphy Switch Inc., of California. The unit is a sealed box with 15 terminals, five possible adjustments and five indicator lights. Terminal hookups include: magneto pickup, oil pressure, water or oil temperature, starter, fuel solenoid, lamp test, automatic running position, manual test, and ground. Indicator lights are displayed on the box and remote lighting can be used to show the same: low oil pressure, high water/oil pressure, overcrank, overspeed, engine running and engine failure. The adjustments allow changing the overspeed rpm, crank disconnect rpm, crank time/rest time, and shutdown lockout delay time settings by way of turning the control screw on four separate potentiometers. A row of five dip-switches makes it possible to change the number of cranking attempts. Several terminals have wire and amperage specifications.

The control unit is positioned on the firewall for easy access and visibility of the indicator lights. Remote lighting is placed in the dash for driver awareness of the engine's condition. Adjustments will not be possible unless the unit is removed from its bolted-down position, except for the main selector switch, with off, auto and test positions, which is in the driver's compartment.

The AC motor control

The AC motor is controlled by the invertor. The invertor maintains a constant 336 volts, but varies the frequency of the AC signal from 0 to 120 Hz. This will vary the motor's speed from 0 to 12,000 rpm as described in the previous section. To control the invertor's frequency, a 0 to 5 volt signal is sent from the operator. This signal is controlled by a potentiometer in the form of a "gas pedal." The gas pedal will be discussed in greater detail in the Ergonomics section.

The vehicle direction is controlled by setting a switch to forward, reverse, or neutral. The direction of travel will be controlled by the invertor instead of using a reversing gear in the transmission.

EMISSIONS CONTROL

The batteries

The batteries used are sealed-recombinant cells. Therefor they only emit hydrogen when overcharged. To help vent this explosive gas out of the battery pack, we are installing a 15 cfm fan. The fan is a brushless 12 V, 0.18A Sunon fan. The air is ducted from the front of the car into the bottom, front of the battery pack. Exhaust leaves the battery pack from the rear, top of the battery compartment. The fan is powered by the accessory port on the invertor, such that anytime the car is either receiving or giving off a charge, the fan is turned on. A gasoline heater is used to heat the batteries. This gives us additional air flow to ensure the proper venting of the battery box.

The exhaust system

The routing of the exhaust system begins at the exhaust manifold which is located on the engine above the alternator on the passenger side of the car. The exhaust manifold exits toward the rear of the vehicle and flares from 1 inch to 1.5 inch diameter pipe. The exhaust pipe exits the front compartment behind the right front tire and runs along the frame rail, outside the passenger compartment, but inside the outer skin. It is then routed behind the right rear tire and up to the muffler. The muffler is mounted underneath the upper rear horizontal cross member at the back of the frame behind the rear suspension. After exiting the muffler, the pipe flares to 1.75 inches and drops down so as to exit the rear of the vehicle. The Kohler engine meets 1994 CARB emission standards with the stock manifold and muffler.

FUEL AND ELECTRICAL POWER CONSUMPTION

The vehicle will consume very little power during it

steady state operation. The Kolher engine will consume 1.9 gallons per hour during full operation and generate 14.5 kW. The AC drive motor will consume 15 kW during steady state operation at 55 miles per. The rest of the electronic will consume only 0.36 kW, except for the invertor which operates at 97 %. This means the total consumption of power is 2.36 kW plus 1.9 gallons per hour during Hybrid mode, or a total of 17.36 kW from the batteries during Zero Emission mode.

VEHICLE STRUCTURE

The chassis

The vehicle chassis was designed of an entirely aluminum structure. This was done because of the favorable strength and weight characteristics of aluminum. The chassis is composed of a two-section design. First, the frame is a wide twin rail design. This design was chosen to accommodate the battery box within the frame rails. In case of an accident, the battery compartment is securely locked within the rail structure and would not break free from the automobile. The frame is constructed entirely of a single material stock. The rectangular beams are three inches by five inches with a 3/8 inch wall thickness. The geometry of these rails provides a large factor of safety in deflection and loading.

The second section of the chassis is the rollover protection cage. The vehicle was required to have two rollover protection hoops and a side impact protection bar. It was decided that a full cage structure would provide a safer vehicle. The cage is made up of a combination of two and 3/8 inch tubing with 3/16 inch wall thickness and two inch square tubing with 1/8 inch wall thickness. These material stock sizes were chosen to satisfy the contest rules.

Both sections of the chassis were fabricated by Liberty Metals of Kent, Washington and all welds are certified. The two sections are attached to provide a rigid substructure for the rest of the vehicle components.

The bumpers

The bumpers were designed to withstand a five mile per hour impact with minimal damage. They are made from a set of energy absorbing bumpers from a Volkswagen Rabbit, combined with steel C-channel bumpers.

The body design dictates the shape of the bumpers. To give the shape to the bumpers, notches were cut at equal intervals. The steel was heated and bent to close the gap left by the notches. The empty areas were welded to add strength back to the steel. Mounting points were drilled out to fit 1/2 inch bolts and spacers were made to mount the bumper at the proper height.

The door frames

The frames for the doors are constructed of aluminum C-channel. In order to make the doors open in a gull-wing fashion, they were hinged on the roof about three inches from the centerline of the car. Two gas springs per door were used to decrease the force needed to operate the doors. The springs are set up so that the door falls shut on its own if it's only half way open. If it is opened any further, it stays up on its own.

The door is latched using a rotating cam that pulls two latching pins. A locking mechanism has also been incorporated into the latch mechanism, and works completely separate from the latch mechanism. The locking mechanism prevents one latch mechanism components from moving. An external key lock is integrated into the locking mechanism as well.

The firewall

The firewalls are constructed of 3/16 inch aluminum plate with fire resistant matting on the passenger side. A firewall is at the extreme front of the passenger compartment to protect the occupants from any fire danger due to the IC engine and alternator. It also helps prevent the charging system from entering the passenger area in case of a head-on collision.

SUSPENSION DESIGN AND MODIFICATION

The suspension of our vehicle is directly out of a 1991 Mercury Cougar XR7. The rear suspension is the fully independent lower "H" arm type. This complete rear suspension system attaches to a subframe assembly that comes out of the Cougar. This subframe bolts to our vehicle's frame with some modification. The front mounting points have been altered to reduce the length of space needed for mounting. A set of air shocks may be used to help support the added weight placed on the rear suspension compared to the stock design.

The front suspension consists of a lower control arm, tension strut, stabilizer bar, and rack and pinion steering that also attaches to a subframe assembly. An upper "A" arm and a coil over type shock assembly mounts to the vehicles roll cage. This is a slight modification from the original design, but the basic function of the stock suspension has not been altered.

We chose this suspension system because of the way it detaches from the car in complete subframe assemblies. The XR7 Cougar, weighing approximately 3800 lbs., weighs virtually the same as our vehicle so the suspension components are heavy enough for our application.

The weight bias of our vehicle is very close to the Cougar, with slightly more weight on the rear suspension than in a stock Cougar. With the battery pack set low in the car and residing between the frame rails, the center of gravity of the car is very low and slightly rearward of the center of the car. The 900 lb. weight of the battery pack does not have detrimental effects on the handling of the vehicle because of this weight distribution. The weight toward the rear of the car increases the vehicle's tendency to understeer. Therefor, when the vehicle is pushed to the limit of adhesion in a corner, the rear end stays behind you and the front of the car starts to slide first.

The brakes

The vehicle has four wheel antilocking disk brakes. The ABS system is adapted from a 1991 Cougar XR7. Each wheel has a speed sensor whose information is fed to a central processor, which in turn controls the master cylinder. The electric master cylinder controls all of the pressures and modulations to each wheel as it is needed to prevent wheel lockup. Unlike a conventional master cylinder that uses vacuum for the power assist, this master cylinder is fully electric.

The wheels and tires

The wheels used on this vehicle are required by the suspension which has a five bolt, 4.25 inch spacing. They also needs to have a diameter of sixteen inches to have clearance for our large disk brakes. The only wheels available with this spacing and size are the original

wheels from a Cougar XR7. The tires are Goodyear's 235/55 R16 Eagle GAs. This tire size was recommended for our vehicle by Mr. Bill Eagon at Goodyear because of its weight handling capabilities and its low aspect ration of 55.

The steering system

The rack and pinion is out of a 1991 Cougar XR7. This rack was originally a power assisted unit. Since we do not have an engine running continuously that can turn a power steering pump, we needed an alternate source of hydraulic pressure. This is accomplished through a 12 volt hydraulic pump. The pressure from the pump will run through a check valve, through a pressure switch, and then into a pressure accumulator. This will regulate the pressure at 700 psi. In this way the pump will not have to run all of the time, and the rack will always have plenty of hydraulic pressure supplied to it.

CHOICE OF MATERIALS

Structural material choice

The material selected for the frame and structure is 5086-H32 Aluminum. This alloy is a marine alloy and therefor more corrosion resistant to salt water than most alloys. This is a work hardenable alloy, instead of a heat treated alloy. Which means that the metal will retain most of its work hardened strength in the weld zone.

The yield strength of

5086-H32 is almost twice that of 6061-T651, which is a commonly used alloy. The strength of 5086 also increases with work and fatigue and therefor the car will actually get stronger with use. This effect will be rather slight in actual practice since the stress on any part of the vehicle is only 20% of the yield strength.

Body materials

We initially looked into several different body construction methods. These included ABS plastic panels, aluminum skin over aluminum body forms, molded fiberglass, and finally foam core fiberglass sandwich construction. The first three methods were ruled out because a correctly scaled mold would be necessary. To make a scale mold, the various panels of the car would have to be created before the mold could be made. This results in building the car twice before the final panels can be completed. Composite foam core methods use the foam as an integral mold which made it necessary to only build the shape once. This not only reduces the time spent creating the final shape, but it also reduces the material cost. Another deciding factor that ruled out the first two options, is that they require special tooling which the school doesn't have access to. This left us with either molded fiberglass or a foam composite. Since we barely have time to build the car, we chose foam core fiberglass construction as our building technique.

Advantages to foam core construction

The three most obvious reasons for using foam core construction are its incredible strength to weight ratio, its ease of manufacturing, and its minimal manufacturing cost. Because the core of the structure is foam, adding insulation to deaden sound and control heat is not necessary. Urethane foam is used as insulation in other fields such as home construction. Another advantage is the fact that foam will absorb energy if an impact occurs. Simply put, if the car gets in a wreck the foam will absorb the crash impact and limit the damage to the automobile, making it easy to repair. A final advantage to using the foam core method is the high degree of flexibility it offers. First, in that it can be bent into slight or even compound curves without stressing or breaking, and second, in the shaping of the surface. Urethane foam is readily sanded into any surface contour desired. In fact, a large enough block of foam could be sculptured into a final body shape. This process that was once done only in clay by major auto manufacturers is now done using foam.

BODY STYLING AND ERGONOMICS

A plexy-glass window is installed in each door. Review mirrors are installed on each door also. The doors have continuous weather stripping around the edge. This also lowers the noise level inside the car. Internal rain gutters along the door catch any water that may be left on the weather stripping.

Body styling

The basic minimum dimensions of the car were set by the space frame and the maximums were limited by HEV contest rules. The basic shape was created from these limitations. The next step was to select a windshield which closely matched the initial concept drawings. Once the windshield was chosen, the basic drawings were developed. Clay models were then constructed using both fluid theories and suggestions from several sources. The first main source was an article in Popular Mechanics about automobile aerodynamics. This article included several good suggestions which included: 1) Flush windows and lights greatly reduce drag. 2) Side skirts both reduce drag and help keep air from getting under the car. 3) Keeping the rear end close to the ground helps the flow off the rear of the car to remain laminar. A second outside source that proved helpful was AERO Environment. They suggested keeping the angle from the horizontal down to the slope off the rear of the car at 15 degrees or less. All of the above information as well as a little artistic styling was then used to create several different clay models. These models were then tested in a wind tunnel using both flow visualization and force balance testing. From this, the final design was determined. Some decisions that were determined from the wind tunnel testing were: 1) A front air dam made little difference so it will not be used. 2) A flat rear deck helped maintain laminar flow across the rear of the car. 3) Enclosed rear wheels greatly improve laminar flow.

Ergonomics

Where possible, the interior of the vehicle was designed to fit the fifth percentile female to ninety-fifth percentile male.

Seating/Vision
The seats were custom build by T.E.A.'s Design. These seats accept a racing harness that attaches approximately 10 cm below the top of the shoulders. The latching mechanism for the harness is a metal, quick release latch.

The seats are positioned at a height and angle where the helmet of the tallest occupant is at least 5 cm below the surface defined by the roll bar and the front roll hoop. A driver can see the ground at least 9.2 meters ahead of the front bumper and can see the top of a target that is 7.3 meters high and 27.5 meters ahead of the front bumper.

The vehicle is equipped

with adjustable rear-view, right, and left side view mirrors. The driver can see head lamps that are 2 feet above and 50 feet behind the rear bumper. There are no blind spots and the driver is not required to turn his or her head.

Pedals

Our accelerator and brake pedals are from an '89 Mercury Cougar. These were chosen mainly because they were readily available and simple to modify for our needs as opposed to constructing pedals from our own design.

The accelerator pedal measures at least 2" X 9" and requires a force of 10 to 20 lbs to depress. The center line of the driver to the center line of the pedal is between 5 and 7 inches and the resting angle is 28 degrees with a 15 degree travel.

The foot brake is at least 4 inches wide and 3 inches high. It is 8 inches off the horizontal and has a resting angle of 39 degrees. The brake pedal has a maximum travel of 4 inches.

Dashboard

The dashboard is from a 1991 Ford Taurus. We decided not to build our own dashboard due to lack of funds and time. The Taurus dashboard fits our frame well and holds most of our instrumentation and controls.

Steering Wheel/Column

The steering column is

taken from a 1989 Mercury Cougar because it matched up with our front suspension. The Cougar steering column includes many controls which are utilized in the HEV. These controls include turn signals, hazard lights, high beam control, windshield wiper control, tilt steering, ignition switch, and horn.

The steering wheel is self centering and has positive stops at the end of travel so that the wheels responsible for steering do not contact the vehicle body. The displacement of the wheel is limited to 120 degrees of primary turning range. A maximum force of 20 lbs is required to turn the wheel.

Headlights

The headlight/parking light control will be the same control used on the Taurus dashboard which is an illuminated 3 position rotary switch.

Gear Selection

Gear selection will be made with three push buttons: forward, reverse, and neutral. These were supplied with the AC drive.

CONCLUSION

The design presented by the University of Idaho/Washington State University team is a series hybrid vehicle. The powertrain begins with a 20 hp Kohler DC Engine that runs on unleaded gasoline. A 400 volt Fisher alternator powered by the engine charges a lead-acid

battery pack that consists of
28 GNB UPSolyte batteries.
This battery pack produces a
336 volt DC current that is
sent through a frequency
controlled invertor. The
invertor powers a 100 kW AC
motor, which was designed and
built by AC Propulsion Inc. A
first gear transaxle, taken
from a Chevrolet Citation,
provides gear reduction of the
AC motor output. A rear sub
assembly from a Cougar XR7
transmits power to the wheels,
completing the powertrain.
The vehicle consists of a 5086
Aluminum space frame, shelled
in a foam-core, fiberglass
body.

University of Illinois Hybrid Electric Vehicle Philosophy and Architecture

David J. Andres, Philip R. Guziec, Robert A. Weinstock
University of Illinois at Urbana-Champaign

ABSTRACT

The University of Illinois at Urbana-Champaign is participating in the Hybrid Electric Vehicle Challenge sponsored by Ford Motor Company, the Society of Automotive Engineers, and the United States Department of Energy. General philosophy and design considerations for the University of Illinois Hybrid Electric Vehicle Team are discussed, including power requirements, battery packaging, control, emissions, regeneration braking, safety, and ergonomics. The series configuration hybrid electric vehicle designed by the team integrates state-of-the-art, off-the-shelf technology and meets or exceeds the performance characteristics of a 1992 Ford Escort Wagon on which the conversion is based.

INTRODUCTION

With legislation in California and other states requiring two percent of automobile sales to be zero-emissions vehicles by 1998, a vehicle design is needed today in order to realize production by 1998. The University of Illinois at Urbana-Champaign (UIUC) Hybrid Electric Vehicle (HEV) Team holds the philosophy that an economically viable vehicle that meets or exceeds the performance characteristics of an original 1992 Ford Escort Wagon is attainable. Using off-the-shelf, state-of-the-art technology coupled with thorough engineering and innovative solutions for design optimization, the UIUC team goal is to produce a commercially viable hybrid electric vehicle.

These philosophies guided the team through the design of the vehicle, influencing the following design categories: power requirements, battery selection and packaging, control strategy, auxiliary power unit scheme and emissions, regeneration and braking strategy, structural and suspension modifications, driver interface, and climate control. Of course, safety, manufacturability, reliability, and serviceability are considered in all of these categories.

DESIGN CONSIDERATIONS

The UIUC HEV utilizes a series design HEV architecture which combines an electric drive with a small engine-generator set (APU). The electric drive permits 100 percent mobile emissions reductions while in electric mode, and the APU extends the vehicle range. The heat engine has no mechanical connection to the vehicle drive axles, permitting the engine to be operated under optimal conditions independent of the vehicle operating state for an additional improvement in emissions reductions. To minimize emissions, the vehicle is operated in zero emissions mode (electric only) for daily commuting in an urban setting and automatically switches to hybrid mode when battery charge is low for extended traveling.

Power Requirements

For a marketable vehicle, the original performance characteristics of a 1992 Ford Escort Wagon must be matched by the conversion, and knowledge of vehicle power requirements is the primary determinant of component selection. The UIUC Team believes that the APU should provide adequate power for steady-state cruising where transient loads are handled by the battery pack. In order to satisfy highway consumer demands, a highway cruise speed in excess of 100 kilometers per hour and a range limited only by liquid fuel capacity were chosen as design goals. The average power requirement of the vehicle on Environmental Protection Agency (EPA) city cycle is used for city range calculations. The power required for the most demanding of the city and highway cases defines the minimum power output of the APU. Steady state cruising is more demanding, requiring 17 kilowatts at 100 kilometers per hour, as shown in

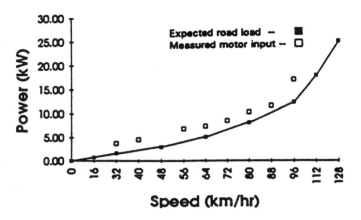

Figure 1 Road power vs. speed

Figure 1. The APU size selected permits a calculated 100 kilometer-per-hour cruising speed and a vehicle range while in hybrid mode limited only by fuel tank volume.

Battery Selection and Packaging

As shown in Table I [1], lead-acid batteries were selected as the best compromise between availability, low cost and maintenance, specific energy, specific power, cycle life, recyclability, and other environmental considerations. Although alternative battery architectures with better theoretical performance were evaluated, cost and availability considerations generally precluded their use. Nickel-Cadmium batteries were also considered, but the voltage levels required for the AC motor result in an unacceptable overall mass. However, characteristics favoring lead-acid batteries are excellent power density which affects vehicle performance, and superior recharging efficiency, which is critical for the charging input power requirements stipulated by the HEV

TABLE I

COMPARISON OF EV BATTERY TYPES

	Lead-Acid	NiCd	NiMH	NiFe	NaS	Li-Polymer
Cost ($/kW·hr)	70	600	600	200	600	200
Energy Density (W·hr/kg)	34	55	55	50	100	85
Power Density (W/kg)	280	180	180	100	140	90
Cycle Life (80% DOD)	300	800	500	900	800	800
Charging h	80%	65%	65%	60%	88%	??
Availability	Excellent	Good	None	Poor	Fair	None
Safety	Excellent	Excellent	Excellent	??	Fair	??
Environment	Fair	Poor	Good	Good	Excellent	Good
Recycle	Excellent	Poor	Fair	Good	??	Fair
Durability	Good	Excellent	Excellent	Good	Good	Excellent
Maintenance	Excellent	Good	Excellent	Poor	Good	Excellent

Challenge [2]. The batteries selected were Johnson Controls UPS 12-95 lead-acid batteries. A number of competing lead-acid batteries were evaluated, but none could match the UPS 12-95 for energy density.

The battery pack was sized so that the points at which the pack failed to provide sufficient power due to voltage sag and due to capacity limits would be coincident. Thus, 26 sealed lead-acid batteries weighing 11.8 kg each (totaling about 307 kg) provide a total of 8.58 kW·hr of energy at a three hour discharge rate.

The 26 batteries are connected in series with a split ground. This yields equal positive and negative DC busses with a nominal voltage of 156 V_{DC} per rail for a total battery nominal voltage rating of 312 V_{DC}.

All 26 batteries are contained in an aluminum enclosure which is mounted between the rear floorpan and the rear suspension crossmember. This packaging geometry was significantly influenced by safety, serviceability, and space efficiency. From a safety standpoint, the box is completely isolated from the passenger compartment, separated by floorboard. In the most severe accident situations, the box would separate from the vehicle and travel underneath the vehicle. From the rear, the box is protected by the bumper and rear chassis structure.

In any event, battery intrusion into the passenger compartment is extremely unlikely. Even with all of its structural protection, the entire battery box is easily and completely removed by a mechanic with proper equipment, enhancing serviceability. The box is not intended for removal by the owner, and the design, requiring removal equipment, inherently insures that the owner cannot remove the box. Finally, the box is space-efficient, because it is placed in a volume only partially used by the spare tire mounting in the original vehicle. The spare tire is relocated behind the rear wheel well in the traditional station wagon location. The placement of the battery box also provides visual concealment. Additionally, spacers are placed between individual batteries to distribute pressure on the center of the battery walls and a foam spring maintains this pressure. This pressure prevents the separation of the electrolyte matting from the plate structure due to

case distortion from internal pressure, increasing battery capacity by approximately ten percent [3]. A floor panel removal tool with a large suction cup was also found to be a convenient battery handling device, greatly facilitating serviceability.

Power System Design

Overall electrical system architecture is illustrated in Figure 2. Overcurrent protection is provided by two (2) 250 V_{DC} rated fuses sized at 250 amps. One fuse is installed in each bus for total overcurrent protection. A maintenance disconnect switch function is provided by a 250 amp, 250 V_{DC} Class, 2-pole molded case circuit breaker and is wired to the output of the battery pack immediately before the fuses. The circuit breaker provides remote operation via the shunt trip mechanism. The shunt trip is powered indirectly

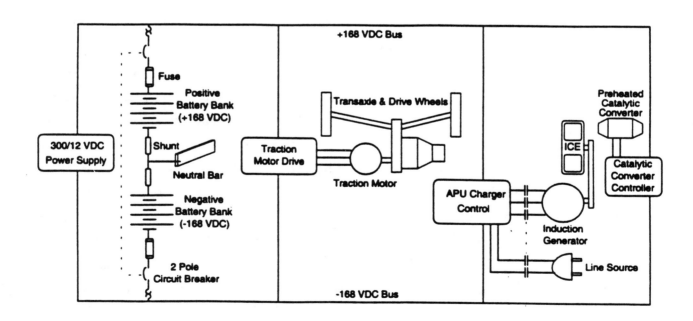

Figure 2 General HEV System Schematic

from the main battery pack via an onboard 312/12 V_{DC} switchmode power supply. To assure shunt trip operation in the event of 12 V_{DC} supply failure, a capacitive energy storage circuit has been implemented. Shunt trip operating push-buttons are located in the vehicle dashboard and underhood, with the underhood push-button operable from outside the vehicle in compliance with the rules of the Challenge [4]. Both the circuit breaker and the fuses are mounted within the main traction drive inverter enclosure for improved volumetric efficiency.

The vehicle high voltage power system is grounded to the chassis at a single point through a silver plated copper bar. All electrical items added by the UIUC Team are connected to this ground bar, which is in turn connected to the vehicle chassis through a single #8 AWG conductor. This configuration prevents any chassis conducted currents from occurring under normal operating conditions other than those designed into the stock Ford Escort 12 V_{DC} electrical system. It should also be noted that all loads connected to the high voltage DC system are operated between the positive and negative supply busses; there are no loads connected between bus and ground. Thus, only during a bus to ground fault will current flow through the high- voltage power system ground. This arrangement permits the use of Hall effect based current sensing with milli-ampere sensitivity for detecting ground faults.

Control Strategy

In order to emulate the look and feel of the original car, a number of functions must be controlled automatically. For this purpose the vehicle features a distributed microcontroller system consisting of four Motorola 68HC11 microprocessors arranged as three control units and one supervisory controller. These microcontrollers are configured to monitor battery state of charge, control APU operation, control commanded motor torque, and control the on-board LCD and supervisory controller. Information is shared between the microcontrollers via an RS-485 network. Control reliability is ensured with the distributed control architecture by minimizing the effects of controller failures.

An on-board LCD is located in the dashboard and serves to monitor vehicle parameters that were deemed inappropriate for the instrument cluster, such as motor winding temperature, battery current, and battery voltage. The LCD display obtains this information by interrogating the RS-485 network for periodic updates. In addition, the LCD display is used to provide complete alarm annunciation and system self-diagnosis for a large variety of foreseen vehicle failures. A keypad is provided to allow the motorist to change displayed parameters.

After evaluating commercially available battery amp-hour meters, a decision was made to develop a suitable meter independently. The algorithm utilized for the UIUC HEV, as shown in Figure 3, is a modification of the TVA method [5] which is based on averaged discharge currents to compensate for the rated amp-hour capacity of the battery pack. As can be seen in Figure 4, lead-acid battery capacity is a strong function of temperature. Consequently, the TVA algorithm used to calculate battery capacity has been modified to compensate for temperature derating. The primary advantage

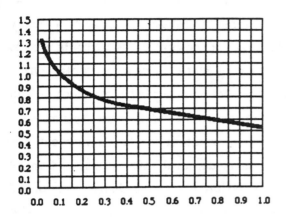

Figure 3 Battery Capacity versus Discharge Current

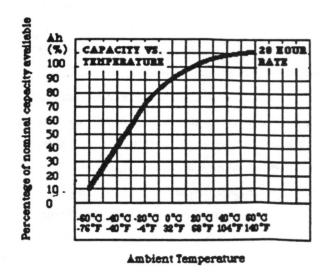

Figure 4 Battery Capacity versus Temperature

of the modified TVA method is high accuracy (median accuracy is approximately 5%) with a relatively simplistic processing algorithm.

In addition to exporting the battery state of charge data to the network for transmission and display in the instrument cluster, the state of charge calculator will also send messages to the APU controller to turn on and turn off the APU. Initial turn on and turn off thresholds were set at 20% and 80%, respectively; but there is some evidence which indicates that battery performance and cycle life can be improved by narrowing the two threshold values. The algorithm allows for easy introduction of battery aging effects as well.

Auxiliary Power Unit -- Engine

An exhaustive search was conducted of small internal combustion engine manufacturers for an engine which would meet the vehicle power requirements as well as maximize specific power and minimize volume, brake specific fuel consumption, emissions, and noise. The APU internal combustion engine chosen is a Kawasaki FD620D which is water-cooled for packaging ease and noise and emissions reduction. This engine has a displacement of 620 cc with a maximum rated power of 17 kW at 3300 rpm. The mass was 37 kg before modification, and the flywheel was replaced by the inertia of a belt-drive pulley. Brake specific fuel consumption values are excellent at a nominal 280 g/kW·hr on gasoline. Testing shows that this rated value is at a rich condition and stoichiometric running on ethanol results in values as low as 370 g/kW·hr, equivalent to 265 g/kW·hr on gasoline. The engine already meets California's 1995 emissions standards for off-road vehicles, and initial testing shows that emissions at stoichiometric air fuel ratio are excellent.

146

Emissions

Ethanol was chosen as the APU fuel for a combination of emissions and environmental considerations. Higher heat of vaporization implies lower evaporative emissions and a lower peak flame temperature, reducing oxides of nitrogen. Additionally, recent advances in membrane separation and distillation techniques may allow more efficient production of ethanol. This could result in an effectively closed carbon cycle with CO_2 produced during combustion and recovered during plant photosynthesis. Also, ethanol is typically non-corrosive, indicating relatively simple conversion from gasoline operation to ethanol operation.

Dynamometer testing of rpm, manifold pressure, load, emissions, air to fuel ratio, and fuel consumption have been performed in an effort to determine an optimization between low emissions and high power output of the APU. The tests with ethanol have shown reduced NO_x emissions by virtue of reduced peak flame temperature. This allows slightly leaner running, reducing CO emissions and brake specific fuel consumption values.

The exhaust system for the APU includes a catalytic converter, a catalyst preheater to reduce cold-start emissions, and a muffler. The catalytic converter is a standard catalyst replacement kit for a small engine and consists of a platinum/palladium catalyst material on a ceramic matrix. A catalyst preheater is incorporated to preheat the initial air charge passed through the catalyst, reducing catalyst light off time and cold start emissions. This is incorporated into the control strategy to allow for a 10 second preheat. The exhaust system upstream of the catalyst is wrapped with fiberglass thermal insulating tape to further reduce warm-up time. Evaporative emissions are addressed using the original vapor recovery system of the 1992 Escort.

Auxiliary Power Unit -- Generator

One of the basic premises for the APU sizing and selection was that the system, when activated, would operate at 100% of rated output. A squirrel cage induction machine was selected for the engine-generator set. As shown in Table II [6], the induction machine is not necessarily the best selection when considering peak torque efficiency only. If peak torque efficiency is the only consideration, then the PM- synchronous machine would be more suitable.

However, the induction machine offers several other advantages that tend to offset efficiency. For example, the induction machine is far less expensive than equivalent rated PM synchronous machines and generally more robust.

To further take advantage of the induction machine, the generator is also used as the engine starting motor. This novel innovation allows the DC starter motor, which is normally used for this application, to be eliminated from the system altogether. In addition to providing a weight savings, eliminating the DC starter motor greatly relaxes the output surge current requirements of the on-board 312/12 V_{DC} switchmode power supply, further reducing weight and cost. The microprocessor-based system controller for the APU incorporates a cycle cranking feature to ensure that the motor will attempt to restart if the engine fails to crank.

TABLE II

COMPARISON OF ELECTRIC VEHICLE DRIVE TYPES

	DC	PM Synchronous	Reluctance	Induction
η at Peak Torque	85 - 89	95 - 97	< 90	94 - 95
η at 10% Torque	80 - 87	73 - 82	??	93 - 94
Relative $/kW	20 - 30	5 - 20	Potentially Low	2.75 - 5.00
Relative Drive $	1.00	3.7 - 6.0	4.0 - 10.0	2.5 - 3.0
Robustness	Good	Fair	Excellent	Excellent
Max RPM	4,000 - 6,000	4,000 - 10,000	> 15,000	9,000 - 15,000

Since an industry standard 254 frame squirrel cage induction motor rated at 15 kW at 60 Hz weighs approximately 110 kg (unacceptable), a standard 56-frame induction machine was rewound and overdriven by a 3:1 ratio Gilmer belt drive system. This drives the generator at 9900 rpm, achieving the performance specifications listed in Table III. The generator has a standard rating of 2.2 kW, and has been rewound for 77 VAC at 60 Hz. By connecting the windings in delta and overdriving the machine 300%, an output of 17.6 kW is achievable with some sacrifice in efficiency.

TABLE III

INDUCTION GENERATOR PERFORMANCE SPECIFICATIONS

	60 Hz Base Ratings	330 Hz Ratings
Voltage	77 VAC L-L	230 VAC L-L
Current	20 A	35 A
Breakdown Torque	32.5 N·m	32.5 N·m
Power Factor	0.90	0.90
Power	3.2 kW	17.6 kW
Slip	9%	8%
η at Peak Torque	75%	77%
η at 10% Torque	60%	62%
Rated RPM	1800	9900
Cost	$ 600	
Mass	20 kg	

The controller used is based on a commercially available sine coded PWM variable frequency inverter, which is used as an induction generator voltage regulator in this application. The drive uses state of the art IGBT switching devices and is 98% efficient. Since the machine is operated at 100% rated conditions, over-torque requirements are not demanding, so a 100% rated inverter drive was selected. The drive itself has been extensively repackaged and is mounted in the same enclosure as the traction motor drive.

The control algorithm for the generator drive is based on a standard scalar V/f control algorithm, and is used to maintain the engine at constant power by adjusting commanded speed and, therefore, motor slip. A block diagram is shown in Figure 5.

Traction Motor Selection

Desirable characteristics for traction motors in passenger vehicles are high torque, low mass, and high efficiency for improved range. In a series HEV, traction motor efficiency is more critical than in other configurations since all the vehicle's energy is transferred through the motor to the wheels. Referring to Table II, an induction motor traction system yields the best balance between efficiency, robustness, and cost. Available PM-synchronous machines suffer from very high cost and questionable reliability. Standard DC machines suffer from high cost, mass, and maintenance when compared to a squirrel cage AC induction motor. Switched reluctance machines offer substantial gains in efficiency and cost, but torque characteristics from currently available models are inadequate for the HEV application.

Two constraints influence the size and rating of the motor. For extended traveling at the maximum continuous cruising speed, the motor should be able to accommodate the corresponding level of power continuously. In general, this constraint is not demanding, considering that the 1992 Escort station wagon typically uses about 17 kW at highway speeds. However, traction applications for passenger vehicles may require 400% or greater over torque capability in order to satisfy consumer transient driving demands. This constraint is more binding since typical over torque capability for a standard NEMA Design B motor is only 250%. The implication is that the motor rating should be selected primarily by peak requirements, which closely parallels how automotive gasoline engines are currently rated.

Performance ratings for the UIUC- HEV traction motor are given in Table IV.

The traction motor is mated to the stock Ford Escort transaxle via a flexible coupling. When driven at maximum torque through the standard

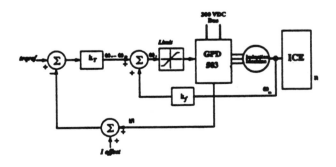

Figure 5 APU Control Block Diagram

149

TABLE IV

TRACTION MOTOR PERFORMANCE SPECIFICATIONS

	60 Hz Base Ratings	180 Hz Ratings
Voltage	67 VAC L-L	200 VAC L-L
Current	88 A	264 A
Breakdown Torque	103 N·m	103 N·m
Power Factor	0.83	0.83
Power	7.5 kW	22.4 kW
Slip	3%	2%
η at Peak Torque	89%	90%
η at 10% Torque	74%	76%
Rated RPM	1800	5400
Cost	$ 600	
Mass	55 kg	

transmission, the UIUC HEV has a 0-100 km/hr acceleration time that is 5% better than the stock Ford Escort Wagon, demonstrating that the original acceleration characteristics can at least be matched.

Variable Frequency Traction Motor Drive

The traction motor drive is based on a 98% efficient, commercially available PWM variable frequency inverter which has been extensively repackaged for this application. The drive is a state of the art component featuring 400 amp IGBT switching devices which are controlled by a 32-bit microprocessor. Judicious repackaging has reduced the mass by approximately 41 kg while providing an enclosure satisfying IP42 specifications for environmental protection and improved reliability. The entire enclosure is shock-mounted to the vehicle firewall for vibration isolation. The rating of the traction drive was selected to permit the motor to develop its maximum over-torque capability. Since power electronic devices are sized based on current ratings, the drive was selected with a 200% overcurrent capability, matching over-torque capacity of the traction motor.

Induction Motor Torque Control & Clutchless Shifting

The traction motor drive was originally designed for industrial applications requiring speed control, but has been modified to operate as an induction motor with torque control. Extensive testing of a prototype HEV with similar design architecture determined that the motor speed control alone will not yield a satisfactory driver interface. Thus, motor torque control has been implemented by developing an interfacing controller which accepts driver inputs corresponding to accelerator and brake pedal positions and generates motor slip commands to the traction drive. Pedal signals are conditioned through a buffer circuit which also provides safe failure modes. The control algorithm uses both machine rotor speed feedback from a variable reluctance magnetic pickup and current feedback from a Hall effect sensor implemented around a standard scalar V/f control algorithm. The method is similar to conventional techniques [7], and a block diagram is shown in Figure 6. This control strategy contrasts to more sophisticated indirect flux vector sensing torque control techniques that are typically utilized for induction motor control.

For high performance applications such as induction servo motors, flux vector control is necessary. However, for a traction application such as the HEV, very high performance flux vector control is excessive, particularly when vehicle reaction time constants are considered. In addition, for direct or indirect flux vector control to operate reliably, extensive knowledge of the induction machine parameters is required to ensure error term cancellation for stable motor operation. Since these parameters often vary with time, there is some

evidence to suggest that flux vector control may not be robust enough to ensure satisfactory motor control over the projected life of the vehicle without adaptive control techniques. On the other hand, scalar V/f control will provide sufficient performance with the additional benefit of providing a more robust control due to its insensitivity to changes in machine parameters.

The clutchless shifting involves a unique procedure made possible by the rapid response of the electric motor. A microswitch from a Porsche auto-stick clutchless shifting mechanism is incorporated into the shifter and determines when a shift is being initiated by registering force applied to the shifter. Applied force to the shifter instantaneously drops the motor torque to zero, allowing movement into neutral. The intended gear is predicted from throttle position and previous shift history and this is used in combination with road speed to determine proper motor rpm for the next gear. While the transmission is disengaged, the motor speed is brought to the calculated speed of the new gear within 0.1 seconds. The torque is then returned to zero and the transmission is manually engaged into the intended gear. Torque is reapplied in a ramping fashion when the hand is removed from the shifter, resulting in smooth, clutchless shifting.

Regeneration and Braking Strategy

To increase vehicle efficiency and electric range, recovering energy that would otherwise be dissipated as heat in the brakes is desirable. This energy can be recovered using a regeneration braking strategy which can significantly increase overall vehicle efficiency.

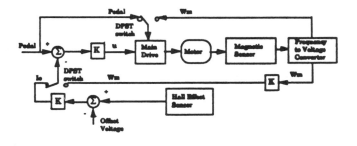

Figure 6 Traction Motor Control Block Diagram

The UIUC team has developed a safe regeneration strategy that involves adding free-play to the brake linkage. For the first portion of brake pedal movement, the spring-loaded pedal arm activates a potentiometer, and braking is accomplished entirely through reverse torque on the motor, resulting in regeneration. The controller determines the torque to be applied by the motor based on pedal position and the current state of the transmission. The reverse torque applied is proportional to pedal position and inversely proportional to transmission gear ratio in order to achieve a constant ratio between wheel braking torque and pedal position. When the brake pedal is further depressed, mechanical braking is introduced at a deceleration rate greater than 0.3g and will operate even in the case of total regeneration system failure. Additionally, this design lends itself to front wheel lockup before rear wheel lockup. Although this implies underutilization of the rear brakes, the vehicle remains stable upon wheel lockup. However, in production, a different proportion should be used to more closely match the lockup points of the front and rear brakes. Simulations of the EPA city cycle show that a 24-percent range increase can be realized using this regeneration strategy.

Structural Modifications

The rear structure of the vehicle requires modification to accommodate the battery pack. This involves modification of the bottom section of the tailgate, removal of the spare tire well, modification of the rear seat mounts, and modification to the crossmember to which the rear suspension attaches. Both the original and modified rear crossmember were tested for structural integrity, and the results are shown in Figure 7.

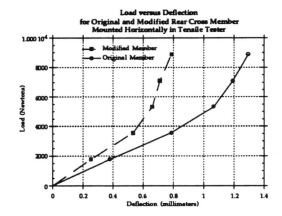

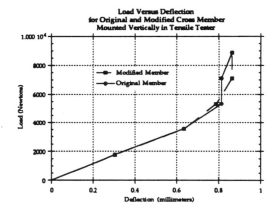

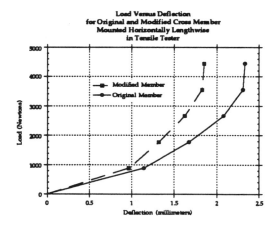

Figure 7 Results of Structural Testing

152

From the graphs, one can see that the modified crossmember is stiffer than the original in the loading configurations tested. This is assumed to imply greater strength although yield testing was not performed due to the high cost of prototype fabrication. This is the most significant structural change.

Suspension Modifications

In order to match original ride characteristics, the natural frequencies of the front and rear of the vehicle were used as design parameters to be matched. With the changes to the mass of the front and rear of the vehicle, one can alter the respective spring rate to keep the natural frequency constant. Thus, with knowledge of both the original and modified vehicle mass distributions, one can calculate the new spring rates and make the necessary changes. Constant natural frequency implies that the ride height remains constant with no changes to spring free length.

However, with modified mass distributions, the front/rear cornering bias of the vehicle is altered as well. Specifically, the weight added to the rear of the vehicle increases the weight transfer at the rear end, resulting in a tendency toward an oversteering vehicle. To compensate for this, the diameter of the front anti-roll bar is increased until neutral to understeering characteristics are achieved. Moreover, tire pressures on the low rolling loss Goodyear Invicta GLR tires are biased higher to the rear to increase the rear coefficient of friction and, thus, stability.

Driver Interface

A goal of the UIUC team is to simulate a driver's experience in a standard vehicle with the HEV. However, new information must be displayed to the driver as a result of vehicle differences. The team made two significant alterations to the vehicle-operator interface by modifying the dashboard and the shifting algorithm. The original instrument cluster has been replaced with a Mazda Protegé dashboard which has been modified to display the new information. Figure 8 depicts the final instrument panel. As illustrated in the figure, the bar graph on the driver's left displays the battery state of charge and battery symbol for low-charge warning. Due to the use of the original 5-speed transmission, underneath the square box indicating power to the high beam headlights is the "upshift" indicator. In a traditional automobile, there is significant audio feedback to indicate to the driver that shifting is necessary even if the driver is not watching the tachometer. However, with a nearly silent electric motor, this feedback may not be audible, and the upshift indicator is provided to emphasize shift points. In addition, a gear position indicator is located on the tachometer

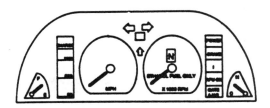

Figure 8 Mazda Protegé dashboard

face. The bar graph on the driver's right displays messages including POWER, BRAKE, !, APU ENABLE, and GATE AJAR. The POWER light indicates to the driver that the vehicle is operational. Unlike conventional combustion vehicles, the HEV does not idle, and an indicator is necessary (for both safety and convenience) to communicate to the driver that the vehicle is ready to drive. Finally, the "!" is used to refer the driver to the LCD display which also provides fault warning and diagnostic information.

Climate Control

Approximately 80 percent of vehicles sold in the U.S. today have air conditioning, indicating that climate control is necessary for a marketable vehicle. Climate control system efficiency is crucial, because the power requirements for operation are significant (around 4.5 horsepower for the original refrigeration system), and energy storage is a fundamental limitation to electric mode operation. This problem is exacerbated by the inability of the drive motor to produce sufficient heat to warm the passenger compartment. Climate control in the UIUC HEV is achieved through a vapor compression cycle which utilizes a reversing valve to toggle between refrigeration and heat pump operation modes as illustrated in Figure 9. This implies that only one system is needed for both refrigeration and heating.

Refrigerant 12 is used due to incompatibility of the high efficiency General Motors V-5 variable displacement compressor with Refrigerant 134a at the time of prototype

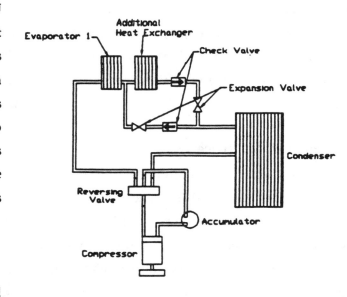

Figure 9 Climate Control System Schematic

construction. Extra evaporator volume is needed to accommodate the heat pump function, slightly increasing total system volume. The compressor is powered from the drive motor, drawing a continuous 2.5 kilowatts.

Manufacturability

Manufacturability has been addressed throughout the component selection process by choosing slightly modified off-the-shelf technology. Structural modifications have been accomplished with the use of materials which match the original structure, allowing volume manufacture with a simple change in die geometry at low cost. In production, all aluminum fabrications could easily be replaced by die castings resulting in a low marginal component cost. The battery box could also be converted to a stamped and spot-welded assembly.

CONCLUSIONS

The manufacturability of the UIUC HEV is achieved, in part, using off-the-shelf technology. With this state-of-the-art, readily available technology, the University of Illinois Hybrid Electric Vehicle Team has demonstrated that a marketable vehicle can be produced by 1998.

The final operational vehicle is the result of 16 months of design, analysis, iteration, and fabrication involving over 200 people at the University of Illinois. One objective of the design is to produce a vehicle capable of winning the Hybrid Electric Vehicle Challenge. However, the team also has an earnest desire to produce a safe, environmentally friendly, marketable vehicle.

REFERENCES

[1]   A.F. Burke, "Battery System Technologies - Overview", presentation at SAE TOPTEC, Dearborn, MI, 14 September 1992.

[2]   "Ford HEV Challenge Rules and Regulations", Edition dated 15 December 1992.

[3]   M.G. Andrew, "Applying UPS 12-95 Batteries", presentation at Johnson Controls, Milwaukee, WI, February 1993.

[4]   "Ford HEV Challenge Rules and Regulations", Section 11, Edition dated 15 December 1992.

[5]   A.F. Burke, "Evaluation of State of Charge Indicator Approaches for EV's", SAE Technical Paper Series, 890816 (1989).

[6]   R. Martin and K. Rajashekara, "Present and Future Trends for Electric Vehicles", pp. 7-12, *Proc. 1992 IEEE Workshop on Power Electronics in Transportation*, October 1992, IEEE Cat. No. 92TH041-5.

[7]   W. Leonhard, *Control of Electrical Drives*. New York, NY: Springer-Verlag, 1985, pp.204-214.

Jordan College Energy Institute

Daniel Cuoghi and Jim Giefer
Jordan College Energy Institute

ABSTRACT

Students at Jordan College Energy Institute are participating in the 1993 Ford Hybrid Electric Vehicle Challenge in which a 1992 Ford Escort Station wagon was converted to run on both electric and a small internal combustion engine. This report describes the modifications that were performed to the vehicle in preparation for the HEV Challenge.

The intent of the design by the students at Jordan College Energy Institute (JEI) has been to keep the concept as simple as possible, and to use current, well proven technology that is already in place. In this way we felt we would be able to avoid technical difficulties that might prove insurmountable in the short time of this project.

SYSTEM CONFIGURATION — We decided to use a parallel rather than a series drive configuration because we did not wish to change the rotational energy of the gasoline engine into electrical energy (See figure 1). Since this additional step would compound the inefficiency of the system. We also decided to leave the standard transmission in the vehicle. This made it possible for us to combine both drive systems, since removing the standard transmission would have necessitated either using multiple electric motors to compensate for the lack of a transmission, or having an increased power output to give us the needed power. Our Alternative Power Unit (APU) was still going to require some sort of transmission because we wanted a reduced size to increase the efficiency of our vehicle. The APU we selected was from a 1988 Kawasaki Ex 500 motorcycle. Modifications to the APU included removal of the transmission, which was not going to be used and which would only add extra weight. Our electric motor has been coupled directly to the standard transmission by the use of an adaptor plate. We also retained the Escort transaxle and clutch assembly, so that we could maintain shifting, while also allowing for disengagement of the driving units from the drivetrain. The Advanced DC electric motor chosen by the JEI team has a double-ended shaft; this enabled us to use the end opposite from the transmission to connect power between the APU and the electric motor. These two units are connected by means of a Gates PowerGrip HTD belt and drive sprockets. Accompanying the driven sprocket on the electric motor is a one-way clutch that will freewheel when the electric motor is the driving unit, and that will lock (no longer freewheel) when the APU is the driving unit. This unit will be in the lock position anytime the APU's speed is greater than the electric motor's speed. Preventing our vehicle from having engine braking during deceleration or over-speeding on down hill slopes. This can be an asset by not pulling extra fuel into the intake during high vacuum situations caused by engine braking.

ELECTRIC MOTOR — Our selection for an electric motor is an Advanced DC series wound 8-inch motor, its advantages being that it is readily available, inexpensive and specifically designed for electric vehicle use. Although this model is not inherently efficient, its cost was the deciding factor in its selection. It also has certain other drawbacks: its weight, the fact that it is not brushless, and the fact that it is not a permanent magnet motor. Because of its inefficiency, it was modified to make it more efficient by installing Magnaquench Type 1B magnets. This increased its overall efficiency and allowed us to perform regenerative braking. It is quite expensive to make these modifications on this motor, but still not as expensive as an off-the-shelf brushless DC permanent magnet motor with regenerative braking capabilities. We are receiving a newly designed controller which should allow us to use our regenerative braking capabilities.

BATTERIES — Our battery selection was partly decided by the structure of the competition. We chose conventional lead acid technology. This had to do mostly with cost, and the infrastructure that is already in place in the United States. Although these batteries need to be replaced every five years, it makes the initial cost of the vehicle much less. Lead acid batteries use a well established technology. When batteries with a higher energy density come down in price, they will become a better choice for this vehicle. Because one of the main things we are being judged on by Ford is cost effectiveness, we wanted to keep our costs down as much as possible. Another factor in the selection of our batteries was that, by our calculations, it would take only one-half horsepower extra on a level road to carry the extra

157

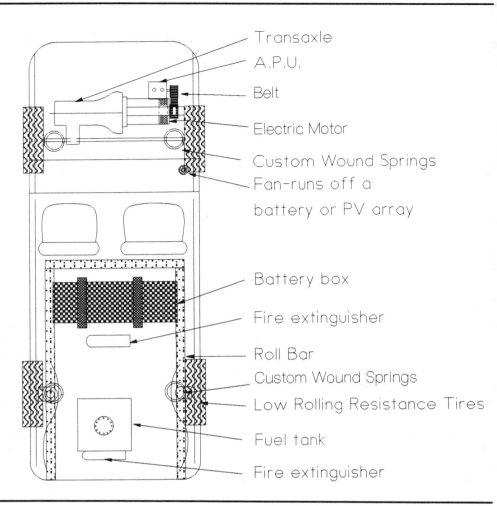

FORD ECOSCORT 1992

Labels (top to bottom, right side):
Transaxle
A.P.U.
Belt
Electric Motor
Custom Wound Springs
Fan-runs off a battery or PV array
Battery box
Fire extinguisher
Roll Bar
Custom Wound Springs
Low Rolling Resistance Tires
Fuel tank
Fire extinguisher

Figure 1: System configuration

weight of the batteries, as opposed to lessening our weight with a smaller battery pack. Recharging of the batteries during the hybrid portion of the competition would have been necessary using an equivalent of 4.8 horsepower. This reasoning led to our choice of Trojan 5SHP batteries. At 86 pounds each they are extremely heavy, but we felt we needed the energy density of these batteries to complete the required 40 miles at 40 to 55 mph. These batteries are rated at 78 min at 75 amp draw, or 97 amphours. Our vehicle is configured at 96 volts for a total of 9300 watthours of energy. This is being calculated at a C/1.25 or 75 amp draw, which is a typical draw for this size and weight of vehicle. The only drawback to lead acid batteries is their energy density, which at this discharge rate is 13.5wh/lb. An advantage over other types of batteries is that there are many recycling facilities in the United States already in place.

ALTERNATIVE POWER UNIT — For the selection of an Alternative Power Unit (APU) we selected an engine from a Kawasaki Ex500 motorcycle. This engine is rated at 57 horsepower (hp) at 9,800rpm, and 34 footpounds (ft-lbs) of torque. We feel that, with the hp requirement of the vehicle at 50 miles per hour (mph) being 12 hp, this engine will have sufficient power to propel the vehicle down the road as well as to accelerate it from a dead stop. An advantage of this engine over industrial engines is that it has

four valves per cylinder; this helps in scavenging the engine, thereby increasing the overall efficiency. A second advantage is that motorcycles have to meet emission requirements in some states. Another major advantage is the power-to-weight ratio of the engine, which went up dramatically with the removal of the transmission, as stated earlier. This brought the engine weight to approximately 120 lbs. The alternator was removed from the engine and a power takeoff shaft was added so that we could mount the pulley for the power transmission belt. Further modifications to the APU included shaving of the head so that we could increase the compression ratio from 10.5:1 to 12.5:1. This was done to allow us to take advantage of the octane in M-85 fuel, which is much cooler burning. An increase in compression ratio increases the amount of work done by the engine per stroke, reducing consumption of fuel. Because the BTU content of M-85 is approximately half that of gasoline, we also re-jetted the carburetors with larger main and idle jets. M-85 should also afford us reduced emissions in hydrocarbons, carbon monoxides, and ground-level ozone. We do realize that our largest increase will be in formaldehydes, a by-product of incomplete combustion. Another modification we would have liked to have accomplished is changing the torque range to a lower RPM. This would have been accomplished by regrinding the camshaft; unfortunately, we ran short of time in engine development.

CONTROL STRATEGY — The control strategy selected by the students of JEI was to use a combination of both systems during The Hybrid Electric Vehicle mode. We combined them by allowing the electric motor to handle acceleration of the vehicle to a preset speed of approximately 35 mph. At this time a signal is sent to start the APU system. When the APU has started, the controller for the electric motor is disabled, and the vehicle runs only on APU power. The reason for this is that the electric motor is a high torque unit and accelerates the vehicle easily. This has allowed us to use a smaller APU unit. When the car is hovering around 35 mph, to prevent the APU from cycling on and off there is a hysteresis built into the controls, allowing the engine to stay on until 25 mph, which is the standard turnoff speed for the vehicle. When decelerating and the APU is still running, electric power will assist the APU until 35 mph is reached. With this scenario the engine is always off when the vehicle is stopped, reducing the running time of the engine and reducing the amount of pollutants the engine produces. With the transmission system discussed earlier, we will also be using the freewheeling clutch when the APU speed is less than the drivetrain speed. This will prevent extra fuel from being pulled into the combustion chamber during times of high vacuum conditions.

EMISSION CONTROLS — The emissions of our vehicle are being controlled in two ways. The evaporative emissions are being controlled by the charcoal canister that was already in place in the vehicle. The float bowls of the carburetors, and the fuel cell vent are both run to this system and should provide adequate protection for it. To control tailpipe emissions we are trying to take advantage of the inherent qualities of the M-85 fuel. This fuel and the modifications we made to the APU should help reduce our overall emissions. To accompany this we are going to place the catalytic convertor as close to the engine as possible. The purpose for this is twofold: one, to help decrease the time for light-off of the catalyst; and two, to help achieve light-off due to the cooler burning of the fuel itself.

FUEL AND ELECTRICAL CONSUMPTION — Data for fuel and electrical consumptions are not available at this time. This is due to the unfinished state of our vehicle at this writing. Preliminary calculations for electrical consumptions are:

MPH	HP	Watts	Amps	Usable Energy (hrs.)	Miles
40.	10.4	7,773.0	81.0	1.20	48.0
45.	13.13	9,795.0	102.0	0.94	42.3
50.	16.3	12,189.0	127.0	0.76	38.0

Based on these numbers and the calculated inefficiencies of our system, which were included in the calculations for horsepower requirements, we should be able to complete the required 40 miles.

Accurate data for fuel consumption is not available at this time, due to dynamometer testing of the engine has not been completed. Data from the manufacturers is not available on motorcycle engines for fuel consumptions,

torque and horsepower curves, it is considered proprietary information. We can only make an assumption that our fuel consumption will be around 15mpg using methanol. We are carrying an 8 gallon tank, this should give us an 120 mile range. This would be more than adequate for the competition.

STRUCTURAL MODIFICATIONS — Modifications to the inherent vehicle structure were kept to a minimum. Changes that were made included the addition of the battery box and the removal of the fuel tank. The battery box was designed to hold five batteries, and is located underneath the rear seat of the vehicle, which was the original location of the gas tank. The structure added to hold the battery pack is now part of the vehicle structure itself. The batteries are sealed in an airtight box (figure 2) made of one-half-inch-thick aluminum honeycomb material, coated on both sides with an epoxy resin coating with inlaid fiberglass cloth that is fire and corrosion resistant. The battery containment box itself is supported by a steel framework that suspends the center of mass of the batteries in line with the floor so that, in the event of a crash, the momentum of the batteries will be absorbed not only by the steel framework but also by the floor and main side rails of the vehicle. This alignment also reduces the chance of the batteries breaking free from the structure and possibly injuring vehicle occupants during a crash.

The battery support structure is a symmetrical framework of 2" x 2" x ¼" steel angle iron attached to the vehicles two longitudinal frame rails. If we assume a 20g deceleration for a head on collision, and treat the support members attached to the frame as a beam problem with a distributed

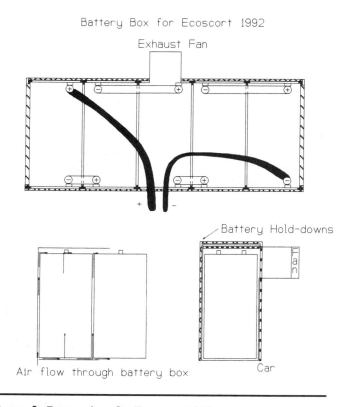

Figure 2: Battery box for Ecoscort 1992

load, the moment on such a beam is given by:

$M = WL^2 / 8 = 50,400$ in-lb,

where M = the maximum bending moment on the beam

W = the distributed load =

5 batteries x 96lb/battery x 20g / 42'' beam

L = 42'' beam.

The stress in the beam is given by:

$Sb = M / Z = 50,400$ in-lb / $.5$in^3 = 100,800psi,

where Z is the section of modulus of the beam:

2 beams (.25in^3) or .5in^3 total.

If the support members were simply supported at the rail ends, the stress in the beams would be twice that of the ultimate strength of steel (50,000psi). To give the beams more support, the beams are welded to the floor and to the frame rails that span the two longitudinal rails. Flat bar stock is also welded to the other members in the framework to connect the beams in the center where the stress is greatest. The result is an integrated framework that distributes the stress to all its members, including the framerails and the floor of the car. The loading on the system is statically indeterminate. However, noting that the load is now supported by four beams instead of two and by doubling the section modulus in the above equation we find:

$Sb = M / Z = 50,400$ in-lb / 1 in^3 = 50,400psi.

Considering that the beams are further supported, the battery framework should keep the batteries from breaking free in a head-on collision. Since a rear collision would result in a smaller deceleration and since the framework is symmetric, the framework should hold up to the resulting stresses. In a side collision, the resulting forces are borne by the framerails themselves; this would necessitate the car being torn in half in order for the batteries to break free.

The battery box is vented according to the rules with a 10 cubic feet per minute brushless fan located at the end of a duct near the top of the box. The inlet vents are located at the bottom of the box, and spacing has been left between each of the batteries to aid in cooling and air circulation in the battery compartment. The batteries are accessible by removing the rear seat. Securing of the battery compartment lid is accomplished by two load straps of a ratcheting style to make the lid seal tightly and to facilitate ease of access. We placed the batteries in this location as opposed to the rear of the vehicle after studying the structure and the way it would be affected in a crash situation. This was emphasized by viewing crash tests of electric vehicles whose batteries were located in the rear. The loading in a rollover situation would be the mass of the batteries with a 10g deceleration ten times the weight of the five batteries, which comes to 4,300 lbs. Each strap is rated at 5,000lb failure, so we have a safety factor of two. Each battery weighs 86 lbs and has a base area of 96 in^2; the resulting stress on the lid for a 10g deceleration is:

10g x 86lb / 91in^2 = 9.45psi (pounds per square inch).

The lid has a rated compression strength of 650psi, so it will remain intact in a rollover. The location of the battery pack has also made it easier to control the weight ratio of the vehicle. Because of this we were able to maintain a 50-50 weight ratio. This change from the standard 60-40 weight ratio made it necessary to add an adjustable proportioning valve to help compensation in the braking ratio of the vehicle.

Battery placement necessitated placement of the fuel cell at the rear of the vehicle. Instead of a standard fuel tank we installed a ''fuel cell'' from a race car. The difficulty with this tank is that the fuel inlet is on the top, requiring that we intrude into the cargo compartment with the fuel inlet. The fuel inlet is sealed from the cargo compartment by a bulkhead and by the fuel cell itself. Our choice of the fuel cell was dictated by the safety of the cell in a crash situation.

The other modification made to the vehicle as required by the rules was the addition of a rollbar. The rollbar is composed of a main hoop section and two supports that extend from the top of the hoop down to the frame rail at the back edge of the cargo area (see figure). The support bars are angled at 5 degrees below the horizontal plane of the ceiling of the vehicle, and are positioned just beyond the rear passenger door to allow easy battery and passenger access. The two supports then bend down toward the floor at a forty-five-degree angle. Due to the high cost and unavailability of the seamless tubing specified, we instead used 1.750'' O.D. and 0.120'' nominal wall thickness D.O.M. tubing in order to satisfy competition requirements.

Since the rollbar is necessary because of the added weight of the batteries, the load on the rollbar is taken to be the weight of the batteries with a 10g deceleration or:

5 batteries x 86 lbs/battery x 10g = 4,300lb.

A simple check of the compressive load such a force puts on the vertical member of the main hoop gives:

Stress = force / crossectional area

= 2400lb / .6in^2 = 4000psi

Where the force is the load on each member or half of the total load.

The compressive strength of steel is 22,000psi, which gives a safety factor of 22,000psi / 4000psi = 5.5. The hoop alone should handle the rollover force. Lateral stability is provided by the rollhoop, which has a horizontal member, and by the supports that extend to the rear of the vehicle.

The rollhoop is positioned behind the front seats in the rear- most position: it is in contact with the ceiling of the vehicle and is padded with one inch of foam.

SUSPENSION MODIFICATIONS — Changes to the vehicle's suspension were limited to changing of the spring rate, because of a weight increase of approximately 200 pounds per front wheel and 400 pounds per rear wheel. The Mcpherson strut cartridges were left stock; higher damping rates would be helpful with the added load of the vehicle. Due to the added weight, a caster change would help ease the steering of the vehicle, but this is not readily changeable.

MATERIALS — The choice of materials has ranged from steel to aluminum. Steel has been used mostly because of the facilities and equipment available to us. Aluminum was used when possible, especially for larger, heavier items. The only exotic material used is a special honeycomb board. This came in two version: one with aluminum honeycomb and an epoxy surface, and the other with a paper based honeycomb and the same epoxy-coated surface. The aluminum unit was used in the construction of the battery box, and the paper was used as a mounting surface for the photovoltaic array.

VEHICLE MANUFACTURABILITY — Because structural integrity of the vehicle was changed so little, manufacturability of the vehicle should require very few changes. Most of the changes are alterations to the vehicle itself and would require different pieces to be used on the assembly line. The only major changes would be the additions of the battery box and the fuel cell. These modifications do require the removal of some of the decking of the vehicle to accommodate the batteries and the fuel cell.

BODY STYLING AND ERGONOMICS — Because the public is the determining factor if a vehicle will be a success or a failure, and because we have used a conversion vehicle, our body styling has not changed at all. Given Ford's proven success with this body design, one wonders if the public would accept a totally new design. Nevertheless, it would help any electric vehicle if its tare weight were less. In the area of ergonomics we have tried to retain the same friendly interior that is already present. We wanted to make sure that the number of passengers and the amount of cargo the vehicle held would not be altered. We did find it necessary to shave the rear seat slightly to gain some space. Because this vehicle has two different methods of propulsion we added extra gauges to monitor the necessary systems. We have added our gauges in the center console area, and have had fabricated a stylish console in which to house the new gauges.

The students at JEI have had an enjoyable time participating in the Ford Hybrid Electric Vehicle Challenge and hope to participate in future events. We wish to thank Ford, SAE, DOE for their support in this program. Along with the tireless efforts of Ford team concept and everyone else involved in the project.

The Lawrence Technological University's "Response" - A Hybrid Electric Vehicle Concept

C. W. Schwartz, Faculty, Doug Callahan, and Norm Harrison
Lawrence Technological University

ABSTRACT

Lawrence Technological University's prototype Hybrid Electric Vehicle, the **RESPONSE,** combines the convenient power of an internal combustion engine with the quiet, environmentally safe power of an electric motor. Lawrence Technological University's (LTU) primary objective was to build a practical, cost-effective vehicle that would be acceptable in today's market place.

The **RESPONSE's** parallel drive system has three modes of operation: electric-only, APU-only (Internal combustion engine), and hybrid. Components were selected on the basis of size, weight, efficiency, adaptability, performance, and cost. Due to time constraints and limited fabrication facilities, as many production components as possible were incorporated into the design. This report discusses several technical aspects of the design and control of Lawrence Technological University's "RESPONSE" to the Ford Motor Company/SAE/DOE Hybrid Electric Vehicle Challenge.

163

INTRODUCTION

The original project objectives listed in the LTU proposal of December 9, 1991 remain essentially unchanged. The LTU HEV team has overcome many obstacles and challenges in constructing a "ground-up" vehicle. The total design, packaging, and construction tasks have resulted in a project that provided an unparalleled experience in both theoretical and hands on engineering. This report chronicles the design and fabrication of Lawrence Technological University's **RESPONSE**.

POWERTRAIN CONFIGURATION

A unique design was created that allows the integration of two power sources to run through one automatic transaxle. Figure 1 shows the **RESPONSE'S** powertrain layout.

This configuration consists of an internal combustion engine (APU), an automatic transaxle, an electric motor, a hydraulically controlled clutch, an intermediate shaft, a powertrain bridge, two toothed pulleys, a drive belt, a support bearing, and a support bearing housing. Each component was selected based upon consideration of size, weight, availability, cost, and performance. These components have the following specifications:

APU - The alternative power unit (APU) is a Suzuki 1.0 liter, electronic fuel-injected, 3 cylinder engine with approximately 55 horsepower at 5700 rpm and 58 ft*lb of torque at 3300 rpm.

TRANSAXLE - The transaxle is a Jatco #JF403E electronically controlled four speed automatic, with a lock-up torque converter.

ELECTRIC MOTOR - The electric motor is a 20 HP, 240 Volt-3 phase AC, two pole, type B induction motor housed in a NEMA 254T frame. The motor provides up to 44 ft*lbs. of torque.

HYDRAUL. CONTROLLED CLUTCH - The clutch is from a Geo metro manual transmission. The clutch is

operated by a hydraulic cylinder and pump for smooth transitions between operating modes. The pump draws power from the APU's 12V electrical accessory system. Under normal operating conditions, the clutch is controlled by the micro-controller, but can be overridden using a two-pole momentary switch on the center console.

INTERMEDIATE SHAFT - The intermediate shaft connects the clutch to the transaxle and includes a pulley for the electric motor drive belt. The design incorporates a support bearing to locate the torque converter and resist bending loads applied to the shaft by the electric motor drive belt. This shaft was designed and fabricated using 8620 steel to withstand the combined power and torque from the electric motor and APU.

POWERTRAIN CONFIGURATION

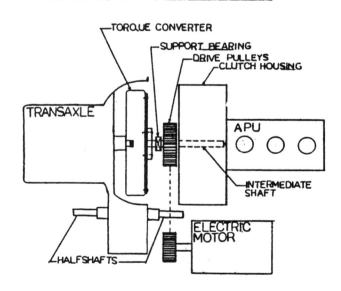

FIGURE 1

BRIDGE - A protective housing or "bridge" connects the APU to the transaxle. The bridge consists of steel plates welded to the ends of a steel tube and mates with existing holes in the clutch housing and the transaxle.

DRIVE BELT AND PULLEYS - Two toothed pulleys and a matching belt provide a no-slip motor drive. The pulleys are aluminum and have a 1.375:1 ratio (electric motor to APU). The drive belt has a 14 mm pitch and is 40 mm wide.

ELECTRICAL ACCESSORIES - In order to provide a constant and reliable power supply for accessory loads (lights, wipers, ECM, micro-controller, etc.), the alternator is belted to the electric motor shaft. Since this shaft is rotating regardless of mode of operation, the possibility of discharging the APU battery when the APU is not run for extended periods is eliminated.

POWERTRAIN SUB-FRAME - The entire powertrain system is supported in the chassis on three liquid filled vibration isolators. A sub-frame from the APU block locates the electric motor. The 3 point mounting system allows the chassis to deflect without stressing the powertrain.

POWERTRAIN CUSHION MOUNTS - A study was done to optimize the locations for the three-point cushion mounting system. For this study a three cylinder internal combustion engine mounted transversely was used. It should be noted that the engine mount system would theoretically be optimized for the internal combustion engine because of the cyclic firing of each cylinder, while the electric motor induces no significant cyclic vibrations into the system. Our powertrain configuration is asymmetric, which makes it more difficult to calculate the optimum mount locations and almost impossible to approach with intuitive methods.

In addition to vibration isolation, which is of paramount importance, it was necessary to design the mounting system to:

* Support static and dynamic loads
* Resist torque
* Limit the static bending moment on the engine block & transaxle
* Provide acceptable service life

Mounts from a Ford Taurus were used since the weight of that system closely matched the drivetrain of the RESPONSE.

MOTOR & DRIVE SELECTION

The electric motor for the RESPONSE is controlled by a variable voltage/variable frequency AC drive. The team selected an induction motor for its efficiency and torque characteristics over a wide speed range. DC brushless motor/controller systems were considered, but because of high costs, LTU opted for an AC motor and drive.

The drive for the motor is an Omega-pak type VT-1000, model #8804 adjustable frequency AC drive donated by Square D corp. Normally operated from a 240 V_{AC} source, the drive required extensive modifications, both electrically and physically, for operation from a DC source.

To modify the drive, rectifying contacts for the AC input were removed. For packaging purposes, eight 270 V, 90 uF input capacitors were replaced with one 300 V, 1600 uF capacitor. With the removal of the AC source, a 12 V_{DC} to 120 V_{AC} transverter provides power to the solid state components internal to the drive.

To incorporate the drive into the vehicle, the components were packaged into a specially designed container. This reduced the drive's weight and volume approximately 45% and 35% respectively.

BATTERY SELECTION

The RESPONSE uses twenty Powersonic model PS-12500 sealed lead-acid gel batteries. The batteries are connected in series to form a 240 volt power source for the electric motor. The battery pack is contained in two areas of the vehicle. Ten batteries are housed in an enclosed section of the passenger compartment along the longitudinal axis of the vehicle and the remaining ten batteries in the rear section of the vehicle behind the passenger compartment (Figures 2 & 3).

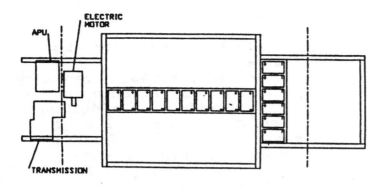

FIGURE 2

REAR VIEW OF
REAR BATTERY BOX

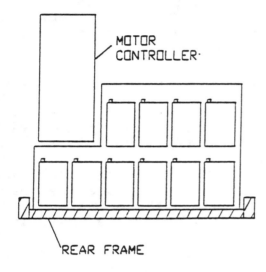

FIGURE 3

This layout was based on overall vehicle packaging and weight distribution targets. Since these are maintenance free batteries, a lower priority was given to accessibility for maintenance. They should need service only in the event of a failure such as; a loose connection, a broken terminal, etc..

RATIONALE FOR BATTERY SELECTION -
For the **RESPONSE**, several types of batteries were considered including:
1. Lead-acid
2. Nickel-cadmium
3. Nickel-iron
4. Sodium-sulfur
Lead-acid batteries are not only the most readily available, but

they also provide the greatest range of packaging options, acceptable energy densities, and lowest power to cost ratio.

The following major constraints were imposed for battery selection, along with other rationale:

1. Minimum 200 volts due to controller current limitations
2. Maximum 30 batteries due to packaging constraints
3. 15 to 16 Wh/lb; minimum energy density

When meeting the above constraints, the team strived to reach the best combination of power to weight ratio, temperature operating range, cost minimization, packaging and safety.

Since the PS-12500 are sealed batteries, they can be installed in any position. This allows greater freedom to meet packaging constraints.

BATTERY SPECIFICATIONS - The Powersonic PS-12500 are maintenance free, sealed lead-acid batteries. Manufacturers specifications follow (1:7):

Physical Dimensions -
Weight (ea.): 31 lbs (14.1 Kg)
Total weight: 620 lbs (281.8 Kg)
        Length: 9.40 in. (239 mm)
         Width: 5.50 in. (138 mm)
        Height: 8.20 in. (208 mm)
Individual Batt. Voltages -
12.00 volts nominal
12.90 volts Full charge
11.64 volts Full discharge
Energy Capacity -
50 AH @ C/20
17.42 Wh/lb per battery
9.72 Kwhr-entire pack

Minimum Battery Life -
350 cycles at 80% D.O.D. per cycle
Operating Temperature Range -
-76°F to 140°F
-60°C to 60°C

BATTERY CHARGER - The two battery chargers for the **RESPONSE** are K & W Engineering's model BC-20. The BC-20 is voltage controlled, current limited, with fully adjustable voltage and current controls. Each charger charges one-half of the total battery pack.

The BC-20 is a very compact and light-weight charger (297 cubic inches, and 9.9 lbs respectively). The BC-20 also provides the most economical choice for in-vehicle installation. These chargers were selected and purchased when the HEV Challenge still required an on-board charging system.

outlet for each pack. When the batteries are to be connected for vehicle operation, a shorting plug consisting of two Anderson connectors connects the positive end of one battery pack to the negative end of the other. This layout joins all twenty batteries in series. A block diagram of the electrical power system is shown in Figure 4.

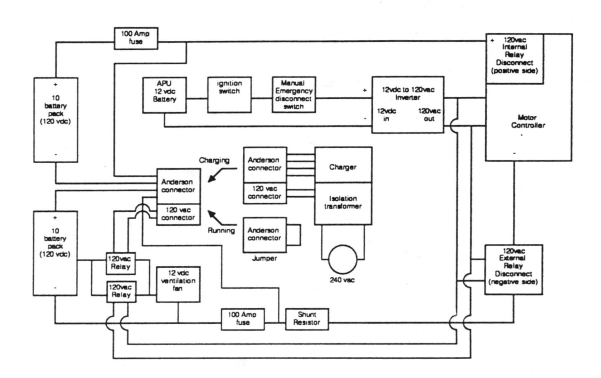

FIGURE 4

The BC-20 accepts a 105-140 V_{AC}, 50-60 Hz, 20 Amp power supply, and provides a 48-140 V_{DC} output(2:9). The isolation transformer between the 220 V_{AC} line and the chargers effectively splits the 220V_{AC} line into two 140 V_{AC} lines.

To accomplish the task of splitting the batteries into two separate and equal packs for charging, one half of each battery pack is terminated at an Anderson connector. This configuration provides an isolated charging

This charging system meets the 30 Amp charging limit specified in the Challenge rules with the 20 amp circuit breakers internal to the BC-20.

SAFETY - The sealed containers for the lead-acid batteries provide a high degree of safety in the event of a collision or rollover.

The PS-12500 uses oxygen recombination (the use of oversized plates in a sealed container) allowing the oxygen produced by the positive plate during charging to be absorbed by the negative plate. Oxygen recombination deters hydrogen from being generated. Along with the obvious safety factor involved, this process keeps the water content of the electrolyte unchanged, providing consistent performance over the life of the batteries (1:5).

CONTROLLER STRATEGY

The **RESPONSE** features three modes of operation; electric motor-only, APU-only, and hybrid. The mode of operation is selected by the driver via a push button switching mechanism located on the instrument panel. The signals from these switches are interpreted by a Motorola MC68HC11 micro-controller, which handles several primary processes for the selected mode.

Additional hardware has been designed and fabricated in the form of an interface board to modify input signals into a form that the micro-controller can interpret. Included, among other components on this board are: power supplies, signal isolation devices, digital to analog converters, and voltage to frequency converters.

The operation strategy for each mode is as follows:

MOTOR-ONLY MODE - Motor only-mode is defined as operating the vehicle exclusively on the electric motor. The APU does not provide any assistance in vehicle operation.

When in motor-only mode, the micro-controller disengages the APU via the hydraulically operated clutch and removes power from the APU's ECM by removing power from a normally open relay. This completely isolates the APU from the powertrain system. The micro-controller then monitors throttle position using a 0-5 volt throttle position sensor. The controller sends a 0-10 volt signal to the motor controller. The motor controller uses this signal to determine the frequency & voltage at which the electric motor is driven (0-10 V relates linearly to 0-7000 rpm on the motor). This method is a speed control system as opposed to power control.

Due to varying slip in the

motor, the output frequency cannot be read directly from the motor controller. A proximity sensor is used to monitor the motor speed directly from the motor shaft to determine the vehicle's shifting strategy and controller operation.

Due to limited development time, vehicle speed is used to determine shift points in motor-only mode. The following is the shift schedule for motor only:

Vehicle Speed[mph]	Gear[]
0 - 5	1
5 - 10	2
10 - 50	3
> 50	4

Table 1

This schedule holds for both upshifting and downshifting of the transaxle. This schedule was based on a vehicle speed of 40 mph at a motor speed of 3475 rpm.

APU-ONLY MODE - In APU-only mode, the electric motor provides no power to the vehicle, and the internal combustion engine provides all the power to propel the vehicle.

When the vehicle is in APU-only mode, the micro-controller engages the APU through the clutch and sends a 0 volt signal to the motor controller. The micro-controller also sets itself up for the APU shifting strategy. Throttle control is handled through the mechanical linkage and fuel control systems of the Suzuki engine. The shifting strategy for APU only is shown in tables 2 & 3.

Vehicle Speed[mph]	Gear[]
0 - 18	1
19 - 33	2
34 - 50	3
> 50	4

Table 2 (upshift)

Vehicle Speed[mph]	Gear[]
> 45	4
45 - 25	3
24 - 12	2
11 - 0	1

Table 3 (Downshift)

To avoid "hunting" around the shift points, a two second delay occurs before downshifting.

HYBRID MODE - LTU's definition of the hybrid mode is to operate the vehicle primarily on electric power, using the APU as a supplement to propel the **RESPONSE** when the battery pack discharges to a predetermined state. When operating in hybrid mode, the vehicle responds in the same manner as the electric motor-only mode. If while driving, the operator depresses the accelerator pedal to 90% or greater of full travel (a region called "detent"), the micro-controller engages the APU; first by turning on the power to the ECM, then engaging the hydraulic clutch. This process effectively bump starts the APU, providing added power for hill climbing or passing. Once the accelerator pedal is in detent, the APU remains in operation for 30 seconds before shutting down, eliminating excessive APU cycling.

When operating on electric power and the batteries' depth of discharge (DOD) reaches 80%, the APU will fire using the same strategy as above. The APU now propels the vehicle and also charges the batteries. Battery charging is accomplished by regenerative circuitry included in the motor controller. When the batteries reach a 10% DOD, the vehicle returns to electric motor operation. When the accelerator goes through detent in the charging phase of hybrid mode, generation stops and the electric motor provides added power.

Although cycling the batteries from 80% DOD to 40% DOD would be the most efficient method (the batteries charge on a linear scale to 40% and a decaying exponential from 40% to 0% [Figure 5]), the **RESPONSE'S** strategy was fit to the parameters of the competition.

State of charge on the battery pack is determined using the KwHr meter provided for the competition.

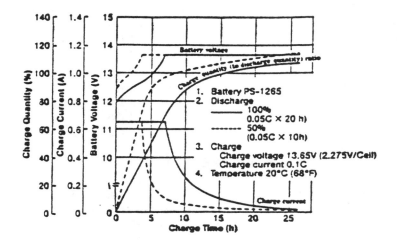

FIGURE 5

TRANSAXLE CONTROL - The transaxle control strategies for the **RESPONSE** are designed to take full advantage of the Jatco (JF403E) electronically controlled, 4-speed automatic transaxle with overdrive.

A transaxle shifting strategy was developed based on the electric motor and APU power curves, and is implemented by the on-board micro-controller. Inputs to the micro-controller include engine/motor rpm and vehicle speed. Transaxle shifting is accomplished by controlling the A and B shift solenoids, over-run clutch solenoid, and the torque converter locking solenoid.

In addition, the internal line pressure of the transaxle is controlled through a separate circuit which has been developed to provide low (70 psi), medium (130 psi), and high (200 psi) line pressures. A variable duty cycle 50 Hz signal is sent to the line duty pressure solenoid in the transaxle. The duty cycle is controlled with one of two LM555 50 Hz astable timers amplified through a npn transistor. One timer is 50% duty cycle (medium line pressure), and the other is 85% duty cycle (low pressure). The system defaults to high line pressure. A bypass system has also been incorporated into the design which allows the driver to control gear selection through the gear shift position lever. This control circuit is independent of the

169

micro-controller and can be used in the event of a micro-controller failure or if driving conditions warrant direct driver input. In the event of a total systems failure, the transaxle's internal default allows drive 2, drive 3, reverse, neutral, park, at full line pressure through the use of the gear shift lever.

POWER REGENERATION - The **RESPONSE** has two electrical power recovery strategies; regenerative braking and regenerative charging. During each of these processes the electric motor is energized to maintain the rotating magnetic field. This field provides the regenerative energy.

The regenerative braking process is only used in motor-only or hybrid mode. When the driver is braking to a lower vehicle speed, a retarding torque occurs and causes the motor to act as a generator. The energy produced from the field is directed back through a transistor which is connected across the DC buss, providing a maximum of 30 amps for up to five seconds.

Regenerative charging is used in hybrid mode only. As the vehicle is powered by the APU, the controller energizes the motor to operate at a speed slightly less than the APU. The difference in potential between the motor field and the DC buss allows up to ten amps of regenerative energy for extended periods of time.

Both of these systems are disabled when the batteries are above 10% depth of discharge.

EMISSION CONTROL

The team's decision was to use the Suzuki engine complete with all production emission controls including: catalyst, EGR, crank case ventilation, and evaporative emissions. It is recognized that considering the power to weight ratio of the **RESPONSE**, recalibrating the diminutive APU would be beneficial for the emissions. Since the APU is under-powered for this application, it operates frequently at near full

throttle, at which time the emissions controls are bypassed. Alternatively, if weight could not be reduced, a larger APU could be incorporated to provide acceptable emission levels.

FUEL AND ELECTRICAL POWER CONSUMPTION

The design of the **RESPONSE** optimized the vehicle for an operating speed of approximately 40 mph. When the vehicle is operating in electric motor-only mode at 40 mph, the electric motor operates at it's most efficient speed of 3475 rpm. At this constant speed, the RESPONSE has a range of approximately 18 miles (this data is preliminary and the system is still being refined). The power consumption for the electric motor drive system is shown in figure 6. The fuel consumption for the RESPONSE operating in APU-only mode is shown in figure 7.

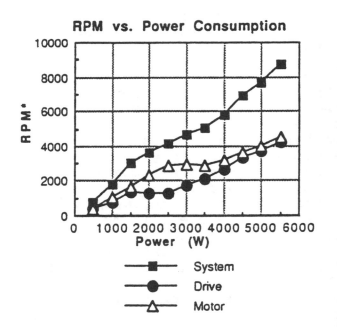

FIGURE 6

* Vehicle speed is dependant upon gear selection from transaxle shift strategy.

170

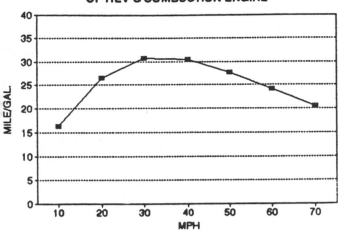

ESTIMATED MPG VERSUS MPH
OF HEV'S COMBUSTION ENGINE

FIGURE 7

VEHICLE STRUCTURE DESIGN

The **RESPONSE'S** frame is constructed from mild, tubular steel of various cross sections and wall thicknesses. As illustrated in figure 8, the passenger compartment lies between the front and rear torque boxes which are the structural components of the frame. One of the two battery storage compartments lies along the longitudinal centerline of the vehicle and connects the front and rear torque boxes. The trussed type battery box frame is constructed from 1010 tubular steel and covered with adhesively bonded, mechanically fastened, thin sheet metal. Trussed side rails also run between the front and rear torque boxes providing torsional rigidity and side impact protection. The floor of the passenger compartment is composed of paperboard honeycomb sandwiched between two layers of sheet steel. The composite floor pan is adhesively bonded and mechanically fastened to the torque boxes, battery box, and side rails. The battery box lid is gasketed mechanically attached to frame members to complete the box structure.

Structural cross-members imbedded in the composite floor support the bucket seats. A roll hoop attached to the front torque box provides protection for the occupants' legs in the event of a rollover. To protect the heads and upper bodies of the occupants, a roll bar is attached to the rear torque box and is reinforced by diagonal braces supported by the rear frame structure.

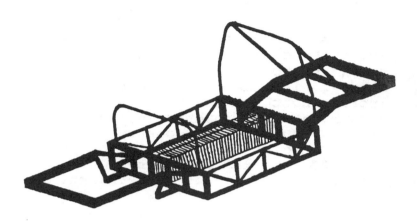

FIGURE 8

The front frame structure extends forward from the front torque box and supports the powertrain and front suspension. A 300 millimeter (mm) crush zone lies at the very front of the frame and only crushable items, such as the radiator, windshield washer reservoir, and carbon canister, lie within this zone. This crush zone can absorb all of the vehicle's kinetic energy at an impact velocity of 7.27 m/s. The maximum deceleration experienced by the occupants during such an impact would be 22.4 g's. This reaction is well below the maximum deceleration limit of 60 g's set by the Federal Motor Vehicle Safety Standards.

The frame structure extends rearward from the torque box and supports the suspension, second battery storage compartment, motor controller, cargo box, and fuel tank. The fuel tank is centrally located between the outer frame rails, directly above the rear axle, to protect it in the event of a collision.

SUSPENSION DESIGN

Suspension, brake, and steering components were selected from current production vehicles with gross vehicle weights approximately equal to the design target weight of the **RESPONSE**. The independent front suspension employs MacPherson struts and coil springs from a Ford Tempo. The rear suspension consists of a solid rear axle with coil springs and gas shock absorbers from a Dodge Shadow. With the exception of increasing the front track width to accommodate the powertrain, the original suspension geometry of those vehicles is duplicated on the **RESPONSE**. The **RESPONSE** also features a four-wheel four-channel anti-lock braking system. The rack-and-pinion steering assembly is adapted from a Saturn.

The effects of center of gravity and weight distribution were considered during the design and construction of the **RESPONSE**. The center of gravity was kept as low as possible by locating the batteries, the heaviest component of the vehicle, at floor level about the centerline of the vehicle. The result is a front/rear weight distribution of 53%/47%, and a neutral (within 2%) side-to-side weight bias. The gross vehicle weight of the **RESPONSE** is approximately 3600 lbs.

CHOICE OF MATERIALS

Material selection for the **RESPONSE** was driven by time constraints, availability, and cost. In order to accelerate the process of frame construction, Rectangular, tubular steel was selected for the basic frame material because it is easily worked, readily available, and relatively inexpensive. Originally, round tubular steel was chosen, but as the design progressed it became apparent that fitting the joints between round stock would be more difficult and time consuming than fitting the joints between rectangular tubing. Mild steel tubing, such as that used in the

RESPONSE'S frame, is readily available from local suppliers, and in fact was donated by one of them. Aluminum was also considered as a weight-savings alternative to steel, but since it is roughly three times as expensive, steel was selected.

VEHICLE MANUFACTURABILITY

The **RESPONSE** as conceived by the LTU team would be fabricated using conventional manufacturing methods except for the need for light weight materials to make it practical for battery operation. Increased attention must be directed toward maximizing electrical and mechanical efficiencies, and minimizing aerodynamic and rolling resistance losses. For the prototype as entered in the Ford/SAE/DOE HEV challenge, the frame has been fabricated from welded tubular sections. In production these sections would be replaced with welded stampings or conventional light weight unibody construction. To save weight, the electrical components including the power distribution for the lighting and instrumentation could be replaced by multi-plexing. The fabrication of the **RESPONSE'S** electrical components such as the microprocessor, motor controller, and transverter were assembled using conventional electrical industry methods. The traction motor is from an industrial application and would be re-engineered for lighter-weight and higher operating temperatures if it were used in large scale production.

The powertrain assembly would be re-engineered for weight reduction and the bridge between the motor, engine, and transaxle could be simplified. A transaxle could be designed and calibrated for this special application. By using multi-function die-casting techniques several components could be combined into a single light-weight part.

Out of necessity, the body shell for the **RESPONSE** is hand-layed fiberglass and would not be recommended for large scale production. Instead, a recyclable SMC (sheet molded compound) over an aluminum or graphite structure would be a prime consideration for the light-weight durable body.

BODY STYLING AND ERGONOMICS

The body of the **RESPONSE** is constructed of fiberglass and is shown in figure 9. The mid-section of the body is the remnant of a 1981 Bradley GT kit car which features gull wing doors. The Bradley mid-section, from A-pillar to B-pillar, was cut and modified to accommodate the **RESPONSE'S** chassis. The interior structure of the Bradley mid-section was removed, leaving a portion of the exterior shell. The mid-section is attached to the chassis to rubber cushions at the corners of the front and rear torque boxes, and reaches from the roll bar to the roll hoop. The windshield wiper armature and motor mechanism is from a 1969 Volkswagen and is mounted to the front of the dash. Side mounted mirrors are from a Geo Storm as well as the interior rear view mirror.

The front and rear body sections of the **RESPONSE** are both student designed and fabricated. The design of the front and rear body sections was initially styled on paper, then transferred to a full size clay model, with the Bradley GT mid-section placed between the front and rear end clay models. After the clay bucks were shaped, fiberglass molds were made utilizing a wax and peel-vinyl release agent. These molds were then separated from the clay bucks and another parting agent was applied directly to the mold. Each section of the body was then hand-layed into the molds and removed. The front and rear sections of the body are constructed of an outside layer of gel coat and three layers of fiberglass cloth and resin beneath the gel coat. The side rocker panels on the mid-section are also made of fiberglass and hand-layed in the same manner as

the front and rear sections.

The hood is reinforced with a filler replacing the second (middle) layer of fiberglass cloth. Each of the body sections are also reinforced to maintain design shape in selected areas.

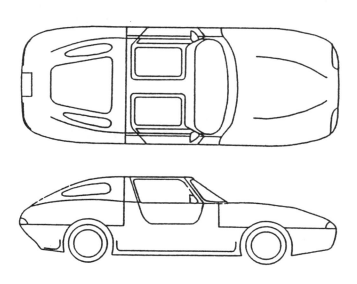

FIGURE 9

The hood of the **RESPONSE** hinges forward at the front cross member. It incorporates an air intake grill for the passenger compartment ventilation. The rear hatch pivots at the B-pillar behind the roll bar and rotates upward.

The headlamps and turn signals are from a 1990 Geo Metro and the rear taillamp assemblies, license plate lamps, and the high mounted stop lamp are incorporated from a 1991 Geo Storm. The windshield and door windows are from the Bradley GT, while the rear windows are constructed of 6.5 mm thick Lexan. The front and rear over-hangs are each 100 cm. The maximum width of the **RESPONSE'S** body is 175 mm and the maximum height is 132 mm.

Normal vehicle controls, such as the brake and accelerator pedals, the emergency battery disconnect switch, the Halon extinguisher release, and mode select switches are within easy reach of the driver. Seating and visibility accommodate a 50th percentile male with the seat in its mid-position.

ACKNOWLEDGEMENTS

The Lawrence Tech. Hybrid Electric Vehicle team would like to express their gratitude to the LTU faculty, staff and administration, corporate sponsors, and individuals who have contributed to the **RESPONSE**. Without their patience and efforts, this project would not have become a reality.

REFERENCES

1. <u>Powersonic, 1992 Sealed Lead-Acid Battery Catalog</u>
2. <u>KTA Services, 1992 Battery Charger Catalog</u>, Vol 2

Michigan State University - Spartan Charge

John B. Gerrish, Gerald L. Park, and William A. Gulley
Michigan State University

ABSTRACT

The design, development, and testing of a hybrid electric vehicle for the 1993 Ford/SAE/DOE competition is described. One objective was to field a competitive car. The more important objective, however, was to develop in a large team of students the skills, knowledge, and behavior needed in a huge technical project. The management and information systems chosen and the key technical features of the vehicle are described. We discuss the decisions for series drive architecture, nickel metal hybrid batteries, vector drive pulse width modulated inverter without encoder, induction drive motor, gasoline-fielded engine, catalytic preheater, permanent magnet alternator, steel tubing and aluminum monocoque frame, anti-lock and regenerative braking, and composite body.

Driving performance and emissions are considered. The role of the computer in controlling the alternator and the operating instrumentation is developed.

Since so much was learned from errors, many of the major ones we made are described.

I. INTRODUCTION

At Michigan State University (MSU) involvement with the Ford Hybrid Electric Vehicle (HEV) Challenge began late due to a communication lapse. Nevertheless, our proposal to build "Spartan Charge" was hurriedly composed and submitted on time.

The most important decision was to enter the "build from ground up" class. MSU is a large school (40,000 students); we wanted to expose as many students as possible to the opportunities afforded by the Ford/DOE/SAE contest. We preferred to make a generic car since we have alumni and friends in many automobile companies as well as in Ford.

The Wankel engine that the faculty initially proposed for an auxiliary power unit (APU) was rejected by the student leaders. Several other features of the proposal were adopted, however, including the organizational scheme which called for student decision-making at all levels. Faculty retreated to advisory roles-- acting as consultants; sources of information and corporate and alumni contacts (very important); and as providers of offices with long-distance telephones (most important for solicitation of information, parts, and support). Faculty incorporated Spartan Charge activities into courses which offered design credits for the engineering students. Another faculty contribution included the organization of a series of seminars early in the project. These seminars were given by engineers from industry or other colleges with experience relevant to EV and HEV design and fabrication. A final faculty contribution to the project was the coordination of this paper--a chronology distilled from minutes, e-mail, records, and students' own submissions near the end of the campaign.

Role of the University. Unlike software or circuits development, building a full-size vehicle requires full-size facilities. At least 2,000 square feet are needed. The main faculty advisor, the model shop and the garage facilities were provided by the Agricultural Engineering Department, which at our land-grant school is connected both to the Engineering and Agricultural and Natural Resources Colleges. In addition, AE had faculty and staff expert in chemical, electrical, and mechanical engineering as well as in technology management. Two MBA candidates from business were student leaders, but it proved difficult to retain additional business students on our team.

In order to finance Spartan Charge, solid University administrative support was necessary. We received this from Engineering, Agriculture and Natural Resources, and Business. The Dean of Engineering was our key supporter. Fund raising in the 1992-93 economy was problematic. Substantial funds are needed when purchase orders must be authorized. While we courted many corporate and alumni donors, our greatest success came from several of the organizations within the University. Financial backing was pledged by the Provost, the VP for Computing, the VP for Graduate Research, the Dean of Business, and the Dean of

Engineering. Several departments found their stock of electronic parts, metal, solvents, and duct tape mysteriously depleted. Academic departments were generous in overlooking our transgressions, believing that we were learning great lessons at small cost.

II. PROJECT GOALS

For many, the goal seemed obvious--win the contest! For us, that was important but secondary to our main goal. The main goal was to develop the skills, knowledge, and behaviors necessary to a project so large that team work was essential. One student included the following quote in his report, "Tell me and I am forgetful, show me and I remember, involve me and I learn."
Some of the lessons students learned include:

- A systems viewpoint is absolutely necessary for a complex machine like a HEV.
- Every mistake is a learning opportunity.
- A fall-back solution is advisable for each major project milestone. For example, if the "high-tech" batteries don't arrive, be ready to fall-back on the lead-acid practice batteries.
- Team work is absolutely necessary.
- The job isn't done until it's all done.
- Information acquired over the phone is more useful than what is found in the library. (Faculty object to this conclusion, but we found it consistently correct.)
- Faculty can provide accurate reference letters for students seeking employment.

III. TEAM ORGANIZATION AND MANAGEMENT

The key words here are speed and concentration. We had to get a team organized quickly and provide an organizational setting where student attention to Spartan Charge would be maintained throughout the project.
The organizing faculty suspected that older and more experienced students would become the leaders and major contributors. A mechanism was needed for insuring the concentration of the student leaders during the initial phases of the project. Thus, we advertised the availability of six one-quarter time graduate student assistantships for Spartan Charge. Many candidates were interviewed: a president was chosen; propulsion, electrical, structural, mechanical, and financial leaders were chosen. There has been very little turnover in these positions. The four technical leaders formed the core of the engineering management. Another ten unpaid student leaders emerged during the first year, mature undergraduates whose work and leadership were acknowledged by their fellow team members. The volunteer leaders led groups responsible for batteries, wiring, APU, controller, inverter, motor, wheels, body, and strategy.
Undergraduate students needed "academic recognition" of the many hours they devoted to Spartan Charge. The Electrical Engineering faculty agreed that a HEV design course would run concurrently with the project. Each of the 29 students enrolled kept a technical

diary and wrote a paper on his or her contribution. Both were reviewed every term by the instructor--one of the HEV advisors. Similar arrangements were made on an individual basis for students in other departments so 35 to 40 students received academic credit for participation (and conversely, the need to pass the course kept students working when attention might have otherwise flagged). Over the two semesters, another 30 students participated with neither pay nor academic credits. Still another 20 students kept nominal contact with the project but were generally unproductive.
The technical teams met separately each week and joined together on Friday afternoon for "coordination" at a local bar. The faculty advisors were often present and can attest that the team members were more interested in the project than in drinking beer. There is hope for the future!
The glue that held the entire team together was the local electronic mail network that all productive team members accessed. Questions, arrangements, announcements, technical debates, reporting of tests, etc., were all broadcast on the network. The communication was not all serious. One team leader shortened one advisor's lifespan when he transmitted on April 1 that a fork-lift truck wrecked our chassis! Functional or frivolous, we cannot place too much emphasis on inter-group communications. An academic environment is usually not team oriented as many "real" engineering environments are. It is absolutely necessary to encourage and nurture a team mentality in a big project.
Many deadlines were imposed by Ford/DOE/SAE. A PERT chart was used to keep track of Spartan Charge's progress in meeting deadlines. The chart is too complex to reproduce for this paper, but the list of definable tasks remaining during
the final six weeks has 108 entries. The PERT chart served its purpose by awakening the overconfident members of the team.
Fund raising is a critical component of any large project. The MSU team tried hard, but didn't acquire the needed level of cash contributions. About $15,000 was raised. Contributions in-kind, however, were much easier to obtain. Gifts in-kind totalled approximately $28,000 in declared value. The value of the car itself as figured by the organizers came to $48,000--a figure based on supposed retail value of components of the car. In spite of these figures, approximately $80,000 was expended on the project through University purchase orders and payroll.

IV. TECHNICAL EFFORTS AND CONTRIBUTIONS

In this section we summarize the key decisions made and the main features of the MSU's Spartan Charge vehicle. The results come from student papers written by team members to summarize their contributions. The categories 1-4 below are convenient to summarize the major technical tasks as each is relatively independent of the others.

PROPULSION AND CONTROLS - This major area included several smaller groups and was supervised by several graduate students working with undergraduate team leaders. A number of the groups had overlapping and shifting membership which worked well and kept a good level of communications. The following groups met weekly: batteries and wiring, central processing unit (CPU), instrumentation, and sensors. Individuals or pairs of students worked on projects such as auxiliary DC power, troubleshooting, ventilation, alarms, sensor interfacing, microprocessor compiler, APU stepper drive, etc.

Drive Architecture - A year ago, there was a major controversy in the Propulsion and Controls group over the series versus split-parallel drive configuration. After initially voting for parallel, the students later reversed their decision. In the series mode the auxiliary power unit (APU), a 983 cc internal combustion (IC) engine, charges batteries and/or feeds the inverter-motor which generates torque for the transaxle. The team believed transient problems in switching between hybrid and electric modes would be awkward and perhaps unsafe, and that the apparent increase in reliability due to redundancy wouldn't actually accrue. Later we came to believe that drivers of parallel hybrids would be tempted to shift to the peppier hybrid mode in areas where electric operation (ZEV) is ecologically necessary.

The overall vehicle design could proceed once this decision was made. The DC versus AC drive motor decision has much less effect on the overall design as compared with the series versus parallel decision.

Batteries, Charging and Wiring - The first major decision was battery technology to supply the nominal 10 kWh of energy storage permitted by the rules. All technologies meeting the rules were considered.

The team originally selected NiCd batteries to use as a stand-in for the more environmentally benign NiMH. The hope was to develop the car around NiCd until NiMH batteries could be procured in early 1993, then the electrically similar NiMH batteries would quickly displace the NiCd set.

The business and finance team members made a major contribution in securing a lease of NiMH batteries from Eagle Picher. These batteries were in development and were very expensive. When the price and delivery date of NiCd batteries were finalized, we became more humble and selected lead-acid gel-cells for the practice batteries because we could afford them, and delivery was immediate. The disadvantage of the plan was that our two battery technologies were dissimilar and required two trips up the learning curve. When ordered, the NiMH batteries were to have weighed about 500 lbs. By the time the batteries were packaged for safe use, they weighed in at 810 lbs. We were tempted to settle for the lead-acid gel-cell batteries (750 lbs.), but we could not because the gel-cells are not rated for the required 300 deep discharge cycles. NiMH batteries are good for at least 1600 cycles. The 60 lb. weight penalty and cost penalty associated with NiMH were to be accepted in favor of excellent power density and environmental design points. It is no less important that NiMH batteries

promised our team a uniqueness that made the project exciting. The idea that ours might be the most environmentally friendly car in the challenge gave our team great enthusiasm.

The NiMH batteries were rated at 35 Amp-hours. 250 cells are packaged into five packs of 50 cells. Mid-discharge voltage is 1.14 v for each cell. All cells are in series. A key feature of the NiMH batteries is an internal resistance of about 0.5 ohm for the entire battery. This is about half the internal resistance of our lead-acid practice batteries. Low internal resistance leads to small variation in APU rpm when motor load fluctuates during on-the-go charging. The reduced rpm variation translates into reduced tailpipe emissions--a benefit we realized late in the game.

All through the winter months, we tested the drive train using lead-acid gel-cells. The NiMH batteries arrived just six weeks prior to the contest. With the onset of warm weather, battery cooling became a problem. Fortunately, some modelling had been done by a group early in the project. The contest car was designed with battery cooling in mind, although the practice car had no provision for removing battery heat.

Wiring, switching, ventilation, and fusing are all important performance and safety issues. AWG #2 copper locomotive cable (rated at 192 A, 90° C) was used to connect the batteries to the inverter. This was adequate for the maximum expected current of 150 A. The battery bank is isolated by a 300 amp manual switch within reach of the driver and passenger. For fault protection, 200 A rated "semiconductor" (fast) fuses were installed in both battery lines. Smaller fuses abound for the lower voltage circuits. The APU-driven alternator has its three-phase AC output fused locally at 40 A. The major wiring circuits are illustrated in Fig. 1. The signal and low current accessory circuits are wired with PVC insulated stranded wire of 16 or 18 gage. The wires are wrapped in helical-cut tubing and connected with molex connectors for ease of service or modification. All current is returned to source via dedicated wiring so the chassis can be grounded for battery charging without excessive induced ground current.

DC-DC converters (donated by Vicor) accept 100 to 400 V at the input and provide power to the following:
- Battery cooling fan: 12 V DC 100 watts. (This is an important safety feature satisfied by a 100 cfm axial fan.)
- APU controller: 5 V DC, 100 Watts.
- Inverter contactor: 72 V DC, 100 Watts.
- Lamps, horn, wipers: 12 V DC, 600 Watts.

The main battery pack is charged by an on-board charger with external 5 KVA isolation and voltage-adjustment transformer. The charging circuit is an adaptation of a "standard" handbook circuit and is efficient and (except for its outboard transformer) compact. The on-board charger is connected to the transformer via a "smart" connector especially designed for electric vehicle charging (Meltric). The initial charging current seldom exceeds 15 A DC. This corresponds to 25 A AC through the smart connector. Typically, charging current tapers to 10 amps in two hours for the NiMH

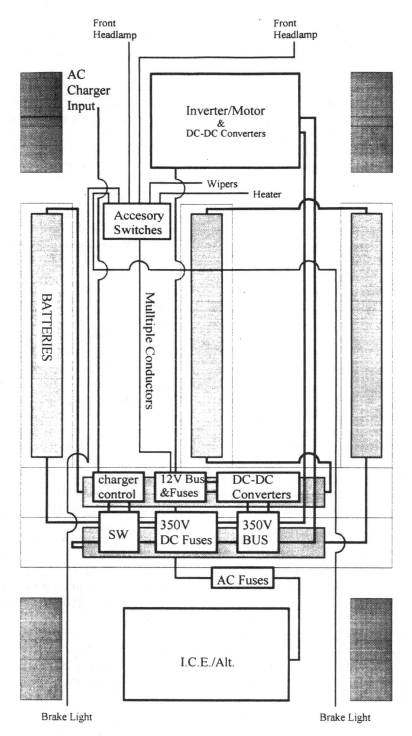

HIGH CURRENT DIAGRAM

Figure 1

Diagram of High Current Wiring

battery pack.

Drive Motor - After initial discussion, the team decided that a single electric motor driving a front wheel transaxle would be most practical. A coast-down test on one student's personal vehicle determined that 11 kW at 45 mph was a reasonable value for a large car. Thus, we began looking for a 15 hp motor which could produce at least 30 hp for short intervals. The choice finally narrowed to a General Electric 3-phase 230 V 15 hp 2 pole squirrel cage motor weighing 134 pounds on a 215T frame.

The reasons for choosing this motor:

- It was simple and durable and could be overloaded for short periods.
- It could be rewound and otherwise modified locally at reasonable cost.
- It was inexpensive. Two units were donated by General Electric.

DC motors were not chosen due to weight and cost. Permanent magnet and other "high-tech" motors were rejected on grounds of cost and reliability.

The GE motors we received have been rewound; one was converted to 4 poles, the other was rewound to 2/3 pitch, 2 poles. The two-pole motor is what we used. The electric motor was to couple directly to the Geo transmission. The transmission from our 1993 Geo gave us ratios of 13 (first gear) through 2.9 (fifth gear). To improve acceleration in competition, we exchanged the transmission for another Geo model which had a higher axle ratio. At the events, our ratios were 15, 8.3, 5.5, 3.9, and 3.3. We decided that the clutch and flywheel would make the easiest connection. Since we were unsure which gear to select, we kept all five and the clutch so that we could change our mind. In the end, circumstances dictated the outcome. At very high rpm in the lower gears, the torque-speed curve of the motor reached a "flat spot." This was predicted by two of our seminar speakers, but we persisted hoping not to have to shift. A consequence of keeping the clutch was that we kept the flywheel. Since the flywheel had been balanced with the engine crank shaft, it had to be re-balanced with the electric motor rotor. We had a noisy ride until we figured that one out. We did remove the ring gear from the flywheel to reduce drag.

Finally since we had to shift, we took pains to have the motor slightly braked (regeneratively) when the driver let up on the accelerator pedal and/or depressed the clutch. The car mimics a standard transmission conventional automobile during shifting up or down. It is very user-friendly in this regard.

Electric Inverter - Once an AC motor was selected, an inverter to convert the battery's DC to AC became necessary. Since the team had neither the time nor the expertise to design an inverter, a survey of inverter manufacturers was undertaken. It didn't take long to determine that a vector drive PWM (pulse width modulated) inverter of 20 to 40 kW rating was a reasonable target. If the inverter could be run without a shaft encoder (to tell the inverter where the rotor is) so much the better. If the inverter would realize torque control--where the throttle setting commanded a torque as

in a conventional auto engine--then our car would respond to foot throttle motion in the same manner as all other cars. A final plus would be regenerative braking capability. We were fortunate to be given a 22 kW Magnetek VCD 703 drive which did all these things plus more. Extra were a complex protection and timing program in the inverter software which indicated when the safe operating envelope of the motor-inverter was exceeded. The software included an induction motor model. The tuning capabilities were needed every time we modified the motor. The three-phase diode bridge in the inverter served to rectify the output of the APU driven alternator. A lap-top personal computer could be plugged into the inverter to gain better access to the inverter's internal software. Another similar smaller inverter was used to test the interface between our APU controller and the inverter. The inverter is mounted over the drive motor with air flow cooling and at the time of writing had never become warm. In electric-only drive at slow speeds, the dominant noise from the vehicle is a tone at 2 kHz, the inverter PWM frequency.

Alternator - We decided a high-tech alternator for battery charging and propulsion in hybrid mode would be a reasonable risk. We chose a 12 kW 3-phase 8 pole unit with a rare-earth permanent magnet (PM) rotor. The team was relieved to learn that rare-earth does not mean that the elements are truly rare enough to limit production. Nor are the rare-earth elements environmentally dangerous (Fisher Electric Motor Technology). The alternator is light (29 pounds) and compact, it generates about 320 V at 2700 rpm, and it can be easily be attached to the mounting face and shaft of a small auto engine. We had some mechanical fastening problems during break in, but since then the alternator has met its specifications. We forgot two things about permanent magnets when we ordered the alternator: 1) the magnets attract all the ferrous dust floating around our shop, and 2) with a permanent (albeit efficient) field, any changes we wished to make in alternator voltage output had to be done by waveform manipulation. In retrospect, a heavier wound-rotor alternator may have been a better choice since (especially for lead-acid gel-cell batteries) we desire to regulate charging current to stabilize the engine rpm to reduce tailpipe emissions.

Internal Combustion Engine (APU) and Fuel Supply - Emissions first and efficiency second were the criteria used for APU selection. The choice was a gasoline-powered 1993 California version of the 3 cylinder, 983 cc, 4 stroke cycle, Suzuki engine used in the Geo Metro. It has the lowest emissions of any small engine on the market, is very low mass, and has very good fuel economy (55 mpg).

The unleaded gasoline-fueled engine was selected because the infra-structure is already in place to provide unleaded gasoline. The supply of M85 or ethanol would have been a headache for our team, just as it would be a headache for anyone who would own a HEV requiring those fuels in the next five years.

APU Controller - The group doing this was called the "CPU group". The Geo engine is injected with fuel pulses whose timing and duration are determine by the standard engine control module (ECM). Although we could have simplified the ECM for our limited application (nearly constant rpm), time did not permit. Rather, we chose to interface to the throttle via a Hurst stepper motor. The scheme was to slowly adjust the charging rate as needed. Should road load change dramatically (e.g., a sudden reduction due to deceleration as when approaching a stop sign), then the throttle would be stepped down one step every two or three seconds in order to charge the batteries at a modest rate. To keep the engine rpm under control, a half-bridge voltage chopper was used to immediately respond to dramatic change (e.g., the same deceleration). The voltage chopper increases the current when the load voltage climbs (due to the battery's reduced load or even regenerative braking). By increasing alternator current, the engine rpm is kept from increasing very much. A second or two later, the throttle will be stepped closed one step (about 500 Watts less) to reduce the charging current toward a target level determined by the battery's state of charge and the operator's pre-selection of rapid or trickle charge.

The APU controller also coordinates: a) catalyst preheating, b) starting the engine either on operator's acceleration to generating speed and power, d) shut-off of the catalyst preheater at the appropriate time, e) orderly shutdown on command or automatically at a pre-set upper state of charge.

Should the APU controller computer fail, the vehicle can be driven only in ZEV mode. The CPU for the controller is Motorola 68332. A multi-position mode switch, engine temperature, engine oil pressure, engine rpm, throttle position, alternator current, and bus voltage are inputs to the APU controller.

The same CPU doubles as a dashboard controller since there is computational power and memory to spare.

Instrumentation and Sensors - Since there is large representation of electrical engineers in the project, instrumentation and data processing received considerable attention. There are several vehicle requirements which involve transducers (sensors), displays and computation. They are:

- Driver operating information: Providing vehicle speed, APU motor rpm, and battery amp-hour charge remaining in both digital and analog formats. Also APU fuel level is displayed. Colored LED's (light emitting diodes) were chosen because special purpose vacuum fluorescent displays are too expensive for "one-off" vehicles and because mixed color LED's can be seen from either side of the front seat. Special colors indicate the limits of desired operation. A diagram of the display panel is shown in Fig. 2. The circuit board-display panel was designed using the ORCAD program. The processing is done by the same CPU that controls the APU.
- Driver warning system: This system of sensors, logic, and display indicates faults in propulsion and control system components (such as overtemperature, inverter failure, CPU failure, etc.) as well as for door ajar, parking brake, and headlight-on warnings (see Fig. 3). A truth table and resultant logic design implemented the audio (buzzer) output of the logic system. The driver warning system is independent of the CPU.
- RPM sensor circuit: This detected the APU rpm from pulsations in the alternator output and processed that signal to inform the ECM of the engine rpm. This was needed because the speedometer signal which formerly was fed to the ECM had to be replaced by a meaningful input.
- Throttle position sensor circuit: This circuit isolated and scaled the throttle position output of the APU for input to the CPU section controlling the APU operation.
- Battery pack voltage sensing: The batteries were five sixty-volt packs. The voltage of each pack was sampled twice per second.
- Several other sensing circuits connected purchased subsystems to the CPU or to other HEV components.

Controls and On-board CPU - Because the implementation of computer control occurred at the end of the project and because considerable specialized preparatory work was required, the CPU group lacked the frequent interaction that other teams enjoyed. Towards the end, their work load and interaction increased dramatically. Once the controlled subsystems had been defined, the CPU group formalized specific goals for its programs. The major goals included:

- Monitoring and possible automatic adjustment and/or resetting of inverter parameters via an RS-232 interconnection.
- Collection and multiplexing of sensor signals and conversion of analog sensor signals to digital format, for example: battery pack voltage, battery current, AC motor current, APU rpm, throttle setting, alternator output voltage, drive motor temperature, inverter temperature, and fuel level.
- Processing of the above signals for APU throttle control, and for alternator output voltage control as described earlier. Operating mode control was also included.
- Display of information based on the above signals.
- Storage of significant operating parameters in non-volatile memory for diagnostic purposes.

The processors originally chosen to accomplish these tasks were the Motorola MC 68332 and the HC 11 controller. The latter was chosen for its analog to digital conversion and real-time data acquisition capabilities. However, coordination between the two processors proved difficult; only the MC 68332 was retained along with a 16 bit 16 channel analog to digital converter (ADC 8016). The CPU, auxiliary logic, storage devices (SRAM and EPROM), and interfaces (UART and ADC) are mounted on two circuit boards located behind the dashboard on the passenger's side. The display logic and drivers are included on the lower half of the custom

Figure 2

Dash Display Panel

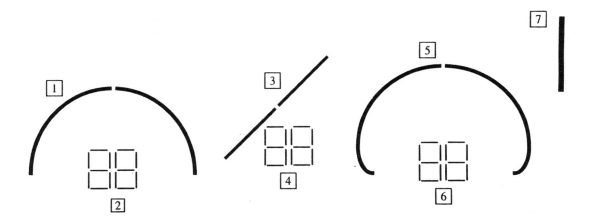

1. ANALOG - ICE Rotations per Minute
2. DIGITAL - ICE Rotations per Minute
3. ANALOG - Vehicle Speed
4. DIGITAL - Vehicle Speed

5. ANALOG - Battery Charge Level
6. DIGITAL - Battery Percent Charge
7. ANALOG - Gasoline Level

Figure 3

Diagram of Driver Warning System

THE DRIVER WARNING SYSTEM (DWS) / INSTRUMENTATION
Functional Block Diagram
(includes CPU contributions)

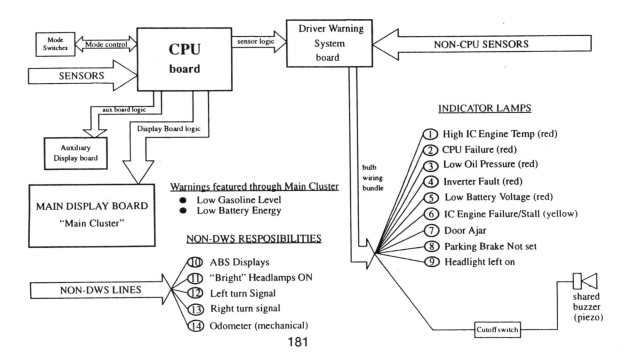

Mode Switches

Mode control

CPU board

sensor logic

Driver Warning System board

NON-CPU SENSORS

SENSORS

aux board logic

Display Board logic

Auxiliary Display board

MAIN DISPLAY BOARD
"Main Cluster"

Warnings featured through Main Cluster
● Low Gasoline Level
● Low Battery Energy

NON-DWS RESPOSIBILITIES

NON-DWS LINES

⑩ ABS Displays
⑪ "Bright" Headlamps ON
⑫ Left turn Signal
⑬ Right turn signal
⑭ Odometer (mechanical)

bulb wiring bundle

INDICATOR LAMPS

① High IC Engine Temp (red)
② CPU Failure (red)
③ Low Oil Pressure (red)
④ Inverter Fault (red)
⑤ Low Battery Voltage (red)
⑥ IC Engine Failure/Stall (yellow)
⑦ Door Ajar
⑧ Parking Brake Not set
⑨ Headlight left on

Cutoff switch

shared buzzer (piezo)

181

display circuit board in front of the driver (see Fig. 2). Since software is so amenable to "improvement," we anticipate debugging programs right up to the start of the contest! We used the C++ language along with our UNIX operating system to program the display drivers and to control digital inputs to the actuators.

Testing and Performance Evaluation of the Propulsion System - Testing began in the Fall of 1992 when the inverter, the stock GE motor, and a 250 volt gel-cell battery bank were installed in a scrapped dune buggy chassis (from an ancient VW Bug!). This ugly configuration ran in our Homecoming Parade without failing. Nevertheless, the battery bank seemed nearly exhausted after three miles and the drive motor ran hot-- even after a few bags of ice had been desperately applied during the parade! This experience was both exhilarating and sobering to the team. We realized we had no monitoring instruments and that our propulsion system wouldn't get us across town--to say nothing about Dearborn-to-Cambridge. The parade was a watershed event which unified the team and got a fire lit under it.

Shortly after the parade, a used Geo Metro (dubbed "Mule II") was purchased to use as a more-realistic test bed for propulsion components and for drivers. The Suzuki engine and associated wiring were removed from the engine compartment and the transaxle lowered so the induction motor and inverter would fit under the hood. An adapter plate between the motor and transaxle was machined. It turned out that our 215T frame motor was the largest motor which would fit the transmission without interfering with the drive shafts. This settled all debate over whether a 20 hp motor would be better than our 15 hp motor. The back seat was removed and 30 gel-electrolyte 12 volt 25 A-h wheel chair batteries were installed and isolated by an AC switch, fused at 60 amperes (motor type). The inverter control panel was put on extension ribbon and mounted in the cab. An analog zero-center ammeter and an analog voltmeter were mounted so the driver and passenger could observe battery conditions. The difference in voltage and current between full and zero throttle gave an on-line approximation of battery source (Thevenin) impedance; this and the no-load voltage indicated state of charge. Later, a donated Fluke Hydra data acquisition voltmeter was installed to record battery and inverter power output conditions. See Fig. 4.

Once Mule II was made, regular testing began and continued right up to the day that the inverter, motor and batteries (later NiMH) were moved to the final chassis. A great deal of "tuning" the inverter (by adjusting the boundaries of the safe operating area and of the induction machine model) was necessary for good performance. Hundreds of inverter parameter changes were made--many in Mule II, others on the rewinder's dynamometer when the motor was modified. Assistance from Magnetek engineers was requested and gratefully received. Two steps forward and one back was the average. Eventually performance increased until Mule II exceeded 80 mph (frowns here from the faculty advisors). The drive train required 6.2 kWh for 26 miles of urban driving (see Fig. 5). Along the way, the Suzuki engine

with exhaust and gas tank was coupled to the Fisher alternator and mounted on a two-wheeled trailer along with an ECM, a stepper motor, and a controller for the APU throttle. The three-phase alternator output was fed through a Hubbell connector and in through the rear of the car to the inverter. Now, we could run in full hybrid mode. A two-hundred mile trip followed. We managed to get 33 miles per gallon while charging the batteries at a slow rate and travelling at 50 mph, pulling a trailer--not bad for the first trip.

A vehicle log and the sampling voltmeter (with a lap top computer for memory) allowed comparison between different motors, between acceleration runs and between steady-state speed versus energy consumption runs. The data were integrated so that accurate energy consumption data could be collected. Regenerated energy was also calculated (it is typically under ten percent). We learned that analog displays (for monitoring) and digital collection (for analysis) were both necessary. The log was necessary to know the time of testing, who did it, and what they did. This was especially true while charging batteries where it was important to estimate the energy put into the batteries by the charger.

Emissions Testing and Control - Rather than attempt work with novel fuels and novel engines, our team chose to improve the emissions from an already clean conventional engine. The only emitter is the APU. The Suzuki motor we tested came with a '93 Geo Metro wrapped around it! Before we "defabricated" this brand new car, we put 200 miles on it, then verified its emission performance at a State of Michigan dynamometer. Series hybrid operation promised to reduce emissions even further than the conventional FUDS numbers since the APU would be controlled to vary slowly (if at all) between 3000 and 3600 rpm as load changed.

As is well known, cold-start emissions are a large part of the tailpipe problem. A hybrid offers an opportunity to clean up cold start emissions since ten seconds anticipation is easy to achieve. To reduce start-up emissions, a 12 V 200 A catalytic preheater (Emitech) was placed at the output of the exhaust manifold, immediately upstream from the Geo catalytic converter. When DC current was applied for ten seconds before start-up and 20 seconds after start-up, start-up emissions were reduced by 70 percent. The preheater volume was 0.1 liter; the Geo catalytic converter was 1.0 liter. Although this device would not figure in the hot-start modified FUDS required in the competition, our team accepted the 8 lb. weight penalty in order to reduce overall emissions. We have tested the device to determine the best operating procedure. A 100 page report is available which gives results for cold start CO, CH, and NOx. The ruggedness of the preheater was in question; a newer model is supposedly good for 100,000 miles.

STRUCTURE AND FRAME - The structures group was divided into a CAD group, a frame building group, a body group, and an interior design group. Since the frame had to be of original student design, the CAD group was the first to become active. The IDEAS

Figure 4

Performance Run Using Lead Acid Battery

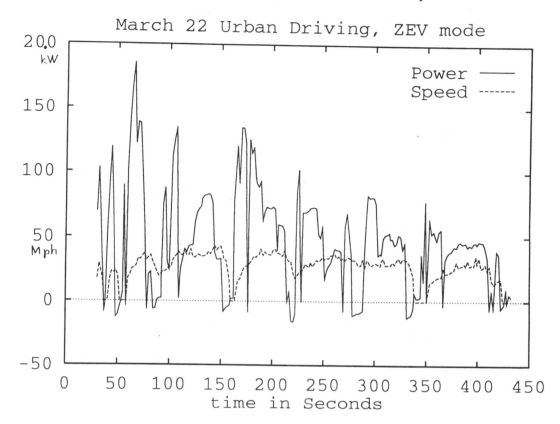

March 22 Urban Driving, ZEV mode

Figure 5

Performance Run Using NiMH Battery

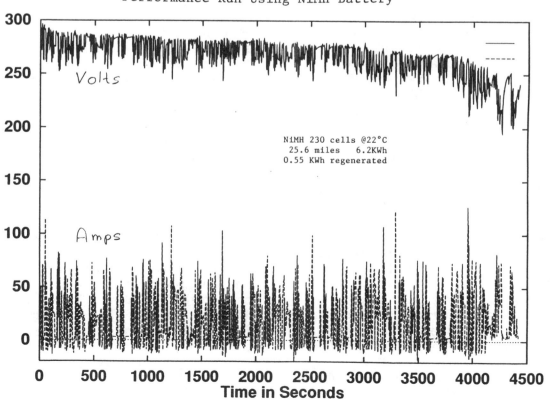

NiMH 230 cells @22°C
25.6 miles   6.2KWh
0.55 KWh regenerated

program in the MSU Case Center for Computing was the platform on which first-stage design work was accomplished.

Choice of Materials and Processes - A field trip to Pratt & Miller, a firm that builds custom cars, persuaded the group to commit to a standard "one-off" method used in building racing cars: square tubular steel space frames, front and rear, joined to an aluminum monocoque mid-section. The detachable space-frames gave the team an opportunity to have a replaceable spare frame in the event of a crash. Square steel tubing was preferred over round because it made the compound angular joints simpler, and provided better opportunities for attachment of the many components needed. The aluminum was to be riveted and glued. Over 1600 rivets were eventually used. Welded aluminum joints are brittle, so the team avoided them. The steel tubing was generally 1 1/4" square x 1/16" wall thickness. In a few places, 1/8" wall tubing was used.

CAD Design - The IDEAS model was developed as part of a design-credit exercise in a Mechanical Engineering course. Frame elements could be easily relocated. Stress testing was carried out on the computer model to elucidate structural shortcomings and over-designs. After some trial and error, a stiff frame evolved which had sufficient room for the components of our hybrid electric propulsion system, which system at the time was improved to the point where the team could proceed with confidence (see Fig. 6).

Sectioned Frame - The frame design incorporated the required steel roll bar and roll hoop. Working with the group designing the suspension, the most severe loading scenarios were established. Subjecting the car to such loads produced computed deflections and stresses in various members. Finite element analysis showed that the aluminum monocoque mid-section was quite capable of bearing loads in the loading scenarios modeled. Figure 7 shows an exaggerated displacement of the front space frame subjected to a severe torsional load (one front wheel hitting a curb while braking) while the rear space frame was held rigid. The displacement was a mere 1/2 mm. A 30 mph frontal crash was also simulated. The frame was a bit too stiff for a 30 mph crash. The occupants would not be pleased that the frame stood up so well; it may be necessary to make certain members more collapsible in the next re-design.

Interference - Major engine components were modeled and entered into the IDEAS database. The APU, the inverter, the transmission and electric motor could all be moved about in the space-frames to determine interference-free locations. IDEAS was also used to plan routes for wiring and brake lines. In retrospect, more use should have been made of the IDEAS model for avoiding interference. Several costly errors could possibly have been avoided. At one point, we abandoned an entire front frame and built another.

Construction - The frame was laid out on an 8 ft. x 6 ft. chassis plate. Our welding of the 1/16" wall tubing was awful at first, but we got much better with practice. All welds that were of doubtful strength were re-worked by an experienced welder who was a patient mentor as

well. Our vehicle frame was strong and accurate; eventually, our welds all passed inspection. When the entire three-piece frame was assembled, diagonals agreed within 3/16", well within suspension adjustment range. The weight of the frame and monocoque was 675 lbs. excluding the roll bar and roll hoop, but including the four wheels, springs and shock absorbers. A constant campaign to trim weight resulted in removal of about 35 lbs. of unnecessary steel. The frame-building group typically worked late nights on weekends. Faculty advisors became "Monday morning quarterbacks" sending signals of approval and disapproval over the execution of joints. Joints were not designed on IDEAS; they were improvised in the shop. Many engineering lessons were learned, hopefully never to be forgotten! Student team members caught on to the process and began themselves to insist on excellent execution and attention to detail. Engineering students acquired respect for technology, the skilled trades, and their practitioners.

MECHANICAL SUBSYSTEMS - Hand in hand with the structural design went the design of the suspension and steering. Much of this work was done with ruler and compass, using formulae from SAE papers and textbooks. A weight budget established some limits and awakened the team to the need for a diet.

Suspension, Wheels, Tires - Since the team had purchased a new Geo Metro, we had to have good reasons to use parts other than Geo parts. Our anticipated gross vehicle weight (GVW) was around 2,900 lbs. The Geo Metro GVW was about 2,700 lbs. Since the rules permitted those who were modifying a Ford Escort to exceed the GVW by 10% (probably because speed limits were to be strictly limited), our team felt that 2,900 lbs. would not be a dangerous overload. Mule II (also a Geo) rode low with the full battery pack; we obtained stiffer Geo rear springs (from Solectria in Massachusetts) to level the ride. These stiffer springs were transferred to the competition car. Adjustable spring stops on the rear springs permitted us some flexibility in trimming the weight distribution. In a production vehicle adjustable stops would not be needed. Our computer models showed tire rolling resistance to be a very important parameter in acquiring points in the competition. Our 2,900 lb. GVW and our search for low rolling resistance tires forced us to select 13" wheels instead of the stock 12" wheels and tires. Goodyear donated Invicta tires to fit lightweight 3-piece alloy rims. Load ratings on the tires were adequate for our GVW. We noticed that the Geo convertible used 13" tires and had 12 mm wheel studs. We decided to replace the Geo Metro's 10 mm wheel studs with 12 mm wheel studs on that basis. At this point we began to wish for anti-lock brakes since low rolling resistance tires at full pressure would probably be prone to skidding. Greater braking torque was also anticipated because of the regenerative braking being combined with disc brakes in the front. 12 mm studs made even more sense in light of these factors.

Steering - The track width of the Spartan Charge vehicle was 13 inches wider than that of the Geo Metro. Thus, the steering rack had to be lengthened by 13 inches, but lengthened in such a way as to locate the

Figure 6

Frame Design

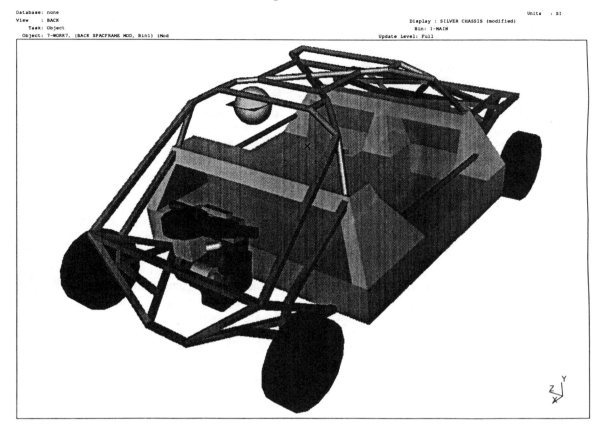

boxchassis

LOAD SET: 2 - TORSION
DISPLACEMENT - NORMAL MIN: 0.00 MAX: 0.000491

Figure 7

Frame Section Deflection Under Stress

steering column in the proper place. We decided to keep the push/pull rods of the original Geo, but this created a geometric problem unless the rack was carefully positioned fore and aft to prevent an over-center lock-up situation on the outer wheel while in a tight turn. In the process of locating the steering rack, we learned that tire side-slip made the ideal tracking path irrelevant, and that an empirical approach to locating the steering rack was adequate. Assurance that we could turn within a 12 m wide lane did make our analysis worthwhile because we had no way of checking this experimentally.

Our team preferred a Ford steering column to the Geo steering column because the dimensions were closer to what we needed. A buyer was found for the entire 1993 Geo Metro body and interior, including the steering column. That made it easier to adopt some non-Geo parts. A Ford steering column seemed like an appropriate gesture.

Safety Features - In an electric or series hybrid-electric vehicle, the parking brake must be set every time the vehicle is vacated. The transmission will not serve to hold the car from rolling since there is no compression stroke in the electric motor. Therefore, the parking brake requires a warning signal in the event the door is opened without the brake being set. Similarly, switching the main switch on while the brake is still set should trigger some sort of warning. These features were incorporated in the driver warning system (see Fig. 3). Many of the safety features mandated by the rules, but which would not be part of a production car, will not be discussed here.

Brakes - Because the front wheels had regenerative braking, the fore/aft distribution of braking effort was bound to be unbalanced assuming the Geo brakes were properly designed. Coupled with our plan for anti-lock brakes as a complement to low rolling resistance tires, it made sense to adopt a split master-cylinder braking system which was available for race cars. The Geo Metro had a vacuum booster on the brake which our team decided to abandon. We replaced the stock Geo brake pads and rear linings with pads and linings of higher coefficient of friction. This had a good effect after break-in. The vacuum assist was not used on the test vehicle, yet braking effort was reasonable and the brakes could be locked by an ordinary human. The final package, then, was to consist of special brake pads/linings, and an adjustable brake pedal which would allow us to tune the braking for front and rear wheels. With regenerative braking helping in front, the additional GVW was stopable when a little more effort was transferred to the rear wheels. The weak link in the chain became the tire-road interface and ABS appeared to help (in theory).

Fortunately, the Bosch Company saw fit to donate an ABS modulator unit to our project. In a remarkable stroke of luck, we managed to inherit the special tone-wheels which had been built and tested on a Chevrolet Sprint or Geo Metro several years ago. The front tone wheels were machined on the outside hubs of the front half-shafts; the rear tone wheels were integral with the wheel bearings (NDH Integral Bearings, Sandusky, OH). By competition time, the brake system worked, since the

Bosch system was made for a vehicle of similar weight. The front-rear tuning of the brake pedal helped greatly. The ABS system added 22 lbs. to the car's weight. Our team elected to accept the weight penalty to make a statement about safety; electric vehicles seem to demand high pressure (slippery) tires and ABS may be a necessity rather than a luxury.

BODY AND INTERIOR - Our team decided that the fastest, most efficient car in the challenge could not beat a good-looking car of lesser (but reasonable) performance. We decided to use modern fabrication techniques and to feature composite materials because we wanted to learn about them and because we hoped to impress the judges and our competitors with a car they would be proud to own.

Seats - Seats became a problem when our luggage box had to be located behind them, accessible from inside the cab. Corvette seats were lightweight and would fold far forward to give good access to the luggage box. We chose leather upholstery, convinced that it is more biodegradable than vinyl upholstery. We did use some matching vinyl upholstery elsewhere on the interior, but not by choice; more matching leather could not be located in time.

Dashboard - The dashboard held the instrument panel and printed circuit board. Also concealed in the dashboard were the APU controller, CPU and associated circuitry, and a heater/defroster. A padded front afforded the driver and passenger a modicum of safety.

Body Design - The frame developed on IDEAS was covered with a shell composed mostly of flat surfaces. A body design resulted which would have been simple to build and quite cheap. It was also rather boxy. A second attempt was made to produce a more rounded, aerodynamically-correct shape. With connections provided by Pininfarina, North America, a stylist was located who volunteered to put professional touches on our amateur attempt at design. Alchemy of Palo Alto took our computer-generated surface and developed it into an exciting, bold design (see Fig. 8). It remained for us to execute this design. We elected to use a very up-to-date method, but at great risk as it turned out. The techniques by which modern concept cars are made are time consuming and expensive. It was agreed, however, that we had the most to learn by the sophisticated method.

Body Fabrication - A male model of the car was made by casting a 5/8" undersize plywood "egg-crate" substructure. The car was done in three pieces: front, middle, and rear. Due to a communications lapse and some format mismatches, at one stage our model was 1.5 cm wider than permitted. Our attempts to "fudge" this by shaving one cm from each side ended up in other disasters. Once the male mold was made, the computer generated surface from the stylist had to be converted into a tool path for a numerically controlled milling machine. Also, we had to locate a machine large enough to accommodate each of our three molds. Demmer Corporation (Lansing, MI) fortunately came to our rescue. Control Data Corp. (Southfield, MI) donated the time and expertise to translate the IDEAS-generated surface into a tool path for Demmer's machine.

Figure 8

Body Design

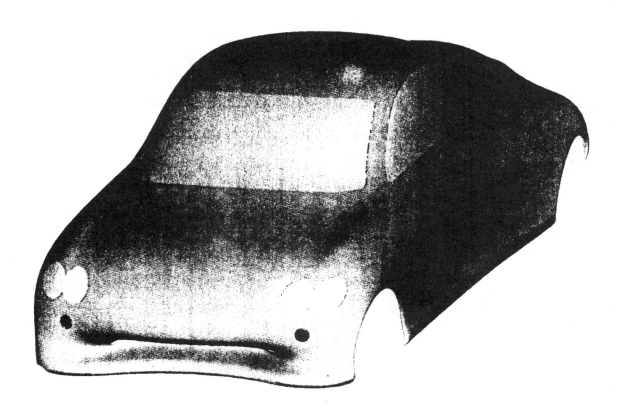

SPARTAN CHARGE HEV PROJECT SPONSORS

Ad-Tech Plastic Systems Corp.
Advanced Lead Acid Battery Consortium
Alchemy
Auto Air Composites, Inc.
Auto Truck Service Equipment
Barry Controls
Boeing Support Services
Borg & Beck Torque Systems
BP Oil Company
Robert Bosch
Campus Ford
Ciba-Geigy Composite Materials
Control Data Systems, Inc.
Copper & Brass Sales
Dexter Automotive Materials
Demmer Corporation
Eagle Picher Industries Inc.
Emitech
Fisher Electric Motor Technology
Ford Motor Co.
General Electric Company

Goodyear Tire & Rubber Co.
Kent-Moore Tool & Equipment
Jet Company
John Fluke Mfg. Co.
Lansing Electric Motor
Lear Seating Corporation
Magnetek

MSU Credit Union
MSU Bookstore
Navistar International Transport Corp
NDH Integral Bearings, Inc.
North American Lighting
North American Rockwell
Oldsmobile Division of GM
Osborne Transformer Corp.
Quadrax Corp.
Siemens Automotive L.P.
United Technologies Automotive
Vicor
Zenith Data Systems

187

Our carpentry was not accurate enough to support the computer-generated surface. We had never properly aligned all three molds, although each mold individually was pretty close. Also our one cm "correction" got us in trouble when the numerically-controlled tool crashed into the egg crate substructure beneath the target layer of epoxy dough. It took us several weeks to repair the damage and prepare a smooth sanded, blemish-free model of our car.

Casting the female mold was next. The car's surface was divided into four regions separated by flanges. Each region was carefully chosen to avoid mold traps--areas which would not release the mold. Materials for the female mold were donated by Ad Tech (Charlotte, MI). Layers were: wax, mold release, surface coat, 3 layers of fiberglass and epoxy resin, 1/2" epoxy dough tooling compound, 3 layers of fiberglass and resin. The process had about 1300 laborer-hours in it by then. The female mold was disassembled, touched-up, and re-assembled. Inside the female mold, we laid up the car's "skin": a layer of fiberglass backed by three layers of carbon fiber cloth, all pre-impregnated with epoxy resin. After oven-curing in a vacuum bag, a good-side-out body resulted.

Windows - Acrylic (Plexiglass) windows were selected for our car. Polycarbonate (Lexan) is difficult to work while keeping optical distortion to a minimum. Safety glass is not practical for a one-off car unless the car is designed around existing windows. The male mold was used to get the exact curvature in the windows. Openings were not cut in the thin carbon fiber skin until window fastener holes had been accurately drilled. Had it become necessary to use the windshield wipers for more than a few hours, we were prepared to buff the windows to restore clarity. Because of time constraints, we abandoned plans to make slider type openings in the side windows.

CONTEST PREPARATION - In one sense, all of the activity reported above is contest preparation as well as vehicle design and construction. Nevertheless, special preparation was needed on training, logistics, strategy, and communications for the actual contest in Dearborn.

Rules Analysis - The spirit of the rules was readily accepted by our team. Nevertheless, some of the rules promulgated by the sponsors were unclear, a few seemed arbitrary, and the interpretation of others changed before the actual contest. Like most engineers and managers, our team members tended to ignore rules that didn't seem logical or justified. We found it necessary to check regularly that our specifications fit the rules so that our vehicle would qualify. We suggest that any agency writing similar regulations pay special attention to clarity, physical reality, and cost of implementation. The rules of the next HEV contest should evolve from the current ones. There should be few substantive changes after the designing begins.

The point allocation for scoring was carefully analyzed early in the game; early design decisions were appropriately affected. For example, a low-cost drive motor was balanced against a higher value inverter. Some "high-tech" innovations were included solely to capture design points. Later, changes in driver training, vehicle controls, and battery-fuel management were proposed as a result of an eleventh-hour iteration of the rules analysis effort.

Strategy Simulation - A simple dynamic simulation of our vehicle was written in FORTRAN. The convex trade-off (Pareto) curves between range and drive efficiency (Btu/mi or kJ/km) were generated for the range and commuter challenge events. Sensitivity analyses and point weighing followed so that relatively simple driving strategies could be generated and their contribution to the vehicle score estimated. For example, acceleration was heavily weighted in the Commuter Challenge and driver training was organized to take this into account. Obviously, propulsive efficiency (Btu/mile) was significant in the range event; therefore, running speeds were chosen for high efficiency.

Driver Training - Because the MSU team started and stayed behind schedule, a lengthy driver training process wasn't practical. Five or six students did most of the test driving in the Mule II test platform; they were logical candidates for contest drivers. However, a written application for drivers was given to all team members so anyone who wanted could try out. The team eventually came to the wise policy of having the most experienced driver and co-pilot in the vehicle when the stakes were highest during competitive events. On the day after the competition ended, every team member present drove the car around the parking lots. It is noteworthy that everyone drove right away without instruction. By design, this was a user-friendly car with driveability similar to a conventional car.

Vehicle Support - Although we had designed and built a reliable vehicle, Murphy's Laws were still in effect. On-site support was obviously wise. A large truck was lent by Navistar for this purpose. Spare parts, diagnostic and test equipment, welder, ramps, compressor, spare batteries, and cabling, plus a plethora of hand tools were to be mounted in the truck. A trouble-shooting guide was prepared to aid students in diagnosing problems. At the competition, our car needed practically no repair or tuning. Our welder and spare parts turned out to be handy for other teams who were in trouble.

Team Communication - For road testing on campus, we were lent two Motorola handy talkies on an MSU Physical Plant frequency just in case we became stranded. For use during the events, Motorola lent us a scrambled UHF system; this was in addition to what Ford/DOE/SAE provided. Team members who were ham radio operators oversaw telemetry of critical vehicle operating parameters to our pit location. Complex communications made the co-pilot's job more critical than the driver's job at some times.

The Events - Twenty-eight of the students who designed and built the components were present at the events. The car performed well in spite of too little testing, a tribute to the students' engineering abilities. The reliability of our car permitted our team members (and faculty advisors!) to enjoy their evenings throughout the five days. We were pleased to win five of eight engineering design prizes and we were honored to have our car chosen for display at the Henry Ford Museum. In retrospect, the decision to sacrifice the cost event in order to expose our students to modern technology was probably a good decision; our goal was primarily educational and our car turned out to be quite modern compared with other cars in our class. In the dynamic events, we could have done better were it not for a little locknut missing from the screw which stopped the clutch-return. This hurt us in the acceleration event. And it makes a wonderful object lesson which will undoubtedly be retold by our alumni at future coffee breaks. Even so, we competed strongly in all events.

We would like to have been recognized for what we think was the most reliable car in the Challenge. We would also like to have been graded by a judge who would have driven every car. All in all, however, we were pleased to place third in the ground-up class. This, together with the Good Sportsmanship award we received, reflects well on Michigan State University and our industrial sponsors.

The competition was well organized and very exciting. Events were cleverly designed. It was an honor to compete with the other fine teams who were present. We are grateful to Ford Motor Company, the Department of Energy and the Society of Automotive Engineers.

SPARTAN CHARGE HEV TEAM MEMBERS

Aerni, John
Alfredson, Stefan
Amrhein, Amy
Armstead, Michael
Bauer, John
Bellfy, Paul
Bergeron, Greg
Berriman, Robert
Bickart, Ted
Blok, Alvin
Boulos, Nermine
Brinker, Greg
Butler, Gib
Cantu, Lisa
Carr, Daniel
Chakravarti, Nav
Ciccone, Jim
Clark, Karl
Connolly, Stephen
Corbeil, Donald
Cramer, John
Danielson, Howard Jr.
Darrow, Jonathan
Dautel, Doug
Davis, Steven
Dhameja, Sandeep
Diehl, Denise
Doyle, William
Drucker, Seth
Durban, Michelle
Eberlein, Brett
Ecker, Karen
Elliot, Troy
Erickson, David
Evans, Lawrence
Faulkner, Ed
Fisher, Jim
Giacoletto, Lawrence
Garza, Todd
Gerrish, John
Gibson, John
Gillian, Michael
Goodman, Amy
Gopinath, "P.G."
Grace, Colleen
Grace, Rob
Gulley, William

Gurney, Eddy
Harris, Bill
Harris, Eric
Herr, Scott
Hilliard, Michael
Hoyns, Diane
Iwamasa, Jonathan
Jennewine, John
Job, Michael
Kalmbach, David
Kaszeta, Richard
Kelly, Thomas
Kendziorski, Matt
Korecki, Steve
Kort, Daniel
Kutchey, Jeff
Landis, Donald
LaPonsey, Brian
Lassini, Stefano
Laurenz, Rodney
Lawhead, Randall
Leach, Christian
Ledebuhr, Richard
LeGassick, Jeff
Lekki, John
Lichon, Richard
Macon, Charles
Makhoul, Walid
Manetsch, Thomas
Manolias, George
McAnnally, Tom
McGregor, Kara
McIntyre, Bryan
McKee, Eric
McNamara, William
Moeggenberg, Ben
Moody, Chad
Mourou, Julien
Moy, Peter
Mueller, John
Nagy, Joe
Nicholson, Gary
Nowicki, Dean
Park, Gerald
Pawl, Nathan
Phillips, Brad
Phillips, Doug

Pittel, Mike
Pomerleau, Marc
Popps, Donovan
Potter, Bruce
Potter, Michael
Pratt, Robert
Pung, Christopher
Quinn, Andy
Rauls, Adija
Richards, Janet
Richlie, Charles
Rodner, Darren
Russ, Brian
Russell, Bill
Sabbagh, Ramzi
Sabina, Steven
Sajovec, Leslie
Sass, Ron
Schaefer, Eric
Schnepp, James
Scott, Barbara
Scouten, Kirk
Shiek, Dawn
Shippell, Joel
Siebert, Marc
Siemen, Brian
Sinaie, Kianoush
Soule, Tim
Strelecky, Rachel
Szmansky, Mike
Trivedi, Dhaval
Truong, Phu
Tsai, David
Twork, Michael
Ulrey, Scott
VanDine, Nathan
Vanniman, Dale
Varton, Eric
Wagner, Mark
Waibochi, John
Walsh, Edward
Ward, Dennis
Watkins, Donald Jr.
Welch, Dennis
Witt, Chris
Wolthuis, Richard
Woodruff, Christopher
Zimmerman, Scott

New York Institute of Technology Hybrid Electric Vehicle Project

**Babak Beheshti, Faculty Advisor, Joe Ambrosio,
Edouard Paknia, and Wonson Park**
New York Institute of Technology

ABSTRACT

The society of Automotive Engineers Student Branch at New York Institute of Technology were selected to be participants in the 1993 Ford Hybrid Electric Vehicle Challenge. After an 18 month development program, the students of NYIT produced a Hybrid Electric Vehicle which optimizes methanol and battery power. In order to reach this goal, the design team applied leading edge motor, battery and methanol engine technology. The solutions presented by the students at NYIT address problems concerning emissions control, fuel and electric power consumption and vehicle manufacturability.

191

ELECTRICAL/CONTROL SYSTEM

The Hybrid electrical vehicle (HEV) is driven by efficient and reliable DC brush electric motors. The motors can operate on the power supplied by the on board batteries, making a zero emission vehicle. The configuration for the vehicle is a series hybrid. When more range and performance is required, the driver or the control system can literally "dial in" the alternate power unit mode (APU) to accommodate conditions. It is accomplished by a commercially available Auto-CrankTM module. This starts up the methanol engine which drives a high speed generator to produce 12KW.

ZEV (Zero Emission Mode)- Power directly from the batteries. This driving mode is intended for city traffic with zero emissions. The regenerative brakes can add up to 20% to the range in city driving. A fully-charged battery package has a driving range of 35 miles at 50 mph cruising with no regen.

HEV (Hybrid Electric Mode)- When a driver turns the key on, the vehicle is in HEV mode automatically. In HEV mode, the vehicle starts in ZEV mode and later when the battery reaches 60 % DOD, APU mode begins. The APU operates in a 60% DOD to 20% DOD window, leaving the last 20% to a slower overnight charge due to the low efficiency of the end of the charge cycle. All power left over from the 12KW generator from cruising will be absorbed into the battery pack.
Tests show a generator on time of 20 to 30 minutes per HEV cycle.

Traction motor -The NYIT HEV has a front wheel drive system and each front wheel has one motor with a belt drive with a 4.48:1 ratio. Each motor has 29 peak Horse Power (HP). Each motor will draw 300 amps peak at starting with 56 N/M torque. Maximum speed of motor is 7000 rpm. The weight of one motor is 43 lbs. The maximum internal temperature of motor is 395 F and the motor will be cooled by the air ducting. This brush motor (K91-4001), which has 89% peak efficiency at 4500rpm, was purchased from Advanced DC motor company. According to the computer software that was used (Performance Analyzer TM), the two motors will move the car, which has a weight less than 2000 lbs, from 0 mph to 45 mph in 10 sec without difficulty. Cruising rpm is also in the high efficiency range of the motor.

Controller for Motor - The

method of controlling the speed of motor is Pulse Width Modulation (PWM). The NYIT motor controller, purchased from CURTIS company (PMC 1221B-74##), has two advantages. First, during acceleration and during speed operation, the Curtis PMC controller allows more current (max current = 300 A) to flow into the motor than flowing out of the battery. The controller takes in low current and high voltage (the full battery voltage = 96 Volts) and puts out high current and low voltage. The Curtis PMC controller gives NYIT HEV dramatically greater driving range per battery charge. Second, Curtis PMC controller has its own safety features. If overheating occurs (>167 F), the current limit decreases steadily until it is reduced to zero at 203 F. Also, the Curtis PMC controller is housed in rugged anodized aluminum extrusions that provides excellent environmental protection. The Curtis PMC controllers limits the motor current to a preset maximum. This feature protects the controller from damage that might result if the current were limited only by motor demand. In addition to protecting the controller, the current limit feature also protects the rest of the system. By eliminating high current surges during vehicle acceleration, stress on the motor and batteries is reduced and their efficiency and service life are improved. Similarly, there is less wear and tear on the vehicle drivetrain. The weight of each controller is 20 lbs.

Regenerative brakes -

Since the DC brush motors used have no magnets an auxiliary system must be used to get regen upon stopping. One rewired alternator is used on each front wheel and connected into the belt system. When the brake pedal is depressed a field is put across the alternators. Each alternator is rated for 3.6Kw. From test data obtained, regen will be possible down to 5mph. The system has provisions for down hill driving so it can be used most efficiently. The penalty for this extra system is weight approximately 10lbs. It is more than made up for in cost and reliability in the DC drive motors chosen.

Wiring - The main wires used for the drive motors, 2/0 and 4/0 welding cables. The battery pack can produce at least 600 amps peak for two motors. 4/0 welding cable can deliver 600 amps peak through battery disconnect switch, to the positive bus. Two 2/0 wires go to each motor. The welding cables are very flexible and 0.71 lbs per foot and kept to a minimum length. The positive bus and negative bus are front of the HEV. The reason is to save weight, each bus has six terminals. The wires were chosen for the safety, taking max amperage into account (wire burning by its own heat, max current over the time limit period).

BATTERY- Lead Acid batteries were chosen for NYIT HEV. Eight batteries connected in series. Battery specifications are as follows:
-Trojan Deep Cycle batteries (27RVH)
-rated 12 volts battery; 96 volt pack
-2.1 volts per cell, 48 cells

in battery pack
-86.6 Ah per battery at 3 hour discharge rate
-8.3 k Wh total power capacity
-300-350 cycles at 80% Depth of Discharge (DOD)
-Operating Temperature between 30-120 F
-Total battery weight is 480 lbs (60 lbs per battery)
-Physical Dimensions per battery:12.0625 x 6.75 x 9.25

Lead Acid batteries are both recyclable (100 %) and very affordable. The batteries are charged with a 96 V 25 A charger by Lester Electronics. The batteries will be charged to 100 % of capacity within the 6 hour limit (experimental charging time: 5 hour 23 minutes).

The voltage of battery pack is 102.1 v at 0 % DOD and 83.6 v at 80 % DOD. Under testing the batteries last almost two hours before dropping below 80 % DOD with a continuous 40 A draw which follows along well within company projections.

NYIT HEV battery pack has its own controller. It is "BADICHEQ". This system was developed by a German company called Mentzer Electronics. The main purpose of this controller is to equalize, with a differential of only ± 0.06 volts, each battery within the pack while both charging and discharging. This procedure will prevent overcharging and high discharge that will lead to an extension of battery life and endurance. BADICHEQ also has useful features which aid in analyzing data. The system displays the energy capacity left in the battery in % and the amount of current being used as a percentage at a maximum value at 300 A. BADICHEQ can also be interfaced with a PC. The PC will give such information as defective batteries, # of deep discharges (>80 % DOD), # of cycles, total charges, and discharges.

Battery cooling fan is connected to the battery pack delivering 12 cfm positive pressure when ever the car is running or charging.

A commercially supplied fuel gauge, Curtis 934EAS, will monitor the battery level and provide the signal which will start APU mode or warn the driver in ZEV mode at when DOD reaches 80 % DOD. DC/DC converter by Uniq mobility provides all 12v power from the main pack for all accessories (signal lights, head lights, field voltages, reverse contactors,etc).

The battery cartridge will be inserted into the center chassis tunnel and has ducts for cooling and terminals for easy connections to the power terminals.

CHASSIS AND SUSPENSION

The chassis on the NYIT HEV is an aluminum monocoque unit with OEM suspension parts integrated into the design. The motivation behind the entire Ground-Up class participation in the Ford HEV challenge was to have the ability to construct a light weight car as a complete unit. The design also is addressing the question on vehicle manufacturability. That certain unibody techniques could be used so that the prototype could easily be separated into easily parts that would be pressed or easily fabricated.The chassis unit is a unitized monocoque tub that has been fitted with SCCA specification roll-over and side impact protection. The main tub and strength in the center battery tunnel. The major challenge of battery placement in EV's was a main design consideration. The monocoque design, lended itself very well to the main center structure. This structure enables the chassis to retain it's rigidity and still have room to fit batteries without interfering with the rest of the components in the vehicle.

The addition upper strength was achieved by constructing a steel alloy roll cage around the vehicle. The tubing spans the vehicle from end to end so as to provide excellent torsional support. The roll bar itself was constructed out of 1.5" Cro-moly steel and at thickness of .083. Side impact protection is also achieved by the steel cage. The side walls of the car were kept high and solid without any breaks for door entry. The entry and egress is over the side wall with upward opening doors. The design allows for easy access for passengers and allows for a 10 sec exit time, within spec.

The suspension for the vehicle utilized many existing OEM parts. The rear suspension was assembled from a 1992 Ford Escort wagon. The focus in the construction was to use as much useful structure as load bearing points. With the help of a Finite Element Analysis program, AnsysTM, we able to optimize the construction of the unit.

The main material used in construction was aluminum. 6061 aluminum sheet (.063) was the main temper used for the forming of the bottom tub. Each panel built into the chassis help distribute and control the 500 lb weight of the battery cargo. The panels were adhered together with Aerospace adhesives and riveted together for strength in sheer and in all other directions. Panels that had to span longer distances were ribbed and pressed to provide additional load bearing strength.

The front suspension was obtained from the 82'+

Volkswagen Rabbit/Scirocco assembly. This was a good choice for our design due the direct drive configuration. The half-shafts from the VW work very well with the in-house built belt driven driveline. The bearing knuckles are all utilized as well as the entire steering mechanism (rack and pinion), including the steering column. The shock and strut assemblies of both suspensions were also used in construction.

Using the OEM parts enabled the chassis design team to have a vast selection of existing parts to solve the problems of overall geometry, safe handling, and mounting ease. The suspension also provide a smooth ride with plenty of adjustment for optimizing the ride.

BODY STYLING AND ERGONOMICS

The body of the NYIT and HEV has been designed with styling and aerodynamics in mind. The body design was modeled after some racing car designs such as CanAm and GTP. The reasoning is two fold; first of all a intensive aerodynamic study would not have been possible due to time and financial constraints and an attempt to use pre-developed styling would allow a good guide for body design.

The material for the body will be a thin aluminum skin. 3003 T4 (.030). This material will give flexibility in styling at a excellent weight savings. The material will also have very good corrosion resistance with it's coating (color) applied. This simple design goes along with the ease of manufacturability trying to be accomplished.

Due to the nature of the competition the interior of the vehicle was designed with the driver in mind, but also competition tailored. The driver and passenger will easily be able to monitor all vehicle functions from the control panel. The main cut-off switch will also be well within reach of the driver and the passenger. The cockpit was kept to a two-seater arrangement for the competition, but the automobile's wheelbase allows for the seating of four people comfortably.

The widow material for the vehicle will be a polymer plastic suited for automotive use. This material was chosen because a stock windshield could not be found that would suit our styling needs, it also went along with the teams vision of the ground up vehicle.

AUXILIARY POWER UNIT

The trend in modern high performance electric vehicle design is toward the installation of an onboard auxiliary power unit (APU).
This feature relieves the propulsion batteries, in sofar as possible, from the responsibility of providing the enormous power demands for a regular electric street car. Those power requirements include accelerations, high speed cruising etc. The installation of a series APU configuration for electric car is an excellent solution to fulfill those requirements. The design of a series APU occasionally suffers because of the tendency to regard it as just another accessory, whereas in fact, it is one more drive component on the vehicle and should be treated as such.

DESIGN REQUIREMENTS

The following is a list of functions and features of the APU that NYIT team includes in the design:

- Be efficient
- Fulfill the stringent emission requirements
- Be as light as possible
- Be as quiet as possible
- Be self sustaining
- Start and operate within the vehicle's control strategy
- Turn ON or OFF on driver's command

SELECTION OF COMPONENTS

The crucial criteria for the selection of the internal combustion engine and generator is to match both so that they operate at maximum efficiency while meeting the power requirements. Both components must also have high power to weight and power to volume ratios.
It was estimated that a 12 KW electric output from the APU would be sufficient to meet those power requirements. Engine and generator would be operating at one steady rpm for maximum efficiency.
The design team selected a UNIQ generator model# DR156X. The unit has a three phase output fully rectified DC with the following characteristics:
- EMF cte   20V/1000 rpm
- Eff.   >90% @5500 rpm
- Weight   18.5 lb

An efficiency map is shown on Fig 1 (Does not include cooling). It can be noted that in the region between 11.22 KW and 13.09 KW the unit is over 95% efficient above 5000 rpm.

A belt drive, the POLY V chain from GATES CO. is selected for the power transmission from engine to generator. This type of belt drive offers the following advantages:

- Lightweight
- 97% efficient
- Various belt sizes to accommodate shaft to shaft distance
- Various pulley sizes to select the desired speed ratio
- Low noise and vibration

The internal combustion engine

is a KAWASAKI FD-620, 617 cc, 2 cylinder, 4 stroke, water cooled delivering 20 Hp at 3600 rpm. The NYIT design team has opted to use methanol M85 as fuel and use a custom designed sequential fuel injection system and a preheated catalytic converter to achieve high efficiency and the emission requirements.

LOCATION

Provided the existence of a centrally located battery tunnel and a front wheel drive configuration, it was decided to locate the APU with the fuel cell and its battery in the rear in order to distribute the weight. Engine-Generator and radiator are located on the left side of the battery box while the fuel cell and auxiliary battery are located on the right side of the battery box. The setup helps the front to rear as well as side to side weight distribution. See Fig 2.

FUEL SYSTEM

The fuel cell, fuel rail, and fuel pump are fully methanol compatible. Although methanol is a highly corrosive fuel, polyurethane materials stand it well. The fuel cell from Aerotech Laboratories (ATL) has 8 gallons capacity and weighs 70 lb fully loaded. It meets all vehicle crash-worthiness requirements. The fuel level sensor, filler neck, are also being supplied by ATL. The level sensor is a float type, variable resistive unit which provides a full range of level indications.The submersible electric fuel pump, with integral check valve (to prevent drainage of fuel lines)

was chosen from AC Rochester Co. Its flow rate of 80 lb/hr is higher than the required 25 lb/hr but it is the smallest methanol fuel pump compatible available in market.

The fuel injection system is custom designed for a 4 stroke V-twin engine and replaces the carburetor. The sequential system injects fuel only during intake stroke. This compensates for the poor vaporization of methanol especially at low temperatures. The fuel line pressure is 45 psi and the brake specific fuel consumption is estimated at 1 lb/Hp.Hr. The fuel injector holders, the pressure regulator holder, the throttle body, pulley system for crankshaft and camshaft triggers have been designed and machined on school premises. See Fig 3. A fuel flow diagram is available on Fig 4.

COOLING SYSTEM

The internal combustion engine comes with its own radiator and mechanical fan which are directly mounted on the engine. Due to the limited space in the rear of the vehicle, the radiator had to be removed and placed in front of the left air duct. Fig B-2.
The mechanical fan is then completely detached from the engine and replaced by an electric fan meeting the same air flow requirements of 60 cfm.
The UNIQ generator requires 65 cfm and 5 in.H2O at 184 in.lb (5200 rpm). NYIT design team has selected a double stage forced air fan from AMETEK Co. to meet the cooling requirements of the generator. The fan model number E-8535-2B*

operates on 12 VDC and draws 146 W from the auxiliary battery at the operating speed. The right side air duct will solely deliver the required air for the generator.

EMISSIONS CONTROL

The exhaust pipe is going to be fitted with 3-way catalytic converter especially designed for methanol. The APU unit would not turn on unless the catalytic converter reaches its operating temperature. From the instant the signal is sent to the APU to the instant it turns on, there is a lag of 20 to 25 seconds if the exhaust is cold. The catalytic converter is from EMITEC Co. It comes with its own controller. The component works best when the number of moles of NOx and CO are relatively. The APU team
is in the process of fine tuning the engine in order to achieve
this. It appears that the amount of NOx and CO in the tailpipe are equal only when the equivalent air/fuel ratio is in the lean region. It must be furthur investigated if leaning the mixture would not harm permanently the engine.

PERFORMANCE CHARACTERISTICS

In order to achieve the desired 12 KW electric output the internal combustion engine must overcome the losses due to cooling, power transmission and generator efficiency.
E cooling= 97%
E belt = 97%
E gen = 95%

P inp= P out / (E coolingxE beltxE gen)
=12KW / (0.97x0.97x0.95)

=13.43 KW
=18 Hp
In order to achieve this, it operates at 3200 rpm with a brake specific fuel consumption of 1 lb/Hp.Hr .
At 18 Hp, the fuel consumption is 18 lb/Hr which is equivalent to 2.87 gal/Hr.
The fuel cell capacity is 8 gallons, so the APU can operate for 2.8 hours delivering 12 KW. The total energy input into the batteries is 12 KW x 2.8 Hr= 33.6 KWH.
Considering a power requirement of 9 KW at the motors to cruise at 55 mph, the APU only can provide enough energy for 3.73 Hours
covering a distance of
3.73 Hr x 55 mph = 205 miles.
The total weight of APU excluding battery and fuel cell is 116 lb (54 Kg).
Power to weight ratio = 12 KW/54 Kg = 0.22 KW/Kg
Power to volume ratio = 12 KW/20 l = 0.6 KW/l

MOUNTING SYSTEM

The engine and the generator will be mounted to a bracket as shown on FIG B-2. The bracket is "L" shaped made of 3/16" steel plate that holds both the engine, generator and their respective pulleys. This configuration helps both units keep the same shaft to shaft distance at all time during driving and minimize power transfer losses. However, the bracket itself is isolated from the frame of the vehicle by special vibration mounts. Four of those mounts are installed beneath the bracket. They are finger flex type mounts model number 10Z4-1552 from STERLING INSTRUMENT. Special straps will also be fitted to contain the fuel cell and auxiliary battery to the chassis.

ACKNOWLEDGEMENTS

The design team would like to thank all the sponsors and supporters of this project especially:

Administration NYIT
Drake Associates
LBD Design Studios
NYIT SGA
Orient Express
Emitec
Amitek
Uniq Mobility
Solar Car Corporation
Trojan Battery Co.

MOTOR MODEL: DR156X

FIG-1

PERCENT PEAK POWER, %, KW

%	0.05	0.10	0.15	0.20	0.30	0.40	0.50	0.60	0.70	0.80	0.90	1.00	0.03
KW	0.94	1.87	2.80	3.74	5.61	7.48	9.35	11.22	13.09	14.96	16.83	18.70	0.50
RPM													
0	0.000												0.000
200	0.369												0.519
400	0.693	0.537											0.795
600	0.824	0.719	0.634										0.973
800	0.878	0.814	0.752	0.697									0.896
1000	0.902	0.865	0.821	0.779									0.980
1200	0.913	0.894	0.863	0.832	0.774								0.896
1400	0.916	0.911	0.890	0.867	0.821								0.889
1600	0.916	0.921	0.908	0.890	0.854	0.817							0.880
1800	0.913	0.927	0.919	0.907	0.878	0.849							0.870
2000	0.909	0.930	0.927	0.918	0.896	0.872	0.848						0.859
3000	0.888	0.927	0.939	0.941	0.937	0.929	0.919	0.908	0.897				0.804
4000	0.847	0.912	0.933	0.942	0.948	0.947	0.943	0.938	0.933	0.927	0.920	0.914	0.751
5000	0.814	0.894	0.923	0.937	0.949	0.952	0.952	0.951	0.948	0.945	0.942	0.938	0.702
6000	0.788	0.874	0.910	0.928	0.945	0.952	0.955	0.956	0.956	0.954	0.953	0.951	0.656
7000	0.748	0.854	0.896	0.918	0.948	0.950	0.955	0.957	0.958	0.959	0.958	0.957	0.614
7500	0.733	0.844	0.889	0.913	0.936	0.948	0.954	0.957	0.959	0.960	0.960	0.959	0.595

REAR CROSS-SECTIONAL VIEW

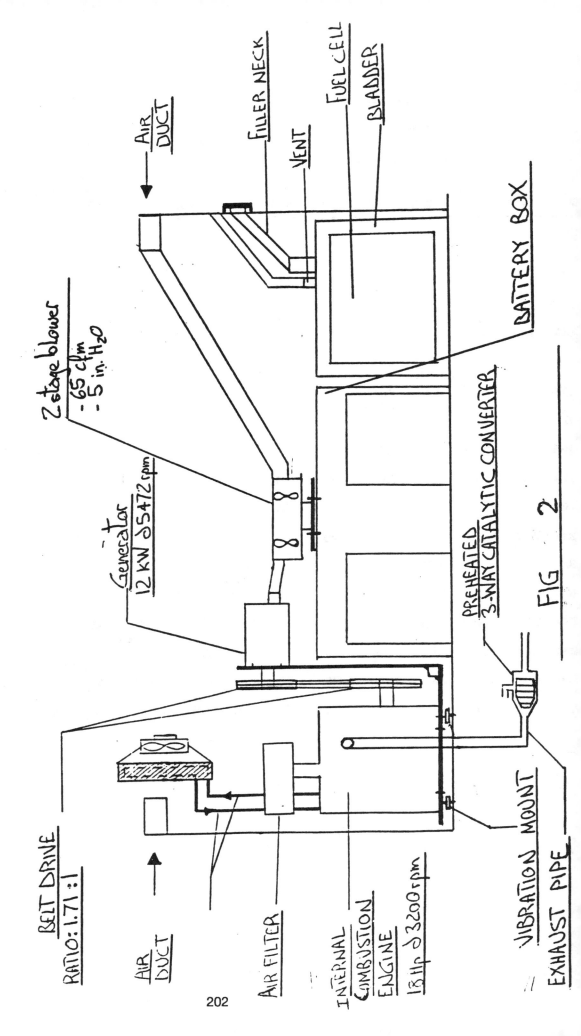

AIR DUCT

FILLER NECK

VENT

FUEL CELL BLADDER

2 stage blower
- 65 cfm
- 5 in. H₂O

Generator
12 KW @ 5472 rpm

BELT DRIVE
RATIO: 1.71 : 1

AIR DUCT

AIR FILTER

INTERNAL COMBUSTION ENGINE
18 hp @ 3200 rpm

VIBRATION MOUNT

EXHAUST PIPE

PREHEATED
3-WAY CATALYTIC CONVERTER

BATTERY BOX

FIG 2

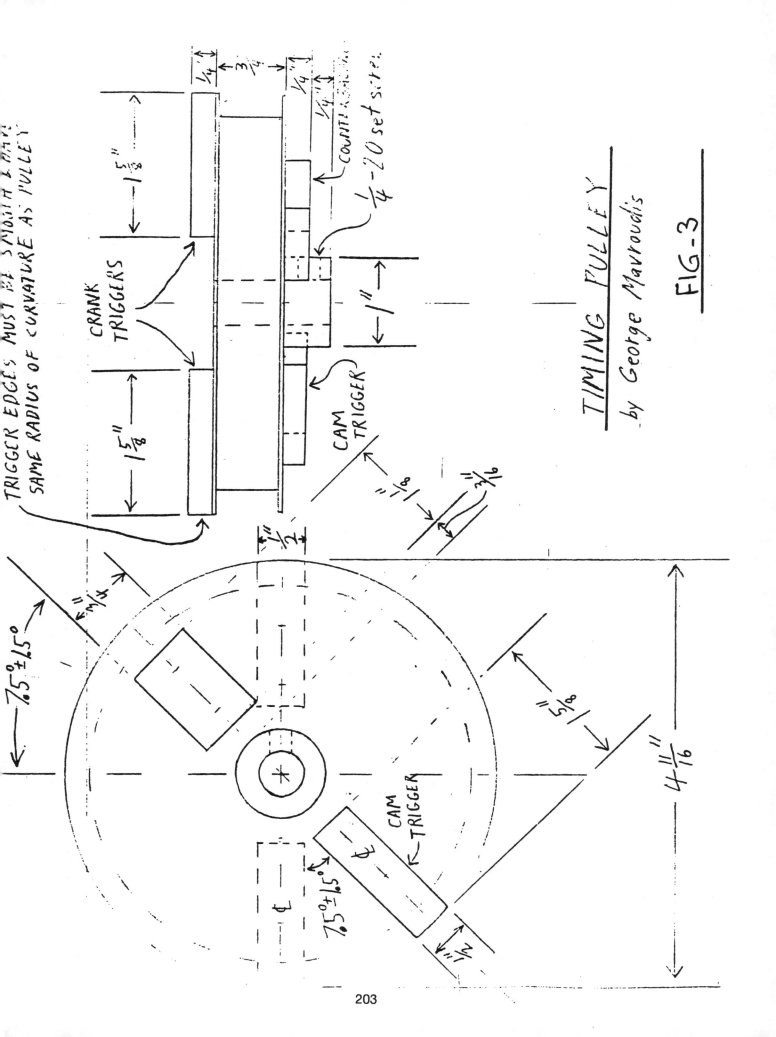

TRIGGER EDGES MUST BE SMOOTH & HAVE
SAME RADIUS OF CURVATURE AS PULLEY

CRANK
TRIGGERS

$1\frac{5}{8}$"

$1\frac{5}{8}$"

$\frac{1}{4}$
$\frac{3}{4}$
$\frac{1}{4}$"

$\frac{1}{4}$"

COUNTER BORE

$\frac{1}{4}$-20 set screw.

1"

CAM
TRIGGER

$\frac{1}{8}$"

$\frac{3}{16}$"

$\frac{1}{2}$"

$\frac{3}{4}$"

$75° \pm 15°$

$1\frac{5}{8}$"

$4\frac{11}{16}$"

CAM
TRIGGER

$75° \pm 15°$

$\frac{1}{2}$"

TIMING PULLEY
- by George Mavroudis

FIG-3

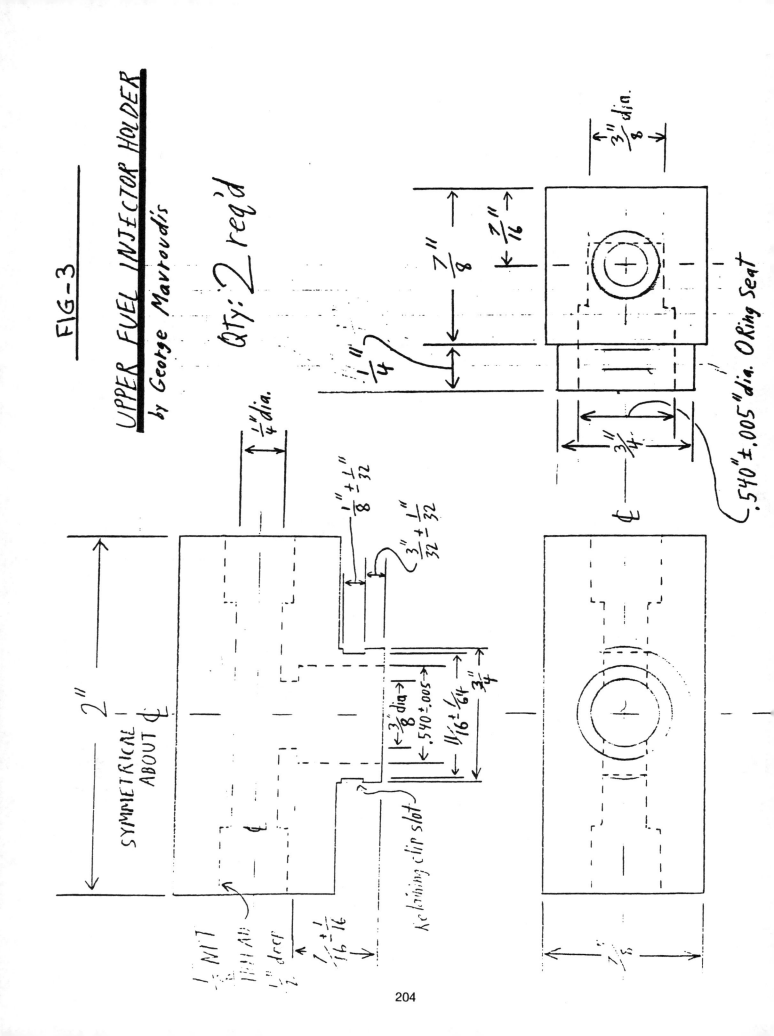

FIG-3

UPPER FUEL INJECTOR HOLDER
by George Mavroudis

Qty: 2 req'd

$\frac{1}{4}''$ dia.

$\frac{1}{8}'' \pm \frac{1}{32}$

$\frac{3}{32}'' \pm \frac{1}{32}$

$2''$

SYMMETRICAL ABOUT ℄

$\frac{1}{4}$ NPT

$\frac{3}{4}''$ DEEP

$\frac{1}{2}''$ deep

$\frac{7}{16}'' \pm \frac{1}{16}$

$\frac{3}{8}''$ dia.

.540 ± .005

$\frac{11}{16}'' \pm \frac{1}{64}$

$\frac{3}{4}''$

Retaining clip slot

$\frac{7}{8}''$

$\frac{7}{8}''$

$\frac{7}{16}''$

$\frac{1}{4}''$

$\frac{3}{4}''$

$\frac{3}{8}''$ dia.

.540" ± .005" dia. O-Ring Seat

℄

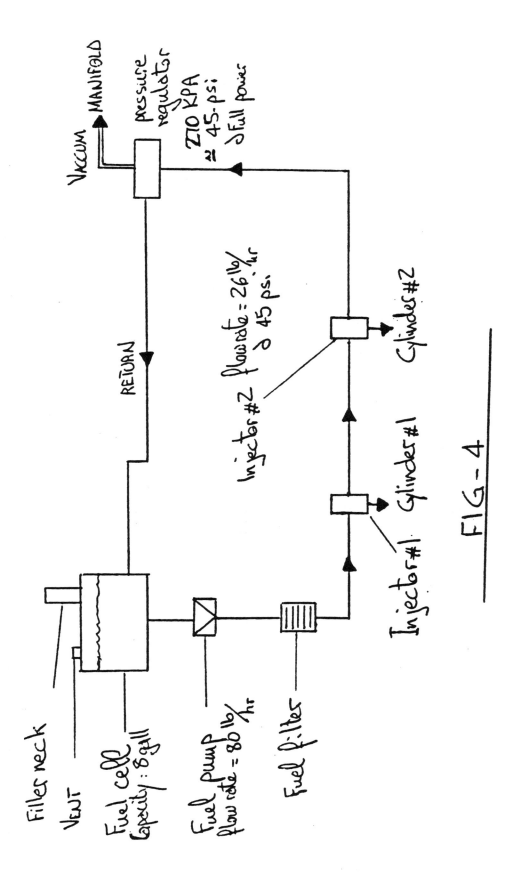

FIG-4

Seattle University - Mach.1

Ray W. Murphy, Marvin J. Baresh, Mark I. Ishida,
Rhonda A. Knutson, and Douglas N. Morrison
Seattle University

ABSTRACT

Concern for the environment has necessitated a viable alternative to gasoline powered automobiles. Hybrid electric vehicles (HEV) present a plausible solution. Seattle University (SU) has developed an HEV to compete in the Ford Hybrid Electric Vehicle Challenge. The SU HEV, which is a conversion of a 1992 Ford Escort, represents a systems approach by engineering students of Seattle University to produce a working vehicle that would be attractive to commuters while meeting the parameters of the challenge. The split parallel configuration of an electric motor and gasoline engine offers a four-wheel drive vehicle with the power to accelerate, climb hills, and have a potential range of 250 miles. The design process incorporated a computer simulation program that modeled the characteristics of an HEV in a real world setting.

INTRODUCTION

BACKGROUND - Growing concern about the environment is forcing automobile manufacturers to develop a new line of pollution free, energy efficient, electric vehicles. One type of electric vehicle, a zero emission vehicle (ZEV), has an electric motor as its only power source. Another type of vehicle, a hybrid electric vehicle (HEV), has two sources of power, an electric motor and an alternative power unit (APU). The APU acts as a range extender or as a power booster for the electric motor.

The Ford Motor Company, Department of Energy, and the Society of Automotive Engineers, interested in advancing their understanding of HEV technology, have sponsored a challenge for engineering schools to design and built an HEV.

PROJECT PARAMETERS - To compete in the challenge, Seattle University engineering students have designed and built a vehicle (SU HEV), dubbed Mach .1, to meet the criteria established by Ford. The criteria for the contest are as follows:

- be able to accelerate from 0 - 45 mph in 15 seconds (recommended)
- be able to climb at least a 15% grade

- have primary power from an electric motor, using an alternative power unit (i.e. internal combustion engine) as the supplemental power source
- provide for acceleration/deceleration cycles typical of city driving
- travel at least 40 miles in ZEV mode at a speed of 45 mph
- have an extended range of 250 miles
- contain specified safety items, including halon fire extinguishing system, seat belts, roll bar, and battery containment box

In addition to the parameters set by the HEV Challenge, the SU team set the following criteria:

- provide an efficient, powerful vehicle that would appeal to the general public
- provide the students with a design experience to fully exploit their academic knowledge, and to prepare them for real world challenges

For more specific contest requirements and specifications see Reference 1.

PURPOSE AND OVERVIEW OF REPORT - The purpose of this report is to provide a technical description and evaluation of the HEV designed by the students in the engineering disciplines at Seattle University. The report is organized as follows: under Methodology and Procedures we discuss team organization and the process by which we made design decisions including analysis of alternative solutions and the use of computer modeling. Under Results we describe the technical features of the HEV and explain its operation. Finally, under Discussion we evaluate the strengths and problem areas of our design approach and also assess what was learned by the participants in the project.

METHODOLOGY AND PROCEDURES

TEAM ORGANIZATION - The HEV design project was incorporated into the Engineering Senior Design Sequence at Seattle University. Due to the size and nature of the HEV Challenge, the team members for the overall project were subdivided into five groups, each consisting of four or five students and a faculty advisor. The total number of students working on the HEV project was 21.

A system for division of labor was established to facilitate effective design of the HEV while giving each student an equal opportunity to learn the design process, and to fit workloads within the curriculum of Seattle University's Engineering Design Sequence. The groups that were developed consisted of: 1) the Alternative Power Unit (APU) and Drive System Group, which was responsible for selecting the type and size of APU, its transmission, the fuel system, exhaust and emissions control, and halon fire protection system; 2) the Electric Motor and Drive System Group, which was responsible for selecting an electric motor, motor controller, and drive system; 3) the Controls Group, which was responsible for designing the overall control strategy for delivering power from the APU and electric motor to the wheels, and to develop the operating system by which the vehicle can be driven; 4) the Battery Group, which faced the task of selecting the quantity and type of batteries to provide the energy for the electric motor, choosing a battery charger, and designing a battery containment structure; and 5) the Suspension and Structural Modification Group, which was responsible for all required modifications to the suspension system of the HEV, including installation of a roll bar, seats, seat belts, and brakes, and for insuring overall vehicle structural integrity. Each group was responsible for ensuring that all choices followed the restrictions and limitations set by the contest rules and regulations.

PROJECT COORDINATION - Though each group had responsibilities of its own area, there was an intricate interconnection between the groups. It was necessary to develop a communication system that encouraged the groups to work together as a team and work out interfacing aspects of the vehicle.

To enhance communication, a Coordinating Committee was established, consisting of one student from each design group, the student team leader, and the faculty advisors. This committee met weekly to discuss progress, budget, and difficulties each group was facing. Major decisions of purchases and vehicle modifications needed to be cleared through the committee to prevent redundancies and to insure that each group's design strategy did not interfere with the other groups. The committee provided central control for the project to enhance the organization of the design groups so that individual efforts worked together smoothly to achieve the team's goal.

ALTERNATIVE DESIGN SOLUTIONS - Deciding on the configuration of the two power sources in the SU HEV was the most important step in the system design of the vehicle. The design team considered both series and parallel approaches (See Figure 1).

Series hybrid configuration consists of an electric motor and drive train that is the sole source of power to the wheels. It utilizes an APU coupled to a generator as a means of supplying charge to the batteries. The APU extends the range of the vehicle by charging the batteries during operation. The rate at which the APU provides charge to the battery is governed by the level of charge in the battery.

Parallel hybrid configurations consist of an electric motor and an APU which can both supply power to the wheels, simultaneously or independently. Within the parallel approach, two configurations were examined: combined parallel and split parallel. The combined parallel hybrid

combines the power output from the electric motor and the APU into a single transmission and driveline. In the split parallel hybrid, however, the two power sources remain independent of each other. The APU drives the front wheels and the electric motor drives the rear, or vice versa.

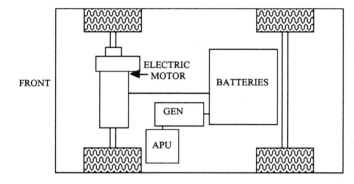

SERIES HYBRID

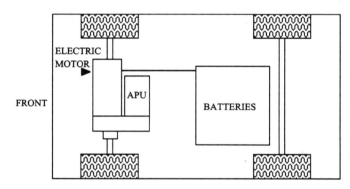

COMBINED PARALLEL HYBRID

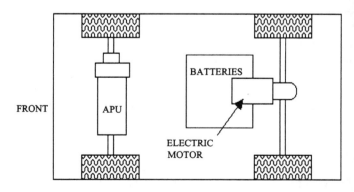

SPLIT PARALLEL HYBRID

Figure 1. Possible Configurations for Hybrid Electric Vehicles

DESIGN SELECTION - To select a drive system several criteria were developed to evaluate the series and parallel approaches. The criteria used to weigh the decision included the following:

- Efficiency
- Performance
- Ability to operate in any mode
- Simplicity and feasibility of design

In terms of efficiency, the system with the least amount of energy loss would be better suited for the contest. The series approach is less efficient than the parallel. In the series mode of operation, the APU would be used solely to charge the batteries. The process of converting fuel energy to mechanical energy (via the APU), then through a generator to create current to charge batteries, and finally to the electric motor and back into mechanical energy involves losses and inefficiencies with each step. In the parallel mode of operation, in comparison, energy loss is less because the APU takes the energy of the fuel and converts it directly to mechanical energy to be transferred to the wheels through a transmission. Similarly, the electric motor takes the energy from the batteries and converts it to mechanical energy to the wheels.

For assessing the second criterion, vehicle performance, the two configurations were judged on how well they would perform in relation to the project parameters. Performance includes acceleration, hill climbing, and range. With the series configuration acceleration and hill climbing are not benefited by the addition of the APU, which serves only to charge the batteries. With the parallel configuration, however, the power of the APU and electric motor can be combined providing the extra power necessary for such tasks. In addition, with the increased efficiency the range of the parallel vehicle will exceed that of the series vehicle.

The third criterion, the ability to operate in different modes, provides the flexibility that we believe will appeal to the general public. The series approach has only one real mode of power distribution to the wheels, which is the electric motor transmitting power to the wheels. This limited mode of operation will leave the operator stranded in case of an electric motor breakdown. The parallel system, however, allows the driver to operate singularly in one mode in case of a break down. This would allow the driver to continue driving in case of a failure of either the APU or the electric motor.

The last criterion is simplicity of design. The series configuration is the simpler approach, in that only one drive system need be designed. Also, the weight savings of using a smaller APU and a single transmission and drive system allows for either a lighter vehicle or a larger battery pack. With the parallel approach, the complexity of mating two power sources with a gear box into a single transmission, the need to work around the extra weight of the second driveline, and the control difficulties of interfacing two different power sources make the parallel system more complex.

In weighing the alternative approaches against these criteria, we decided that a parallel approach was superior to a series approach. Though the parallel approach appeared more difficult, the SU Design Team felt it was within our abilities to develop a working design that would provide the performance characteristics we were looking for. Though we agreed that a series system could compete in the Challenge, we didn't feel that it could win.

Having chosen a parallel approach, we next had to decide between a combined parallel or split parallel approach. To decide on which of these methods to use, the following criteria were considered:

- Mechanical simplicity
- Greater redundancy

In the combined parallel design approach the electric motor and the APU output power are combined into one gearbox and drive one set of wheels. At this time there is no off the shelf device to mate these two power sources easily and effectively. This alternative would require an intricate design to mate the two power sources, which was considered beyond the scope of the 21 students in the project. For the split parallel system, separate transmissions that accept only one power source are simple and readily available and can be easily adapted to alternate power sources and drive trains.

The combined parallel system also offers little flexibility in the case of a mechanical breakdown in the transmission. For the case of the split parallel system, in contrast, the greater redundancy of a drive system on both the front and the rear will enable the driver to continue home on either system if one should fail. In addition, with the split system a four-wheeled drive configuration is available if more traction is needed. We thus decided on the split parallel approach.

COMPUTER MODELING TO OPTIMIZE PARAMETERS - Having chosen the split parallel approach, it was necessary to determine how much power would be necessary to achieve the best results concerning the established criteria. The performance in the hill climbing and acceleration events needed to be maximized, and to accomplish this we needed an electric motor and APU that could provide the right amount of power. Having already researched several electric motors, APUs, transmissions, and batteries, we needed some method of modeling each configuration to determine which APU and which electric motor, when working together, could best fulfill our needs. A system analysis was necessary to accept inputs from all of the groups to determine in which direction a universal solution lay. Two computer programs written in QuickBASIC by one of the students provided the system analysis that was required.

Use of Computer Models - The system analysis necessary to determine the power requirements of the APU and of the electric motor was provided in two parts. The computer program, POWER, was initially developed in the summer of 1992. Its purpose was to determine the type and size of electric motor and APU that would be necessary to accomplish specific acceleration and constant velocity climb requirements. These requirements would be entered by the user. The results obtained would narrow down the choices of electric motors and APUs.

The second program, SIMULATOR, was begun in late September, 1992. This program would model an HEV to determine the expected performance with specific APU and electric motor choices. The desired results for a selected configuration would include a demonstration of the vehicle's acceleration, battery drainage, and fuel consumption. Ideally this program would model every changing aspect of a vehicle as it is being driven. In addition to choosing the components of the vehicle and environmental conditions, the user could input the road trip specifications, which include the mode of operation, initial and final velocities, any grades that need to be climbed, and the maximum amount of throttle the driver may request. Figure 2 presents a block outline of the available inputs and outputs of the two computer programs.

Mathematical modeling to simulate the vehicle characteristics was developed with the principles of energy conservation and vehicle dynamics. See Reference 2 for further discussion of the computer programs.

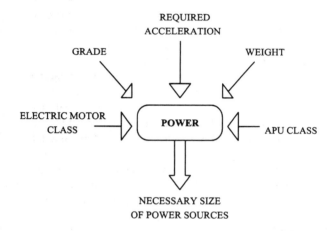

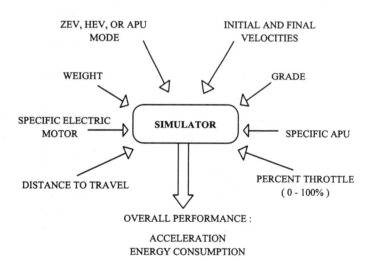

Figure 2. Block Diagram of Computer Modeling Programs

Decisions Made With Computer Models - The initial narrowing down process of the APU and electric motor selection was accomplished with the POWER program. The SIMULATOR program was used extensively to determine which specific APU and electric motor would best suit the needs of the contest.

Based on the results of these computer models, the team chose for the APU the 52 hp engine of a Geo Metro. According to the SIMULATOR, using the Geo engine with the original Ford Escort transmission would allow an acceleration of 0 to 45 in 24 seconds on APU power alone.

The modeling of the electric motors led to the final selection of the UNIQ SR180S motor. The program demonstrated that a direct drive mechanism would allow the desired acceleration of 0 to 45 in 15 seconds, however, it limited the velocity of the vehicle to that less than freeway speeds. Therefore a transmission was modeled to determine to what extent performance could be improved. The need for a multi-speed transmission became evident by the results of the program, and we chose a Volkswagen transmission.

The programs gave a tremendous amount of insight into how much difference in performance there was by changing the weight of the vehicle by 100 pounds or by limiting the amount of throttle used over a period of time. The benefits of the programs were evident not only in the choice of components, but also in the lesson they provided of how dependent each part of the vehicle is on every component of the car.

RESULTS

OVERVIEW OF VEHICLE - The SU HEV is a conversion of a 1992 Ford Escort wagon with a split parallel drive system (see Figure 3). With a split parallel drive the vehicle can be run in three different modes: electric motor only (ZEV mode), APU only (APU mode), or with both the electric motor and APU operating together (HEV mode). A gasoline powered internal combustion engine drives the front wheels of the car through a multi-speed manual transmission. The electric motor drives the rear wheels through a second multi-speed transmission. The electric motor is powered by sixteen 12-volt deep-cycle lead acid batteries connected in series. The batteries are housed in a carbon graphite composite box located in the midsection of the car just behind the front seats. The vehicle is controlled in the ZEV and APU modes through the normal vehicle controls, supplemented with special switches and logic to allow for operation in the HEV mode. Depending on the mode of operation, supplementary information is given to the driver through a special display unit. The rear suspension of the vehicle has been replaced by a Mazda Protegé independent rear suspension to provide the rear wheel drive capability. Heavy duty struts, springs, shocks, and higher load rated tires have also been added to accommodate the increased weight of the vehicle. A roll bar, restraining harness, and a halon fire extinguishing system have been added to provide additional safety to the vehicle and its passengers. The SU HEV has a seating capacity of two and weighs approximately 3400 lbs, unloaded. The expected vehicle range on a full charge of batteries is 50 miles. The anticipated fuel consumption is 25 mpg, giving the APU mode a total range of 200 miles. Further detailed breakdown is done in the following sections. For a full discussion of the design process for each section, see References 2 through 6.

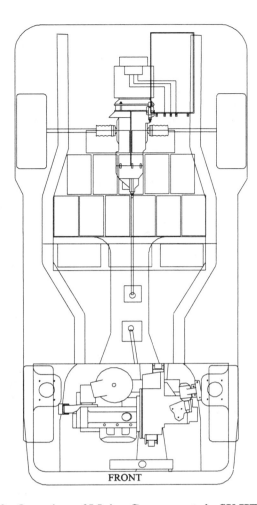

Figure 3. Overview of Major Components in SU HEV

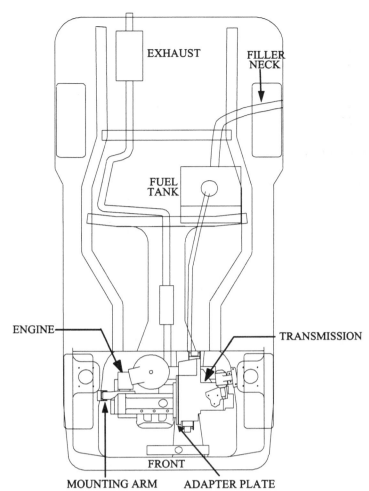

Figure 4. APU Components Within SU HEV

APU AND DRIVE SYSTEM - Figure 4 presents the placement of all APU components within the SU HEV. The APU is a 3 cylinder, 1 liter internal combustion engine, produced by Suzuki for a 1992 Geo Metro. It is rated at 52 hp at 5700 rpm and provides a torque of 57 ft-lbs at 3300 rpm. The engine runs on unleaded gasoline. The unit weighs 160 lbs. Included in the overall system is the ignition system, coolant system, and fuel injection system from the Geo Metro. Also included is the Geo's emission control system, including the exhaust gas recirculation system, positive crank case ventilation valve, and a charcoal vapor canister. The exhaust manifold and catalytic converter of the Geo Metro were mated to the existing Ford Escort exhaust system. The routing of the exhaust was not altered from the original Escort design.

The transmission is the 5 speed manual transmission that was supplied with the Ford Escort. Mating the engine to the transmission required modification of the Geo clutch assembly (see Figure 5). This included replacing the clutch disk with one from a 1989 Dihatsu Charade and machining the hub of the clutch disk to fit the spline shaft of the Ford transmission. The flywheel of the engine was machined to fit a new pilot bearing to accommodate the transmission shaft. Also required was the design and manufacture of an adapter plate with the appropriate bolt patterns to mate the engine to the transmission. The plate was produced from a 3/4" thick 7075-T651 aluminum plate. Additionally, a 3/4" spacer was utilized to move the flywheel onto the transmission shaft.

To mount the engine assembly into the engine compartment, it was necessary to construct a mounting arm and bracket to support the engine on the passenger side. Since the Ford transmission was utilized, similar mounting modifications were not necessary for the driver's side.

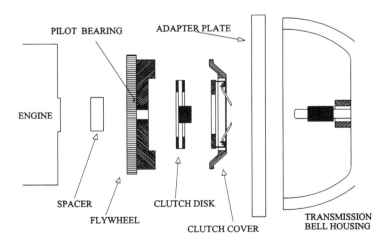

Figure 5. Mating the Geo Engine and Ford Transmission

The fuel tank was designed and constructed out of 1/8" thick 6061 aluminum. It has a capacity of approximately 8 gallons. The submersible fuel pump from the Geo Metro gas tank was incorporated into the design. The tank is mounted under the vehicle beneath the battery box on the driver's side. The original Ford Escort filler neck, fuel lines, and fuel gauge are utilized with some slight modifications. (Ref. 2)

ELECTRIC MOTOR - Details of the electric motor components and their placement within the vehicle are shown in Figure 6. The electric motor selected is the UNIQ SR180S permanent magnet, brushless DC motor. It has a horsepower rating of 43 hp, maximum torque of 66 ft-lbs, and a maximum voltage and current rating of 200 and 300 respectively. The UNIQ motor weighs 52 lbs and has a efficiency of up to 95%. The motor has regenerative braking capabilities to zero speed.

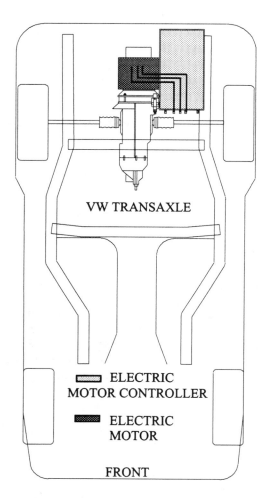

Figure 6. Electric Motor and Drive System

The electric motor is mounted in the rear section of the vehicle to power the rear wheels through a multi-speed Volkswagen transaxle. An adapter plate was machined using a 7075 - T6 aluminum block to mate the electric motor to the transaxle. There were several modifications made to the VW clutch assembly. First, the teeth on the flywheel used by the starter were machined down to make the system lighter. Next, a second adapter was machined out of 7075 - T6 aluminum to rigidly attach the flywheel to the shaft of the electric motor. Lastly, a high performance Kennedy pressure plate was used in the clutch system to help withstand the higher rpm of the electric motor. To incorporate the Volkswagen transaxle into the Mazda Protegé rear end, extensive modification was done

to the rear end. The Protegé differential was removed and part of the metal was cut away to house the Volkswagen transaxle in its place. The shift linkage from the transaxle to the shifter was shortened to allow for installation of the gear shifter to the space originally occupied by the parking brake. Figure 7 presents the mating configuration of the electric motor and drive system.

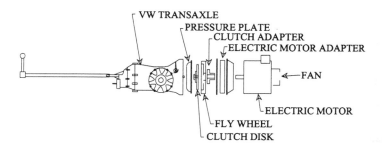

Figure 7. Mating of the Electric Motor and Drive System

To control the electric motor output, the UNIQ CR20 - 300 controller was selected. The controller has a minimum and maximum input voltage of 30 and 200 volts, respectively. It is located in the rear of the vehicle above the electric motor. The controller weighs approximately 50 lbs. (Ref. 3)

CONTROL SYSTEM - Initially, a programmable multi axis motion controller (PMAC) built by Delta Tau Industries was selected as the centralized computer component of the control system. This was to work with a three position rotary select switch to allow the control system to be dynamically reconfigured for each of the three modes: ZEV, APU, and HEV. The computer system would display vehicle status information to the driver via a liquid crystal display (LCD). A six button interlocking switch array was to be used to provide gear selection logic and data to the computer system.

In the late stages of system development, an unfortunate event occurred which rendered the PMAC computer inoperable. This required devising a new control strategy utilizing logic boards to process data from various sensors and activate appropriate switches to control vehicle operation. At the time of this writing, the system is under development.

The vehicle has two manual shift transmissions. One shift linkage is provided for the APU and a second shift linkage for the electric motor. The clutch pedal operates on both transmissions simultaneously and uses a micro switch that limits electric motor RPM to prevent electric motor over-speed. One accelerator pedal sends a zero to ten volt signal to a vacuum servo on the APU carburetor and the electric motor control unit. Two micro switches are attached to the accelerator pedal to indicate full lift or full depression of the driver's foot. Full lift of the accelerator pedal engages regenerative braking. Full depression of the accelerator pedal will provide maximum performance. (Ref. 4)

BATTERIES - The battery pack used in the SU HEV consists of 16 Dyno 27M, lead acid, 12-volt batteries configured in series which provides the electric motor with the necessary 192 volts nominal. The total pack weight is 800 lbs plus an additional 100 lbs for accessories and enclosure. The energy capacity of the pack is 14 KWh measured at the 3 hr rate. Each battery has 6 cells with a nominal voltage of 12V

(2V/cell). The minimum cycle life of the battery is 300 charge-discharge cycles measured at 80% depth of discharge. The battery pack can operate optimally between the temperatures of 0 °F and 110 °F.

The battery box is made of an aircraft quality light weight carbon graphite composite material. This construction provides the strength needed for containment as well as the low weight that this vehicle design demands. Three of the batteries are located in the foot rest area behind the front seats with the remaining thirteen in the back seat area. The batteries were placed as far forward as possible to reduce the load on the rear wheels and to maintain an acceptable center of gravity. The sheet metal beneath the rear seat area was removed and leveled using metal straps and panels (18 gage sheet steel). The box and reinforcements serve to seal off this area as well as maintain the structural integrity of the uni-body construction. The box is vented, while the pack is being used, with two SHICOH 13 cfm fans running off a VICOR DC/DC converter (192V to 12V). These fans draw air from the underside of the vehicle into the bottom front of the box and vent the air and fumes from the top rear of the box through the floor back to the underside of the vehicle (see Figure 8). This design insures that any gaseous discharge/recharge byproducts are completely removed from the vehicle. The batteries are restrained from movement within the box by framing at the base of each battery and by a cross member across the top of the batteries which is bolted to the vehicle frame. (Ref. 5)

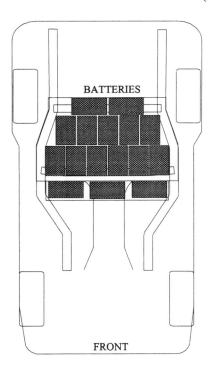

Figure 8. Battery Placement Within SU HEV

SUSPENSION/STRUCTURE - The SU HEV's primary vehicle structure and critical areas as defined in the rules and regulations were not modified. However, some parts of the vehicle floor were cut to allow space for the electric motor and the battery box as shown in Figure 9. The mid-section area

was reinforced using the battery box floor, and the rear area was strengthened with a sheet metal cover.

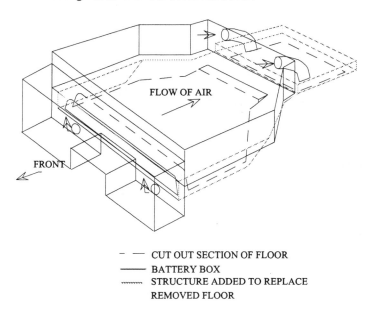

- - — CUT OUT SECTION OF FLOOR
———— BATTERY BOX
~~~~~ STRUCTURE ADDED TO REPLACE REMOVED FLOOR

Figure 9. Battery Box and Midsection Reinforcement

The contest rules and regulations state that the gross vehicle weight + 10%, which is 3812 lbs, could not be exceeded. The weight was a major concern since there were additions to the vehicle such as the batteries (800 lb), Mazda Protegé rear end (142 lb), and the electric drive system (143 lbs). This concern was addressed by taking the following steps:

- Replacing the stock FORD engine (300 lbs) with a Geo engine that weighs 160 lbs.
- Using composite material for the battery box.
- Using a light weight gas tank.

In addition, all the new components added to the vehicle were selected to minimize the weight.

The weight distribution has been changed dramatically from 59% of the total weight on the front and 41% on the rear to 38% front and 62% rear. Shift in weight distribution is mainly due to the need to locate batteries in the rear seat area and the added weight of a rear drive system. The problem was minimized by optimizing the location of the battery box, and modifying the suspension.

The front suspension of the vehicle remains unmodified because the final load is 6% below the original load. The rear suspension was modified to handle the increased load on the rear end by using the original McPherson strut assembly with stiffer springs and strengthened shock absorbers.

The brakes have been modified in the rear of the vehicle only. The replacement of the Ford Escort rear end with the Mazda Protegé rear end added rear disc brakes to the vehicle. A secondary DC vacuum source was needed, since the APU will not be able to provide vacuum for braking when in ZEV mode. To accomplish this a vacuum pump and reservoir were added in the engine compartment for the power assisted braking system.

The stock tires of the original Escort have been replaced with low rolling resistance tires. The front tires are Goodyear P185/70 R13 rated for a load of 1135 lbs each. The rear tires are Goodyear P185/80 R13 Invicta GL. rated for a load of 1301 lbs each to handle the increased load in the rear of the vehicle. The original stock seats have been replaced with light weight racing seats that allow for a five point racing harness type seat belt system. The racing seat belt had been specified in the rules and regulations. A roll bar was designed and fabricated from AISI 1020 seamless steel tubing of 1.50 inch o.d. and 0.120 inch nominal wall thickness to meet the HEV Challenge specifications. The roll bar hoop is secured to the vehicle's frame rails, located behind the front seat, and the fore and aft braces are attached to the rear shock towers using existing fastener locations as shown in Figure 10. (Ref. 6)

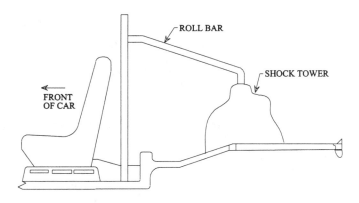

Figure 10. Roll Bar Location

VEHICLE OPERATION - The HEV control system relies on the operator's discretion for many of the coordination tasks of the power sources. Due to the complex nature of the design, the driver must fully understand the vehicle control logic and vehicle strategy. To assist the driver, a two line 40 character alpha numeric, liquid crystal display (LCD) may be used to present data such as vehicle target speed, actual vehicle speed, percentage of regenerative braking used, and power consumption (see Figure 11).

The driver interfaces with the vehicle using many of the original instruments, though their operations have changed slightly. For instance the clutch pedal disengages and engages both clutches in the vehicle. Also, the accelerator pedal sends signals to either the APU, the electric motor controller, or both depending upon the mode of operation.

Prior to any mode changes, both vehicle power sources must first be in neutral. To drive the vehicle in APU mode the driver must select the APU position on the mode selector. In this mode the driver shifts the five speed manual transmission of the APU as typical of any standard transmission vehicle.

To operate in ZEV mode the driver selects the ZEV position on the mode selector, then with the electric motor gear shift system, shifts into low gear, and then selects the appropriate button from the shift selector array. In this mode the driver shifts the 4 speed manual transmission of the electric motor as typical of any standard transmission vehicle. Reverse is available through either the front wheel

transmission in APU mode, or though the electric motor controller in ZEV and HEV modes.

To operate in HEV mode the driver selects the HEV position on the mode selector. For low gear the driver must shift the APU into neutral, shift the electric motor into low, and select the low shift array button. For second gear the driver must shift the APU into fourth gear, shift the electric motor into high gear and select the combined gear shift array button. This gear is used for increased acceleration and hill climbing. Operations in this gear are combined power source output. When the car achieves a cruise speed the driver must shift the APU into fifth gear, shift the electric motor into neutral and press the high gear selection button from the selection array.

As this is a fairly complex system, to drive the vehicle requires extensive practice to ensure a safe yet effective driving experience. Note: at the time of writing the vehicle was still under testing and development leaving controls and vehicle operation subject to change.

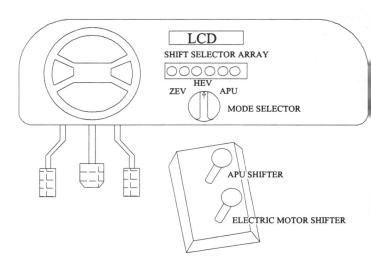

Figure 11. Driver Interface

MANUFACTURABILITY - The choice of the split parallel configuration allowed the majority of the components to be purchased "off the shelf". The APU is an engine from a 1992 Geo Metro. The front wheel transmission is the manual 5-speed from the 1992 Ford Escort. A Dihatsu clutch disk was modified for use in the system. The coolant system, engine control module (ECM), and emissions control system of the Geo Metro were incorporated. The exhaust system of the Escort was mated to the Geo catalytic converter. Modifications were necessary to mate the engine to the transmission and to mount the engine in the engine compartment.

The fuel tank needed to be designed specifically for the SU HEV. Space limitations did not allow a commercial tank to fit. The tank was welded out of aluminum, and was connected to the existing Escort fuel lines and filler neck.

The UNIQ SR180S electric motor and UNIQ CR20-300 controller were readily available. The Mazda Protegé rear end required some modification to mount to the Escort frame. The Mazda differential was removed, and a Volkswagen 4-speed manual transaxle was mounted in its place. An adapter plate was designed to mate the electric motor to the transaxle. Some modification of the clutch assembly was required.

The springs and shocks of the rear suspension were replaced with market products. The seats and seat belts were also readily available items. Though a commercial roll bar was available to fit the Escort, the SU Design Team developed a superior design and had the pieces manufactured. The tires were replaced with Goodyear P185/70 R13 in the front and Goodyear P185/80 R13 Invicta GL in the back.

The batteries are available through Dyno Batteries of Seattle, WA. The battery containment structure needed to be designed to fit the space and weight limitations of the vehicle. Building the structure was a relatively simple operation.

By limiting the number of specialty items, and using primarily readily available components, the SU Design Team constructed a vehicle that could be easily duplicated.

COST - The sticker price of an HEV such as ours will be of intense interest to consumers. The vehicle will need to be comparable to standard automobiles in price as well as performance for the consumer to be interested. With this in mind, it is helpful to place an estimate on the purchase price of the SU HEV if mass production were to begin.

Although the prototype was developed at a retail cost of $49,000. It is our estimate that a mass production version of the SU HEV could sell for much less given the cost of materials, components, and labor. The technology is available today to build an SU HEV; thus extensive funding for development and design is not necessary.

While the majority of the components utilized in our vehicle were off the shelf items, some of them had not been on the shelf for very long (i.e. the electric motor and controller). This led to a high introductory cost for the component. However, with mass production we can expect the price to drop dramatically. The price of batteries, when produced by the millions, will decrease as well.

TESTING - To ensure proper operation of all components several tests have been performed or are scheduled to be performed upon completion of the vehicle.

At the start of the project, the team tested the characteristics of the unmodified Ford Escort such as rolling resistance and handling. For handling, the car was driven through a course of four cones at ten meter centers. There were various runs through the course each attempting to obtain information about the handling under various payloads that simulated batteries in the rear of the car. Also performed was a weighing test to determine the exact weight of the vehicle to provide the team with a starting point from which to base future weight calculations. To test the performance characteristics of the APU, a direct dynamometer test was performed. Data from this test were used to plot trends of torque, horsepower, and fuel consumption versus rpm. These trends were fed into the program SIMULATOR to derive an effective strategy.

At the time of this writing, many tests have been scheduled, though not yet completed. Proposed tests involve testing the braking, handling, and performance characteristics of the vehicle. Also proposed are various tests of the electric motor, the APU, and the control system.

Testing of the vehicle's ride characteristics will entail the following types of tests. The center of gravity and weight distribution need to be verified to meet the challenge regulations. Also necessary is a tilt test to ensure that the vehicle will not roll on a 35° angle. Handling of the vehicle will be tested in a variety of road tests to check suspension, braking, and maneuverability in a slalom course.

Testing of the electric motor and APU will entail detailed control type tests to ensure the components are consistently controllable. Also to be performed are tests of the vehicle performance in acceleration, hill climbing, and endurance in all modes of operation. Fuel consumption and battery drainage will be monitored for acceleration, range, and stop-and-go performance tests.

DISCUSSION

This section analyzes the strengths and problem areas of our design approach and also summarizes what we learned about real-world engineering from participating in the HEV Challenge.

In choosing a split parallel design for the SU HEV, the Design Team intended to create a vehicle that would be easy to manufacture, that would be attractive to the general public, and that would be capable of winning the Ford HEV Challenge. The results of our entry show that our vehicle has a number of strengths combined with some notable problems.

STRENGTHS OF THE DESIGN APPROACH - Four major strengths of our design approach can be highlighted. First, our split parallel configuration, as opposed to a combined parallel design, enhances the manufacturability of the vehicle. A major drawback of the combined parallel approach is the need for a complex transmission/drive system that would accept input from two power sources. The split parallel approach, however, allows each power source to drive a set of wheels independently, using its own transmission. This approach simplifies manufacturability by using available technology. This aspect allows for easy duplication for others interested in building their own HEV, including automobile manufacturers. Though they would design new components, manufacturing such components would not involve major retooling. The "off the shelf" components simplified the overall design, and also demonstrates what can be done with the products available to the average consumer.

A second strength of our design approach is the enhanced performance characteristics that allow for greater acceleration and hill climbing. The parallel configuration allows an integration of power from the APU and the electric motor that is not available in a series design. In ZEV mode we expect an acceleration of 0 to 45 in under 15 seconds. With HEV mode, and the additional power available, the vehicle will perform even better. Climbing 15% grades will not be a problem in HEV mode. Additionally, the vehicle can operate in a 4-wheel drive mode.

A third strength of our vehicle is its flexibility of operation, which should make it especially appealing to the general public. Our goal in making an HEV that is attractive to the consumer was accomplished through several features: Our approach provides the power required for acceleration and hill climbing. Our approach also provides extended range. With an anticipated ZEV range of 50 miles, and an additional 200 miles on APU power alone, commuters can achieve short trips to the supermarket and still be able take the long Sunday drive on the highway at highway speeds. Another attractive feature of our design is the redundancy of the split parallel approach which allows the driver the peace of mind of limping home on one power source in the case that the other source fails. Also, the ability to operate in 4-wheel drive adds increased traction during times of inclement weather. Lastly, since the majority of the components are off the shelf, any spare parts necessary for repairs or maintenance are readily available.

A last strength, not of the HEV, but of our design approach, is our success in developing two computer programs that allowed us to model the HEV throughout the design. The main purpose of the simulation programs was to help the team optimize parameters when selecting and matching components within the split parallel design. By specifying performance criteria, we found solution space that included many available components. The solution space also showed that many of our possible choices would not be effective. By modeling an HEV with any combination of components (electric motor, APU, transmissions, etc.) and by specifying real world driving conditions (with hills, wind, and mechanical inefficiencies), we were able to conceptualize our design and analyze expected performance before any money was spent. When the pieces finally came together, we did not want any surprises. Computer modeling allowed us to design a vehicle that could best meet or exceed the acceleration, climb, and range requirements established by the HEV Challenge. Although testing of the vehicle is not yet complete, the projected performance in these areas anticipates a successful vehicle.

PROBLEMS ENCOUNTERED IN DESIGN - As our work progressed, three major problem areas became apparent. The first problem area involves all the difficulties associated with the overall weight of the vehicle. Due to the current level of technology, the choice of batteries left few alternatives. Lead acid batteries are not the best choice for HEVs of the future, but no other battery is currently available at a reasonable price. At the moment it is also the most environmentally friendly battery, and protecting the environment is the whole point of the HEV. The maximum weight of the vehicle is a boundary that was difficult to work within. With the 800 lb battery pack, little room to improve the electric portion of the vehicle was available. Because of the weight of the batteries, a main criterion in selecting the other components was also weight. It affected the choice of APU, electric motor and controller, transmissions, seats, fuel tank, and so forth. If the weight boundary had not been there, or if current battery technology allowed a lighter yet comparable alternative battery, some of our selected components may have been different. Two heavier automatic transmissions, for instance, would have been much easier to control than the manual counterparts.

The need to limit transmission weights thus leads to a second major problem area -- the complexity of the current operator control. With two manual gear shifts and a push button array to manipulate in HEV mode, the driver must learn new driving habits. Developing a reliable control strategy was a challenge, given the limitations placed on the components. Many ideas for improving the controls aspects were explored, but due to impending deadlines they had to be scrapped.

A third problem area resulted from the time constraints of this project. By placing the bulk of the design within the final school year, to serve as the Senior Design Sequence, we attempted to squeeze a very large project into a very short amount of time. Students dedicated more effort and time into this project than could ever have been expected for a normal Design project. Even with the extra effort, deadlines were difficult to meet. Some of the minor designs were not fully developed and left room for improvement. The area most affected by the time crunch was testing. Developing a testable vehicle earlier would have been a great improvement. Though we originally anticipated a 10 week testing period, we managed to get only three weeks.

WHAT WAS LEARNED - The HEV Challenge project was incorporated into the Senior Design sequence of Seattle University's engineering curriculum. This program provides a three-quarter, 12-credit-hour design experience for engineering students aimed at exposing them to real-world engineering while drawing on their traditional academic learning. Within the context of this curriculum, the HEV Challenge provided a particularly rich engineering experience.

Within this project, the SU Design Team learned and utilized the entire design process including establishing the need for zero emissions vehicles; understanding the problems associated with HEV design; generating potential solutions for the HEV concept and for each of the minor designs that went into the product; and evaluating the potential solutions to decide which is the best one. In addition the students learned a great deal about documenting the work, about writing technical reports, and about giving concise, clear, oral presentations.

Given the complexity of this project, and the number of students working on it, the students also learned a great deal about team dynamics. The communication and coordination between the teams was vital in the making of engineering decisions. With each of the groups codependent on the others, the importance of each step within the whole scheme of things was particularly evident. The project was like a large puzzle, in which moving one piece affected the placement of all of the others. When one group wanted to move one piece the entire HEV team was affected, requiring the need for numerous coordination meetings.

The students also learned how to use the resources that are available. Four main resources were utilized whenever the team attacked a new problem. First the students looked for the answers within themselves; having spent four years in the study of engineering, team members have begun to develop a good sense of problem solving. We incorporated our academic knowledge into the task at hand. Second was research. When solving a problem, we found it helpful to see how others solved similar problems. Through magazine articles, technical papers, and textbooks, feasible solutions and their drawbacks were identified. Faculty advisors represented a third source of information. Their engineering design knowledge, as well as their industry experience, was beneficial in analyzing the potential difficulties and attributes of each aspect of the project. Often the advisors provided more questions than answers to the students, which ensured that it was the students who solved the problem and gained the experience. When technical questions arose that were beyond the expertise of the advisors, and not readily available through publications, the students turned toward a fourth source -- consultants in the field. Discussions with auto mechanics, vendors, manufacturers, and local electric vehicle organizations provided insight that was previously lacking. Professional opinions were extremely valuable when making important decisions.

CONCLUSION - The SU Design Team had two major goals to achieve with the HEV Challenge project. The first was to design and build a viable HEV that could perform well both in the competition and for commuter use. Projected results with the simulation program indicate that the SU HEV will perform acceptably. The second goal, though by no means less important, was to give the engineering students of Seattle University an opportunity to apply their textbook knowledge to a real life engineering challenge. The students feel they have excelled within a design experience much beyond the scope of previous Senior Design projects. This aspect alone is enough to call Seattle University's entry in the HEV Challenge a success. Doing well in the competition will simply be icing on the cake.

ACKNOWLEDGMENTS

The manufacture of the Seattle University HEV (Mach .1) could not have beeen possible without the dedication, hard work, and time put forth by the following mechanical and electrical engineering students who make up the SU HEV Design Team: Marzouq Alghanim, Osama Alhouri, Rogelio Baldevia, Marvin Baresh, Richard Batuna, Brian Berryessa, Peter Cao, Mark Henry, Jonas Hinton, Mark Ishida, Phil Kartes, John Kladorus, Rhonda Knutson, John Luoma, Doug Morrison, Paul Roos, Jim Swanson, Anthony Teo, Steve Thompson, Peter Trinidad, and Robert Vawter. The project also could not have been completed without the help of faculty advisors, Dr. Robert G. Heeren, Dr. Jack D. Mattingly, Professor Ray W. Murphy, Professor Steven B. Robel, Dr. Dennis W. Wiedemeier, all of whom provided guidance and occasionally a shoulder.

The students would like to extend special acknowledgment to Blaine Shaffer for his contribution in the form of patience, wisdom, and expert craftsmanship. Also, special thanks to Dr. John Bean and the Writing Center for their assistance in editing this document.

REFERENCES

1. "Ford HEV Challenge Rules and Regulations," Ford Motor Company, Dearborn, Michigan, January 1993.

2. "Alternative Power Unit and Drive," Project Report: Hybrid Electric Vehicle Project, Engineering Design Center, Seattle University, Seattle, Washington 98122-4460, June 1993.

3. "Electric Motor and Drive," Project Report: Hybrid Electric Vehicle Project, Engineering Design Center, Seattle University, Seattle, Washington 98122-4460, June 1993.

4. "Battery System," Project Report: Hybrid Electric Vehicle Project, Engineering Design Center, Seattle University, Seattle, Washington 98122-4460, June 1993.

5. "Suspension and Vehicle Modifications," Project Report: Hybrid Electric Vehicle Project, Engineering Design Center, Seattle University, Seattle, Washington 98122-4460, June 1993.

6. "Driver/Vehicle Interface and System Controls," Project Report: Hybrid Electric Vehicle Project, Engineering Design Center, Seattle University, Seattle, Washington 98122-4460, June 1993.

Leland Stanford Junior University
"The Winds of Freedom"

Stanford Hybrid Automobile Research Project and Martin Hellman
Leland Stanford Junior University

ABSTRACT

SHARP, the Stanford Hybrid Automobile Research Project, has built The Winds of Freedom, a prototype hybrid electric vehicle (HEV) conversion of a 1992 Ford Escort. The vehicle is a series type, electric/gasoline hybrid. It principally operates as a purely-electric vehicle, powered by an electric motor and batteries for 60-80 miles. Subsequently, a 17 kW auxiliary power unit or APU (consisting of an internal combustion engine coupled to an alternator) produces electricity to drive the electric motor and recharge the batteries. The series system allows for full performance capability even in purely-electric operation and non-polluting driving for most of a user's needs. However, the APU provides The Winds of Freedom with a projected range that may even exceed conventional gasoline vehicles. This design's advantages include efficient and clean operation of the APU and the elimination of cold-start emissions. Features such as a highly efficient AC electric motor, the APU, and regenerative braking will most likely reduce the vehicle's operating cost/mile to a fraction of that of a conventional gasoline car and give it performance characteristics which are comparable to current vehicle standards.

PROJECT SYNOPSIS

The first hybrid cars were developed in the late 1800s because neither gasoline engines nor electric motors were powerful enough to drive a car. Their use was eclipsed with the rapid developments in the combustion engine. However, increasing concern for the environment and for energy conservation has once again caused hybrids to become an attractive alternative to the conventional automobile.
SHARP was formed to create a hybrid vehicle that addressed the needs of the public. Our primary goals in building an HEV were to create a design that: 1) had the greatest benefit for the environment and 2) produced a vehicle that would fit in with the existing infrastructure. Based upon these goals, we decided to convert an existing vehicle into a series hybrid configuration.
By converting an existing vehicle, we are able to demonstrate the immediate viability of this technology to the public. The ability to see a vehicle in which people can sit as they are used to sitting, carry groceries as they are used to carrying, and drive as they are used to driving, will make this car attractive and marketable. At the same time, this exciting concept will benefit the environment.
By utilizing a series configuration, we are able to offer a vehicle that will perform equally well in both ZEV (Zero Emission Vehicle) mode and HEV mode. If the general public is to truly embrace this technology, they cannot feel that they are only getting peak performance some of the time. The environmental impact of the vehicle, however, stems from the fact that 95% of the vehicle's operation will be in ZEV mode.
Throughout the project, SHARP tried to probe the limits of technology. Because of this focus, many engineering decisions were made, valuing performance enhancement over cost. We believe that once the capabilities of hybrid vehicle technology are demonstrated, less expensive methods of implementing it can be developed. Since these vehicles and their associated technologies, such as AC induction drive motors, are still in the prototype phase, they will most likely prove to be very cost effective once they are mass-produced and utilized to their full potential.
Based upon our goals, the series hybrid offers some significant technological advantages. First it allows normal day-to-day operation without loss of performance. Since 95% of people's daily driving needs are comprised of less than 60 miles, the series hybrid allows for good performance throughout vehicle operation. The series offers the opportunity to operate the Alternate Power Unit (APU) at a constant speed, thereby making it extremely clean and efficient.

VEHICLE CONFIGURATION

ELECTRICAL CONFIGURATION —Because the Winds of Freedom is a series hybrid vehicle, the car's wheels are driven solely by the electric drive motor. The electricity for this motor is supplied first by a 108V, 15 kWh Ni-Cd battery pack and subsequently enhanced by the 17 kW APU.
All high-power electrical components in the vehicle are wired, in parallel, to a central power bus. This power bus routes electricity from all sources, to all destinations. The

components located on this power bus are the drive motor, the APU, the traction battery pack, the battery rechargers, and the DC-DC converter (which provides power to a 12V accessory bus). For example, if the vehicle is fully charged, during normal operation, the batteries supply energy to the power bus while the traction motor and DC-DC converter draw from it. During regenerative braking, the traction motor supplies energy to the bus, and the DC-DC converter and batteries draw from it. When the APU is operating it supplies 17 kW to the bus. The traction motor would draw 12 kW, the DC-DC converter about 0.25 kW, and the remaining 4.75 kW would go to the batteries.

<u>System Evaluation</u> — While the car's electrical configuration is quite satisfactory, a holistic, production-oriented design would lead to significant integration of components, especially controllers and rechargers: For example, the motor controller, alternator controller and chargers all contain inverters/rectifiers which could be integrated into one unit, significantly more compact and efficient.

PHYSICAL CONFIGURATION — SHARP's overriding goal in component placement was to preserve as many of the ergonomic advantages of the Escort as possible. Preserving seating for five, full rear cargo space, and maximum leg and foot-room were prime considerations. Items which would not be included in a production vehicle, such as a roll cage and a halon fire extinguishing system, were not placed with any less consideration for space preservation. Refer to Figure 1 for a schematic diagram of the location of main components.

SHARP's original goal was to fit all components except the batteries in the original engine compartment, and place the batteries in locations which would not interfere with passenger or cargo space. The primary location for batteries is beneath the cargo area floor. Thirteen of the eighteen batteries in the car are in a fully enclosed box in this area. These batteries are arranged in three rows: the front row containing three batteries and the other two with five batteries each. By tightly locating components, we were able to place the additional five batteries in the front driver's (hereafter left) side of the engine compartment. These five batteries are in two layers: three on top, and two beneath. Because these five batteries account for 90 kg, this placement greatly improves the weight distribution compared to putting all 18 in the rear.

The differential unit was removed from the original Escort transmission, the final gear was replaced with a sprocket and High-Velocity (HV) chain, and the entire assembly was re-cased. We selected an HV chain because of its high strength and high efficiency. The case was designed to be able to accept the original half-axles and be located where the differential had been in the original Escort. The chain was added because it enabled the motor to be mounted transversely above the right half-axle. As the traction motor has an eight inch diameter, if a final gear reduction had been used instead of a chain, the motor would have interfered with the half-axle. The chain was also used because it was significantly more cost effective in a single-vehicle application. The motor is attached through a 4:1 planetary gear reduction to the pinion gear of the chain system.

The traction motor power inverter is located directly above the motor, and sits in a flat plane. The main contactor is

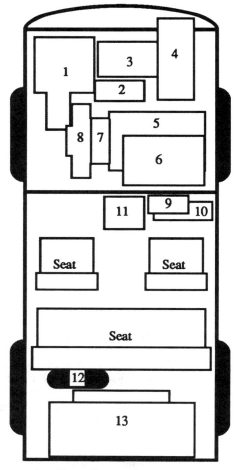

1: Front Battery Box
2: Alternator Controller
3: Alternator
4: Combustion Engine
5: Electric Motor
6: Motor Power Electronics
7: 4:1 Planetary Reduction
8: Chain Reduction/Differential
9: Motor Controller
10: Vehicle Controller
11: Rechargers
12: Spare Tire
13: Rear Battery Box

Figure 1

between the motor and the firewall. Beneath and slightly forward of the motor is the one gallon oil tank which holds the oil to cool and lubricate the motor, gear reduction, chain reduction, and differential.

In front of the motor is the 250cc motorcycle engine, which composes half of the APU. The engine is transversely mounted such that the front cylinder of the V-Twin protrudes forward of the radiator support into the front fascia of the vehicle. The engine's fuel injection system controller is mounted outside the right frame rail, in front of the wheel well, and to the right of the engine. As the alternator (which forms the other half of the APU) is coupled directly to the crankshaft, it lies to the left side of the engine.

The left half of the original radiator area is used for the engine's radiator, the traction motor's oil cooler, and the engine's oil cooler. An electric fan is mounted to draw air through the radiators. The alternator controller sits in a vertical plane between the alternator and the differential/chain case. Outside the left frame rail lie the two DC-DC converters, the 12V emergency/accessory battery, and the fuse blocks.

The main vehicle controller and the traction motor electronic controller are mounted under the passenger's side of the dashboard, and the recharger units are under the center of the dashboard. This setup allows the main battery cables to run along the left side of the car, under the driver's seat, along the center console, and to the rechargers, main contactor, traction motor power electronics, and alternator power electronics all in one line. The cabling from the front battery box is able to go directly to the DC-DC converters, run along the left frame rail to the rear of the engine compartment, and meet the rear battery cables in the center of the firewall. Routing these cables together reduces the space they occupy and minimizes electromagnetic radiation.

System Evaluation — Working within the original Escort design significantly constrained the physical configuration of The Winds of Freedom and forced SHARP to locate certain components in less than ideal locations. For example, the front row of the rear battery box intrudes four inches into the cargo area because it had to be located above an already-existing suspension arm. In addition, the motorcycle engine's air intake and exhaust system are routed rather circuitously because the engine was approximately two inches taller than the original engine compartment. However, working within these constraints allowed SHARP to achieve its goal of demonstrating that an existing vehicle could be retrofitted with a hybrid-electric drive system.

The car's physical configuration within the Escort's constraints is acceptable. We were able to locate most of the high power components in the car in the same order that they attach to the high-power electrical system, thereby creating a fairly straight wire route from the rear battery box to the center of the engine compartment. We were able to locate the motorcycle engine far enough forward to secure significant natural cooling, and were able to maintain enough frontal area to place all the radiators in the coolest area of the engine compartment. We were also able to stagger components and preserve "crush zones" in the engine compartment such that the compartment has sufficient room to buckle in the event of a frontal impact.

VEHICLE SYSTEMS

The car's systems are divided into five main groups: the traction drive system (Motor, transmission, differential), the battery system (batteries, rechargers), the alternate power unit or APU (combustion engine and alternator), the vehicle control systems, and the vehicle structure itself.

TRACTION DRIVE SYSTEM: Components 5,6,7,8,9

SPECIFICATIONS — A 56 kW continuous 3-phase AC induction motor and controller coupled to a 4:1 planetary gear reduction, a 3.5:1 High Velocity chain reduction, and the original Escort differential gears composes the traction drive system.

DRIVE MOTOR — The car uses a 3-phase AC induction motor for the main vehicle propulsion system. Decision matrix 1, Appendix A, demonstrates our evaluation of possible drive motors.

The AC induction motor, in production, seemed to be the best choice, because of its low cost, high specific power, high efficiency and rugged durability. Through arrangements with FMC Corporation, we were able to overcome some of the prototype AC induction difficulties and utilize this technology in our prototype vehicle. To obtain the desired acceleration and gradability, the vehicle's motor is a 56 kW continuous motor with a maximum speed of 15,000 rpm. The high speed and torque of the motor reduces its size and weight and eliminates the need for a multi-speed transmission. The dimensions of the motor are: 7.5 inch diameter, 12 inch length and a weight of approximately 35 kg.

This motor was designed as a joint effort between FMC and Stanford University. The system was designed to perform to the following specifications. Simulations indicate that it will meet or exceed all of these requirements:
- 0-60 mph in less than 12 seconds
- Gradability at least 30% (gradability is the maximum grade that the car can climb. 30% is equivalent to the car pushing its front wheels over a curb from a full stop.
- Capable of maintaining 55 mph on a 6% grade.

The magnetic elements of the motor, along with the controller circuitry were designed and manufactured by FMC. The housing, cooling system, and lubrication system were designed by SHARP students. SHARP also bore responsibility for design and construction of the dynamometer test setup, data acquisition system, and drive system integration. This in-house design allows the motor's cooling and lubrication oil to also lubricate the planetary gear reduction, H-V chain reduction, and differential. This custom design, coupled with the Stanford-designed chain reduction and differential unit creates an well designed, fully integrated traction drive system.

MOTOR CONTROLLER — The FMC/Stanford unit utilizes state-of-the-art AC induction controller technology. The heart of the controller consists of an inverter that uses IPMs: intelligent power modules rated for 400 Amps per phase. IPMs consist of a integrated package of two IGBTs, diodes and thermal protection circuitry. The use of IPMs in the design has decreased the overall size, and increased the reliability of the inverter. These devices carry their own thermal and electrical protection, substituting for MOSFETs or IGBTs, traditionally the Achilles' heel of AC induction power electronics. In addition to drive circuitry required by the IPMs, the inverter package also houses the main control circuitry. A speed signal from the motor through a magnetic pickup is used to close the control loop. An input at the accelerator pedal by the driver through a potentiometer, commands a required motor torque by varying the slip frequency.

The controller and motor are capable of alternator operation and hence allows regenerative braking. Simulations indicate that in a SFUDS cycle, this regenerative braking increases overall efficiency by 15%. The regenerative braking system on the car incorporates dual sensing mechanisms: one on the accelerator pedal and a second on the brake pedal.

Upon fully releasing the accelerator pedal, 10% of regenerative braking capability is activated which serves two purposes. First, it encourages efficient driving: the normal driver releases the accelerator pedal when he wants to slowly decelerate the car, for example when approaching a red light. Using small amounts of regenerative braking for a longer time is more efficient than allowing the car to coast and then forcefully depressing the brake pedal. Since an electrically driven car has significantly lower parasitic drive system losses, it will tend to coast much farther than a gasoline-powered car. Hence a normal driver would tend to release the accelerator pedal much later than would be optimal. Second, the system increases the apparent drag on the vehicle (though in this case it is not parasitic), and makes the car feel more "normal" to the average driver used to a gasoline car.

Having released the accelerator pedal, the first inch travel of the brake pedal provides direct regenerative braking. Maximum regeneration is achieved at the end of this first inch of travel. If this is not sufficient, the brake pedal can be depressed further and the vehicle's original hydraulic brake system is activated.

One potential problem in a regenerative braking system is the variance in braking "feel" depending upon the batteries' ability to absorb energy (state of discharge, operation of APU, etc.). Such variance in braking would be not only uncomfortable, but dangerous. To ensure consistent braking response, any energy which cannot be absorbed by the batteries is diverted to a resistor bank.

Air cooling would be inadequate to fully utilize the motor's capabilities. An integrated cooling and lubrication system utilizes turbine oil to lubricate all bearing surfaces and to cool the rotor and stator. Oil ports direct oil through the stator and rotor shaft, as well as through the controller. The oil from the motor then flows through the planetary gear reduction, is subsequently misted to lubricate the H-V chain, after which it flows into the differential for lubrication, and finally to the bottom of the case where a scavenging pump returns the oil to its holding tank.

TRANSAXLE — SHARP also designed the final reduction/differential unit (hereafter: final drive). The differential gears themselves were removed from the Escort transaxle to be used in our unit. Using the Escort gear package allowed us to keep the existing half-axles, which we saw no reason to replace. The bottom half of the final drive was manufactured to place the differential in exactly the same location as in the original Escort, and mounts were designed to attach to SHARP's lower mounting platform. The final drive reduction, a High-Velocity chain, extends vertically, where its pinion gear is concentric with the traction motor and planetary gear shafts. The final drive case is directly coupled and bolted to the planetary gear system, which in turn is bolted to the traction motor. These four components (motor, planetary gears, chain reduction, and differential) compose the car's unified traction drive system. The unified system, rigidly integrated, is then vibration isolated from, and mounted to, the vehicle structure.

System Evaluation — Though the system has not yet been sufficiently tested to permit a conclusive evaluation, preliminary testing indicates that this system is extremely successful. In production quantities, the HV chain would almost certainly be replaced by gears. In addition, a more holistic design of the entire system would have lightened the system by some 15-25 kg by eliminating unnecessary adapter plates and a fully integrated casing design. The system is able to generate a large amount of power and do so very efficiently and in a compact space.

BATTERY SYSTEM: Components 1,11,13

SPECIFICATIONS — The battery pack consists of 18 Saft STM 5.140 (6V) Nickel-Cadmium batteries. This is a nominal 108V, 140 A-hr pack which should provide 60-70 miles of range at a constant 55 mph and have a listed life cycle of 2000 cycles at 80% DOD. The pack weighs 300 kg when fully hydrated, and occupies 0.176 m^3. The batteries are recharged by two interconnected 3 kW rechargers.

BATTERIES — Batteries were evaluated on the criteria shown in Table 3, Appendix A. Energy density is energy storage capability per unit weight (wh/kg); power density is power release and charging capability per unit weight (w/kg). Voltage density is a measure of how many volts per unit weight without a significant reduction in energy density (for example, since Ni-Cd batteries are chemically limited to 1.2V per cell, achieving a high system voltage with a realistic amount of weight calls for so many small cells that the weight of cell casing begins to approach the weight of the cell material itself: hence, Ni-Cd's have a poor voltage density). Temperature is a compilation of efficient operating temperature and charging temperature. The remainder of the criteria should be fairly self-explanatory.

Although contacts with a Nickel Metal Hydride (NMH) battery company led to a tentative agreement to provide Stanford with a test set, the company was not able to produce enough batteries for us before the HEV challenge. Due to their extreme cost and minimal availability, we were not able to procure Nickel Iron batteries. Based on availability and state of development, we purchased Nickel Cadmium batteries. It should be noted that our use of Ni-Cd batteries is intended to simulate performance of NMH batteries and that except where noted, all characteristics of Ni-Cd batteries listed below are also applicable to NMH batteries. We reject Ni-Cd batteries for use in a production vehicle for two reasons: the serious recyclability and potential health problems related to cadmium, and the scarcity of this element.

Our battery pack was designed to meet or exceed the following specifications:

- more than 55 mile ZEV range
- 60 kW required for acceleration and regenerative braking
- High enough running voltage to allow sufficient motor power and system efficiency
- Recharge fully in 6 hours
- Weigh under 350 kg to meet GVWR requirement.

RECHARGERS — The batteries are recharged by two interconnected, fully automatic 3 kW recharging units. These units are automatically controlled for quick and efficient charging. The chargers' power cords are attached so that the units plug into a single 220V 30A outlet. When charging begins, both units are active (producing 6 kW) until the batteries reach their nominal 108V. Subsequently, one recharger turns off, and the other charger slowly reduces its output until the batteries are fully charged at 20% over their nominal voltage.

System Evaluation — All characteristics herein described for Ni-Cd batteries are also true for NMH batteries, except as noted. Ni-Cd batteries do offer the advantage of a well-developed technology. These batteries are well documented, and fairly commonplace both for household and electric vehicle applications. Although projected, the same is not yet true for Nickel Metal Hydride batteries. Nickel-cadmium bus voltage does not drop appreciably until over 80% depth of discharge. This advantage allows us to maintain 55 mph over most of the batteries range. Also, Nickel-Cadmium batteries have been shown to have long life cycles. Life spans of 2000 cycles (80% DOD) and user lives of 10 years or more are very common. While damage can quickly occur if excessive overcharging occurs (> 10% overcharge), this problem can be easily overcome with carefully designed rechargers.

This battery pack offers the user a purely electric range long enough to have a significant impact on the environment. According to information obtained during a telephone conversation with the California Air Resources Board, 95% of all daily driving needs are under 60 miles. Therefore, the APU would only operate 5% of the days. In addition, the high power density of this pack allows for efficient and effective regenerative braking capabilities, as well as exceptional motor power and acceleration.

Despite weighing over 300 kg, this battery pack's nominal voltage is only 108V. This low voltage creates performance compromises, since most electrical components in the vehicle are current limited, not power limited. In addition, lower voltage necessitates higher amperage and therefore higher losses in wiring, fuses, contactors, and controllers. This problem would be reduced through the use of Nickel Metal Hydride batteries.

ALTERNATE POWER UNIT (APU): Components 2,3,4

SPECIFICATIONS — The APU is a Honda 250cc liquid-cooled V-twin 4-stroke engine, grouped, throttle-body, computer controlled fuel injection, coupled to a 17 kW 3-phase AC induction alternator with controller.

ENGINE — Having decided upon a series hybrid impacted our APU strategy. We decided that the APU should provide sufficient power to drive the car on a flat road at highway speeds (13 kW, as determined by coast-down tests), and 25% extra to slowly recharge the batteries. This yielded an APU power requirement of 17 kW, and assuming 90-95% alternator efficiency, we concluded that we needed an engine which would supply a constant 18 kW.

Since our strategy called for our engine to run a constant speed at its most efficient point, we were left to research engines and find one whose emissions were low and efficiency was high at 18 kW.

We researched two stroke, four stroke, rotary, and gas turbine engines. The decision matrix based upon this research appears in Table 2, Appendix A.

As can be seen above, the two stroke engine had a definite power to weight ratio and size advantage over a four stroke, but fully developed two-strokes suffered emissions and efficiency handicaps. Although some information on recent two-stroke engine developments indicated that they could be considered a viable choice in the future, these developments have not yet led to fully developed, proven systems.

Rotaries' high power to weight ratios and extremely compact size was also attractive, but we could not find any rotaries in the size range we required. One, slightly underpowered, was made in England to power remotely controlled drone (target) aircraft. It's reliability was suspect due to its intended application, and its $9000 price tag and 3 month production lead time made it a poor option. Sealing problems remained a question, as did emissions, efficiency, and cold start difficulties.

Gas turbines were excluded due to high cost and limited development in small power versions as would be required for a hybrid electric vehicle.

Having decided upon a four stroke engine, power requirements of 18 kW (23 hp) excluded all car engines. Three separate motorcycle engines met our requirements and seemed essentially equivalent for our application. The Honda VTR250 was selected because of the higher availability of engines, parts, and information regarding the engine.

Subsequent Engine Modifications — Having selected the engine, we made the following modifications to enhance its performance for our application:

1) Since they were unneeded, the transmission, clutch, starter motor, alternator, and flywheel were removed to conserve weight and reduce parasitic losses. This forced us to modify the engine case to both seal now-open oil passages and drive the alternator directly off the crankshaft. A flexible chain coupling serves to isolate the vibration inherent in the engine from the alternator.

2) A tuned exhaust system was created to minimize back-pressure losses and further decrease fuel consumption at 18 kW output.

3) To eliminate evaporative emissions and enhance engine performance, efficiency, and control, the carburation system was replaced by dual throttle body fuel injection and computer control system. This system allowed us to find the optimal operating point for the engine at 18 kW, while minimizing fuel consumption and emissions. This system also allowed us to tune the fuel system for efficiency and

emissions control, rather than for power as in a standard motorcycle application.

4) To alleviate the temperature problems created by running this engine at constant high speed, an external oil cooler was added. This system draws lubrication oil from the oil pan, pumps it through a radiator, and feeds it back into the top of the oil pan.

ALTERNATOR — Our first major alternator decision was whether or not the alternator needed to be controllable. As our overriding reason for designing a series hybrid was to allow for constant RPM operation of the engine, our alternator necessarily had to be controllable. Operating the engine at constant RPM necessitates a constant load be placed on the engine by the alternator. To accomplish this, the current and the voltage output from the alternator may vary, but their product must remain constant. Since the power bus voltage rapidly fluctuates with changes in motor current draw and regenerative braking, the alternator controller needed to compensate by varying the output current. In addition, we use the alternator to start the engine, thereby eliminating the need for the engine's starter motor. This operation also necessitates alternator control.

Having concluded that we needed a controllable alternator, our decision on type matched our decision for type of traction motor. Again, due to weight and efficiency considerations AC induction seemed the logical choice. Further supporting this decision is the fact that the optimal speed for our engine was 8500-9500 RPM. Using an AC induction motor eliminated the need for a gear reduction between engine and alternator, as would have been required with a DC generator.

System Evaluation — Though the engine has performed much to our expectations, some aspects of the system have surprised us. Initially, we did not foresee the need for an oil cooler, though the system we have implemented seems to be sufficient. The engine's size has been somewhat of a liability. Due mostly to time constraints, we have not been able to reduce the size of the engine case to reflect the components removed. As such, and compacted with the fairly bulky cooling jackets necessitated by a liquid cooled engine, fitting this engine within our crowded engine compartment has taken considerable efforts. Given more time, the size difficulty could be overcome. Except for those two difficulties, the engine has exceeded our expectations. It was readily adaptable to fuel consumption, and removal of unneeded parts such as the transmission, clutch, and flywheel was not as difficult as expected. The power output of this engine was as we expected it to be, and its particularly low fuel consumption has exceeded our expectations (BSFC appears to be 4.6-4.7). General knowledge concerning this engine has been readily available, as have replacement parts. The engine has an excellent reputation and has proved exceptionally adaptable. This engine seems to be an excellent choice for our application.

The basic operation of this alternator has been tolerable for our prototype application. Some aspects of the alternator, however are less than optimal. The alternator, although only capable of 1/4 the power, is nearly the same size as our traction drive motor. By scaling our traction drive motor to meet our alternator requirements, we would trim 2-3 inches from the overall length and about 2 inches from the diameter of the alternator. Some of the discrepancy is because the alternator is air cooled, and therefore has large cooling fins which surround the case.

Using an AC induction alternator was a good decision, not only because it increased APU system efficiency by 4-7%, but because it eliminated the need for a speed reduction between engine and alternator.

EMISSIONS

The hybrid vehicle concept is based largely upon its reduced emissions over normal automobiles. While a hybrid provides several unique methods of reducing emissions, the APU emissions of the hybrid vehicle must still be reduced.

SYSTEM OVERVIEW — Overall emissions are reduced in a hybrid concept by several means: decreasing total fuel consumption, increasing efficiency, constant speed operation, and maintaining the air-fuel ratio close to stochiometric. In the SHARP design, fuel consumption is reduced by using a small but powerful 250cc motorcycle engine. The engine is run at close to its minimum specific fuel consumption point, approximately 8500 rpm. To ensure continuous operation at peak efficiency, the engine's speed is held fixed at its optimum point. In addition, the engine, as indicated above, was retrofitted with a computer-controlled fuel injection system. This system allows for significantly faster and more accurate control of air-fuel mixture and emissions.

Evaporative emissions — Evaporative emissions in the crankcase are eliminated with the installation of the fuel injection system. Evaporative emissions from the fuel tank are controlled by the stock pressure control valve which routes fuel vapor back to the fuel tank. This system, included on the original Escort, was unmodified.

Exhaust emissions — Exhaust gases are the primary source of emissions, and require one or more catalytic converters in order to eliminate HC, CO, and NOx. Since a disproportionate share of the exhaust emissions occur in the first few minutes of engine operation, before the catalytic converters reach light-off temperature, the initial SHARP design incorporated an electrically-heated catalytic converter (EHC). This system would heat the catalytic converter before engine start (since the engine is started by the vehicle controller, it is easy to heat the catalytic converter 10-15 seconds before ignition). Preheating the catalytic converter eliminates the large amount of emissions normally released before a car's catalytic converter can reach operating temperature. Eliminating these emissions is extremely significant since a study by the California Air Resources Board estimates that these emissions account for 70-90% of all emissions released during a normal round-trip.

A second down-stream catalytic converter would then provide most of the emissions reduction during normal engine operation. Depending upon the nature of the emissions emerging from the electrically-heated catalytic converter, the second converter could be a two-way or three-way converter, and could include air-injection.

SHARP obtained all the necessary components for such a system and consulted extensively with other organizations experimenting with electrically-heated catalytic converters. However, examination of the contest procedures revealed that the emissions testing would not include cold-start emissions. In fact, the engine and catalytic converter would have run for an entire test cycle before the emissions testing would begin. While an electrically-heated catalytic converter is a preferred design for any real-world application, such a design would be inefficient and irrelevant for the contest. In the interest of maximizing simplicity and minimizing weight, the system was not installed, though this electrically heated system has been installed and proven on another hybrid vehicle at Stanford University.

Contest Configuration — The emissions system installed on the car consists of two relatively small catalytic converters (to ensure fast heating), and an air injection system. This air injection reduces unburned hydrocarbons (HC) and Carbon Monoxide (CO) at the expense of Nitrogen Oxide emissions (NO). By varying the level of air injection, the emission system can be fine tuned to achieve desired emissions levels.

System Evaluation — SHARP has been satisfied with the car's emissions system, with respect to contest parameters. We feel that the system would be inappropriate for production use, since cold start emissions are of significant concern in a production vehicle. Hence we include the description of the electrically heated system which would be installed. Installing the electrically heated system necessitates the addition of either a larger accessory battery, larger DC-DC converter, or modification of the EHC's controller to heat with higher voltage or less current for a longer time. These modifications proved an unnecessary effort, as they would in no way benefit the car's performance in the HEV Challenge.

CONTROL SYSTEMS

As The Winds of Freedom is a prototype vehicle, many systems have individual control units. In addition to the overall vehicle controller, the AC induction motor and AC induction alternator, fuel injection system, and rechargers, each have a controller. The vehicle controller is discussed below. Each system controller is discussed in that system's description.

OVERALL VEHICLE CONTROLLER

SPECIFICATIONS — The vehicle controller is constructed from the following components.
- Microcontroller: Motorola MC 68HC16 - 16MHz 16-bit microcontroller with built-in Analog-Digital converter, general purpose timer, serial I/O unit.
- Sensor input: built-in A/D converter, general purpose timer.
- Data Output: Computer terminal / LCD connected through serial unit.
- Control Output: through D/A converter (Burr-Brown PCM56P)

SYSTEM OVERVIEW — Utilizing a Motorola 68HC16 microcontroller, the vehicle controller serves three distinct functions in the car. First, it carries the overall vehicle control strategy, monitoring battery state of charge and determining when to activate the APU. Second, it controls the APU

output and ensures constant speed operation of the engine when active. Third, it monitors all vehicle systems, activates cooling systems, controls driver display, and activates warning lights when necessary.

The first function of the controller entails monitoring battery state of charge and activating the APU when necessary. The controller reads the operation mode (ZEV, Zero Emission Vehicle, Batteries Only; HEV, Automatic Hybrid Operation; or APU on) from a manual dashboard switch. ZEV mode and APU on mode override the HEV mode operational strategy. ZEV and APU on modes are required for the HEV challenge competition and for testing of this prototype vehicle. This switch would not be included in a production vehicle. In HEV mode, the controller monitors the battery level from the amp-hr meter. At 80% Depth of Discharge (DOD), the controller activates the APU (see appendix A, Table 2). At about 85% DOD, the batteries' performance will begin to decrease sharply. However, 80% was selected because at that DOD, there is still enough energy left in the batteries to compensate for peak demands.

When the controller determines that APU activation is required, it proceeds through the strategy illustrated in controller strategy figure 1 (see appendix B).

Having followed this flowchart, the engine begins constant RPM operation, the second controller function. To maintain constant RPM entails keeping a constant load on the engine. This is equivalent to keeping a constant power output of the alternator. Power is the product of the current and voltage output. Since the main power bus voltage fluctuates with acceleration and regenerative braking, the vehicle controller must fluctuate the alternator output current inversely to maintain constant power. The controller outputs a -6V to +6V to the alternator controller which varies the output current accordingly. This control method allows the engine to run constantly at its cleanest, most efficient speed.

The controller's third function, a system watchdog, is perhaps the controller's most vital function. The controller monitors critical temperatures in the motor, both battery boxes, the engine, and the alternator. It also monitors battery state of charge, fuel level, currents, and voltages. The controller activates warning lights when it detects a system malfunction, and will, in potentially dangerous situations shut systems down automatically. The controller is normally powered by the DC-DC converter, but a separate 12V battery is included to ensure controller operation in the event of a battery pack failure.

BASIC CONTROL STRATEGY — The product of the main bus current and voltage is also integrated to determine the total energy to and from the battery to determine the remaining battery level, and when running in hybrid mode, when to turn on or off the APU.

The controller controls the APU by varying the throttle position and alternator load on the engine. The RPM of the APU sub-system is closely monitored both for strategy and for ensuring proper operation. Stalling, over-heating and other malfunctions of the APU sub-system are dealt with by the controller, and the APU is shut down in an emergency.

When the APU needs to be turned on in either the APU only or HEV mode, the controller goes into the start-up cycle. First, the alternator is used as a motor to start the engine up to a set RPM, after which the engine will be run at a certain speed until warm up. When the engine has reached the desired temperature, it is sped up by increasing the throttle, while the alternator load is carefully adjusted to control the RPM of the APU.

When the optimal point is reached, the controller goes into APU on mode. For optimal efficiency, the engine is kept running at constant speed and constant load. When the battery is fully recharged, or in any other situation when the APU needs to be shut down (apart from an emergency), the engine speed is decreased to idle after which the fuel injection will be cut off.

System Evaluation — The vehicle control system, is satisfactory for a prototype vehicle. Its functions provide exceptional vehicle safety and system monitoring. The control algorithm for engine control seems quite satisfactory.

In a production vehicle, the overall control system would be integrated with all other control systems in the car to eliminate redundancy. Set algorithms, such as regenerative braking operation, could be varied based upon battery state of charge to ensure optimally efficient operation. In addition, integration of low power control systems would simplify electrical insulation and electrical noise reduction.

VEHICLE STRUCTURE

STRUCTURAL MODIFICATIONS — The structural modifications to the car are intentionally minimal. The most significant modification was a removal of the cargo area floor between the frame rails to accommodate the battery box. The area removed mostly served to house and support the spare tire, which has since been relocated to the backside of the rear seat. This modification, for safety reasons, did not cut or alter any of the structural members in the car. The floor was replaced by a fiberglass/Nomex composite box which houses the 13 rear batteries. As this box is rigid, it is isolated from the more flexible Escort structure. Steel straps are enclosed in the fiberglass structure of the box, which are then bolted to the frame of the car through rubber vibration isolators.

We made small modifications in the engine compartment (cutting of sheet metal) to install various components such as the engine, DC-DC converters, and radiators. Various holes were drilled and sealed in the firewall to allow proper wire routing. We were able to rout most wires and hoses through holes which existed in the original Escort.

We modified the dashboard and instrument panel to incorporate appropriate indicator lights and gages, fire extinguishing system and power interrupt controls, and operational switches. In keeping with SHARP's goals, we were able to make most of these modifications while preserving the original Escort's ergonomic features.

SUSPENSION — Final curb weight is about 3200 lbs (700 lbs heavier than a production Escort). However, the weight distribution improved from the original 59% front/41% back to 51/49. To compensate for the change in weight and weight distribution, we replaced the original springs with stronger and stiffer ones. In addition, we replaced the fluid in the shock absorbers with a more viscous fluid, to achieve approximately the same damping rate and ride as in the original Escort.

System Evaluation — SHARP was successful in achieving its goal of minimal structural modification, even though many aspects of the Escort's original design (soft handling and a flexible body) made it less suited than other cars to adding 300 kg of batteries in the rear. Strengthening of and rigidly connecting the rear strut towers makes the car handle better with or without the batteries in back. We were pleased with the adaptability of the original instrument panel to a hybrid design. The original instrument panel was equipped with enough indicator lights and gages that no additional positions would be needed in a production vehicle. (Some additional displays, such as an oil pressure gage were incorporated in the car to allow us to monitor the operation of various operating systems.)

This minimal modification and adaptation of existing components demonstrates the manufacturability of this vehicle.

APPENDIX A: SELECTION MATRICES

Table 1: Drive Motor Selection Matrix

Criterion	Weight Factor		AC Induction		DC Brushless		DC Brush-Shunt		DC Brush-Series	
	Proto.	Prod.	Proto.	Prod.	Proto.	Prod.	Proto.	Prod.	Proto.	Prod.
MOTOR:										
Specific Power	2	3	8	10	8	8	4	4	4	4
Cost	2	5	6	10	4	4	4	6	6	6
Reliability	2	3	6	8	6	8	6	6	6	6
Durability	3	2	8	8	8	8	6	6	6	6
Efficiency	2	3	6	8	6	8	6	6	6	6
Regen. Braking	1	2	8	8	8	8	6	8	2	4
Design Feasibility	4	2	6	8	6	6	6	8	6	8
State of Development	3	2	8	8	6	6	8	8	8	8
Lead Time	4	2	4	6	8	6	6	6	10	8
CONTROLLER:										
Specific Power	2	2	6	6	6	6	6	8	8	10
Cost	2	5	4	4	4	6	6	8	10	8
Reliability	2	3	4	6	4	6	6	8	8	8
Efficiency	3	3	8	8	8	8	8	8	8	8
Regen. Braking	1	2	8	8	8	8	6	6	2	4
System Integration	1	1	6	8	4	8	4	6	4	6
Design Feasibility	4	2	4	8	6	8	6	8	8	8
State of Development	3	2	4	6	6	6	8	8	10	8
Lead Time	4	2	4	6	6	8	6	8	10	8
TOTAL			258	348	284	312	274	320	332	316

Table 2: Engine Selection Matrix

Criterion	Weight	Four Stroke			Two Stroke				Gas Turbine
		Car	Motorcycle	Wankel	Orbital	Ultralight	Motorcycle	Outboard	
Emissions	5	10	8	4	1	4	4	4	9
Cost	3	4	10	2	3	2	10	5	1
Power / Wt.	3	7	7	10	1	3	8	5	5
Availability	1	10	10	5	4	5	7	7	1
Fuel Cons.	4	7	10	5	1	4	8	5	5
Development	6	10	9	7	1	5	9	8	3
Size	4	1	7	10	2	6	8	6	6
Reliability	4	10	8	6	1	4	8	6	5
Total		225	295	187	43	126	231	173	155

Table 3: Battery Selection Matrix

Criterion	Weight	Pb-Acid	Ni-Cd	Ni-Metal-H	Ni-Fe	Na-S	Bi-polar*
Energy Density	5	1	7	9	8	8	10 (est.)
Power Density	4	1	9	9	8	6	10 (est.)
Voltage Density	2	10	1	8	8	5	10 (est.)
Temperature	2	9	9	9	9	1	10 (est.)
Availability	2	10	7	2	2	1	?
Projected Avail.	4	10	9	5	4	3	?
Recyclability	3	3	1	9	9	2	3
Cycle Life	2	6	10	10	9	5	6
Production Cost	4	10	8	9	7	5	?
Current Cost	1	10	4	3	2	2	?
Total		178	199	225	202	128	N/A

*Though not yet developed enough to have been considered for use in this competition, these batteries are listed because, if developed and tested, they would be an excellent candidate.

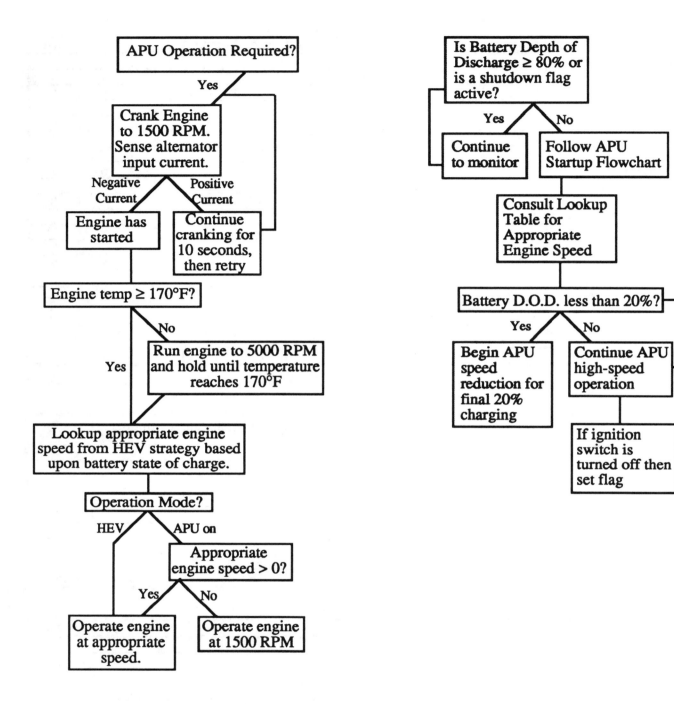

Figure 2: APU Startup Procedure

Figure 3: HEV Mode Operation

1993 Ford Hybrid Electric Vehicle Challenge

Final Design Report

The University of Tennessee

Authors: Bryce Anderson, Mark Bailey, Ken Cookson, Mike Dodd, Robert Maybury, Allen Miller, Wendy Moore, Chris Plucker, David Yarberry,

Faculty Advisors: R.K.Adams, J.W.Hodgson, F.W.Symonds

The University of Tennessee College of Engineering, Knoxville, Tennessee

ABSTRACT

Students from the University of Tennessee's College of Engineering have designed and built a hybrid electric vehicle to compete in the "ground-up" division of the 1993 Ford Hybrid Electric Vehicle (HEV) Challenge. The vehicle was specifically designed to compete in this competition held in June of 1993; therefore, design considerations focused upon the competition as being the team's "customer". The consequence of this is that the vehicle is a two passenger series hybrid (heat engine) with a pure electric range of 33 km and an acceleration capability of 0 to 75 km/hr in 10 seconds. In addition, recyclability of components was integrated into the design wherever recyclable components were available and cost effective. The steel chassis and aluminum body house a hybrid electric vehicle drivetrain featuring an air-cooled 623 cc displacement two cylinder spark ignition engine fueled with reformulated gasoline, an air-cooled brushless permanent magnet DC motor and a 180V pack of deep-cycle lead-acid batteries having a total energy storage capacity of 7.46 kW-hr. Reliability, cost effectiveness, and recyclability were the focus of this hybrid electric vehicle design effort.

DESIGN CONCEPT

The University of Tennessee's 1993 entry was developed in such a manner that a vehicle would be fully operational for this competition and would also be flexible enough to allow changes in the control and powertrain configurations as necessary for future HEV competitions. The highlights of the design and strategies implemented follow:

POWERTRAIN CONFIGURATION - The HEV team, in the spring of 1992, made the decision to use a series drivetrain. The choice of this configuration over a parallel setup was made for the following reasons:
1) Potentially higher overall efficiency
2) Lower weight
3) Greater flexibility of driving modes
4) More acceptable chassis compatibility
5) Greater ease of implementation

In the series configuration, there is no direct connection between the drive wheels and the Auxiliary Power Unit (APU). (Fig.1) The APU is directly connected to the generator which, electrically in parallel with the batteries, powers the electric motor to turn the wheels through a transaxle. A discussion of how the powertrain components were selected follows.

Computer Simulation - The University of Tennessee team decided that the vehicle should be capable of accelerating from 0 to 75 kilometers/hr in ten seconds or less. The required motor size was determined from computer simulations (SIMPLEV modelling software)The Simple Electric Vehicle Simulation Program (SIMPLEV) by Idaho National Engineering Laboratory, was used to perform parametric studies of electric vehicles based on user input driving cycles. In addition, a student generated acceleration program (EMAC) was developed to provide a simple cross-check of the results obtained from SIMPLEV. The EMAC also enabled the team to simulate a 3-speed transmission arrangement (the SIMPLEV program accomodates only one or two speed gearboxes). The in-house program agreed with SIMPLEV for one and two speed transmissions, giving the team confidence in the EMAC model.

Transaxle and Tires - Based on acceleration simulations, a Volkswagen GTI transaxle was chosen with the first 3 speeds used in the acceleration run. In order to reduce the tractive power requirements, special low rolling resistance tires provided by Michelin are used. These tires have a coefficient of rolling resistance of 0.0067.

Electric Motor - After a thorough search, the team chose the Unique Mobility SR180 motor and controller. A novel motor developed at the University of Tennessee was considered but a unit designed to suit the HEV application could not be assembled in time for the competition. The SR180 is a permanent-magnet air-cooled motor which operates from a DC supply up to 200 volts. However, maximum performance is achieved from a 180 volt DC supply. This motor is rated at 50 hp (peak) and 25 hp (continuous). (Fig.2) The SR180 is current limited by its controller to 275 amps.

Generator - Sizing of the generator was based on the objective of having the batteries charged completely during hybrid operation between the two ZEV portions of the range event. During this period, the generator must provide electrical power to charge the batteries and to supply the traction motor. From SIMPLEV simulations, it was determined that a 12.5 kW generator would be needed and the team chose to rewind a Delco-Remy DN50 generator to meet this need. This decision was made for several reasons. The team's initial search revealed that most generators of this size are used in high power applications such as for cranes, and they were much too heavy (approx. 300 lbs.). The Delco-Remy DN50 weighs approximately 110 lbs. Although the team did find a generator that would work for this application, it was deemed to be too expensive. In addition, the team decided that the rewinding of an existing generator would be a good design experience. The DN50 generator was rewound to the team's specifications by Southern Armature Works, Inc. of Knoxville, Tennessee. This generator was originally rated at 24 volts and 300 amps. After rewinding, it has a rating of 180 volts and approximately 65 amps. The field coil was rewound for 180V operation. Both stator and field windings were isolated from the generator frame to permit ungrounded battery operation.

APU - The generator is powered by a small internal combustion engine. The selection of an appropriate APU was based on considerations of: weight, volume, efficiency, and power output. The SIMPLEV simulations led to the conclusion that the APU should be capable of producing 15 kW of brake power. The obvious source of such engines would be engines manufactured for use in motorcycles, but it was found that these engines were often designed to produce their rated power at very high engine speeds which results in high engine friction power losses. After dynamometer studies of several motorcycle engines it was realized that they did not produce enough horsepower at low speeds, a Kohler CH-20 industrial engine was therefore selected. This engine produces 20 hp at 3600 rpm. (Fig. 3) In addition, this engine is considerably lighter than the other engines considered. The engine is air-cooled and is available as a completely assembled unit. Modifications to the APU are discussed below in the section on emissions control.

Batteries - Simulations revealed that it made no sense to carry more batteries than were necessary to meet the 33 km (20 mile) pure electric range requirement. These simulations also indicated a battery pack energy capacity of 7.46 kW-hr would be sufficient. During ZEV mode, the SR180 motor is powered by a 180 volt battery pack consisting of 15 deep-cycle twelve volt batteries connected in series. The UT vehicle uses flooded electrolyte lead-acid batteries for the following reasons:
1) Lead-acid batteries have been extensively tested and information is available on them.
2) This type of battery takes voltage variations well whereas most sealed types do not.
3) Flooded electrolyte lead-acid batteries are economical, readily available, and recycling technology is mature.

The team chose to use fifteen Trojan Corporation brand 22NF wheelchair batteries giving total battery pack energy capacity of 7.5 kw-hr. This battery is rated at 56 Ahr at the 20 hr rate (41.4 at the 3 hr rate). This battery has dimensions as follows: Length = 9.5", Width = 5.5", and Height = 8.812". According to a wheelchair manufacturer which uses these batteries, they last an average of 18 months in a wheel chair without replacement. The vehicle's auxiliary systems have a separate 12 volt battery power supply located in the front of the vehicle and this battery is charged by the APU's generator. The main traction batteries are located in a tunnel through the center of the

vehicle. (Fig. 4) The passenger compartment is completely isolated from the batteries by the use of a Lexan cover secured over the top of the battery tray which fits inside the tunnel. This also helps to protect the team members during loading and unloading the pack. The batteries are separated in the tray by the use of a series of separators and bolts or J-hooks. (Fig. 5) Ventilation is provided by the use of a 12 cfm fan mounted in the top of the tunnel which draws air from the open-bottomed tray and discharges it out the top. The Lexan cover channels air flow over the top of the batteries.

Off-Board Charger - Out-of-vehicle charging of the battery pack is accomplished by the use of a Good-All Electric model C90-1Z 260-12 offboard battery charger. This charger is a 240 volt DC charger, which can be adjusted to 216 volts which makes it capable of charging the battery pack in a maximum of 6 hours with an output current of 12 amps. The adjusting range for this model is 7-14 amps. It has an isolation transformer located between the AC source and the charger. For safety, the charger also has a DC output breaker installed. The charger requires 220 volt AC single phase service. This charger is built to NEMA PE-7 specifications with operating temperature between 0 and 50 degrees C.

High-Voltage Wiring - Two options were investigated for wiring the battery pack: copper bus bar and 2/0 welding cable. The welding cable was chosen over the copper bus bar because of concerns over corrosion problems with the copper bus bar. Welding cable was chosen over standard battery cables because of the higher current rating and greater flexibility. The neoprene covered welding cable has an ICEA rating of 375 amps and a voltage rating of 600 volts. There were three types of battery connectors chosen in order to reduce the cable lengths as much as possible thus reducing weight and resistance. The battery terminals are tin plated cast copper construction. This allows for better strength and current carrying capabilities than the standard cast lead battery terminal construction. Black welding cable was chosen for the wiring on the battery pack. Colored battery terminal protectors provide an easy way to tell if the battery pack is wired correctly and provide electrical isolation. 2/0 welding cable is used in all electrical connections in the high voltage system (red for positive polarity, black for negative polarity). Heavy wall copper lugs are used on all connections in the high voltage system requiring terminal lug connection. There are three fuses in the system: a 300 amp fuse in the motor controller circuit; a 100 amp fuse in the generator circuit, a 400 amp use in the main battery circuit. (Fig. 6) Current shunts are used in the ground legs of the motor, generator, and battery pack. These are used by the microprocessor control to monitor the operation of the electrical system. A 400 amp General Electric switch is used as the main disconnect switch. All connections for the high voltage system are made in an enclosure on the back firewall. The main disconnect is also mounted in this enclosure such that the switch can be operated by reaching alongside the drivers seat. A cable is also mounted to the switch to disconnect from outside the vehicle.

CONTROLLER STRATEGY - The purpose of the HEV control package is to provide system control and driver information. A system control structure providing the necessary minimum system automation was conceived and the microprocessor, development platform, and a basic system design are described below. (Fig. 7)

The microprocessor chosen for the system controller is the Motorola 68HC11 with the FORTH compiler masked in ROM. This complete controller board is manufactured by New Micros, Inc. of Dallas, TX. By using the New Micros embedded controller, a complete system controller can be constructed easily via the expanded bus structure and support boards. The FORTH language provides a fast and efficient platform for code development.

The main function of the system controller is to provide vehicle system monitoring and driver instrumentation. Key elements of this monitoring system are as follows:

Battery State of Charge: The battery state of charge is determined by monitoring the traction battery voltage and current and is displayed on the instrument panel as the "battery fuel gauge". Battery terminal voltage is derived from a resistive divider network and an isolation amplifier. Battery current is monitored by a current sensor that provides a bipolar output to indicate either charging or discharging of the battery pack. This information is also used to determine the point at which the vehicle switches from ZEV mode to HEV mode. At a predetermined set point, the systems controller will instruct the APU to come on and power the generator until the batteries are returned to the desired state of charge.

Battery Temperature: This information is used to avoid possible battery damage due to over-charging or extreme power demand. Each battery is individually monitored in sequence. The desired temperature setpoint has not yet been determined.

Instrumentation Panel: This is the main feedback for the driver. The micro controller interface provides the required signals for vehicle speed, electric motor RPM, battery capacity, and APU fuel capacity. This information is displayed on the instrument panel as in a standard vehicle, resulting in a feel the driver is more accustomed to.

An important goal of the systems group was to implement the vehicle controls in a manner as to create a feel and response matching as closely as possible those of a standard vehicle. With this in mind, the control system provides an interface between the standard vehicle controls and the powertrain. Examples are microprocessor conditioning of the signals from the accelerator pedal to provide smooth acceleration and cruise control, and the brake pedal for regenerative braking of the electric motor.

The control of the APU is handled by a separate 68HC11. The function of this processor is to:
-Start the APU for HEV mode.
-Adjust the APU throttle according to the generator load.
-Adjust the generator field control to achieve the desired rate of charge to the traction battery pack.

EMISSIONS CONTROL STRATEGY -

The emissions control strategy employed for the APU is standard automotive industry practice. A three way catalyst (TWC) is utilized with the engine controlled to run at stoichiometric air to fuel ratio. The TWC reduces the emissions of all three major pollutants; oxides of nitrogen, carbon monoxide and unburned hydrocarbons but requires that the engine operate under stoichiometric conditions (Fig 8). The engine control system used is an Electromotive electronic fuel injection system which uses a heated exhaust gas oxygen (EGO) sensor to ensure that the engine runs at stoichiometric conditions. The engine was modified to accept two Bosch electronic fuel injectors, one in each intake port. The engine's standard magneto ignition was replaced by the Electromotive waste spark system.

The evaporative emission control system incorporates a standard carbon canister that collects the vapors from the fuel tank and fuel system, and burns them in the engine when the vehicle is in operation

The challenge organizers limited the fuel choices to reformulated gasoline (RFG) M85

(a mixture of 85% methanol and 15% gasoline, by volume), and E100 (pure ethanol). Although both M85 and E100 have high octane ratings and may have other favorable characteristics (low ozone forming potential, low global warming potential, potential for being formed from renewable resources), the energy densities of these two fuels are significantly less than of RFG. It is this last consideration that led the UT team to adopt RFG as its fuel for the competition.

FUEL AND ELECTRIC POWER CONSUMPTION

- The energy consumption of the UT HEV has been estimated at a steady speed of 80 km/hr on level ground. Two cases are examined: (1) a fully-charged battery pack and (2) a maximum charging rate. It is felt that these two cases represent the two extremes that should be encountered. In both cases, the power required at the drive wheels to overcome estimated aerodynamic drag and rolling resistance is the same and is based on a drag coefficient of .35, a frontal area of 22 ft2, a coefficient of rolling resistance of 6.7 kg/ton @3.4 KPA, and a vehicle mass of approximately 1,134 kg. Thus, the power required at the drive wheels is 6.9 kW. Using a transaxle efficiency of 95% means that the electric motor most produce 7.2 kW.

In the case of fully-charged batteries, the generator must deliver 8.5 kW if the motor/controller efficiency is 85%. Using a generator efficiency of 85% requires that the APU deliver 10 kW. If the APU operates at wide-open throttle, its brake specific fuel consumption will be 0.321 kg/kW-hr and thus the fuel consumption will be 3.21 kg/hr. At 88.5 km/hr (55 mph), the vehicles' fuel economy will be 27.6 km/kg or 46.6 mpg.

In the case of maximum charging, the generator will be loaded to its maximum output which is 12.5 kW. Using an efficiency of 85%, the APU must deliver 14.7 kW and its fuel consumption will be 5.03 kg/hr. The resulting vehicle fuel economy will be 17.6 km/kg or 29.7 mpg.

VEHICLE STRUCTURE DESIGN - The development of the chassis structure began with a conceptual design done during the spring semester of 1992. During this time, the team researched monocoque, space frame, and semi-monocoque types of chassis construction. Various materials were also studied during this time, ranging from steel and aluminum to modern carbon fiber composite. Three combinations emerged as possibilities: an aluminum monocoque consisting of riveted box sections, aluminum space frame, and steel space frame. After considering each of the designs, a steel space frame was chosen for several reasons. Design and analysis are relatively simple for space frames and there is widespread experience in designing and building steel tube frames in racing/prototype applications. In addition, modifications could be easily implemented with this type of construction.

The next phase of the design process was the detailed design. During the summer semester of 1992, other vehicle parameters affecting the structure were decided upon. Ergonomics, battery placement, suspension design, and placement of the APU and electric motor. were considered. A structure was designed that connected all of these components while taking other factors such as safety and strength into account. Finite element analysis was then used during this process to examine the strength of the structure. The actual construction of the chassis was done to team specifications by an outside vendor. This was done to ensure quality and safety in construction and welding, as this source was experienced in building racing cars to very high standards.

The finished chassis is a conventional steel tube frame, similar to those used in various types of racing. The design is conventional, using the required roll cage as a basis for the structure. The main strength of the structure is from the steel space frame. However, aluminum bulkheads and shear panels add considerable rigidity to the space frame. (Fig. 4) The frame is constructed of mild steel (SAE 1020) tubing of two sizes; 1.5 inch O.D. .095 wall seamless round roll bar tubing and 1.5 inch .063 wall square tubing. The front and rear bulkheads, floor, side panels, and battery tunnel are an integral part of the design, acting as shear panels. They are rivet- bonded to the steel structure.

SUSPENSION DESIGN - The suspension utilizes existing components with student designed geometry and modifications. The use of existing components saved the engineering effort of designing and building the structural members. The roll centers and camber gain curves were calculated using student written computer programs. The roll centers were designed at 3 inches in the front and 4 inches at the rear. The camber gain was designed to maintain the 1 degree negative camber up to the maximum body roll of 5 degrees. The car has relatively stiff springs and sway bars to aid in the handling of the vehicle in events like the commuter challenge.

The front suspension uses an unequal length a-arm setup with concentric spring/damper assemblies. The components are from a Triumph sportscar which weighed about the same as the UT HEV. These components were selected because of their lightweight construction and their availability.

The rear suspension is a configuration utilizing front wheel drive McPherson strut assembly for its components. This configuration was chosen as the best method of independently suspending the drive wheels. The McPherson strut was designed for the front wheels so it had steering capability. To convert the struts to rear use, the tie rods were fixed rigidly to the chassis. The possible bump-steer problem associated with this design is recognized, was taken into account in the design. The design was tested for toe-in during bump travel. The components are from a Ford Fiesta, and like the Triumph pieces, they were chosen because of their lightweight construction, availability, and the fact that they were originally designed for use on a vehicle having about the same weight as the UT vehicle.

The braking of the HEV is handled by disk brakes on all four wheels. The front disks and calipers are 12" solid disks with cast iron twin cylinder calipers from a triumph GT6 sportscar. The rear braking system is from a Ford Fiesta, incorporating 11" solid disks and floating calipers. These systems were chosen mainly because of their compatibility with the front and rear suspension components. Proper fore and aft balance was insured by using a dual master cylinder arrangement. The rough sizing of the cylinders was calculated and the final brake balance will be determined by testing and adjusting using a balance bar. Power boost was not felt to be necessary because the calculated maximum pedal force required was less than 100 lbs.

CHOICE OF MATERIALS AND VEHICLE MANUFACTURABILITY - The choice of material for the exterior of the vehicle was driven by the need for material that was economical, sturdy, and recyclable. After evaluating the recent trend in the automotive industry towards aluminum body panels, the decision was made to design a vehicle that could be easily formed (no complex curves) and fitted to the steel chassis. The high cost of most composites and the limited recyclability of fiberglass also were factors in the decision to use aluminum. The team designed the exterior of the vehicle and then hired a local fabricator to construct the

panels. Several of the students assisted in the construction and finish of the vehicle.

VEHICLE STYLING - Styling for the body and interior began during late August of 1992. Many designs were considered before a final overall design was selected.

In March of 1993, the body construction was underway. Only during the construction were final decisions on body styling actually made. The first idea of an all aluminum body turned out to be impractical. A more sensible solution turned out to be a body that consisted of an upper steel and lower aluminum body. Using steel for the upper portion of the body allowed the roof of the car to be welded directly to the chassis which would increase strength and lower the profile of the car. The steel A and B posts made for strong window frames that were also welded to the chassis. An aluminum nose, hood, doors, quarter panels, and rear end were riveted to a steel sub-framework.

A long and highly arched front windshield frame was made to improve aerodynamics. Next, the roof was made with the help of an English wheel. The top half of the car was finished with the determination of the window line which in turn allowed for the construction of the rear and quarter glass frames. The window line created a long wedge type shape suited for the hatchback; this let a 19 degree rear glass be placed so that the aerodynamics would be greatly enhanced. Also, the wedge shape made the front sighting distance minimal 8 feet. With the completion of the top of the body, work was done to construct from rear to front. With the window line in place, a single piece of aluminum was formed and attached to the sub-frame. To add styling and strength, a groundkit was also formed into this piece. Using a long piece of aluminum allowed or both the door and quarter panel to be made at the same time. With completion of the doors, a nose piece had to be made before final designs for a hood and fender could be completed. The nose was then placed in position so that it was proportionally similar to many vehicles. The nosepiece and fenders were made as one which allowed for them to both be removable from the chassis. The hood was made with three breaks which was just enough strength to support its own weight. Detailing such as recessed rear lights, glass installation, and cargo area were made after completion of the body.

The interior of the HEV started with design of the dash. Using an instrument panel from another car, a dash was shaped out of hard core foam and covered with vinyl. The dash was formed so that sun glare was minimal and the remaining gauges would fit ergonomically. The dash was complemented by a door attachment that created a wrap around effect inside the HEV. Vinyl was used to cover the top half of the doors as well as the side posts. Felt was used to make an attractive headliner which finished the upper half of the interior. The lower half of the interior was made out of foam that was covered with no-back carpet. This allowed for the structure to be padded and at the same time deaden most of the exterior noise without adding the extra weight from a padded carpet. The interior was finished with the construction of the door seals.

BIBLIOGRAPHY

Amann, C., "The Passenger Car and the Greenhouse Effect", SAE Paper No. 902099

"Automotive Newsfront", Popular Science, December 1991, p27.

Banthia, V., Miller, J., "Lightweighting of Cars with Aluminum for Better Crashworthiness" SAE Technical Paper Series #930494

"Braking of Road Vehicles ", Assorted authors, Institute of Mechanical Engineering Conference Publications 1976.

Costin, M., Phipps, D., "Racing and Sports Car Chassis Design", Robert Bentley, 1962

Cramer, R., Machine Design, Addison-Wesley, 1968

Dewan, S., Straughen, A., Power Semiconductor Devices, Wiley, 1975.

"Electric Vehicles", Road&Track, March 1991, p133.

"Electric Vehicles", Road&Track, March 1992, p126-136.

Electrotek, Inc., "The ABC's of EV Technology Seminar, June 25-26, 1991. (Also, test data on Trojan 22NF deep-cycle battery).

Fornier, R., Metal Fabricators Handbook, H.P. Books, 1982, p55

Heywood, J., Internal Combustion Engine Fundamentals, McGraw-Hill, 1988

Linden, D., Handbook of Batteries and Fuel Cells, McGraw-Hill

Nordmark, G., Miller, J., "Joint Design for Aluminum Automotive Structures", SAE Technical Paper Series #930492

Puhn, F. How to Make Your Car Handle, H.P. Books, 1981

Puhn, F., Brake Handbook, H.P. Books, 1985

Rashid, M., Power Electronics, Circuits, Devices and Applications, Prentice Hall, 1988.

Reuyl, J., "XA-100 Hybrid Electric Vehicle", SAE Technical Paper Series SP-915

Sanders, R., Wood, C., "Aluminum Automotive Recycling and Materials Selection Issues" SAE Technical Paper Series #930493

Sen, P., Principles of Electric Machines and Power Electronics, Wiley, 1989.

Smith, S., "Stock Car Chassis Technology", Steve Smith Autosports, 1983.

"The Dawn of Lightness" Car Design, Oct. 92, p30

Wong, J., "Theory of Ground Vehicles", Wiley-Interscience Publications, 1978

ACKNOWLEDGEMENTS

In addition to those organizations that made the 1993 Hybrid Electric Vehicle Challenge possible, the University of Tennessee HEV Team would like to thank the following organizations and individuals who made the UT effort possible:

Tennessee Valley Authority
Tennessee Valley Public Power Association
Lane-Magneto and Electric
Kohler Co.
Electrotek
Honda
Kawasaki
Analog Devices
Michelin Tire
Hallmark Electronics
ALCOA
Textron Aerostructures
East Tennessee Race Prep
British Cars, Ltd.
Trojan Battery
General Electric
East Tennessee Battery
Dave Munday Race Cars
Southern Armature Works, Inc.
SDRC
Mechanical Engineering Machinists
Dr. William Snyder, Chancellor of the University of Tennessee
Dr. Jerry Stoneking, Acting Dean of the College of Engineering
Janene Connelly, Director of Development, College of Engineering
Dr. John Snider, Industrial Engineering Department
Dr. Milton Bailey, Electrical Engineering Department

HEV Team Members:
Chris Plucker, Ken Cookson, Chester Duffield, David Yarberry, Sean Howley, Rob Norton, Robin Winton, Steve Lampley, Bryce Anderson, Mark Froning, Robert Maybury, Allen Miller, Karen Miller, Jon McCoy, Roman Kickirillo, Rick LeQuieu, Tim Wheelock, William Moon, Brad Caldwell, Mike Dodd, Kenny DeHoff, Mark Bailey, Steve Bivens, Michael Loope, Mike King, Mamar Gelaye, Mir Azam, A.J., Wijenayake, Trish Yancey, Nicole Vickery, Jorge Carreras, Rob McClean, Jennifer Wilkinson, Scott Sluder, Renu Rajput, Charles Finney, Reuben Israel, Alva Davis, Chris Liposkey, Stuart Schuessler, Richard Mitchell, Charles Bozman, Todd Smith, Angela Walton, Kevin Swanson, Wendy Moore

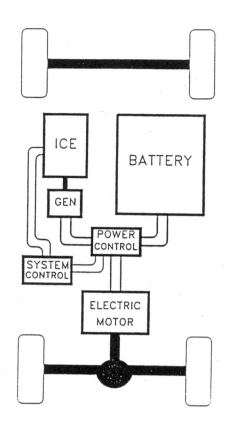

Figure 1: Series Drivetrain Configuration

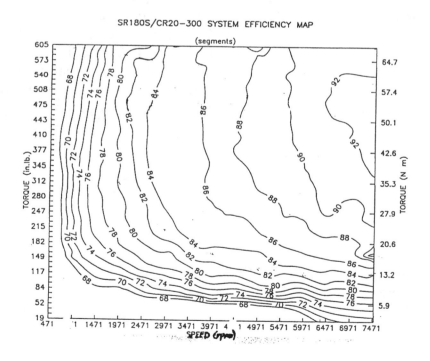

Figure 2: Electric Motor Characteristics

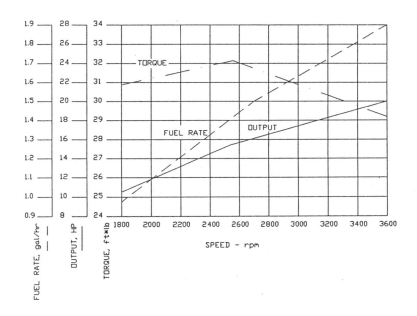

Figure 3: APU Characteristics

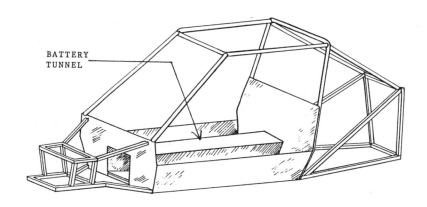

Figure 4: Chassis View Showing Battery Tunnel

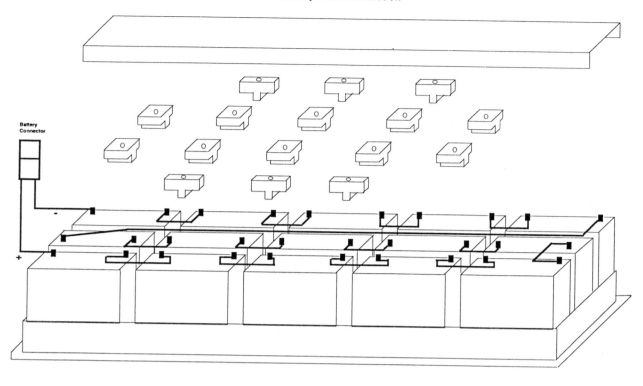

Figure 5: Battery Placement With Shield and Mounting Hardware

Layout and wiring of main disconect switch, fuses and current shunt. This assembly is to be mounted on firewall behind driver.

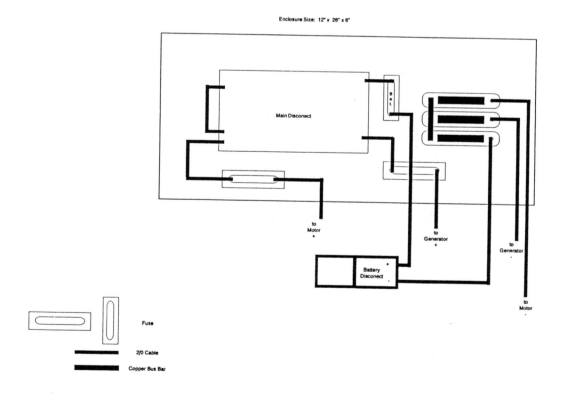

Figure 6: High Voltage Wiring Schematic

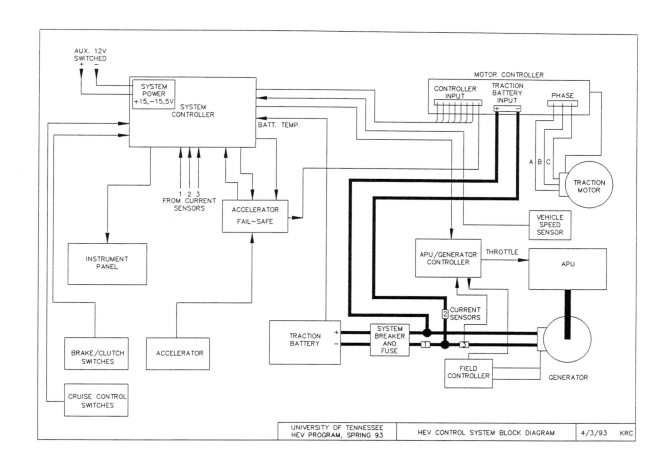

Figure 7: HEV Control System Block Diagram

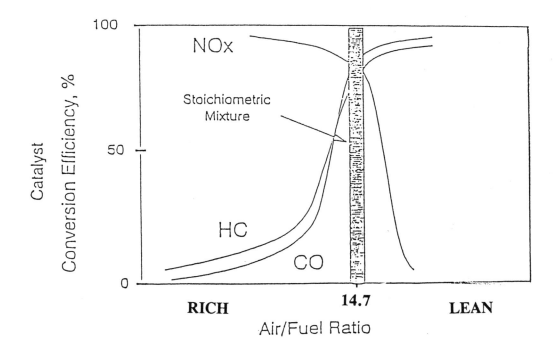

Figure 8: Three-Way Catalyst Efficiencies

The University of Texas at Arlington - "High Bred"

Robert L. Woods, Stephen T. Kugle,
Kliffton M. Black, and Keith A. Sauer
University of Texas at Arlington

ABSTRACT

Presented in this paper are the design concepts and implementation of the Hybrid Electric Vehicle from the University of Texas at Arlington. This project is part of the "Hybrid Electric Vehicle Challenge" sponsored by Ford Motor Company, the Department of Energy, the Society of Automotive Engineers, and numerous other sponsors. The basic concept of the UTA vehicle is a high-performance, sporty, hybrid electric vehicle that has the aesthetics, performance, handling, and attractiveness of a true sports car combined with the utility and desirability of electric-drive vehicles.

The car uses a brushless DC electric motor with a power rating of 16 horsepower continuous and 39 horsepower intermittent. The battery pack is 120 Ni-Cad cells with a voltage of 144 volts. In the electric mode, a continuous speed of 55 MPH is expected with a intermittent speed of 90 MPH.

The combustion engine is a 600 cc motorcycle engine with turbo, electronic fuel injection, using M-85 fuel. The combustion engine delivers in excess of 100 horsepower and drives the differential directly with a parallel mechanical drive system from the electric motor, so that either can propel the vehicle. The combustion engine can be used to recharge the drive batteries if desired.

The body is fiberglass with gull-wing doors for the two-seat configuration. The battery packs are located in the side pods on both sides of the vehicle. The tube frame is constructed with mild steel. The engine and the electric motor are both located in the rear of the vehicle.

INTRODUCTION

Due to the ongoing concerns of pollution control and the increasing restrictions placed on automobile emissions, the search for alternatives for the internal combustion engines has intensified. Electrically-powered cars are thought to be a viable replacement to current automobiles in the near future; however, today's battery technology limits the useful range of an electric car. Consumers are not interested in purchasing these cars that have less than 100 miles range. With increased political pressure on auto makers, new alternatives are being researched to bridge the gap between internal combustion and electric power.

One alternative is the hybrid electric vehicle (HEV). A HEV is a vehicle that utilizes an electric motor drive system as its main power source for inner city driving while using a combustion engine as a supplemental energy source for highway operation and to extend the useful range of the car. To accelerate the research into such alternatives, the Department of Energy, Society of Automotive Engineers, and Ford Motor Company have teamed together to sponsor the Ford Hybrid Electric Vehicle Challenge.

This paper presents the University of Texas at Arlington's technical design of a completely manufactured and functional hybrid electric vehicle named "High Bred".

OVERVIEW OF THE UTA VEHICLE

A "Commuter Vehicle" conjures images of an unstylish utility vehicle (e.g., golf cart) that is predominately functional and not particularly exciting or fun to drive. While our goal is to meet emissions, fuel economy, and range standards, our basic concept is to build a two-seat, mid-engine, sports car that looks great, handles well, and has good acceleration.

POWERTRAIN - There are two types of HEV powertrains recognized for the competition. A series type powertrain uses an electric motor as the main power source while using a combustion engine to regenerate the batteries. This allows an increase in range for the vehicle but limits the acceleration to the electric motor power. A parallel-type powertrain uses an electric motor in conjunction with a combustion engine to power the car. This set-up allows the option of either driving in electric mode when low pollution is desired (such as in the inner city), or in combustion mode when good acceleration or long range is needed (such as entering or driving on a highway). The parallel powertrain allows the best of both situations. Therefore, UTA has chosen the parallel system.

BODY - In order to create a unique look for "High Bred" and maintain a true sportscar appearance, a fiberglass body was designed and built. See Figure 1 for side profile of the body. To manufacture this body, styrofoam molds were poured and carved by hand to an approximate shape. The rough shape was then laboriously sanded to a smooth finish. The styrofoam was coated with a hardener, then fiberglass was laid to form a positive mold. The entire body was made from several molds making up all of the panels.

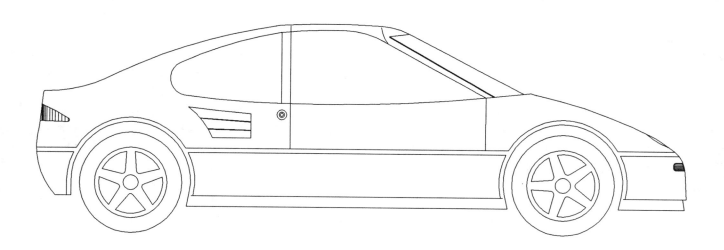

Figure 1. "High Bred" Body Design.

CHASSIS - The vehicle structure is designed to integrate well with the suspension, drive train, and batteries while allowing passenger comfort. The chassis is a steel tubular space frame that allows easy access to components. The frame was analyzed with computer programs to insure structural integrity and driver safety under impact loads. The battery cells are grouped into two packs that are located in the chassis side pods. See Figure 2 for chassis design.

DETAILED DESIGN ANALYSIS

ELECTRIC MOTOR ANALYSIS - The first step of the design phase is choosing the powertrain components. The electric motor and battery selection is important to make very early because the chassis is designed to integrate theses components. Therefore, the powertrain design can create a 'bottle neck' for the remaining car components if not designed early.

The electric motor was analyzed and sized by modeling the motor and vehicle with static and dynamic spreadsheet simulations, HEV ANALYSIS and HEV SIMULATION, to determine required performance characteristics.

The performance specifications in the competition rules, when in the electric mode, are:

1.)   Accelerate from rest on a 15% grade.

2.)   Accelerate from 0 to 45 mph in less than 15 seconds.

3.)   Sustain a speed of 40 mph for at least one hour.

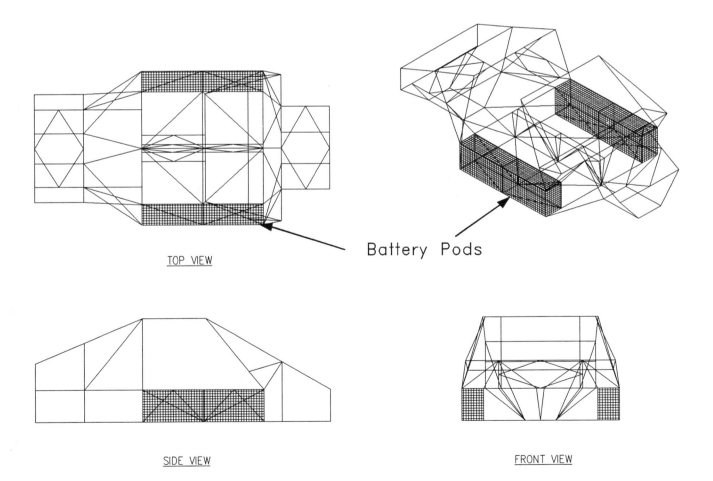

Figure 2. Chassis Design with Battery Pods.

The following are some of the vehicle design parameters considered in the analysis programs.

1.) drag coefficient - 0.3

2.) cross section area - 15 ft.^{2}

3.) weight - 1575 lbs.

4.) mechanical efficiency - 85%

5.) gear configuration - varied in analysis

6.) voltage configuration - varied in analysis

These parameters were chosen by making educated guesses from our automotive experience.

The method of analysis included a systematic use of the programs mentioned previously. Using HEV ANALYSIS at various voltage configurations, plots were analyzed that showed performance characteristics that include: motor torque, reflected load torque, battery current, vehicle speed, horsepower, and efficiency as functions of motor speed. Holding voltage constant and sweeping through a range of gear ratios, data was gathered from these plots in order to construct other plots of all the various performance characteristics as functions of gear ratio. Additionally, the acceleration profile data produced by HEV SIMULATION was obtained and plotted with the other performance characteristics. From these plots, voltage, current, gear ratio, acceleration, and maximum speed were optimized. Figures 3 analyzes the Solectria BRLS16 motor with a 7.8 speed reduction, where;

Tm - torque of motor (ft lb)

Im - current to motor (amp)

Eta - efficiency of motor (%)

Tload - aerodynamic reflected load (ft lb)

HP - horse power

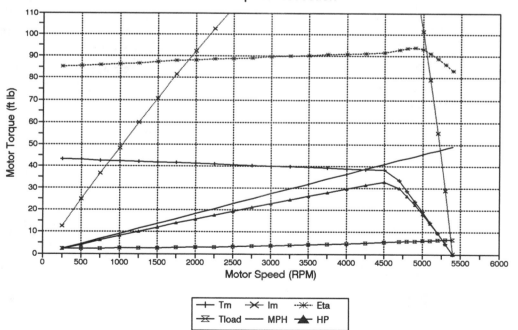

Figure 3. Static Motor Performance (Speed Reduction = 7.82).

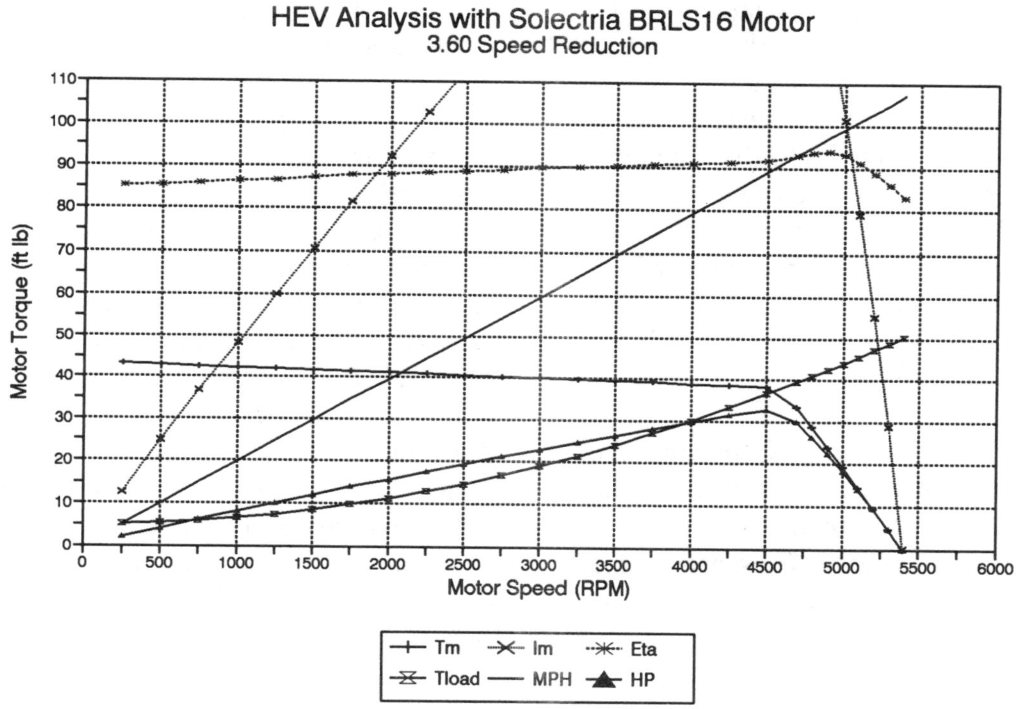

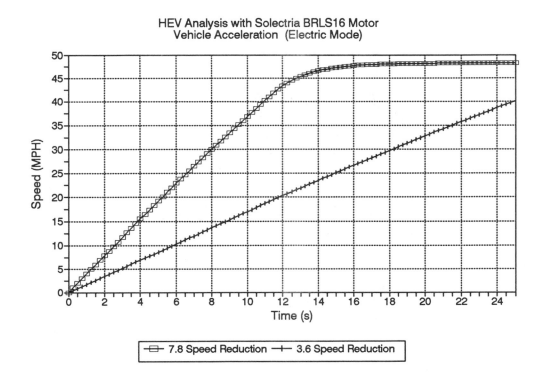

Figure 4. Static Motor Performance (Speed Reduction = 3.60).

Different speed ratios were selected based upon the trade-off between top vehicle speed and the time required to reach 45 MPH. A high speed reduction gives good acceleration but limits the top speed of the vehicle. Figure 5 shows vehicle acceleration in electric mode.

Figure 5. Vehicle Acceleration with Different Speed Reductions.

Since the motor is directly coupled to the drive train, it is possible to over-speed the motor and cause rotor damage. Therefore, a two-speed transmission is used to give good acceleration and yet allow high speeds required for highway operation. A two-speed gearbox with a first-gear ratio of 7.8 allows acceleration from 0 to 45 MPH in 11.25 seconds. A second-gear ratio of 3.6 allows a top speed of 90 mph. This gear ratio also allows the motor to withstand overdriving with the combustion engine to 104 MPH.

To eliminate the concern of spinning the combustion engine while in electric mode, when the engine is turned off and the oil pump is not working, a one-way sprag clutch is used to separate the combustion engine from the drive train while the engine is idle. See Figure 6 for the electrical and mechanical drive train drawing.

The sprag clutch allows the vehicle to be powered by the electric motor without turning the combustion engine. While driving in electric mode, and needing power from the auxiliary power unit, the combustion engine spins up until it overtakes the speed of the electric motor. After that point, the car is being powered by the combustion engine. To eliminate the concern of overdriving the electric motor, the two-speed gear box is shifted into neutral disconnecting it from the drive train. If the electric motor is left in gear and the combustion engine is producing excess torque, the electric motor works as a generator storing energy in the batteries. This is an added advantage to the parallel drive train system.

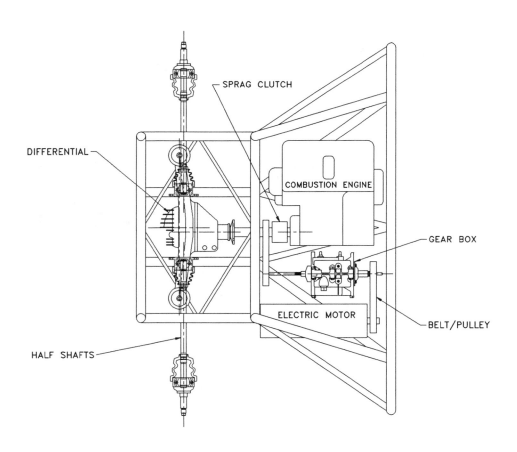

Figure 6. Electrical and Mechanical Drive Train.

248

In summary, the Solectria BRLS16 motor with accompanying controller was chosen as the main power source for the hybrid electric vehicle. A two-speed gearbox is used to allow good acceleration and top speed. A one-way sprag clutch is used to disconnect the combustion engine from the drive train while in electric mode. The combustion engine can power the car and work with the electric motor to generate electrical power simultaneously. With these choices, the following characteristics are achieved:

1.) 11.25 seconds to accelerate to 45 MPH.

2.) 90 MPH top speed in electric mode.

3.) 104 MPH possible @ 5400 RPM.

4.) The vehicle will accelerate from rest on a 15% grade.

5.) The steady state current demand is 24 Ah @ 40 MPH.

BATTERY ANALYSIS - Various battery technologies were investigated for this vehicle. These technologies include lead-acid, sodium-sulfur, nickel-cadmium, nickel-iron, and nickel-metal hybride. It became obvious early-on that in order to maintain a light-weight sporty vehicle a high power and energy density battery is needed. The lead-acid batteries were eliminated since their weight would be about 700 pounds. Some technologies were very expensive while others were not available. However, the nickel-cadmium batteries were ideal for several reasons. The Ni-Cad batteries are high power and relatively light while maintaining a fast recharge time of less than six hours. Therefore, the SAFT Ni-Cad batteries were selected.

To determine Ni-Cad suitability, the actual capacity of a 20 cell pack was tested by Texas A&M University Center for Electrochemical Systems and Hydrogen Research. A&M determined the specific power and specific energy of the batteries. These quantities were used to size the battery packs for our vehicle. From this we calculated the complete battery source should consist of 120 cells connected in series to give a 144 volt bus. The total battery pack weighs 420 pounds.

APU & EMISSIONS - To maintain the concept of a sportscar design and performance, a Honda 600 cc motorcycle engine is used as the auxiliary power unit (APU). This engine will produce in excess of 100 horsepower with a turbo, electronic fuel injection, and M85 fuel. The combination of these components are desirable for the vehicle since UTA uses the same configuration for their Formula SAE race cars. Extensive time and research has been spent on tuning this configuration for performance and efficiency.

Methanol fuel serves two purposes in this vehicle. The methanol allows higher performance than regular gasoline and operates better at higher compression ratios. The addition of a turbo supplies the higher compression ratios and increases the performance of the engine. M85 fuel (85% methanol / 15% gasoline) is also used to reduce NO_x emissions.

One method used to reduce NO_x emissions was to move the fuel injectors a distance of 15 inches upstream of the inlet valve. A large temperature drop occurs as the fuel vaporizes due to the latent heat of vaporization of methanol. This lower air temperature reduces the presence of NO_x emissions in the exhaust. Figure 7 shows experimental data for air inlet temperature vs. probe distance from the inlet valve as the fuel injectors were moved away from the inlet valve. This figure shows that placement of the injectors further upstream in the intake runners allows the fuel enough time to take heat from the air to fully vaporize the fuel. Air inlet temperature reduction and full fuel vaporization are two advantages to moving the fuel injectors upstream. The only negative effect is a slight delay in throttle response. However, this can be controlled by adjusting the electronic fuel injection computer.

Another method of reducing emissions is to use a tuned intake and exhaust systems. The intake system is designed as a dual speed tuned manifold. For light load, low speed situations, about 3500 RPM is selected as a tuning point. For high power, high speed situations, 8000 RPM is selected as a tuning point. These points are dependent on air inlet temperature. Figure 8 shows that as the inlet air temperature increases the RPM at which resonance occurs increases. A tuned manifold allows excess air into the cylinder and lowers the emissions. When using a dual speed tuned inlet manifold there is a point at which the tuning is causing a negative effect on emissions. This occurs around 6000 RPM on this manifold. To combat this effect the exhaust is tuned for an RPM slightly higher than 6000 RPM. This point was picked because it would overcome the negative effect of the dual speed intake manifold and increase mid-range power. Since this point is one of the earliest tuning waves, there is no opportunity for the exhaust system to go into a

resonance that would adversely affect emissions or performance.

In summary, a Honda 600 cc motorcycle engine is used as the auxiliary power unit to achieve good acceleration. M85 fuel is used to increase performance and reduce NO_x emissions. Other steps were taken to reduce emissions. The fuel injectors were moved upstream of the inlet valve by 15 inches to allow the latent heat of vaporization of methanol to cool the inlet air temperature and to allow complete vaporization of the fuel. This reduces the presence of NO_x emissions in the exhaust. Tuned intake and exhaust systems were also used to reduce emissions.

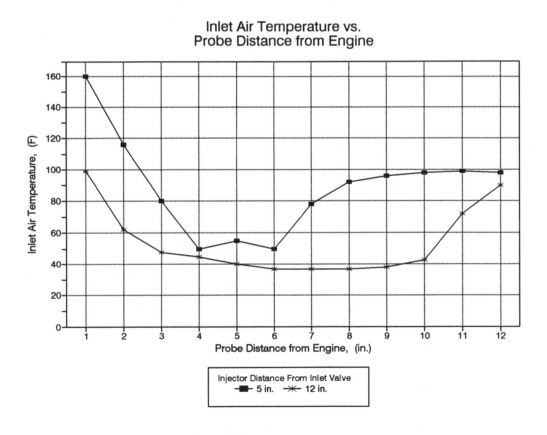

Figure 7. Intake Air Temperature Distribution (Experimental).

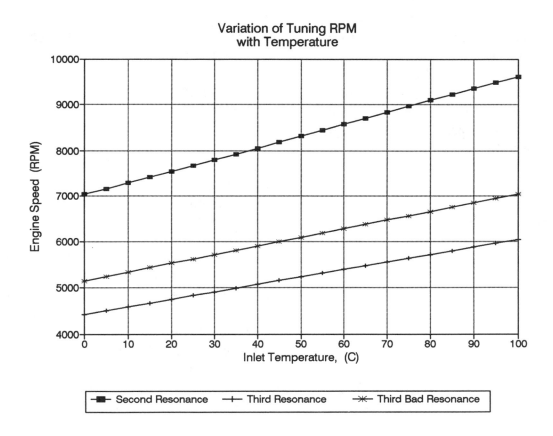

Figure 8. Effect of Temperature on Tuning Speed.

VEHICLE STRUCTURE - The objective for the vehicle structure is to design a light weight chassis that will integrate well with the suspension, drive train, and batteries while allowing passenger comfort and maintaining relative structural integrity in light crash situations. Finite element analysis is used to evaluate stresses and optimize the vehicle structure. Finite element programs MSC/NASTRAN and ANSYS are used for the loading simulations. The different simulations included static loading, torsional rigidity loading, side-impact, front-impact, rollover and the addition of the engine into the model.

The conclusions show that the safety factor increased with the addition of the engine structure into the model. The chassis can withstand a side-impact of an 8 g force at a speed of 13 mph, a front-impact an of 8 g force at a speed of 19 mph and a roll-over simulation of approximately 4 g's based on ultimate tensile strength of 1020 steel.

The type of element selection for the simulation must be considered carefully for different types of stress requirements. The degrees of freedom for the constraints have to be evaluated carefully for a realistic simulation. The application of forces is another important factor to be evaluated for each simulation. The dynamic impact load cases such as front impact, side impact and roll-over are more complex to analyze than the static load cases. The engineer is faced with having to design a structure while considering its deformation under impact. Structural deformation must be controlled and the energy of deformation must be balanced against the kinetic energy of impact. The integrity of the passenger compartment must be maintained with the extremities crushed in such a way as to minimize the occupant deceleration rate. Though it is not necessary for the structure to stay perfectly elastic, it is obvious that collapse or ultimate strength due to the impact must not be exceeded.

Finite element simulation requires the loading conditions and the appropriate boundary conditions to be specified for each load case simulation. The finite element analysis for this project was concentrated on two static load cases and three impact load cases. The engine structure was added to the model to simulate the actual structural rigidity of the chassis. The various loading conditions are as follows:

1.) Static loading

2.) Torsional rigidity loading

3.) Side-impact

4.) Front-impact

5.) Rollover

The C-bar element was selected for all the simulations because this element allows the following stresses to be output:

1.) Tension

2.) Compression

3.) Bending

4.) Shear

5.) Combined Stress (Von Mises's)

C-bar is defined as an infinitely stiff element and the calculated stresses are linear until the yield strength of the material is reached. NASTRAN does not provide an error message for loading that exceeds the yield strength (which actually is nonlinear for carbon steel). Infinite loading in a C-bar element does not break the element due to the infinite stiffness of the element. Therefore the output is not valid for stresses that exceed the yield of the material. Each node has six degrees of freedom, three translations and three rotations. The translations are along the x, y and z axis and rotations are about the x, y and z axis. The boundary condition representations are 1, 2, 3 (translation in

x, y and z), 4, 5, 6 (rotations about x, y and z) respectively. The engine was added in the model using solid tubes to simulate the engine's stiffness. Adding the engine into the model improved the stiffness of the entire chassis structure. The safety factor increased by about 50 percent with the addition of the engine.

All safety factors were based on the yield strength (57 kpsi) of 1020 cold drawn, seamless steel tubing. Impact loadings were tested to the ultimate tensile strength (68 kpsi) and assumed to have failed at ultimate tensile strength.

Static Loading - The four suspension points on the chassis were constrained in 1, 2, 3 and the forces on the chassis were estimated and loaded appropriately. The force estimation was based on the mass of the car including the mass of two passengers (approx. 1500 lb). Triangulation was added to reduce the stress concentration on certain critical members. The safety factor for static loading was about 3.6 with a maximum displacement of about 0.1 in. Triangulation was added in high stress areas to equalize stresses.

Rigidity Loading - Torsional rigidity loading was done to simulate the rigidity of the rear of the chassis hit by a bump force on one tire to simulate a hard turn. The front two suspension points were constrained in 1 and 3 and the neutral axis of the chassis with respect to the forces applied was constrained. A force of 500 lb was applied on each rear suspension point to twist the chassis. A safety of about 3, maximum displacement of about 0.14 in. and a torsional rigidity of 1,333 ft-lb/deg. of roll angle was found.

Side-Impact - Side-impact loadings were calculated using conservation of momentum and energy theories. Failure of the material was assumed to be at ultimate tensile strength. The stress of the material was also assumed to be linear until its ultimate tensile strength. The calculated forces were distributed to the members in the direction of the forces on the side of the chassis. The other side of the chassis was constrained in 1, 2, 3. The chassis was fixed by the boundary conditions and the wall was accelerated in the direction towards the side of the chassis with a certain g force. The

252

battery compartment on the side of the car was found to fail at an 8 g force at a speed of 13 mph with side impact simulation.

Front- Impact - The front of the chassis was found to be able to withstand a 4 g force at a speed of 14 mph using the ultimate tensile level. Triangulations were added and the chassis was able to withstand about 8 g force at a speed of about 19 mph.

Rollover - Rollover was simulated with the forces acting on the top of the chassis as though a wall was crushing from the top. The four suspension points were constrained in 1, 2, 3. Stress analysis output shows that it failed at about 4 g force when tested to the ultimate tensile strength. In the development of a new car design, the roof must pass certain physical tests. One such test states that the roof be subjected to a force equal to 1.5 times the vehicle weight or 5000 lb which ever is less. In our case, we used a 2,250 lb applied to the roof structure. A maximum deflection of 0.26" was the result of this loading. The criteria for such a test is the roof can not deflect more than 5". Therefore the chassis roof structure is adequate for this type of loading.

In summary, the vehicle structure was designed to integrate well with the suspension, and engine components, while remaining ergonomical and safe. The chassis is a steel tube space frame that is designed for manufacturability and ease of repair. The space frame allows good accessibility of all components. The chassis utilizes space for the two battery pods while using the stiffness of these pods to add strength to the chassis and increase safety to side impact. See figure 2 for the chassis drawing.

SUSPENSION DESIGN - To achieve sportscar handling, a double A-arm suspension is used. Through UTA's experience in Formula SAE competitions, the double A-arm suspension offers good cornering performance. Kinematic analysis is performed on a computer program to optimize camber change, roll center position, roll center movement, scrub, damper length, motion ratio and wheel rate for static bump and rebound conditions. The bump and rebound travel is six inches.

The geometry of the suspension is established to provide shock clearance and good connection points to the frame. These connection points minimize the amount of stress transmitted to each frame member.

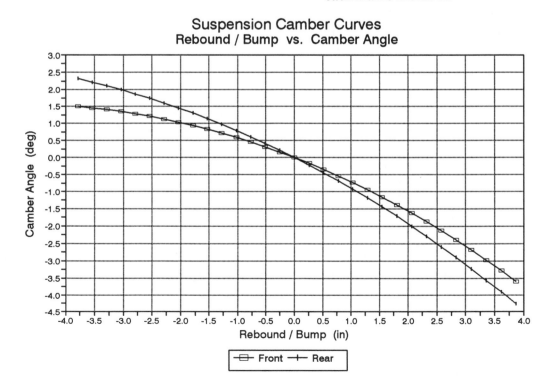

Figure 9. Camber Change in Bump and Rebound.

Once the geometry is set, the A-arm tubes were analyzed using loading cases of 1g brake, 1g cornering and a 2g bump. Given the force in each member, stresses can be calculated for various tube diameters and wall thicknesses. The forces generated are larger for the 1g brake force than for the other loading cases. Therefore, our design parameters are based on this load. The analysis shows that the forces in the bottom A-arm is twice as much as in the top A-arm.

Determination of outside diameter and wall thickness of the A-arm tubes is based on a fatigue failure safety factor of four. This is chosen due to the possibility of impact loads or combination loads of braking, cornering, acceleration and bumps. The stresses developed in the top A-arm are factors of O.D. and wall thickness. Using these stresses, safety factors are determined based on Soderberg equation. One half of the suspension components weight is unsprung mass. Unsprung mass is a consideration for dynamic response of the suspension, as well as the overall performance for the car. Therefore, 4130 steel is a good choice for material since it is about 50% stronger than mild steel.

Rod ends are used to connect the suspension to the chassis. The rod ends selected for the top A-arms are Aurora VCM-6 and for the bottom Aurora VCM-7. The specifications given for these rod ends are very adequate for the forces encountered. The bottom king pin bearing is a self-centering bearing made by Torrington and top connection is an Aurora VCM-6 rod end, this also enables camber adjustments.

The rear suspension geometry is identical to the front and the car's static weight distribution is about 50-50. Therefore, the forces in each rear A-arm is relatively similar to the front.

In summary, the suspension is optimized according to given design parameters and criteria. It is light weight with good strength and reliability. Its connection to the frame is simple but effective.

SUMMARY AND CONCLUSIONS

The hybrid electric vehicle designed and built by UTA meets our expectations as a high-performance sportscar and will have the impressive performance, range, and aesthetics that was our goal. The Ni-Cad batteries combined with the brushless D. C. motor and drive train will provide the weight, acceleration, cruise speed, top speed, and range that were desired. The combustion engine and drive train will provide exceptional acceleration, range, emissions, and the ability to recharge the batteries.

The tubular steel frame has the structural stiffness and factor of safety to maintain the integrity of the vehicle and suspension while providing for adequate factors of safety and crashworthiness. The suspension system will provide exceptional handling and will provide good ride qualities. The fiberglass body has the aesthetics and ergonomics that were desired and are light weight.

This exercise in engineering a new hybrid electric vehicle has introduced young engineers to the problems facing industry and our nation, and has brought great insight into the problems and compromises required in a major project such as this. UTA feels that it has met the challenge in an optimum manner based upon our concepts of the car.

ACKNOWLEDGMENTS

This paper is an accumulation of student projects written over a period of 16 months. The following people are responsible for the data and analysis: Khader AbuKhadijeh, Terry Autrey, Soloman Aregay, Kevin Bevans, Bobby Brown, Doug Box, Bob Bundy, Mike Burns, Yean Neng Choong, Greg Cleveland, Scott Crowder, Kevin Culver, David Dillmore, Dang Dinh Nick Dringenberg, Doug Evans, Richard Fallas, Mark Fisher, Mike Fortner, James Gorden, Boyce Hardin, Craig Henry, Kevin Hill, George Ipe, John King, Thun Kham, Pete Leboulluec, Kris Little, Tim Lockhart, Richard Martinez, Ben McCarley, John McFadden, Steve Nance, Thuan Nguyen, Steve Oliver, John Pullman, Kevin Rainey, Scott Rice, Keith Sauer, Steve Stahl, Faiz Taqi, Zeb Tidwell, Brent Warren, and James Whitt, Jeff Zimmerer.

UTA is greatly indebted to the following sponsors and contributors that have helped with parts or cash: A. E. Petsche Wire Co., Allied Signal, Arendale Ford, Arlington Fastener, Aromat, Associated Fiberglass, Aurora Bearing, Bowman Industries, Buz Post Auto Park, Dayco, Foam Supply, Ford Motor Co., Fluke, General Motors, Goodyear, Hayes Brake, Hillard Auto Park, Hinderliter Heat Treating, Honda America, J & H Machine, Marshall Electronics, Martin Sprocket and Gear, Mazda, Microtooling Systems, Mikuni, Motorola, Nicole Scales, Nohau, Peterbilt Motors, Raychem, SAFT America, Siemans, Spectra Technologies, Solectria, Texas Electric Utilities, Texstar, Thomas Industries, and Wiseco. Numerous other companies have provided direct funds as major or associate sponsors of the HEV Challenge Event which has also been critical to our project.

Texas Tech University Hybrid Electric Vehicle Challenge Final Report

Vince Tyson, Casey Bowles, Mike Lewis, Steve Nisbet, Krista Reed,
Brad Stover, Dan Boschen, Michael W. Canning, Brian Cross, Jessie Hyman,
Richard S. Klepper, Stephen Lamb, Matt Ramon, Gary Romero, Terry Wright,
Matt Adelman, Mike Bock, Phil Guppa, Carlton Lawler, and Doug Meek

Texas Tech University

ABSTRACT

This paper describes the conversion of a Ford Escort station wagon to a Hybrid Electric Vehicle. The converted car is an electric vehicle with an auxiliary power unit (APU). The APU is used for range extension and for low battery charge. The APU is an internal combustion engine running on ethanol. A special hybrid configuration minimizes emissions from the APU. This system was developed by Texas Tech University in response to the Hybrid Electric Vehicle Challenge sponsored jointly by the Ford Motor Company, the U.S. Department of Energy and the Society of Automotive Engineers.

INTRODUCTION

The Ford Motor Company, in conjunction with the U.S. Department of Energy (DOE) and the Society of Automotive Engineers (SAE) has organized an intercollegiate competition focusing on the advancement and use of practical hybrid vehicle technology. A hybrid electric vehicle (HEV) for this competition is defined as an electric vehicle with an auxiliary power unit (APU). The APU in this project involves the use of an internal combustion engine (ICE). Texas Tech University has been selected as one of thirty universities in North America to compete in the HEV Challenge. The HEV Challenge is designed to provide an exciting and practical interdisciplinary experience for university engineering students. The Texas Tech team includes students from the Electrical Engineering, Mechanical Engineering and Engineering Technology Departments.

The HEV addresses two major areas that have prevented wide acceptance of electric vehicles. The HEV can provide for long distance driving capability and for continual operation, even with a low battery pack. The Texas Tech team is converting a Ford Escort Station Wagon to a hybrid electric vehicle that will assure minimal emissions from the vehicle. The alternative power unit for the Texas Tech HEV is a small ethanol fueled internal combustion (IC) engine.

Of major concern to the Tech team is the removal of barriers that have prevented EV's and HEV's from being accepted by consumers. As mentioned above, the primary problem with electric vehicles is the limited range. The average EV has a range of 30 - 60 miles on a single charge. It can take up to twelve hours to fully recharge a depleted battery pack. Although charging can be done overnight, in off-peak hours of electrical usage, most people prefer having an extended driving range capability readily available. The auxiliary power unit will provide the energy to drive the car when needed, and any excess energy will be used to recharge the batteries. The APU will be optimized to reduce emissions and will be used only when necessary.

The design objectives for the HEV which are common to any transportation vehicle, include:

    (1) safety, fuel economy, and reduced emissions;

    (2) driving range, handling and performance;

    (3) cost and driveability.

POWER TRAIN CONFIGURATION

The Texas Tech Hybrid Electric Vehicle (TTHEV) utilizes a quasi-parallel configuration which allows for battery recharge during cruising. The basic layout for the TTHEV is shown in Figure 1. A power train block diagram for the vehicle is shown in Figure 2. The vehicle is powered by the electric motors at slow speed and during driving situations requiring frequent stops, such as in-town driving. The APU is an ethanol powered internal combustion engine (ICE). Ethanol fuel was selected due to its very low emissions when compared to gasoline. The APU is used when the vehicle is driving in cruising situations, such as highway driving. The APU is operated at a constant load during driving and the electric motors help the APU if extra power is needed for passing another vehicle or climbing a hill. Since the design of the system does not provide for independent operation of the car by the APU, it is not a true parallel system.

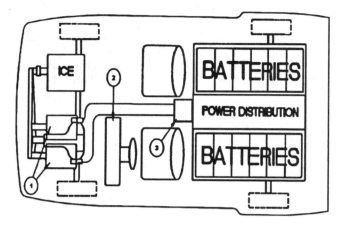

Figure 1. HEV Layout

vehicle speed of 60 mph, the input shaft to the differential rotates at 2500 rpm, the electric motors rotate at a peak of 5000 rpm, and the output shaft of the APU rotates at 2500 rpm, which requires a 2:1 reduction for the chain drive for the electric motors and a 1:1 drive for the APU.

AUXILIARY POWER UNIT - The APU is a 650 cc single cylinder, water cooled motorcycle engine powered by ethanol. The ethanol is fed to the engine via a carburetor that has been modified to use ethanol. The throttle and clutch of the APU are controlled by electric solenoids and the output from the engine is engaged by a mechanical sprag clutch. The sprag clutch allows the engine to be isolated when the APU is not in use. The clutch in the APU is used only when the vehicle is in reverse. The engine is started by the controller and runs at a low rpm for a short time to allow for warm up. After the warm up time, engine speed is synchronized with the differential. When the speed is obtained, the mechanical

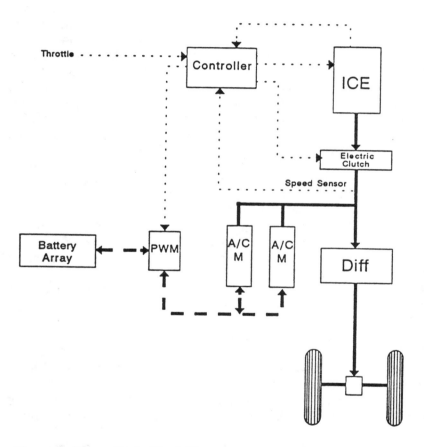

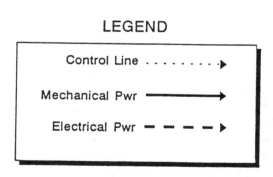

Figure 2. Power Train Block Diagram

The drive train utilizes a differential unit from a Datsun 280Z. This differential connects to the existing drive shafts and support members in the Escort station wagon. The two electric motors and APU connect to the input shaft of the differential via two separate chain drives. The electric motors are permanently connected to the differential which requires them to rotate whenever the car is moving and to be used as an alternator when the APU is powering the car. The APU is isolated from the differential via a sprag clutch. At a

sprag clutch engages, and the APU powers the car. The power required from the APU is kept constant to keep emission levels low. When more power is needed to pass another vehicle or climb a hill, the electric motors will help the APU drive the car so that it still sees a constant load. The car requires 15 hp to drive the car 50 mph on a level road. The output of the APU is 47 hp at 3500 rpm which is well above the requirement for the vehicle.

ELECTRICAL SYSTEM - AC motors were

selected for the electric drive due to cost and capability. The use of AC motors allows for the elimination of the transmission with its associated weight and volume. To meet the acceleration and range requirements of the competition, two Solectria #ACgtx-20 28 HP AC induction motors were chosen. The Dynasty #UPS12-300 deep-cell lead-acid battery was chosen as the primary energy source. The Dynasty battery is rated at 12 volts with a 90.8 amp-hour rating on a ten hour rate. The Dynasty batteries are sealed to minimize gassing. Since 144 volts is required to effectively drive the vehicle, twelve Dynasty batteries are connected in a series configuration. The battery array is totally enclosed and located behind the front seats. A fan is utilized to vent the batteries. The batteries are arranged in two rows of six and secured to minimize the possibility of movement.

A motor controller is necessary to change the DC power from the batteries to a 3-phase AC power. The AC motor controller and an IC motor controller were designed and built at Texas Tech due to cost restraints and to insure flexibility. Figure 3 is a block diagram of the total control system. The control system is based on two Texas Instruments TMS370C850 microcontrollers. TMS370C850 #1 controls the AC induction motors while TMS370C850#2 controls the IC engine.

frequency generated by the TMS370C850.

All electrical devices, cable and terminations were selected and constructed so that safety was of highest priority. An 800 amp Square D circuit breaker was used as the battery safety switch. Since it is totally enclosed there is minimal safety hazards in switching up to an 800 amp DC load. Circuit breakers of this type are thermally sensitive, and thus, have the same trip rating on AC as DC. The battery safety switch is located between the battery enclosure and the front seats. A Bussman fuse is utilized to satisfy the requirement of the competition for a main fuse. Two Square D 200 amp 3-phase circuit breakers are utilized to provide the short-circuit and over-current protection for the two motors. All three circuit breakers are equipped with a shunt-trip option to allow the microprocessor or driver to disrupt the power flow if needed.

All wiring in the HEV is accomplished with diesel locomotive cable. The cable has a rating of at least 600 volts DC. All cable has a current rating of at least 125% of the full load current. Terminations were made with copper compression lugs. All of the high power wiring is installed in a liquid tight flexible metal conduit or a metal enclosure.

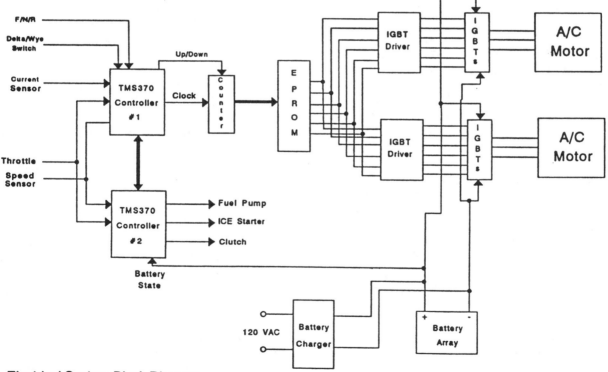

Figure 3. Electrical System Block Diagram

The AC motors controller is a variable frequency DC-AC inverter. Pulse width modulation (PWM) is used to accomplish the DC-AC conversion. The PWM data is stored in the EPROM in discrete form to accomplish the switching of the DC source. To incorporate the variable speed requirement to drive the vehicle, the data in the EPROM is clocked out of the EPROM at a variable

CONTROLLER STRATEGY

The controller strategy chosen for the Texas Tech HEV is based upon the responses of the AC motors and the response of the ICE. The response of the AC motors is optimized for maximum acceleration while the response of the ICE is optimized for emissions. The controller for the ICE is designed to operate the ICE at a constant set point. The controller turns on the ICE and increases the power output at a slow rate of change until the desired setpoint is reached. Likewise, when the controller turns off the ICE, the power output will be decreased at a slow rate of change. This operation is suitable for normal operation, however, under emergency conditions the vehicle will need to stop quickly, making it necessary to reduce the power output of the ICE quickly. To accommodate this situation, the ICE controller will monitor the vehicle speed. The controller will quickly reduce the power output if the deceleration (dv/dt) is large.

To control the power output of the ICE, the butterfly in the air intake will be operated by a stepper motor controlled by the ICE controller. To operate the ICE at a constant setpoint, the butterfly valve will be placed in a fixed position by the stepper motor. However, merely placing the butterfly valve in a fixed position will not ensure that the ICE operates at a fixed RPM and power output. The ICE must have a constant load to operate at the fixed RPM and power output.

The AC motor controller is designed to operate the vehicle at a constant velocity, which is determined by the operator input through the accelerator pedal. The AC motor controller monitors the speed of the vehicle through an RPM sensor mounted on one AC motor. The AC motor controller will adjust the slip in the AC motor to increase or decrease torque to operate the vehicle at constant velocity. Therefore, if the AC motor controller detects a change in load through a change in velocity, the controller will adapt to the load change by adjusting the slip. If the ICE is operating and the load changes as required for a hill, the ICE can maintain constant power output provided the AC motor controller's response is much faster than the response of the ICE.

If the ICE power output is larger than the power needed to operate the vehicle at the desired speed, the AC motors will be operated as generators by providing a negative slip to convert the additional power into current to recharge the batteries. The amount of load the AC motors place on the ICE is variable proportional to the slip. Therefore, if a hill is encountered, the AC motor load is decreased, thus allowing more power from the ICE to climb the hill. With this control strategy the ICE can be operated over a small operating region. The better the response of the AC motor controller, the smaller the operating region.

SYSTEM CONTROLLER - The TI TMS370C850 is used to control the mechanical drive system, which includes the internal combustion engine(ICE), and the stepper motors used to control the throttle body input (TBI) to the carburetor and the ICE clutch. Also, the controller is responsible for monitoring the current and voltage throughout the system, the rpm and speed of the vehicle, the depth of discharge (DOD) of the battery array, and the fuel pump.

The ICE system is centered around the AC system, which will be controlled by another TMS370C850. Communication between the two controllers is

accomplished via the serial interface port. To keep emissions at a minimum, the AC system is used for dynamic changes in speed and the ICE system is used during constant load conditions.

The ICE controller constantly monitors the DOD of the battery array. When the DOD reaches 60% depletion, and the speed of the vehicle is greater than 30 mph, the ICE controller prompts the AC controller to begin its regenerative configuration. At this time, the ICE controller begins the ICE starter procedure.

The control of the ICE will be completely autonomous. A stepper motor is used to control the butterfly to the TBI, which determines the amount of air that enters the carburetor. Using a stepper motor allows for exact positioning of the butterfly, which in turn, keeps the ICE operating at its optimum point so that emissions are kept at a minimum.

INSTRUMENTATION AND SYSTEM CONTROLS -The function of the instrumentation and system controls is to provide an interface between vehicle operator and vehicle function. Instrumentation provides feedback to the operator about the current status of various systems. System controls allow the operator to give input to the system.

Instrumentation installed in the vehicle provides voltage and current measurements at various points in the power distribution system. Also provided is a digital speedometer operated by the systems controller. A depth of discharge meter provides the systems controller with information to determine the need for battery recharge.

System controls include Forward-Neutral-Reverse (FNR) inputs and a variable voltage throttle controller. The FNR inputs will provide a high signal to the electrical system controller. When this input is received, the controller will respond by switching on a light which corresponds to the input signal. The throttle controller is spring loaded and provides a variable voltage (0 to 5 volts) to the electrical system controller.

EMISSIONS CONTROL STRATEGY

The electric vehicle is being developed to reduce or eliminate emissions, especially in urban areas, and to reduce dependency on foreign oil. Therefore, the controller strategy must be in line with these objectives to be practical. Since an IC engine is added to the electric vehicle to extend the range, the operation of the ICE must minimize emissions and be at the most efficient operation point, if possible. With the above objectives, the ICE should be operated with a constant load, which implies constant RPM and constant torque, and if a change in power is required, the change should be at the slowest rate possible to reduce emissions. However, the slow changes in power output must not affect the response of the vehicle.

The emissions from the use of ethanol are controlled by catalysts and engine tuning. The operating speed and load of the engine is controlled and kept constant which allows the engine to be tuned for a specific operating point. The engine is tuned to run at 2500 rpm with a lean mixture which produces very little emissions. The exhaust system for the APU is the stock Escort exhaust system that has been modified to include an ethanol catalyst. The crankcase and fuel tank are vented to the carburetor intake.

FUEL AND ELECTRICAL POWER CONSUMPTION

Ethanol was chosen to power the APU to promote it as an alternative to gasoline. Ethanol is a renewable fuel with a one year cycle where as gasoline is processed from fossil fuel, which takes thousands of years to produce. Ethanol can be produced from corn, which is in excessive supply and no shortages are foreseen. The fuel produces very low emissions and has a higher heating value than methanol.

In an electric vehicle, the efficiency of the AC induction motors is a primary consideration. Two primary areas of the DC-AC inverter influence the efficiency of the controller. First, the power dissipated by the semiconductor switches directly influence the efficiency of the controller. To minimize the power dissipated, Fuji 200A IGBT semiconductor switches are utilized. The Fuji IGBTs have a low saturated on voltage of 3.5 volts which minimizes the power dissipated in the IGBTs while they are conducting. Additionally, the IGBTs are switched at approximately 10 KHz. To minimize the power dissipated while the IGBTs are operating in the active region, the switching time should be small. The Fuji IGBTs were selected since they have a switching time less than one microsecond. The second area which affects the efficiency of the controller is the harmonics generated by the PWM. The PWM signal is used to generate a fundamental frequency which determines the speed of the AC motors. However, harmonics are also generated. To minimize the harmonics, a variation of the standard PWM process (called vector PWM) is used. In standard PWM, the logical relationship between a sinusoidal signal and a triangle signal determines the switching time. Rather than use a simple sinusoidal signal, a signal consisting of the sinusoidal signal plus 21% of the third harmonic is used to compare with the triangle signal. Adding 21% of the third harmonic increases the power in the fundamental frequency, thereby reducing the power in the harmonics. With the vector PWM, the fundamental RMS voltage is 6% greater in magnitude using an amplitude modulation ratio of 1.0. Therefore, the overall efficiency of the controller is improved.

BATTERY CHARGERS - Two battery charging systems are used. One system charges the batteries when the vehicle is operating. This charging mode occurs when the AC induction motors are acting as generators to charge the motor during ICE operation. The second system is an off-board charger which recharges the batteries at the end of each day's events. The charging circuitry that has been selected for the internal charger is relatively simple. The three dual-

module IGBT's will not be in operation during the ICE mode, so these transistors will be used for charging the batteries. Each IGBT has a soft recovery diode. These six diodes can be used as converter circuitry. This diode rectifier design will achieve the AC to DC conversion needed to charge the battery array.

The hybrid electric vehicle must also be capable of accepting a battery charge from an external off-board charging system. To provide for maximum life of the batteries, the off-board charger is designed to follow a safe charging cycle. Inherent features of the charger are voltage and current monitoring, overcharging protection, and faulty battery determination. The charger has a 220-volt input. This input will provide greater power than the 110-volt input, so the batteries can be charged quicker. The charging circuitry is a one-phase thyristor rectifier bridge. This design consists of a thyristor module, a B642-2T, and a triggering circuit, a PTR6000. The triggering circuitry controls the firing of the thyristors. A transformer provides isolation for the charging system. The entire battery array can be charged with this design.

VEHICLE STRUCTURE MODIFICATIONS

The structure of the Escort frame has not been modified in any way. The battery box is located in the passenger cargo compartment behind the front seats. The battery box contains the twelve batteries and the engine controller needed to power the car.

BATTERY ENCLOSURE - The enclosure contains three separate compartments. The outer compartments secure a total of twelve batteries. The center compartment contains two trays for electrical equipment. Each compartment was welded in a manner that each compartment is completely separated from adjacent compartments. The width of the enclosure is approximately 38.5 in. The length and height are 45.5 in. and 19.5 in. respectively. Enclosure supports were made separately because of lengths longer than 39.0 in. The battery compartment was constructed with 0.100 in. thick Aluminum 5052-H32 because of low weight and high yield strength (27 kpsi). A 12 volt, brush-less, 32 cfm. fan was installed in the enclosure for ventilation of the battery compartments.

Angles were welded to the bottom of each compartment to separate each battery. Each angle was welded in place so that the angle could contain the force of one battery. Nylon straps surround each battery to secure the batteries in case of vehicle roll-over. Gaskets were applied to all flanges to insure air-tight seals to the interior of the vehicle. Two smaller braces were attached to the rear of the enclosure for additional support. The total weight of the enclosure (including batteries, support members, and electrical equipment), in the vehicle is 1125 lbs. Ample viewing area was provided using the rear view mirror.

The four components required for the hybrid drive train; a 1978 280-Z differential, two A.C. motors and one

Kawasaki I.C. engine, are being supported by compact, simple structures. The foundation for these structures is the O.E.M. undercarriage member and two rubber motor mounts fixed to this member. The differential utilizes the two motor mounts for support and two adapter plates for connection to the drive shafts. The adapter plates are necessary to connect with the O.E.M. tripod joint at the inside end of the drive shafts. By locating the two electric motors directly on top of the differential, the three shafts are parallel and when viewed from the front, they form a triangle, The electric motors are supported by means of an aluminum plate and a steel frame that bolts to the mounting holes of the differential. The motors are flush mounted to the plate which is then bolted to the steel frame. The I.C.E. is supported on the driver's side by a fabricated steel bracket that originates from the front differential support. On the passenger side of the engine, a steel structure attached to the O.E.M. motor mount holds the engine at it's original mounting point. To minimize the forward and backward torque that will ensue from driving the car, a brace was added to the top of the engine on the driver's side. This brace attaches to existing bolt holes on the two motors and extends laterally towards the passenger's side of the engine bay. In conclusion, there are a total of five individual structures made from numerous parts that make up the support frame. These five components have been designed to be light and strong but also very serviceable.

SUSPENSION MODIFICATIONS

The suspension and braking systems of the Ford Escort Wagon were modified because of the increased weight added to the vehicle. The altered weight distribution is shown in Figure 4. These modifications required minimal compromise in vehicle handling with no change in track width or ground clearance.

The current rear suspension was not capable of handling the additional load. Therefore, the strut assemblies were removed and replaced with strut assemblies which could support higher side loads with spring rates of 300 lbf/in., which is 250 percent greater than the stock rating of 85.1 lbf/in. A shim, shown in Figure 5, was fabricated out of aluminum and installed in the lower strut spring cup to fill the gap caused by the smaller outer diameter of the 300 lbf/in spring. This shim aids in keeping the spring's base from shifting within the cup. The top spring cup, in Figure 6, was also altered to hold the new spring. A new smaller diameter centering section was used in place of the existing centering piece. Also, the existing rubber bushing for the top cup was cut and shortened and placed around the new centering section.

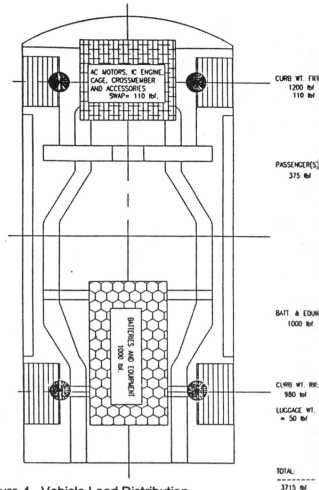

Figure 4. Vehicle Load Distribution

The front suspension spring/strut assemblies were replaced with springs from the Escort GT package (167.9 lbf/in.), with rates approximately thirteen percent higher than original factory equipment (151.3 lbf/in.). The struts were replaced with after market replacements capable of enduring high vertical and side loads. No additional modifications were required to install the GT springs.

The added weight of approximately 1200 pounds force was a major concern with regard to the handling characteristics of the Ford Escort wagon. To improve these characteristics, stiffer after market sway bars and struts with increased damping were installed. This was considered necessary for the maneuvering events of the competition, which include the slalom, U-turn and lateral stability tests.

Low profile tires mounted on fifteen inch wheels from the Escort GT package improves both the braking and handling ability of the vehicle. A vacuum pump for the brakes was needed. An electric pump was selected because of the ease of mounting and power usage. The use of a large vacuum reservoir with an adjustable vacuum control switch solved the problem of the electrical vacuum pump having to run continuously.

The braking system proportioning valve was reversed to provide a 40/60 front/rear pressure split, diverting more braking force to the rear brakes. This modification was performed because most of the vehicle

262

weight is in the rear.

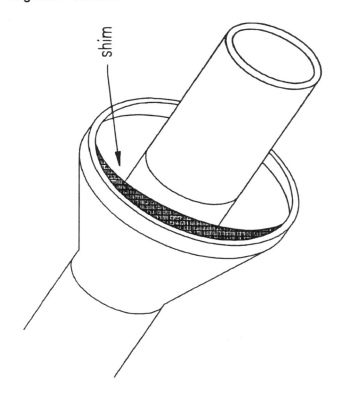

Figure 5. Shim/Spring Cup Assembly

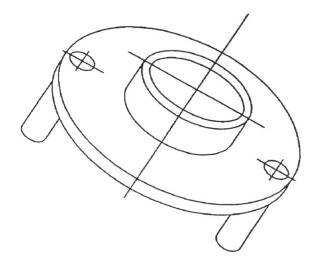

Figure 6. Top Spring Cup Assembly

CHOICE OF MATERIALS

ROLL BAR - The roll bar is made of seamless mild steel tubing with a 1.5 inch outer diameter and a wall thickness of 0.120 inches. The roll bar is no more than 3 inches from the ceiling of the automobile. The roll bar has 2 support bars (4-point roll cage) extending from the hoop at an angle of about 30 degrees from the vertical

position. The roll cage has 1 inch of padding with a 3/8 inch inspection hole drilled into the main hoop. Two steel mounting plates hold the main frame rails in compression with the frame of the car to avoid welding to the thin unibody floor pan. The bar is bolted with 3/8-inch diameter hardened steel bolts using self-locking nuts. The required support arms were fabricated from material identical to the main hoop and were mounted to the shock towers using a steel plate integrated into the shock tower. Using the shock tower for the connection of the rear support arms provides a strong roll bar and also helps maintain lateral stability in the rear suspension.

VEHICLE MANUFACTURABILITY

The goal of the Texas Tech HEV team was to develop a hybrid electric vehicle that is cost effective and realistic to produce on current assembly lines.

To assure this is the case, all components used in the TTU HEV are readily available, off-the-self items. Changes to the basic Ford Escort were kept to a minimum while still assuring the vehicle would meet all requirements. The number of major components was kept to a minimum. One of the advantages of the quasi-parallel configuration is that an alternator for charging the batteries is not required.

CONCLUSIONS

The Texas Tech University's entry in the HEV Challenge has been designed specifically to minimize emissions. This criteria has led to the quasi-parallel configuration and the use of ethanol as the fuel for the APU. Performance requirements, cost and reliability concerns led to the use of two 28 hp AC motors. Reliability, longevity and cost were primary factors in the selection of the deep cycle lead acid batteries. All of the design choices were based on minimizing emissions and cost while assuring performance capability and safety. All of these factors are necessary to make the HEV a viable and attractive form of transportation for the general public.

A majority of the funding for the project was provided by the Texas Corn Growers Association. The association donated $10,000 and two 55-gallon drums of ethanol to promote the use of the alcohol as a fuel. Also, the DOE is donating $3000 upon the arrival of the HEV in Dearborne for the use of ethanol as a fuel. Ford donated the Escort wagon with the company's approval of TTU's initial HEV proposal.

POSTSCRIPT

The Texas Tech team experienced many problems along the way, both technical and financial. The students worked long and hard to have the car ready for the competition. Although over 75% of the students graduated in May 1993, graduation only slowed them down for one day. The student's dedication and perseverance under difficult circumstances was remarkable. During the final days of the project one student got married, had a brief honeymoon, and was back on the job working long hours and nights to complete the project.

The car was final ready to go just in time for the competition. After reaching Dearborn, final adjustments were being made to the car when a major component of the controller failed. After working around the clock for several days and searching Dearborn for parts, the car was not able to compete in the final events. Although the students were disappointed, they realized the experience they gained from the project was invaluable and would serve them well in their future role as practicing engineers. Texas Tech was one of the few schools that designed and built their own ac motor controller. Although this path was chosen for financial reasons, it was a tremendous learning tool.

LESSONS LEARNED - Actually, the greatest difficulty throughout the project was financial. Funding considerations not only dictated the choice of controllers but also limited the number of spare parts. In addition, financial constrains limited the choice of batteries, resulting in heavier batteries that pushed the car over the weight limit. But the greatest problem, which was again tied to funding, was the lack of laboratory facilities to be able to complete characterize and test the system before putting them into the car.

Since the competition, a basic laboratory facility has been developed to test the motors and motor controllers independently. In addition, an extensive fund raising campaign has begun and has already secured as much funding as was available for the past two years.

Although the Texas Tech entry had many problems, the faculty advisors and all of the student participants agreed that the competition had achieved its primary goal of increased knowledge and an appreciation of teamwork. The main thought from all of the students at the end of a long and difficult task was " Wait until next year!".

THE UNIVERSITY OF TULSA

"HYBRID HURRICANE"

The Sun Storm Organization

Advisors: John M. Henshaw & Robert D. Strattan
Students: Irvin Smith, Eric Sager, & Charles Tompkins

ABSTRACT

This report chronicles the journey of the University of Tulsa's hybrid electric vehicle team, code-named Sun Storm, in creating the "Hybrid Hurricane". This vehicle is a sport-utility truck combining the flavor of Oklahoma with the benefits of a multi-purpose vehicle. By use of an AC induction motor, coupled with a transmission, powered by lead-acid batteries, and controlled by a variable speed controller the vehicle employs the latest in electric vehicle technology. Alternate power is drawn from a gasoline powered electric generator placed in series with the other powertrain components. Fabrication of the structure and body from aerospace fiberglass lends to the creativity of design. Suspension modifications have been tuned to the requirements for handling and performance in relation to hybrid vehicles. This report also stresses the manufacturability, reasons for materials chosen in construction, and body styling/ergonomics. Figures 1 and 2 show a photograph and computer aided drafting representation of the "Hybrid Hurricane".

This report is proudly submitted in accordance with rules set for the Ford/SAE/DOE Hybrid Electric Vehicle Challenge.

BACKGROUND

Hybrid electric vehicles are an integral step in the implementation of zero emission vehicles into the automotive infrastructure. Hybrid electric vehicles showcase the good characteristics of electric vehicles combined with the those of currently available automobiles. This allows the consumer to be gradually drawn into the exciting new world where gasoline transportation is phased out to make way for alternative fuel technologies. The Ford/SAE/DOE Hybrid Electric Vehicle Challenge is a competition that will showcase the best engineering student designs in hybrid electric innovations .

The Sun Storm organization is an interdisciplinary team of Mechanical and Electrical engineering students at the University of Tulsa committed to creating a radically new prototype in hybrid electric transportation. By drawing on experiences with solar electric and mini-baja projects, the organization has been able to learn from the past and readjust to implement the best possible technologies to a hybrid electric situation.

Since The University of Tulsa is a small university, with roughly four thousand total students, the project team has been able to educate and draw the support from the many varied departments and groups that make up the campus community. The team has also tried to educate the general populace of the city of Tulsa in the aspects of hybrid electric automotive technologies and their implications. The team feels that through education, the consumer will be more attuned to electric vehicles an their rapid approach into mainstream life.

One of the main goals of this project is to educate engineering students in the concurrent design of automobiles. The focus has been on how a project of this magnitude would be dealt with in industry. Therefore, the breadth of this project goes well beyond the mere design and implementation of engineering design by giving students responsibility for financial matters, organizational and daily management, public relations, marketing, presentations to sponsors and interested groups, and other facets involved in a real-life industrial design and development project. By using the rules and lines of communications more representative of what would be expected upon designing in the corporate world, the students involved in this project have become better prepared for the rigors of industry.

MOTOR DESIGN

At the beginning of the project, the motor design team concentrated their efforts on DC motors. These have an advantage in that the speed is easily controlled, and they can be readily run from a battery bank. One concern was that normal DC motors employ brushes on a commutator. There was some question as to the durability of the brushes during heavy use.

To deal with this problem, we looked into brushless DC motors. As the name indicates, this design does not employ brushes to create the excitation field. Motors of this type use rare earth magnets for a permanent magnetic field.

FIGURE 1- Photograph of "Hybrid Hurricane" taken
March 29, 1993

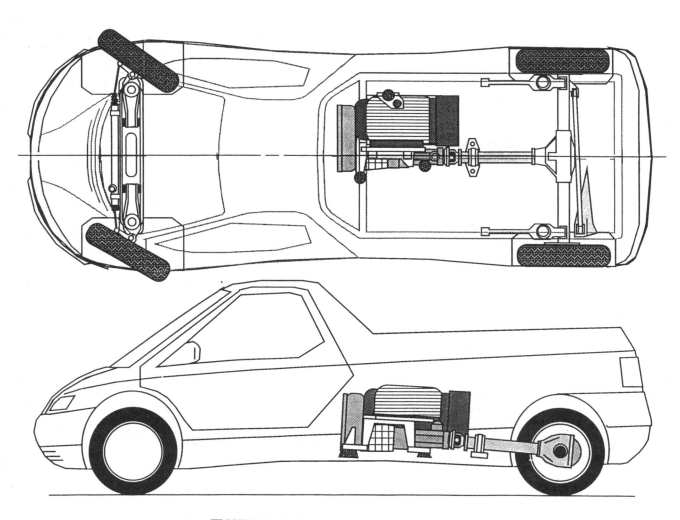

FIGURE 2- CAD Representation of Vehicle

This does solve the problem of brush wear, but brings on another concern. Rare earth magnets, when exposed to high temperatures, have the tendency to demagnetize. These temperatures could occur with only a slight overload of the motor, when extended over a period of time such as a race day. Once the field magnets have lost their magnetic properties, they need to be replaced. This results in down time to make the repair, and a great deal of expense to replace the magnets. Also, the commercial availability of brushless DC motors in ratings suitable for a vehicle of this size is limited.

Through conversations with Baldor Electric, of Fort Smith, Arkansas, a decision was made to use an AC induction motor, controlled by a variable frequency flux vector controller. By using this state of the art smart controller, the AC induction motor is able to run at variable speed, like a DC motor.

Through team consultation, a decision was made to use a 4-speed manual transmission rather than a direct drive system. This meant that a smaller horsepower motor could be used.

The horsepower requirement that would suit the needs of this vehicle necessitates a motor of approximately 15Hp. To have reserve capacity of the motor/controller set for short term acceleration, the controller was oversized to 25Hp, as recommended by Baldor.

CONTROLLER STRATEGY

The motor controller is a variable frequency flux vector AC controller, rated to be used with up to a 25Hp motor. The controller and the 15Hp AC induction motor were donated by Baldor Electric in Fort Smith, Arkansas. The controller was oversized to 2Hp to allow the motor to be operated at peak power output of over 30Hp, while still allowing high resolution control at low horsepower. With new technology easing the complexity of control of AC motors, this arrangement gives us the flexibility in adapting AC induction technology to automotive applications.

The controller was originally meant to be powered from a 240 volt, three phase source. A few modifications were necessary for operation on the 264 volt DC bus used in this vehicle. The sensors sensing the 3 individual phases were disabled and the DC was brought directly past the 3 phase rectifier bridge. The only other modification needed was to exchange the AC cooling fans for brushless DC models of the same dimensions. The controller is capable of operating at supply voltages of between 220 and 385 volts. It controls the motor with a 210 volt line to line three phase, 0-250 Hz. variable frequency AC signal. The 264 volt bus will allow the controller to stay above the low cutoff at a battery discharged state, while still allowing room on the top end for charging from the APU or regenerative braking. Figure 3 shows a schematic for the control system of the "Hybrid Hurricane" vehicle.

The current strategy is to allow the controller, through an auto-tuning technique, to determine the optimal values for such parameters as slip, proportional-gain, windage and friction loss, and maximum current. This auto-tuning can be accomplished through using either the display panel on the controller itself, or through the use of a terminal emulation by a portable laptop computer through an RS232 port on the controller. These parameters, once tuned, will provide the controller with the best control strategy for the application of power to the motor.

Another aspect of controller strategy is the user interface. The controller is capable of responding to either a speed or a torque command mode input. With the torque/speed being proportional to a 0-10 volt input signal to the bipolar-analog input. The variable torque mode is being used. A positive 0-10 volt signal from the accelerator pedal is input to control the torque output to the motor. A simple double throw/double pole switch is used for the reverse signal. Another feature we have utilized is the forward and reverse enable function. We have installed an "electronic clutch" to disable the motor during shifting of gears in the transmission, as a mechanical clutch is not used. This controller also allows for implementation of regenerative braking. Our design supplies a negative torque command to the motor when the brake pedal is depressed. This operates the motor as a generator and recharges the batteries. If the negative torque signal is still applied when the vehicle is stopped, the vehicle would move in reverse if not corrected. This was solved by sensing the analog speed output signal of the controller to disable the braking signal when the speed falls below the reference value. Figure 4 shows the schematic of the regenerative braking system.

BATTERY DESIGN

At the beginning of the project, the design was orientated toward competition in the commuter class of the American Tour De Sol, in 1992. Rules for competition in this class called for a maximum electric energy storage capacity of 7.2 kWhrs. This, along with the motor requirements, was the controlling factor for the battery system design.

As the motor/controller design changed, the battery design needed to be modified as well. Each change in the motor requirements resulted in a analogous variation in the battery design requirements.

The final battery design for the Tour De Sol competition supplied 360 volts DC to the vector drive controller. The controller can accept voltages of 225 to 380 volts DC. 30 EXIDE DC-9 batteries each supplying 12 volts and 20 amp-hours at the five hour rate provided a total battery capacity of exactly 7.2 kWhrs.

For the Ford/SAE/DOE HEV Challenge, a new limit of 10 kWhrs. was set on the electric energy storage capacity. The battery bus still needed to remain within the controller limits, 225-380 volts. At 22 batteries a new bus voltage of 264, nominal, is obtained. Therefore, at full charge the batteries are at 277.2 volts and at full discharge the batteries are at 237.6 volts. At a 3 hour discharge rating of 18 amp-hours the energy storage capacity is 4.75 kWhrs. A second string of 22 batteries was designed and paralleled with the first string. This gives an electric energy storage capacity of 9.5 kWhrs. This battery design is also compatible with the rectified output of the APU generator.

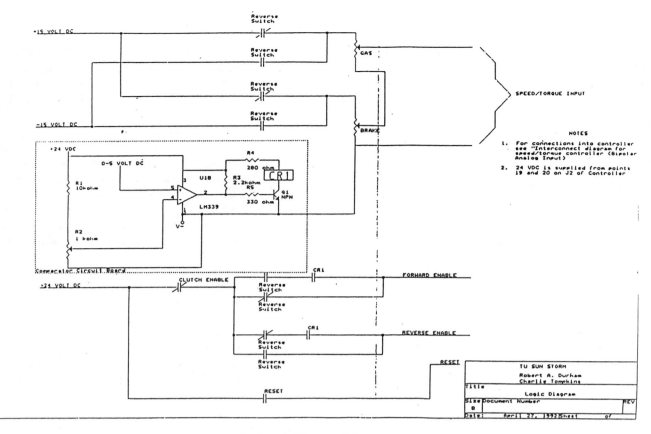

FIGURE 3- Control System Schematic

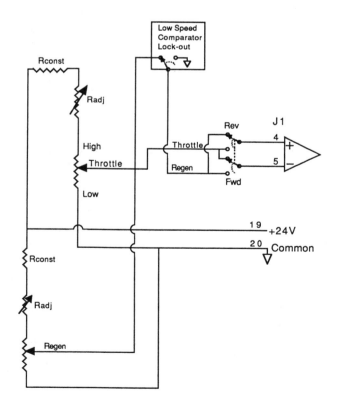

FIGURE 4- Regnerative Braking System Diagram

The team chose Exide Battery Corporation because they were willing to donate the needed batteries. From the battery selection available at Exide, it was decided that their heavy duty deep cycle marine/wheelchair batteries would be the best choice for reliability reasons.

ALTERNATE POWER UNIT DESIGN

The alternate power unit is an intricate part of the "Hybrid Hurricane" vehicle. The alternate power unit used by the Sun Storm team is a modified Honda ES6500 gasoline-powered electric generator. Listed here are some of the generator and engine specifications.

Generator

Maximum Output	6.5 kW
Rated Output	6.0 kW
Rated Voltage	120/240 V
Rated Current	50.0/25.0 A

single phase, Frequency = 60 Hz

Engine

Type	4-stroke, O.H.C., 2-cylinder
Displacement	359 cc
Maximum horsepower	9.1 kW @ 3600 rpm
Maximum Torque	240 kg-cm

unleaded fuel, liquid cooled

This liquid cooled generator design was chosen for its ability to be implemented into the present vehicle design and also for its off-the-shelf ability to provide maximum proven power. The ES6500, shown in Figure 5, has been modified to fit into the vehicle. The modifications to the generator are divided into four major areas; motor/generator assembly, radiator relocation, exhaust relocation, and electrical.

MOTOR/GENERATOR - The first modification involved locating the motor/generator assembly. This assembly was modified slightly. Modification involved readjusting of the mounting brackets for placement into the vehicle. With the orientation of the assembly, the front being the internal combustion housing and back being the generator portion, the front mounting brackets were modified to allow the apparatus to fit within the center channel of the vehicle bed. The modification consisted of removing the existing mounting brackets and welding two L-brackets under the engine. The rubber bushings used for mounting the assembly to the Honda frame were also modified. This modification involved drilling a 3/8 inch hole in the bushing for mounting the assembly to the floor of the bed.

RADIATOR - The radiator is mounted in the rear of the vehicle. Its placement allows it to use air flow from under the car. Two modifications to the existing radiator were necessary. The first was to the radiator itself. The entrance and exit ports were cutoff and welded back to the radiator, to allow proper flow of coolant into and out of the radiator. The second modification to the radiator consisted of lengthening all hoses.

EXHAUST - The exhaust modification consisted of lengthening the tubing approximately 2 feet from the engine header to the muffler and adding a catalytic converter. The muffler is located within the rear compartment of the vehicle. It is mounted vertically within the car with the exit being from beneath the car and out the rear of the vehicle.

MAJOR ELECTRICAL MODIFICATIONS- The existing control box from the ES6500 is repackaged in the rear compartment. Remote controls and indicators were added to the cab. Ignition/starting switch, temperature gage, current warning, and oil warning lights are all part of the recabling to the cab of the vehicle for easy access by the driver. This allows the driver to start the APU from the rear of the vehicle, for testing purposes, as well as from the cab. Also, since the APU power output is 240 volt single phase, a full wave diode rectifier bridge is used for conversion to DC. The DC output is paralleled with the 264 volt DC battery and controller busses.

APU MODIFICATIONS SUMMARY

Modifications to the Honda ES6500
1. Mounting brackets width reduction.
2. Cooling hoses lengthened and repositioned.
3. Exhaust lengthened and repositioned.
4. Addition of a catalytic converter.
5. Lengthening of electrical wiring.
6. Addition of cab remote.

Other Modifications:
1. New fuel tank added.
2. A fuel pump added to facilitate easy fuel flow for gravity feed tank.
3. Automation of choke and idle controls.

EMISSIONS CONTROL STRATEGY

The team attempted to use the most simple and most effective emissions control strategy available. Since our alternate power unit is located in the center of the vehicle, the first priority was to install an exhaust system that would run exhaust from the APU to a muffler at the rear of the vehicle. This systems allows this vehicle to meet the Ford HEV Challenge specifications on exhaust leaving the vehicle in the rear. As shown in Figure 6, the exhaust system and muffler are both located inside of the vehicle instead of underneath as in most commercially available automobiles. This was done in pursuit of our general goal to make the underbody as clean and unobtrusive as possible.

The team approached Allied Signal Automotive Catalyst Company about a catalyst that would suit the special needs of our vehicle. After running several tests which included measurements of exhaust temperature, air/fuel ratios, and several other factors, a catalyst was chosen. The catalyst used in this vehicle is 2.23 inches in diameter by 6 inches in length. This gives us a catalyst volume of slightly over 33 in^3. This is slightly oversized since the engine displacement of the APU used in this vehicle is only 22 in^3. This will not be a problem since the emissions testing at the HEV Challenge will be done after the engine and catalyst

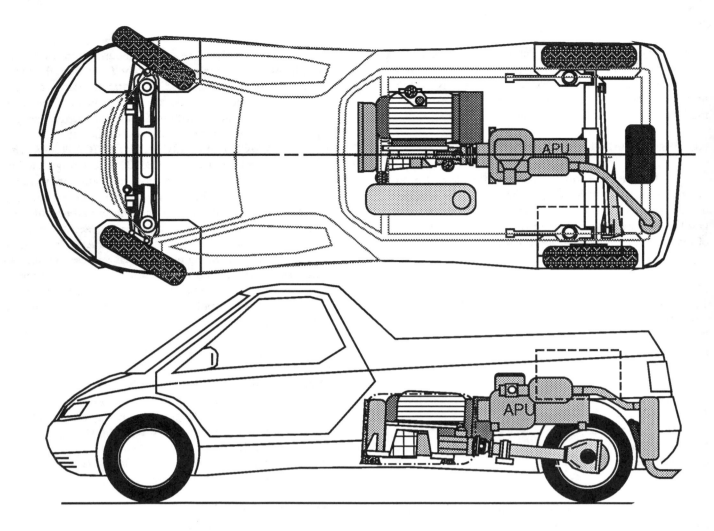

FIGURE 5- APU Placement in Vehicle

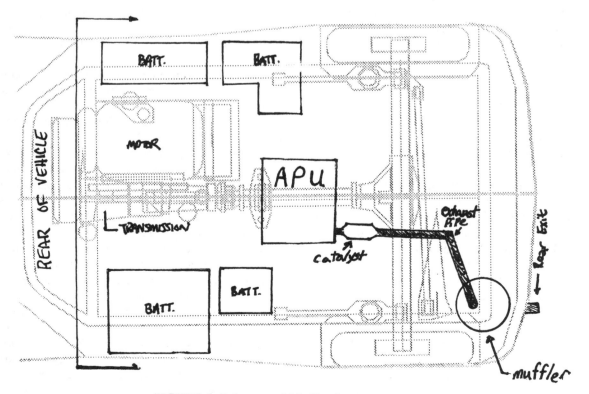

FIGURE 6- Exhaust and Muffler System

have had the chance to warm up, thus allowing the use of an oversized catalyst.

The catalyst was canned (sealed in an insulated metal container) and placed in the exhaust system. It is located approximately 6 inches from the exhaust outlet on the APU (see Figure 6). This is where exhaust temperature is at its maximum and also where the catalyst will work most efficiently.

At the present time, emission testing has been rather minimal as the attentions of the team have been focused on other matters. Future testing is eagerly anticipated to judge the merits and drawbacks of this system.

ENERGY AND FUEL CONSUMPTION

The "Hybrid Hurricane" motor requires about 25 amps at 40 mph. This conclusion was drawn from data gathered during road testing. The voltage provided to the motor's controller is approximately 255 volts with the alternate power unit on. Since the APU's max current is 27 amps, which is close to a 25 amp average, the 25 amp value was used as APU current for the range and fuel consumption calculations. The APU's fuel tank holds 4.4 gallons of gasoline and is capable of running for 5 hours at full load on a full tank of gas (APU specifications provided by Honda). With the APU running at full load, at 40 mph it takes 5 hrs to use 4.4 gallons of fuel resulting in an estimated range of 200 miles and fuel consumption of 45.5 mpg.

The battery bank has a energy capacity of 9.5 kWhrs. At 40 mph the motor is pulling 25 amps resulting in a power demand of 6375 watts plus or minus 500 watts (uncertainty is due to varying voltages in the battery bus depending upon load). At 6375 watts, total driving time on batteries alone will be 1.49 hrs for a total range of 59.6 miles. At 6375 watts minus 500 watts the driving time will be 1.59 hrs for a range of 64.8 miles. At 6375 watts plus 500 watts, total time is 1.38 hrs for a range of 55.3 miles. Because of the higher demand placed upon the batteries during acceleration and inefficiencies in other parts of the system the lower estimate for battery range will be used. The resulting theoretical total range for the Sun Storm "Hybrid Hurricane" electric vehicle will be about 255.3 miles.

VEHICLE STRUCTURE DESIGN

Before initial construction of the body could begin, a concept of the performance needed from the vehicle was developed. To accomplish this a set of design criteria was established:

1. Provide support and room for two people.
2. Provide sufficient strength without being excessively heavy.
3. Provide storage room for batteries.
4. Provide proper support and room for motor, transmission, and suspension.
5. Have a pleasing appearance.

The initial structure design began with a "wire frame" built from PVC tubing. This accomplished two things; it defined the shape of the final load-bearing frame and also served as a three-dimensional model with which the team could work. Figures 7 and 8 show the wire frame in the side, front, and rear views.

Following completion and modification of the wire frame, the team needed to add structure to the body. After researching various materials, it was decided to use composites to complete construction. The composites were chosen for their good strength-to-weight ratio, relative ease of handling, adaptability to mass production, corrosion resistance, and (insulating properties that increase the safety of the passengers of the vehicle from deadly voltages in the battery bus). The materials chosen were aerospace grade fiberglass and vinyl ester resin.

To add structure to the tubing, PVC foam was secured between members of the PVC wire frame tubing. This foam was then sandwiched between layers of glass and resin to form a monocoque structure. It is very important to have a good bond between foam and glass to prevent the glass from delaminating. To insure a good bond, a thin layer of microballoon/resin mixture was used to seal the foam. Microballoons are microscopic, hollow, glass spheres that form a putty-like substance when added to the resin. When the microballoon mixture dries, it forms a surface that can be ground smooth to allow a good interface for the glass and the foam. It also helps seal the foam preventing excess amounts of resin from being soaked into the foam; this helps reduce the overall weight of the vehicle.

For those areas requiring mechanical fasteners, a special type of construction is used called a hardpoint. A hardpoint is made by removing one layer of glass and the foam underneath. This hollowed area is then filled with layers of microballoons/resin. After grinding the micro-balloons, a layer of glass is laid for the one that was removed. Hardpoints provide excellent compressive strength, which makes them ideal as mounting points for the motor, suspension, and other components that must be attached to the structure of the vehicle.

The structural integrity of the vehicle is obviously one of the main concerns of the body design. Calculations and recommendations were made to alleviate the questions of bending moment, deflection, and torsion. The maximum bending moment was found to occur 83 inches from the front of the vehicle. A structural channel was built to separate the motor and battery compartments, and to relieve some of the bending stress in the exterior walls of the vehicle. With this channel, it was found that at a two-G load, four layers of glass arranged in a 0-90 degree orientation (the orientation axis that runs from the front to the back of the vehicle) provides sufficient strength for the calculated bending stress.

The deflection of the vehicle was calculated by breaking down the loads into three categories; the motor & batteries, passengers and seats, and the weight of body and other considerations. The total maximum deflection was found to be approximately 0.04 inches.

Torsional forces were calculated to simulate effects that the vehicle would encounter in everyday driving. The load that the front wheels will transmit to the road has been measured at 595 lbs., but for the calculations, twice this amount will be used to account for dynamic effects of the

SS-2 06NOV91 JCO SCALE= 1:18 SUBFRAME SIDE VIEW

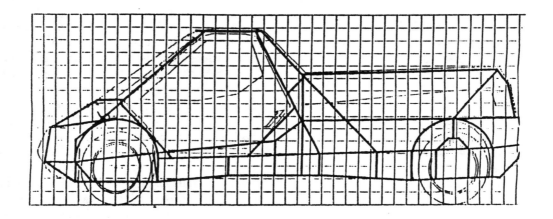

FIGURE 7- Side View of Wire Frame

SS-2 06NOV91 JCO SCALE= 1:18 SUBFRAME REAR VIEW/ FRONT VIEW

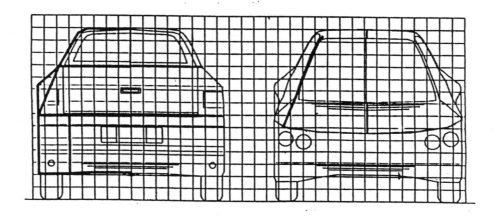

FIGURE 8- Front & Rear Views of Wire Frame

torsional loading. Results of the calculation show that torsional forces can be brought under control by applying two layers of glass at a +/- 45 degree orientation in addition to the 0-90 degree orientated layers.

To achieve the final design criterion of producing a pleasing appearance, the outer surface of the vehicle was coated with a special micro-balloon/resin mixture which included a wax additive. This wax mixture provided a much smoother surface, but some depressions still existed on the outer surface. Body putty was then applied and ground smooth to fill these depressions.

SUSPENSION MODIFICATIONS

Two original suspension design scenarios were envisioned for the Sun Storm "Hybrid Hurricane". One: design and manufacture an entirely original front and rear suspension, and two: integrate an existing suspension system into the truck's load-bearing structure (underbody). The design/fabrication scheme was deemed too complex, expensive, and time-consuming to be undertaken with enthusiasm, whereas the adaptation scheme was seen to offer many benefits with few disadvantages. The choice was made to use a 1982 Chevrolet Chevette's suspension.

The front suspension is dominated by three dynamic control arms including an upper A-arm, a lower control arm, and a lateral control arm that bolts to the body aft of the suspension proper. The static sub-frame of the front suspension is a large, trans-structural U-shaped beam that nestles against and bolts to the monocoque body structure of the "Hybrid Hurricane" truck. This trans-vehicle structural beam is important not only for proper stiffness and strength, but because both the upper and lower control arms mount directly to it, thereby assimilating single-wheel impact loads (e.g. a pothole strike) into the entire structure and "sharing" the stresses experienced over a greater load area. Mounted between the upper and lower control arms is a coil spring, while above the A-arm, a shock absorber can be found. An anti-roll bar is mounted underneath the front of the car, attaching to the left and right side lower control arms and the car structure itself underneath the front overhang area. The front suspension's track is 54 inches. Figure 9 shows detail of the front suspension.

Dissecting the rear suspension, a rigid beam-axle extends across the rear of the vehicle, broken only in the middle by a differential. Outboard on the axle, coil springs and trailing control arms maintain proper suspension action, alignment, and fore/aft containment while a Panhard rod controls the lateral movement of the vehicle. Two shock absorbers (one per side) damp suspension motion and enhance driveability; they are bolted between the body and the aft side of the beam-axle. As with the front, the track is 54 inches; the wheelbase is 113 inches. Figure 10 shows the rear suspension of the "Hybrid Hurricane".

When attaching the suspensions to the composite body structure, steel plates were used. The removed Chevette sub-frame structural plate contains two threaded bosses to which the actual suspension is bolted. Three bolts secure this sub-plate to the truck's vertical (composite) mounting superstructure using a backing plate of steel and

3M micro-balloon/resin hardpoint material within the composite. Additionally, the aft lower control arm is secured to the body structure through a bolted bracket which clevises hardpoints within the floor structure.

The rear suspension has nine points where a connection is made to the body structure: the two control arms (one per side), the torque-tube/U-joint bracket, the two coil springs (one per side), the Panhard rod, and the two shock absorbers. Each of the control arms is bolted to the body using a bracket in double shear, while the torque-tube bracket is through-bolted to the bed of the truck. Both springs rest in their respective spring-seats and compress against shaped, rubber-lined depressions in the body; the Panhard rod is bolted to the body using a hardpoint, and the shock absorbers are mounted to a bracket that uses hardpoints and composites to achieve its strength.

CHOICE OF MATERIALS

The Sun Storm "Hybrid Hurricane" is fabricated almost entirely from a structural glass composite. Ease of manipulation by students and a good strength-to-weight ratio were key factors in the choice of Sun Storm's materials. Specifically, two types of fiberglass were used, a nine ounce satin weave and a six ounce plain weave. Vinyl-ester resin was the hardening agent for both the plain and satin weave fiberglass. Four layers of fiberglass were deemed structurally sufficient for the majority of the car; heavily stressed areas received as many as seven layers. One may ask, "why was fiberglass chosen as the construction material?" The main advantages of using the aerospace grade fiberglass over metal were: easy to manufacture, good specific modulus, and non-conductive and non-corrosive to battery acid (important in an electric vehicle) and also amenable to mass-production.

Additionally, the structure is crafted using PVC tubing and an aerated PVC *Klegicell* foam. Now, before Dali-esque shapes of hot, twisted plastic come to mind, know that the PVC tubing was used merely as a three-dimensional model around which composite could be laid. The *Klegicell* foam spanned the distance between the PVC tubes, fleshing out the 'wireframe' body and giving the fiberglass a surface upon which to harden smoothly. Structurally, the fiberglass bears all of the loading of the car; the foam and PVC are negligible contributors in this arena. Furthermore, the car's monocoque is about one year old and has cured to an impressive level of strength; from a 'seat of the pants' perspective, bending and torsional modes of deflection are reduced to levels not traditionally found on street vehicles.

VEHICLE MANUFACTURABILITY

The "Hybrid Hurricane" is a one-off, *a-mano* creation; the methods used in the fabrication of the truck were extremely time-consuming and labor-intensive. Indeed, the very nature of the vehicle (a non or pre-production testbed) precluded the Sun Storm team from any sort of assembly-line techniques. To wit, every step of construction, from the heating, bending, and fitting of the

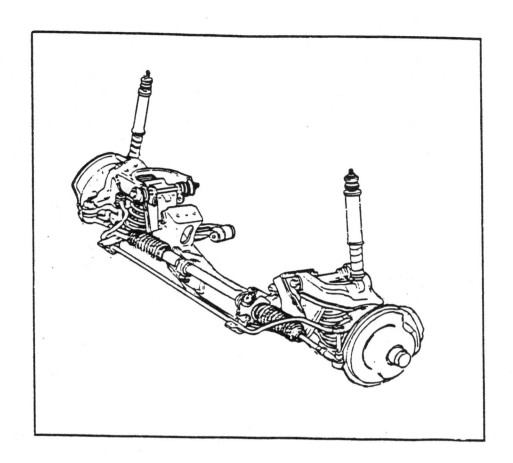

FIGURE 9- Detail of Front Suspension

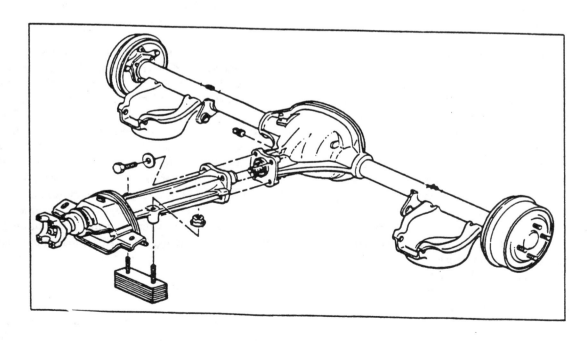

FIGURE 10- Detail of Rear Suspension

274

PVC tubing to the laying of the fiberglass was done by hand using blood, sweat, and a lot of elbow grease; the methods used were completely intractable for volume production. Producing automobiles to sell by this same method would be prohibitively expensive as well as giving the aforementioned low production volume (approximately 10 cars per year using parallel teams of dedicated, experienced craftspeople).

The "Hybrid Hurricane" could be adapted to a production process relatively easily, using custom molds and High Speed Resin Transfer Molding Composite technology as pioneered by Ford. Improved production tolerances and a vastly increased production rate would be the main benefits along with interchangeability of the product or sub-product, (i.e. a hood or other minor assembly). For body panels, Sheet Molding Composite technology such as used in the Pontiac Fiero and the GM minivans including the TransSport, Silhouette, and Lumina APV could be employed. Additionally, the Chevrolet Corvette is made from fiberglass and meets the rigors of production with aplomb.

The initial production runs of zero/low emissions vehicles will be low with corresponding high prices. However, in order to meet the current legislative legerdemain, these vehicles *will* have to be sold, with tax breaks and other incentives defraying the initial cost of purchase. Therefore, even though the "Hybrid Hurricane" would be a more expensive vehicle, it is not precluded from production.

BODY STYLING AND ERGONOMICS

A pick-up truck was chosen as a unique platform with which to display the University of Tulsa's hybrid vehicle concept. Prosaically, the Sun Storm Hybrid Hurricane is an urban sport-utility commuting vehicle. Practically, it is a small, low-emissions commuter vehicle that can carry two people plus cargo in an aggressive yet efficient package.

Upon viewing the truck for the first time, several features make themselves immediately apparent: first is the very form of the vehicle - it is a smallish pickup truck that sits low to the ground on low-profile tires; second is the interior roll cage/exterior rollhoop. Safety is paramount! Walking around to the front of the vehicle, the tall, relatively narrow windshield is seen to be unique (indeed, it was a custom creation of Ford Glass of Tulsa, Oklahoma). Wrap-around aero headlamps are well integrated as are the small mouth-like ventilation holes down low on the front of the truck. Open a door, at the touch of a button, and one notices their aggressive forward-tilting gull-wing design. Moving towards the rear of the vehicle, one's hand traces the body crease along the flanks of the truck about one foot below the top of the bed. Intersecting this styling line are the integrated tail lights that wrap around the rear. Viewed from the rear, the vehicle's 'coke bottle' narrowing of the center section of the vehicle becomes apparent. From this same vantage-point, a modified Ford Ranger backlite with sliding window is seen. Returning to the door opened moments ago in order to look inside the truck reveals a cockpit unlike most production vehicles. Ingress-egress is slightly more complex

that in your father's Oldsmobile due to the five-point racing harnesses and roll cage side bar. Once comfortably ingratiated into the cab, major controls fall readily to hand; the manual shift lever is just where one would expect as is the turn signal paraphernalia. Not familiar, however, is the abundance of data gathering equipment including a data-logger and laptop computer. Looking out of the vehicle, large A-pillars are noticed along with a substantial dashboard area indicative of the cab-forward design (a la GM's plastic minivans such as the Pontiac TransSport).

SUMMARY

The Sun Storm team has focused its efforts on creating a vehicle uniquely applicable to the needs of the urban commuter. The "Hybrid Hurricane" sport-utility truck will allow the owner the practicality of a truck while creating the fun and excitement of a sports type vehicle. Most of the major components have been implemented on the basis of reliability and low cost. This project has also served as an educational test-bed for engineering and other student and the general Tulsa community as a whole. As the future looms ever closer and the monopoly of gasoline powered vehicles begins to ebb, the University of Tulsa students and community are ready with the creative initiatives that will eventually prevail in electric vehicle technologies.

ACKNOWLEDGMENTS

The Sun Storm team wishes to thank the many and varied sponsors that have helped with in-kind, technical, and monetary support for this project. The Ford/SAE/DOE group in charge of this event have had great success in raising funds for all of the teams and have enhanced the University of Tulsa's efforts to complete this project without financial tangles. Also, the various sponsors here in the greater Tulsa metropolis have gone out of their way to make this project a success. Through the efforts of the sponsors of this project, many an engineering student as well as other various people who have heard presentations, read of this project in the media, or otherwise came in contact with the "Hybrid Hurricane" have come away with a greater understanding of hybrid electric vehicle technology and the aspects it represents.

United States Naval Academy, AMPhibian

Gregory W. Davis, Gary L. Hodges, Frank C. Madeka, Jason L. Pike,
Joseph Greeson, Dennis Klein, and John Boone
United States Naval Academy

ABSTRACT

The U. S. Naval Academy's entry for the Hybrid Electric Vehicle Challenge is a 1992 5-door Ford Escort LX Wagon with a manual transmission which has been converted to a series drive hybrid electric vehicle(HEV). A DC motor, coupled to the existing transaxle provides propulsion. Lead-acid batteries are used to store the electrical energy. The auxiliary power unit(APU) consists of a small gasoline engine connected to a generator. The AMPhibian is designed to be a feasible HEV, for use in near term applications. To accomplish this, all components are based upon existing technology. Further, this vehicle was designed to retain, to the greatest degree possible, the basic driving characteristics of a conventional gasoline powered vehicle. The major performance design goals for the AMPhibian include 1) the ability to travel 64 Km as a zero emissions vehicle(ZEV) using battery power alone, 2) operating in hybrid mode, the ability to travel 320 Km while meeting the transitional low emissions vehicle(TLEV) air pollution standards, 3) achieve a time of under 15 seconds when accelerating from 0 to 70 Kph, and 4) climb a minimum of a 15% grade.

OVERVIEW

The USNA midshipmen accepted the HEV Challenge as an extension of their commitment to serve their country -- in this case, to help America preserve its resources. The vehicle name, **AMPhibian**, was chosen by the midshipmen because, just as a real amphibian spends time both on land and in the water, by analogy the vehicle will operate using electrical energy from the battery system, and at other times with electrical energy derived from the gasoline powered generator. As a reminder that electricity will be the primary power source for the vehicle, the first three letters of **AMPhibian** were capitalized to represent the ampere, the basic unit of electric current. Finally, the name also acknowledges the military role provided by the Navy and Marine Corps amphibious team.

The dual nature of a hybrid electric vehicle also led the midshipmen team to choose **"96"** as the vehicle's number. The number can be read from two different directions with the same result, just as the AMPhibian can be easily driven by stored electrical energy from the batteries or by generated electrical energy from the auxiliary power unit.

DESIGN OBJECTIVES

The U. S. Naval Academy HEV, AMPhibian, was designed to be a feasible HEV for use in near term applications. The challenge involves many aspects including cost effectiveness, acceleration, range, safety, and emissions. These design goals were considered when designing the vehicle.

COST - Since the AMPhibian was designed to be economically feasible, minimizing cost was considered to be a major design goal. All design decisions were made only after the associated costs were analyzed. To help attain this goal, all components were to be based upon existing, available technology.

PERFORMANCE AND EMISSIONS - The major performance and emissions design goals for the AMPhibian include 1) the ability to travel 64 Km as a zero emissions vehicle(ZEV) using battery power alone, 2) operating in hybrid mode, the ability to travel 320 Km while meeting the transitional low emissions vehicle(TLEV) air pollution standards, 3) achieve a time of under 15 seconds when accelerating from 0 to 70 Kph, and 4) climb a minimum of a 15% grade. The vehicle was also to maintain driving characteristics as similar to that of conventional gasoline powered vehicles as possible(e.g. one brake pedal, shift gears normally, etc.).

RELIABILITY AND DURABILITY - The AMPhibian was to have reliability and durability similar to that of a conventional gasoline powered vehicle. Using existing components would not only help to limit the costs, but also to help ensure reliable and durable operation of the vehicle.

SAFETY - Occupant safety was a prime concern. The frontal impact zone and original vehicle bumpers were to be maintained to provide sufficient collision protection. The original power-assisted braking system was also to remain intact to ensure proper braking. A fire suppression system was to be added to the vehicle and battery compartments, as well as to the engine bay to minimize the chances of injury and equipment damage. Due to the additional vehicle weight, the roof structure was to be augmented to provide additional protection in case of a vehicle roll-over. Finally, the competition rules required the use of a five point harness system for both the driver and passenger.

WEIGHT - One major disadvantage of electric vehicles has traditionally been the large weight due to the propulsion batteries required to provide the energy storage capability for extended range. An advantage of the HEV concept is to allow for less energy storage capability of the batteries by replacing some of these batteries with a small auxiliary power unit(APU) which provides the equivalent amount of energy with less weight. However, battery weight was still considered to be a major concern, requiring the team to consider all options for reducing vehicle weight. The AMPhibian was to be designed to weigh less than the gross vehicle weight rating(GVWR) of the 1992 Escort LX Wagon plus an additional 10%. This results in a maximum allowable vehicle mass of 1729 kg. Further, to maintain acceptable handling, the side-to-side bias must remain within 5% of neutral, and the front-to-rear bias must not drop below about 40%/60%.

PASSENGERS AND CARGO - The HEV was to carry one driver and one passenger, along with a volume of cargo(50 cm by 100 cm by 25 cm). The total combined weight of people and cargo was a minimum of 180 kg.

BATTERY CHARGING - The HEV charging system was designed to recharge the battery pack in six hours. This should reduce daytime charging demand on electrical utilities. Daytime charging, if necessary, could be accomplished using the APU. The charging system was to accept either 110V or 220V, 60 Hz AC power.

STYLING - Vehicle styling changes were to be minimized to maintain continuity with existing vehicle designs. No external glass or body sheet metal was to be modified except to provide additional ventilation.

VEHICLE DESIGN

The relationship of the design goals was studied, and compromises were made to provide near optimal system design, given the severe budgetary and time constraints. This process resulted in the selection and design of the major vehicle components. The following discussion details the design decisions, this is followed by a summary table of the actual vehicle components.

POWERTRAIN - The AMPhibian is propelled using a series drive configuration. That is, the only component that is mechanically connected to the drive-train of the vehicle is the electric motor. This arrangement is depicted in figure 1, located in the appendix. This arrangement was considered to be superior to the parallel drive arrangement, in which both the electric motor and the APU can propel the vehicle, for the following reasons. The series drive would require less structural change to install, and thus provide a lower cost. The parallel drive system would also require a more sophisticated control system to minimize driveability problems such as those associated with the transition from electric vehicle(EV) mode to hybrid electric vehicle(HEV) mode. This would, again, result in higher cost, and, possibly, reliability problems due to the added complexity. The parallel drive is enticing because it has the potential to provide improved acceleration since both the APU and the electric motor are used to propel the vehicle. However, when the battery is discharged, the parallel system cannot easily be used to recharge the system, thus the potential for daytime use of electrical energy for charging is increased. Overall, the series drive was seen to be the best choice to meet the design goals.

The conversion to a series drive system required the removal of the standard Escort engine. Since the Escort has front-wheel drive, the standard engine is mounted transversely in a transaxle arrangement. Thus, the transaxle was left intact so that a new axle would not need to be designed. The electric motor was attached directly to the existing bell-housing and flywheel. This arrangement also allows full use of the existing transmission, thus allowing for variable gear ratios. This was considered an advantage since it would allow the electric motor to be operated closer to its preferred operating speed over varying vehicle speeds.

Prior vehicle testing and simulation indicated that the vehicle would require a power of approximately 9 kW in order to maintain a steady 80 Kph. Acceleration from a stand still to 72 Kph in less than 15 seconds would require a peak power of 32 kW(at approximately 35 Kph) for a short duration. Motor controller cost and availability became the critical design factor for the selection of both the type of motor and the system operating voltage. The use of an AC motor was investigated due to its inherently higher power density compared to a DC system. However, it was rejected due to the cost, availability, size, and weight of the associated motor controller. A series wound, 15.2 kW(@ 90 VDC) DC motor was chosen instead since DC motor controllers are more widely available, less costly, and lighter in weight. The combination DC motor and controller weighs approximately 82 kg, the engine that was removed weighed 113 kg, thus resulting in a net weight savings of 31 kg. Although the steady state rating is less than the peak incurred during the acceleration, the motor can provide a peak power 2-3 times its steady state rating for short duration. To provide maximum torque, a high system voltage is required. Cost, size and the ready availability of a proven motor controller dictated the controller choice. A controller rated at 120 VDC(160 V peak) was chosen, thus this determined the system operating voltage.

BATTERY SELECTION - USNA AMPhibian has two battery power systems. One system is at 12V and one at 120V. The 12V system is used to power the 12V lighting and accessories. The 120V primary battery powers the prime mover and supplies power to recharge the 12V battery.

USNA AMPhibian battery selection was overwhelmingly driven by cost considerations. Secondary considerations included: 1) the HEV Challenge constraint of 400V or less battery stack voltage, 2) the motor controller rating of 120V, 3) the HEV Challenge constraint of no more than 20 kW-hr capacity at a 3 hr discharge rate, 4) the gross vehicle weight rating constraints and 5) practical considerations. In general, an inexpensive, small, lightweight battery having high specific power and high specific energy is desired for use in the AMPhibian. Additional considerations included the desire to maximize voltage thereby minimizing I^2R losses due to lower operating currents. Also, to help to maximize KW-hrs capacity, and, therefore, ZEV capabilities, the amp-hr battery rating should be maximized. Since the maximum rating for the motor controller is 120V, 120V was selected. This enabled, AMPhibian to determine an order-of-magnitude calculation of the costs of batteries having characteristics superior to those of conventional lead-acid batteries. Results of this analysis lead the AMPhibian design team to limit battery selection considerations to off-the-shelf lead-acid batteries. For example, Nickel-Iron batteries were found at a cost of $1800 per six volt battery or $36,000 for a 120V battery stack. Nickel-Cadmium were found at a cost of $964 per six volt battery or $19,280 for a 120V battery stack. Both estimates far exceeded AMPhibian budget constraints, hence, the self-imposed limitation to lead-acid.

Discussions with EV enthusiasts,[*] battery suppliers,[**] and professional EV converters[***] helped team AMPhibian to focus on several battery features. These features included the following: wet-celled batteries can provide a slightly higher capacity, are typically less expensive than, and require a less complex charging system than gel-celled batteries; however, gel-celled batteries do require less maintenance than wet-celled batteries; "flag" or "L" type terminal configurations have proven to be more reliable and durable, and provide greater contact surface area(helping to minimize corrosion problems) than standard automotive post type terminals. Ideally, the battery stack would be composed of individual, replaceable cells to facilitate replacement of only bad cells as opposed to the replacement of entire multi-celled, batteries having only one bad cell. AMPhibian decided to go with 12V batteries for cost and weight considerations.

The task of battery selection was complicated due to the general lack of published, comprehensive, technical battery performance data covering an extensive number of battery models and manufacturers which had been verified by an independent source. This limited information is shown in the following figures. From figures 2 and 3 of the appendix, the selection of batteries was reduced by eliminating those batteries exceeding 20 kW-hrs at a 3 hour discharge rate and those batteries which would exceed an absolute maximum battery stack weight allocation of 500 kg. With the number of batteries reduced, batteries were compared on a specific volume to weight and capacity to weight basis, see figures 5 and 6 of the appendix. Figure 7 shows the energy capacity per unit volume. Based upon the evaluation of this limited data, and relying upon the advice of EV owners and professional EV manufacturers, the Trojan 5SH(P) battery appeared to be the best choice . The Trojan 5SH(P) battery is a deep-cycle, wet-celled, 12V battery. The "L" type terminals were selected for this application. With the primary battery selected, the 12V system needed to be defined and selected.

Several approaches were considered to power the 12V system. This included the extremes of using the existing 12V system, as is, or converting all 12V components to 120V. Engineering judgment indicates the latter option is not practical. One approach for providing power to the 12V system was to utilize the output of one twelve volt battery from the 120V stack. This approach has the advantage of simplicity. One disadvantage of this approach is that, using the existing 12V components which are grounded to the chassis, means that the battery stack is no longer

* Mr. David Goldstein, President, Electric Vehicle Association of Greater Washington, D.C., private conversations.

** Mr. Bill Kump, GNB Incorporated, Automotive Battery Division, private conversations.

*** Mr. Douglas Cobb, President, Solar Car Corporation, private conversations.

electrically isolated from the chassis and, thus, the chance of injury in the event of failure is increased. Another problem, is that, since the batteries are connected in series, if the battery used for the 12V system fails, the whole battery stack will become inoperable. The chance of battery failure can be reduced by inserting a higher amp-hr rated battery into the 120V stack to compensate for the added use. The disadvantage is that this local change to the series of batteries imparts an unknown on the primary battery stack performance (i.e., internal impedance and resistance). This lead to the decision to have two separate battery systems, a 120V primary system and separate 12V system.

Several options were considered for the 12V system. One option was to incorporate a single, independent high amp-hr rated battery required to provide several hours at a relatively high discharge rate (e.g., driving at night and in rain/use of head lights and wipers). This battery would then be recharged externally during refueling and/or recharging. This option was rejected due to the resulting high weight of the battery. A DC/DC converter, powered by the 120V stack, could be used to meet all of the 12V demand. However, this converter must meet the peak 12V load, which is estimated to be 210 amps during starting of the APU. This option was rejected due to the heavy weight and size of this converter. A DC/DC converter, sized to handle the sustained accessory loads under moderate to heavy use, was incorporated in parallel with a small 12V battery, sized to accommodate the APU starting loads. This design saves both space and weight. The estimated sustained load encountered during moderate to heavy accessory use is 20A. However, a 30 amp DC/DC converter was selected to accommodate the future addition of a climate control system for the passenger compartment. The APU starter requires a battery rated at 210 cranking amps. The ultra light Pulsar Racing Battery, offered by GNB Incorporated, was used since this battery weighed only 4.5 kg, or approximately 50% less than other conventional lead-acid batteries, and provides 220 cranking amps. AMPhibian's net 12V accessory system, occupies the same volume as the OEM 12V battery, but weighs approximately 9.5 kg less than the OEM battery alone.

BATTERY COMPARTMENT - The hybrid electric vehicle battery compartment is required to support, protect, and ventilate ten 12V batteries.

The competition requirements dictate a container that could withstand a vehicular roll over, with a complete ventilation unit isolated from any passengers. When the design was started it was not certain which batteries would be chosen due to available funds. Therefore, a design was based upon a single base plate in which a variety of batteries could be supported, as shown in figure 8 of the appendix. Weight balance calculations were made and it was determined that the battery compartment should be placed as far forward as the existing internal features would allow.

The next step was a calculation of impact forces for a thirty-five mile an hour frontal impact. This velocity was chosen to coincide with the speed used in frontal impact barrier testing. Calculations made under these conditions were used to select the size of bolts needed to secure the base plate. Once the base plate was built, additional structure was welded and bolted in order to provide a sealed enclosure. The battery compartment contains two grid structures. These structures provide lateral, longitudinal and vertical support. Additionally, they maintain spacing which is needed to allow ventilation of the batteries. The upper grid structure was also designed to facilitate electrolyte servicing while the batteries are secured. the top of the battery enclosure was made of Plexiglas to allow easy viewing of the battery stack. This was done for the following reasons. Since this is a prototype vehicle, it was desired to have the ability to visually inspect the stack, looking for problems. Additionally, this would help in the design of an adequate ventilation system, through flow visualization. Finally, since one objective of the vehicle is to increase public awareness of HEVs, this feature would allow easy public viewing of the battery stack.

Ventilation of the battery compartment was designed to serve two purposes. First, during charging, excess hydrogen is vented from the batteries, this hydrogen presents a safety hazard. The HEV Challenge requires only 0.28 cubic meters per min to alleviate this concern. Second, during charging, it is estimated that batteries produce about 50 W/battery, or 500 W total excess thermal energy. This excess thermal energy will raise the battery operating temperatures. Although, increasing temperature increases the battery capacity, useful battery service life decreases. It is estimated that the battery life is halved for each 8 C increase in ambient temperature.* Therefore to maintain maximum service life, this excess thermal energy must be removed in order to maintain recommended battery temperature of not in excess of 50 C. Assuming hot ambient conditions, such as those encountered during the summer, thermodynamic calculations indicate the need for about 4.7 cubic meters per minute of air-flow at 43 C will be required to maintain a maximum of 50 C. Therefore an off-the-shelf, ignition protected(meeting BIA, ABYC, and Coast Guard safety standards) ventilation bilge blower with an open-flow rating of 6.4 cubic meters per minute was chosen. This fan draws fresh outside air through the battery compartment, exhausting the warm air outside the vehicle. The blower is positioned near the top of the battery compartment, to ensure the removal of excess hydrogen. Just as high operating temperatures reduce service life, low temperatures substantially reduce battery capacity. Therefore, the optimum blower would be capable of variable speed operation from a minimum of 0.28 cubic meters per minute, to alleviate safety concerns, and thermostatically adjust the flowrate to maintain optimum temperature for peak battery capacity. The chosen arrangement, then, is not the optimum choice. The current design is a compromise based upon availability and schedule constraints. Future plans include the installation of either a second small fan, or the addition of a variable, thermostatic control, to the existing fan.

Due to availability, the container is made out of aluminum. Since this material is susceptible to an electrolyte spill, it will be coated to minimize reaction in the event of a spill. The design team feels that the ideal compartment would be constructed of a blown polyethylene.

AUXILIARY POWER UNIT - The design specifications for the auxiliary power unit (APU) were derived from the mechanical power necessary to achieve the 320 km desired range while maintaining highway speeds, and allowing for reasonable accelerating and coasting time periods with the batteries at 20% of full charge at the beginning of APU operation. These vehicle operating conditions were then modeled to determine electrical power requirements based on estimated efficiencies, both electrical and mechanical. Calculations based on these estimates of driving conditions (drag

and rolling resistance) and drivetrain efficiency resulted in a minimum desired electric power availability of 10 kW. If the APU could deliver this power, the HEV would be able to sustain highway speeds for the full range, limited only by the amount of onboard fuel. However, this power capability alone would not allow for reasonable accelerations over this distance. Therefore, the APU must be capable of charging the batteries while at highway speeds so that if acceleration becomes necessary, the power may be drawn from both the batteries and the APU. Estimates for this power were based on assumptions that the HEV would not need to meet competition acceleration requirements, but would have to perform reasonably. Also, regenerative braking would be available during coast down periods.

The total calculated electrical requirement resulted in a specification of 12.5 kW output from the APU. Estimating the overall efficiency of the APU to be 80%, the engine then must be capable of mechanically developing 15.6 kW.

With the design parameters determined, the selection of the actual components centered around availability of "shelf" items, size and space limitations, emissions and ultimately and most significantly the cost. Ideally an engine-generator set could be found meeting all the requirements. However, a review of the available market provided no likely candidates, particularly in terms of weight and space requirements. Therefore, the engine and generator were selected separately.

Different types of engines that were considered, included rotary, stirling, gas-turbine, and spark-ignited. Three different operating fuels for use were considered. These fuels are: E100(ethanol), M85(85% gasoline/15% methanol, by volume), and gasoline. Based upon time constraints and availability, the design team limited the choice to a conventional, gasoline powered spark-ignited engine. Of the available engines, the 17.9 kW Onan model P224G, twin cylinder, electric start promised to be the best choice for all considerations. Weighing approximately 61 kg, and small enough to fit under the Escort's hood, the air cooled engine requires only a fuel inlet and an exhaust connection to function and can be mounted using the same existing engine supports as the series DC motor. Speed is regulated by a governor to 3600 RPM and is adjustable. Since Briggs & Stratton donated a 13.5 kW "Vanguard" series engine, the procurement of the previously selected engine did not occur. The donated engine weighs 40 kg and does more easily fit under the hood, while retaining the desirable qualities of the larger engine with the exception of the power output. An additional feature of the Briggs and Stratton Vanguard engine is a pull-cord starting mechanism. The design team elected to retain this feature to ensure that the vehicle could be started in the event of complete battery discharge(both 12 and 120V stack batteries). To meet TLEV emissions requirements the APU exhaust will be connected to a United Emissions Catalyst catalytic converter which contains a ceramic monolith substrate. An air pump, electrically or belt driven may be added to provide fresh air for the catalytic converter after light-off to ensure complete oxidation of un-burned hydrocarbons and carbon monoxide. At the time of this writing, the design team is planning to operate without a pump, pending acceptable emissions test data. The outlet of the catalytic converter will then lead to the existing vehicle exhaust system.

To meet the electrical requirements, a number of alternatives involving both AC and DC generation were explored. To minimize space and weight, a custom built alternator was considered the best choice. However, the cost for this item would make it the most

---

* Johnson Controls, Inc., Specialty Battery Division, Dynasty Battery Literature, Form number 41-6416(rev 5/92).

expensive single component added to the car. After approaching several major electrical machinery manufacturers with the generator requirements, and receiving estimates ranging from several thousand to fourteen thousand dollars for components that weigh as much as the DC drive motor (or more), a lower cost manufacturer was located. Fisher Technology, Inc. was contracted to build a custom 13.5 kW, 150 V, 3 phase alternator. The voltage was selected based on providing 144 V DC from a three phase bridge rectifier, the maximum recommended charging voltage for a 120 V battery stack. However, this voltage is well above the rated voltage for the Curtis 1221B controller. Therefore, a 50 watt 130 V zener diode will be used to limit the controller voltage while charging. Additional voltage control can be obtained by varying the speed of the APU. Beside meeting all electrical requirements, this alternator weighs only 4.6 kg, is 0.276 m in diameter and when mounted directly on the APU shaft, extends a mere 0.19 m from the engine block, making it the most feasible option.

The strategy for controlling the APU was developed for manual operation and will be incorporated into a digital control system with a goal of making driving the HEV as much like driving a conventional vehicle as possible. The system must sense battery voltage to determine battery condition and control the APU operation. It must also control ancillary functions such as insuring the battery box exhaust fan is on whenever charging and monitoring APU current to prevent overload.

A three position switch will be mounted in the passenger compartment to start or stop the APU or place control in the strategy mode. The first two positions are self explanatory and will override the strategy mode, allowing the driver to make the decision to start or stop the APU while monitoring battery voltage, motor and APU current along with other pertinent parameters. However, while in the strategy mode, the system will be make decisions and carry out programmed actions, while signaling with status lights to keep the driver informed.

With the AMPhibian, it is necessary to closely monitor the power consumption rate. In order to do this effectively, the vehicle has three ammeters and one voltmeter. One ammeter monitors battery stack drainage, another checks the output of the APU, and the third ammeter monitors the electric drive motor. The bus potential is displayed by the voltmeter. All meters are located near the center console for easy viewing.

SAFETY - To enhance the roof structure, a Sports Car Club of America approved roll-bar was purchased and installed in the vehicle. Obviously, the structure of the roof itself in a production vehicle would be enhanced to meet the additional weight demands.

In the event of fire, a halon fire suppression system was installed. This system can provide a significant suppression of an electrical fire.

The original power-assisted braking system was to remain intact to ensure proper braking. Since the engine was removed, the vacuum assist was disabled, therefore an electrically powered vacuum pump and reservoir were installed to replace this loss of vacuum.

Additional safety devices include a panic switch that can be used to disconnect the battery pack from the vehicle in the event of emergency. An in-line fuse and single-throw, double-pole circuit breaker are also installed to add additional redundancy for protection of the occupants and equipment. The circuit breaker also serves to isolate the batteries to allow for safe maintenance and testing of

other components. Since a high voltage and current system is used, the chassis is not used as the ground as is the usual case in conventional vehicles. Both positive and negative cabling is used to minimize stray currents and voltages, and to isolate the system from the chassis. Additionally, circuit breakers, both 110V and 220V, have been installed between the on-board charger and the external power connections to ensure safe charger operation independent of the power source.

The AMPhibian no longer has a defogging capability, this safety issue has been recognized and, as an interim solution, a transparent polymer coating manufactured by UNELKO Corporation, sold under the trade names Rain-X and Rain-X Anti-fog, has been applied to exterior and interior windows to minimize fogging. Long term solutions could include the utilization of resistive heating and/or waste heat.

CHARGING SYSTEM - A MOSFET on-board battery charger was chosen for use in the vehicle. This charger is both lightweight and can accept either 110 V or 220 V, 60 Hz, AC power. To reduce weight, an isolation transformer is used as an off-board component. It was felt that future infrastructure could provide adequate isolation at the stationary charging connections.

SUSPENSION - The large increase in vehicle weight due to the extra load of the HEV conversion required the suspension to be altered. The original springs did not provide adequate jounce. The conversion weight bias of 48% front weight/52% rear and accounting for the limit of 5% left/right bias from neutral resulted in the following added weight to ground per wheel from the original configuration: 91 kg front, and 235 kg rear. Four new springs were purchased to meet these new loads. See figure for a representative comparison of the change in spring characteristics. The damping coefficient of the MacPherson strut was not modified, hence the suspension characteristics have changed to a degree. However, after discussion with a strut manufacturer, Gabriel Ride Control, this change should not cause any significant problems.

SUMMARY - The following table provides a summary of the systems used in the AMPhibian.

Table 1. Summary of Components used in AMPhibian.

Chassis:	'92 5-door Escort LX
Stock GVWR:	1572 kg
Converted GVWR:	<1729 kg(est. 1475 kg)
Maximum Carrying Capacity(passenger and cargo):	>180 kg(est. 254 kg)
DC Motor:	General Electric model 5BT1346B50
Motor Controller:	Curtis PMC 1221B-1074
Batteries(propulsion):	10 arranged in series, 12VDC Trojan 5SH(P)
Bus Voltage:	120 VDC
APU Engine:	Briggs and Stratton Vanguard V-twin, 13.4 kW @3600 RPM, two cylinder
APU Alternator:	Fisher Technology, Inc., 13.5 kW, 150 Vpeak

Tires:	Goodyear Invicta GL P175/65R14, low rolling resistance
Conversion Component Net Cost: (exc. safety items, credit for 1.9l engine)	est. $10,000

PRELIMINARY PERFORMANCE RESULTS

As of this writing, the AMPhibian has undergone only limited testing and evaluation. However, it has demonstrated the ability to accelerate from a stop to 70 Kph in less than 15 seconds. A maximum vehicle speed has not been determined although the vehicle has exceeded speeds of 80 Kph on a tightly confined course. Due to lack of an appropriate grade, the vehicle has only been tested on a 6% grade from a standing start. It should be noted, however, that the vehicle was able to accelerate up the grade when starting from second gear without difficulty. The total vehicle range in either EV or HEV mode is unknown. Based upon initial observations, the EV distance on one charge should exceed 64 km. The emissions when operating in HEV mode have not been tested.

SUMMARY

The design of a feasible hybrid electric vehicle for use in near-term applications has been presented. Continued testing and evaluation will reveal the reliability and durability of the various system components. However, the chosen batteries are expected to only maintain peak performance, under normal daily use, for 18 to 24 months before requiring replacement at an approximate cost of $1500. This cost is offset somewhat by the slightly reduced operating expenses due to the reduced use of gasoline, assuming electric power discounts for charging, and battery recycling. Another costly system component is the lightweight alternator used in the APU. This item cost about $5000. The cost of this component would be greatly reduced if it were mass-produced. The total cost of components(less safety items and including a credit for the stock engine) came to about $10,000. So the cost of the alternator is a major portion of the total cost. Obviously, since the standard Escort cost about $10,000, the conversion is not yet a cost effective alternative to existing gasoline vehicles. However, the potential reduction of smog in urban areas will continue to dictate the use of these vehicles.

Future vehicle enhancements include the addition of small alternators to be used in conjunction to the existing brake system, to provide regeneration. Simulations provided by other authors[*] have shown potential energy savings from 6 to 20%, depending upon the driving conditions.

ACKNOWLEDGMENTS

The United States Naval Academy AMPhibian team would like to thank the following sponsors for their generous support.

Advanced Lead Acid Battery Consortium
Aeroquip Corporation
AutoPower Industries
Battery Automated Transportation
Borg-Warner Corporation
BP Research
Briggs and Stratton Corporation
Coil Spring Specialties
Curtis Instruments, Inc.
Dana Corporation
Detroit Edison Company
Du Pont Automotive
Elec. Vehicle Assoc. of Greater Washington DC.
Fisher Electric Motor Technology, Inc.
Ford Motor Company
General Electric Corporation
GNB Incorporated
Goodyear Tire and Rubber Company
Heinemann Electric
Johnson Controls Battery Division
Koons Ford
Magnesium Products, LTD
Naval Academy Research Council
Onan Corporation
Pegasus Auto Racing Supplies, Inc.
Quick-Cable Corporation
Racer Wholesale Safety Equip & Accessories
RayChem Inc.
Robert Bosch Corporation
Rockwell International
SAE International
Siemens Automotive
Solar Car
Sony Corporation of America
The Dearborn Inn
Tribotech
Trojan Battery
United States Department of Energy
United Emission Catalyst
United States Naval Academy
United Technologies Automotive
Webasto

---

[*] Floyd A. Wyczalek, SAE paper #920648.

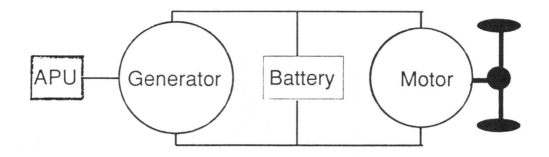

Figure 1. Series Drive Diagram.

AMP HRS @3 Hrs
120 VOLT ARRANGEMENT

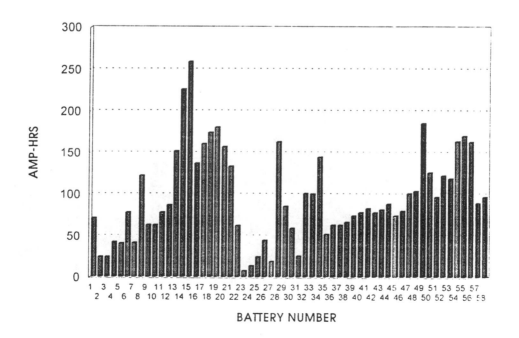

Figure 2. Battery Capacity at 3 Hour Discharge Rate, 120 V stack.

TOTAL WEIGHT OF
120 VOLT ARRANGEMENT

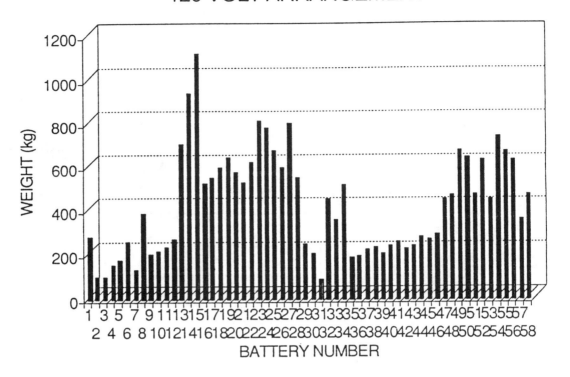

Figure 3. Battery Stack weight, 120 V.

KILOWATT-HOUR CAPACITY
120 VOLT ARRANGEMENT

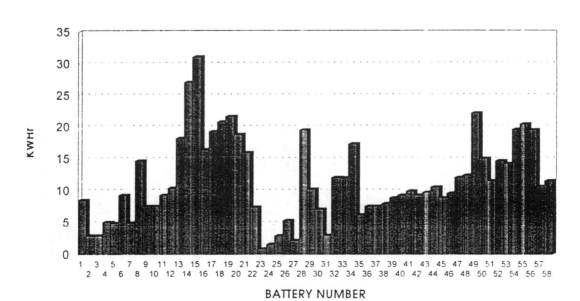

Figure 4. Total Energy Capacity for 120V Stack.

SPECIFIC VOLUME
120 VOLT ARRANGEMENT

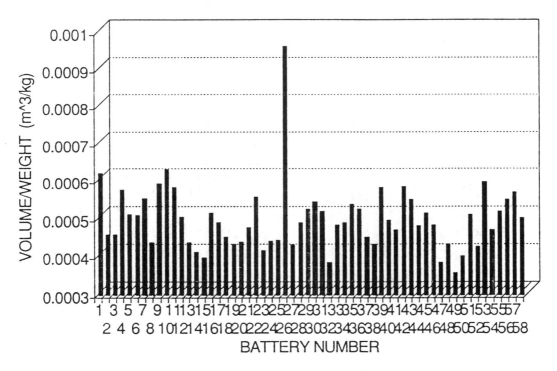

Figure 5. Specific Battery Volume.

CAPACITY PER UNIT WEIGHT
120 VOLT ARRANGEMENT

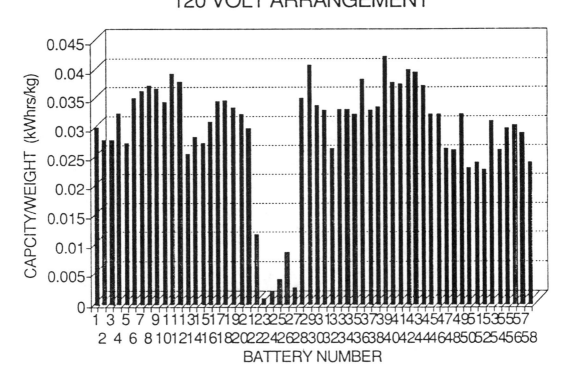

Figure 6 Battery Capacity per Unit Weight.

CAPACITY PER UNIT VOLUME
120 VOLT ARRANGEMENT

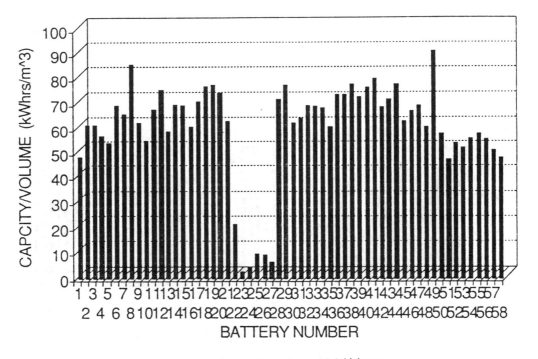

Figure 7 Battery Capacity per Unit Volume.

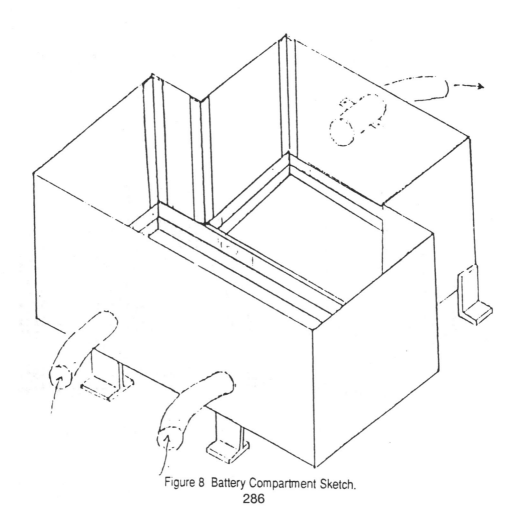

Figure 8 Battery Compartment Sketch.

USNA---AMPhibian 96
Spring Data

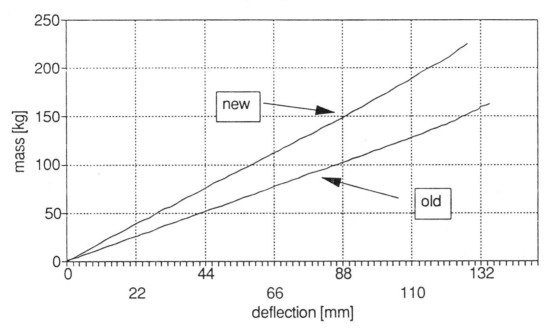

Figure 9. Spring Characteristic Comparison

The Wayne State University Hybrid Electric Vehicle with Independent Drives

Wayne State HEV Team
Advisors: Jerome Meisel, ECE Department
Naeim Henein, ME Department

Abstract

The vehicle designed for the Ford HEV Challenge by the Wayne State University Team involved the conversion of a stock Ford Escort stationwagon. The design centered on the principle that this vehicle should have very adequate performance in either its ZEV or HEV modes. Thus the stock 1.9 liter Ford engine is left unmodified as a drive on the front wheels. A separate electric drive was constructed and installed on the rear wheels after substantial modifications were made to the rear suspension. This electric drive includes two dc-separately excited motors each capable of producing 24 kW peak output power. Thus the ZEV mode has reasonable performance with a computed 100 m acceleration time of 8.4 sec. However, the ZEV range is severely limited to approximately 30 miles due to weight limitations on the lead-acid deep cycle battery pack being used. Additional ZEV range is available following an HEV operational mode due to a specially designed 145 Vdc alternator belt-coupled to the ICE. In addition to a complete description of the Challenge vehicle, this report also contains a discussion of our recommendations for future HEV research and development.

1. Introduction

The design of the hybrid electric vehicle, through the conversion of a Ford Escort stationwagon, by the Wayne State University Team meets two main specifications:

1. To provide a zero emission operating mode as the primary driving mode.

2. To have a vehicle whose operation in both its zero emission mode and hybrid mode are reasonably similar to the original unmodified Escort stationwagon.

The first specification, apart from being required by the Challenge, is needed to meet new State mandated air-quality legislation. The second specification stems from our own discussions that a vehicle acceptable to its ultimate purchaser must operate in both modes in a fashion similar to present-day internal combustion engine (ICE) vehicles. Even if its zero emission range, as described below, is severely limited, operation as a zero emission vehicle (ZEV) should not feel restricting to the driver.

Similarly, in its hybrid mode, with the ICE operating, the driver should again feel that he/she is operating a conventional vehicle. Thus this second specification, as is clarified below, is key to our final design. After lengthy considerations, we do not believe that a useful hybrid electric vehicle (HEV) design acceptable to the U.S. public, can be achieved with sub-normal performance in either the ZEV or HEV mode, the ZEV range may be limited, but the performance should not be.

At present, the first specification for zero emissions translates into a battery-electric vehicle. However, in order to construct a battery-electric drivetrain, it should be kept in mind that the utility of an automobile is directly related to the amount of energy which can be stored on-board the vehicle. Comparing the energy content of gasoline to the energy stored in deep-cycle lead-acid batteries, one finds that gasoline has 494 times as much energy as the batteries, per unit weight, and 167 times as much energy per unit volume.[1] Now the conversion of the electric energy to driving energy is on the order of five times more efficient than the conversion of gasoline to driving energy. Thus, the above values should be divided by a factor of five giving gasoline 99 times as much driving energy as batteries per unit weight, and 33 times as much driving energy per unit volume. This huge energy advantage of gasoline over batteries as an energy storage medium is the primary reason that ZEVs can only be built with substantially reduced range as compared to conventional ICE vehicles.

This reduced range for a ZEV means that vehicle usefulness is severely limited. However, battery packs are capable of delivering substantial peaking power, such that ZEV performance need not be substantially reduced if adequately sized electric controllers and motors are used. In order to add overall range to the ZEV, the concept of a HEV has been developed. Such a design includes this ZEV mode whereby the vehicle is powered by an electric energy store (i.e. a battery pack) which produces no emissions. When this electric storage is depleted, an on-board ICE running

---

[1] Note: (These calculations are based on gasoline having 42.7 Mj/kg specific heating value, and a density of 0.74 kg/liter. The 12 V lead-acid batteries have a unit weight of 15.0 kg, a volume of 6.85 liters, and a 1 hour discharge rate of 30 A.)

on chemical fuel, such as gasoline, gives added range. If the normal use of the vehicle were limited such that the electric energy stored in its batteries in each 24-hour period were sufficient to meet the daily needs, then the vehicle would indeed produce zero emissions. The ICE would then simply serve as an emergency backup alternate power unit (APU). This description of a hybrid vehicle is the one prescribed by the Challenge, and the one the HEV Team used in meeting the two specifications listed above. The vehicle that the HEV Team designed is known as the *Waynescort*. Further discussion of an alternate design for a hybrid vehicle is contained in Section 12.

The electric drive on the Waynescort must have sufficient torque and power ratings such that, in its ZEV mode of operation it is similar to the stock Escort in order to meet the second specification. The details of the electric drive added to the Waynescort are the main elements of this final report. The most direct way of meeting the requirement that the ICE be able to drive the Waynescort in a manner similar to the stock Escort is to simply leave the front-wheel ICE/transaxle drive intact, as supplied by Ford. If the ICE were downsized, then, with exhausted batteries, the HEV mode of operation would not be adequate, particularly with respect to vehicle acceleration rates. Switching the ICE to another engine of similar size to the 1.9 liter engine supplied makes little technical sense, as no real improvements seemed likely. Thus, the HEV Team decision was to leave the Ford front-wheel ICE drive intact as supplied. The only engine compartment modifications involved the following:

1. The addition of a second specially designed high-voltage (145 V) alternator belt-coupled to the engine.

2. The insertion of the required Halon fire extinguishing system.

3. The inclusion of an additional throttle pedal position sensor for controlling the electric drive.

With no possible space in the engine compartment for an electric drive, the HEV Team decided to modify the rear suspension into an independently driven design with the electric motors and transaxle in the rear cargo area of the Waynescort. The two half shafts driving each of the rear wheels are coupled to a differential through two manually controlled hydraulic clutches. Thus, usual HEV operation includes de-clutching the electric drive, such that the transaxle and electric motors are not producing a drag torque on the rear wheels when the ICE is driving the front wheels. Hence, when driven in the ZEV mode, the ICE gear box is in neutral such that the front wheels are producing minimum drag torque for the driven rear wheels. An additional four-wheel drive mode is also provided for peak HEV acceleration, whereby both the electric drive on the rear wheels and the ICE drive on the front wheels are propelling the vehicle.

2. Powertrain Configuration

Figure 1 shows, schematically, the overall layout of the parallel HEV drive on the Waynescort. The mechanical drive from the Ford 1.9 liter ICE through the transaxle/gear box to the front wheels is the standard drive on the Escort stationwagon. A specially designed high-voltage (145 Vdc) alternator has been belt-coupled to the ICE. This alternator provides a charging option when driving in HEV mode should ZEV mode driving be anticipated. The major modification to the Escort involved adapting an electric drive to the rear wheels. The components for this electric drive are shown in Fig. 2. These components were obtained from a Department of Energy (DOE) research vehicle

known as the ETV-2, with the Garret AiResearch Corporation as the prime contractor. This vehicle was donated to Wayne State University previous to the announcement of the Challenge. This section discusses the design of the electric drive shown in Fig. 2, the modifications made on the rear suspension of the Escort to accept this drive, and the details of how this drive is mounted.

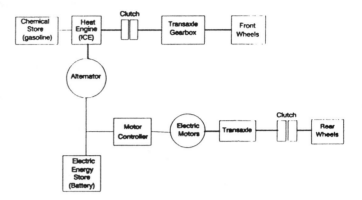

Figure 1 The parallel HEV drive used on the Waynescort.

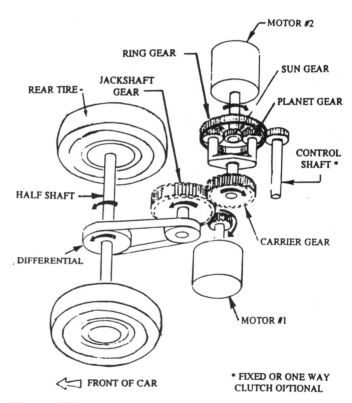

Figure 2 Electric Drive transaxle coupled to the two electric motors.

2.1. The Electric Drive Transaxle

The original electric drive on the Garret ETV-2 vehicle is shown in Fig. 3. This rear wheel drive included a drive motor geared to a differential through a belted chain. In addition, the drive incorporated a flywheel capable of storing 1 kW-h of energy at a rotational speed of 22,000 RPM. The energy flow in or out of the flywheel was controlled by an electric generator. The generator was coupled to the outside ring gear of a planetary gear set, with the flywheel connected to the sun gear. The design of the ETV-2 allowed the flywheel to load-level the battery pack which supplied energy to the drive motor, and also to provide peaking drive power to the wheels.

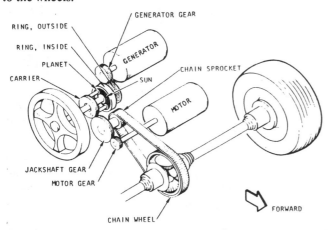

Figure 3 Original Garrett AiResearch ETV-2 rear transaxle drive with flywheel assist. (DOE/CE/5/213-01, April 1981).

The transaxle case, containing the gearing shown in Fig. 2, is cast out of A356-T6 aluminum. The case supports all the loads developed by both motors, the gears and bearings, the differential, and the oil pump. It also dampens any vibrations generated while the drive is operating, and maintains the alignment of the gears within a reasonable tolerance similar to those found in automotive transmissions. The bearing bores are sleeved with a steel support ring that is pinned to the case, which gives added strength and robustness to the case in critical areas. The two electric motors and the oil pump are mounted to flanges for easy replacement if they should fail. The transaxle case has an integral oiling system built into the walls. These passages direct oil to critical areas such as the planetary gear set and the bearings within the case. The oil is moved about by a Gerotor pump delivering the oil at 3.5 liters/min with a pressure of 1.5 atmospheres. The remaining components are oiled by the splash method. The power requirement for the oil pump is approximately 25 Watts. The oil pump operates only when the motors are running, using Mobil Jet II lubricant, commonly used in jet engines.

The ETV-2 transaxle was modified as shown in Figure 2. The major modification included:

1. The electrical generator shown in Fig. 3 was removed. Also, the flywheel was removed.

2. An aluminum cover was fabricated to cover the generator opening on the transaxle. In addition, a spline-retaining block mounted to the cover served as a pin to prevent rotation of the planetary outside ring gear.

3. An adaptor plate was fabricated, using the inside facing of the flywheel housing to allow the generator to be mounted in the position of the flywheel on the transaxle case.

4. A special coupling shaft, shown in Figure 4, was designed such that the original generator machine can serve as a second drive motor with its shaft splined directly to the sun gear of the planetary gear set.

Figure 4 Coupling shaft designed to connect motor 2 to the transaxle planetary sun gear.

The final result of these modifications is that the transaxle transmits all of the power developed by the two electric motor to the rear wheels of the Waynescort. Beginning with motor 2, power is transmitted directly into a planetary gear set. The planetary gear set reduces the speed and increases the torque from motor 2 and transmits it directly to the ring gear. Since the generator gear is pinned, the ring gear in the planetary set is also fixed. This causes the power to be transmitted directly to the carrier gear. From the carrier gear, the power is delivered to the jackshaft gear, where it is combined with the power from motor 1. Again, the torque increases and the speed reduces. The jackshaft gear is connected to the input sprocket of the chain drive. The power transposes to the sprocket which, in turn, drives the differential and finally the rear wheels.

Table 1 includes the details of all gears in the rear transaxle. Also shown is the overall drive ratio between each of the two motors and the rear half-shafts driving the rear wheels. (Note that the ratio of motor 1 is 12.632:1, while the ratio of motor 2 is 15.604:1).

Table 1
Rear Transaxle Gear Specifications

GEAR NAME	GEAR TYPE	NUMBER OF TEETH	PITCH DIAMETER	
			mm	in.
GENERATOR	HELIX	49	64.42	2.536
RING OUTSIDE GEAR	HELIX	82	107.81	4.245
RING INSIDE GEAR	SPUR	102	107.95	4.250
PLANET	SPUR	39	41.28	1.625
SUN	SPUR	24	25.40	1.000
CARRIER	HELIX	85	111.76	4.400
JACKSHAFT	HELIX	96	126.22	4.969
MOTOR	HELIX	20	26.30	1.035
CHAIN SPROCKET	-	19	-	-
CHAIN WHEEL	-	50	-	-

Drive Ratios:

$$\frac{N_{Motor\,1}}{N_{Wheels}} = \left(\frac{96}{20}\right) \cdot \left(\frac{50}{19}\right) = 12.632$$

$$\frac{N_{Motor\,2}}{N_{Wheels}} = \left(1 + \frac{102}{24}\right) \cdot \left(\frac{96}{85}\right) \cdot \left(\frac{50}{19}\right) = 15.604$$

The relationship between vehicle speed and motor shaft speed is

$$N_m = \frac{168.07\,G\,V}{R} \qquad (1)$$

where N_m is the motor shaft speed in RPM, G is the drive ratio between the motor shaft and the wheel shaft, R is the dynamic rolling radius of the rear tires in inches, and V is the vehicle velocity in (mph).

The stock Escort tires are size 175-70-R13, which have a dynamic rolling radius of 11 inches. Consequently, the vehicle can only achieve a maximum velocity of 48.9 mph when motor 2 reaches its peak rated speed of 11,650 RPM. In order to achieve a higher vehicle speed, the rear tires on the Waynescort are increased in size to a 195-75-R15, which has a dynamic rolling radius of 13.76 inches. The maximum vehicle speed, limited by motor 2 reaching 11,650 RPM is thus increased to 61.1 mph.

standard front knuckles were then welded to the lower portions of two standard rear knuckles. The rear two knuckle halves were milled after cutting to assure a flat surface, and MIG welded so that the suspension geometry remained unchanged.

The rear drum brakes were removed and replaced by stock Escort front disk brakes. These disc brakes bolted directly to modified knuckle since the upper half of the knuckle is a standard front knuckle. The stabilizer bar was mounted to the lower control arm, since the bottom knuckle was not changed from a stock rear knuckle. However, the inside mounting brackets for the stabilizer bar needed to be relocated.

The rear struts were modified to compensate for the added vehicle weight by adding stiffening springs. The bottom of the struts had to be modified to adapt to the modified top portion of the knuckle, achieved by filling the structure mounting bracket with weld material, and then redrilling relocated mounting holes to match the top half of the knuckle. More details on the rear suspension design are in Section 8.

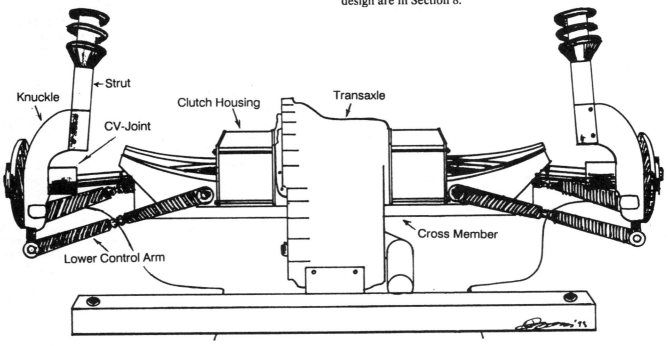

Figure 5   Independent rear suspension for the rear wheel electric drive

2.2. Independent Rear Suspension

Figure 5 shows the major components of the independent rear suspension constructed on the Waynescort. The output shafts of the differential in the rear transaxle case described in Section 3.1 are coupled to the input of a hydraulic clutch. As shown in Figure 5, the hydraulic clutch is mounted in a support housing which also contains the bearing for the clutch output shaft. This supported output shaft is connected to a universal joint. A splined half-shaft connects the universal joint to the CV-joint on the rear wheel. The half-shaft, with splines at both ends, is allowed to have axial travel.

A key component of the rear suspension are the redesigned rear knuckles, used to allow the rear wheels to be driven. The design in the Waynescort is based on the design of the front wheel drive present on the stock Escort. Two front knuckles were modified by cutting off their lower portions. These upper portions of the

2.3. Mounting of the Rear Transaxle Case

One of the most difficult problems faced in redesigning the Escort to accept a rear-wheel electric drive involved the mounting of the transaxle case. Since the HEV Team decided to use the transaxle from the ETV-2, modified as described in Section 3.1, its overall geometry could not be modified. As shown in Fig. 5, in order to minimize losses, the shaft axis of the transaxle differential should be in a straight line with the wheel shaft axis, thus keeping the CV-joint at the wheel and the universal joint at the clutch housing as near to an angle of zero degrees as possible. Thus, the optimum design would have these angles at zero degrees with the Waynescort fully loaded. Hence positioning of the transaxle case required significant modifications of the two rear body cross members, as described in Section 7.

292

3. Battery Pack Design

3.1. Vehicle Requirements

To supply the electrical energy demand for the HEV, a battery pack had to be chosen that would meet certain critical criteria. Of foremost concern were weight, voltage, energy capacity and power. The two electric motors used in our drive can handle a peak voltage of 240 V. The armature current required to maintain a constant vehicle speed of 55 mph is 56.1 A at a field current of 4.5 A. Thus the total electrical input power required to maintain 55 mph is computed to be 13.6 kW. Now assuming that a range of 40 ZEV miles are required, an energy content of 9.9 kW-h are required, with a speed of 55 mph maintained. Including the field supply, the battery must be able to maintain approximately 61 A for 0.73h. The peak power requirement under peak torque output is limited to approximately 230 A at 240 V or 55.2 kW for not greater than 15 sec.

The weight of the battery pack is a major design constraint. The HEV Team decided that the battery pack should weigh no more than 650 lbs. if the total vehicle gross weight is to be kept under the maximum allowable weight of 3812 lbs. With 20 individual 12 V batteries required to give a total pack voltage of 240 V, this allows 32.5 lbs/battery.

3.2. Battery Selection

In our original proposed design, it was anticipated to use NiCd batteries. Our analysis showed that these had excellent energy and power densities. While these are very appealing qualities, there was a drawback. These batteries are primarily available in 2 or 6 Volt units. The weight of the string necessary to achieve the voltage required by our batteries exceeded our limit. We found that 12 V NiCd batteries are available, however their energy characteristics are found to be unattractive. Based on this study we concluded that Lead-Acid would be our best alternative choice. More exotic high temperature batteries, such as Sodium-Sulfur were not considered feasible for this project because of their 300°C operating temperature in addition to prohibitive cost.

The batteries finally selected are deep-discharge Lead-Acid. Detailed specifications are listed in Table 2.

The peak power requirement, with the delivery of 230 A, appears well within the capability of the battery in Table 2. The energy requirement of 9.9 kW-h with a 0.73 h rate is greater than the pack's energy of 7.7 kW-h. This energy short-fall requires that some recharging is necessary during the 80 mile HEV portion of the Range Event in order that enough energy is available for the second 20 miles of ZEV driving. The weight constraint does not allow for larger batteries to be used in the Waynescort. This recharging is accomplished with a specially designed ICE driven alternator producing 4 kVA at 150 V, when rotating at 6000 RPM, corresponding to approximately a 50 mph vehicle speed.

3.3. Battery Mounting and Venting

During charging and discharging, the internal resistance of the batteries causes heat to build. As a result hydrogen is emitted. Thus, to control battery plate temperature in order to maximize our charge and discharge efficiency and to prevent accumulation of dangerous gasses, a closed battery compartment had to be designed and built. This compartment allows the necessary air-flow in order to cool the batteries, remove emitted hydrogen gas

and exhaust this gas from the rear of the vehicle. This enclosure had to be securely mounted in the vehicle to ensure vehicle occupant safety.

Table 2
Battery Specifications

Manufacturer:	Johnson Controls
Model No:	SRM-22NF Interstate Battery
Type:	Lead Acid, deep discharge
List Price:	$49/battery
No. of batteries:	20
Voltage:	12 V/battery, total pack voltage = 240 V
Weight:	32 lb/battery
Total Weight:	640 lbs.
Individual Size:	9 3/8" x 5 1/2" x 8 3/4" high
A-hr l hr rate:	32 A-hr/battery
Max Cur. Draw:	320 A at 0°F for 30 seconds (cold cranking) 320 A at 80°F for 1-1.5 minutes
Cycles:	More than 500 charge/discharge cycles.

Figure 6 shows the basis construction of the battery box in the Waynescort. The 20 batteries are located on a battery platform in the rear of the vehicle. The battery box has replaced the rear seat and passenger compartment of the Escort. The batteries sit on a 4' x 3' plywood platform, as shown in Fig. 7 arranged in three rows. The platform is supported in a number of places with vertical 2 x 6 wooden columns attached to the floor panels. Steel 90-degree angle irons circumvent the outside of the battery box platform. This prevents the batteries from sliding horizontally in the box. Wooden strips 1" x 1" nailed to the plywood separate each column of batteries from other columns, and also hold each battery from sliding horizontally. With these wooden strips, the batteries have a 1" gap between columns for cooling and venting. The ends of the batteries do not have space between them in order to keep the temperature of all battery plates as uniform as possible.

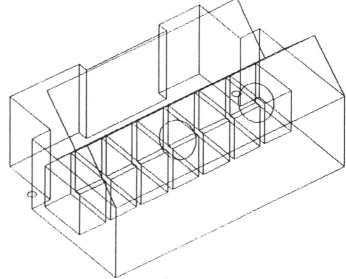

Figure 6 Battery box construction with ventilating air flow from a plenum under the floor of the box.

To keep the batteries from moving vertically, long wooden strips are used over the tops of the batteries to clamp them down. Such strips (about .75" wide) fit between the plastic battery caps. Since there will be no horizontal battery movement, these strips hold the batteries from moving vertically on bumpy roads.

All these batteries, once mounted and clamped, are covered and sealed with a light cover with vertical walls. Since structurally, the batteries do not need to rely on the cover to hold them in place, the cover and walls of the battery box are made of a light-weight material whose function is simply to enclose and seal the batteries from the rest of the vehicle.

Scoops have been incorporated in the underbody of the car to allow an inlet vent for air at a standstill, and to increase the flow as the velocity of the vehicle increases. The design of the battery box uses a sealed plenum under the base platform into which the drawn air flows. Refer to Fig. 6. This is the skirted volume shown. This volume also uses the cavity between the battery compartment, and the back seat. From here, air is drawn through slots in the platform of the box along the wide sides of the batteries. The batteries are cooled only along the wide sides to produce a more uniform heat transfer effect perpendicular to the planes of the battery plates.

During high steady speed operation, the battery pack produces approximately 26 W of heat. When the batteries are aligned, as shown in Fig. 7, the configuration resembles a three tube tube-bank with the air stream in cross-flow. Based on an assumed temperature differential of 30°F between the walls of the battery bank and the ambient, an average convective heat transfer coefficient was determined. This led to the conclusion that two 350 cfm exhaust fans were needed to maintain this temperature differential.

3.4. Battery Cabling

As shown in Fig. 7, the twenty batteries are arranged in two rows of seven and one row of six. Our control scheme requires that the batteries be wired into two series strings with ten batteries in each string. After some consideration the cabling pattern shown in Fig. 7 was designed. This arrangement is an effort to minimize cable lengths. The conductors are constructed of 0-0 size wire capable of carrying the 250 A occurring during peak acceleration. Battery connectors are crimped to cable ends and are all covered after installation to prevent accidental shorting when adding water to the batteries. Taps are provided in the center of each ten battery string to allow the pack to be recharged from the utility supplied chargers in strings of five. Thus four chargers at 60 V nominal are used for recharging.

4. Electric Motors and Controllers

This section contains a detailed description of the electric motors used in the Waynescort and their method of control.

4.1. Description of Electric Motors

The electric drive shown in Fig. 2 includes two electric motors mounted on the transaxle case. These motors are essentially identical having the same power and thermal characteristics. Table 3 lists the detailed parameters of each of these two machines. They are designed as dc-machines with four poles, a shunt control field, interpole and pole-face windings. Their peak

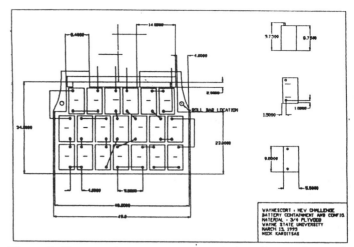

Figure 7 Battery placement and wiring into two strings with 10-batteries in each string.

rated output is 24 kW with a speed range of 0-11650 RPM. Their rated armature voltage is 108 V. The maximum armature current is 250 A, and the maximum field current is 14 A. The motors were special designs by G.E. for the Garrett AiResearch ETV-2 vehicle.

Table 3
Motor Design Parameters

Ratings	
Power, kW	24 max. at 3000 to 10 000 rpm
Speed range, rpm	0 to 11,650
Power source voltage, V	108
Power source current, A	250 max. up to 10 000 rpm
Dimensions,	
Diameter	231 mm (9.1 in.)
Length	369 mm (14.5 in.)
Radial air gap (armature to field)	0.84 mm (0.33 in.)
Circuit Resistance at 20°C, ohms	
Armature winding	0.0215
Shunt (control) winding	3.488
Interpole winding	0.0060
Pole face winding	0.0095
Circuit Inductances, mH	
Armature winding	0.097
Shunt (control) winding	81.9 to 409.6
Interpole winding	0.125
Pole face winding	0.0469
Electrical Loading, A	
Maximum armature current	250.0
Maximum shunt field current	14.0
Winding Descriptions	
Armature:	75-bar commutator, 25 slots, 6 conductors/slot, wave winding, rectangular wire of 8.9 mm² (0.0138 sq in.)
Shunt field:	144 turns No. 16 AWG wire
Interpole:	5 turns rectangular wire, 33.5 mm² (0.0052 sq in.)
Pole face:	5 turns rectangular wire, 19.6 mm² (0.0304 sq in.)
Materials	
Housing	AISI 1010 steel
Wire	Annealed copper, Kapton wrapped
Shunt poles	Silicon steel
Armature laminations	2V Permendur
Interpoles	Silicon steel
Commutator	Silver bearing copper
Brushes	Electrographitic
End bells	Aluminum

4.2. Computed Performance

The motors have speed vs. torque boundary characteristics as shown in Fig. 8. Note the speed limit of 11,650 RPM, the hyperbolic power limit of essentially 24 kW between 3000 and 11,650 RPM, and the torque limit of 72 N-m. The two motors are each mechanically connected to drive the rear wheels by the fixed-gearing transaxle described in Section 3. The gear ratio of motor 1 is 12.63 and for motor 2 the ratio is 15.604. Now assuming the gross vehicle weight (GVW) to be its maximum allowable value of 3812 lbs., and assuming that each motor is controlled to be on the boundary of its admissible operating range, as shown in Fig. 8, the peak ZEV performance of the vehicle can be computed. The results of this computation are shown in Fig. 9. Figure 9a shows the vehicle velocity vs. time starting at a standing start. Note that the maximum velocity of 58 mph is reached in 16 sec. when motor 2 reaches its peak allowable speed of 11,650 RPM. Figure 9b shows the corresponding distance travelled vs. time. The distance of 100M is reached in 8.4 sec. These results are computed using a vehicle drag coefficient of 0.36, frontal area of 21.3 sq. ft., coefficient of rolling resistance of 0.01402, rear wheel dynamic radius of 13.26 inches, on a zero-percent grade.

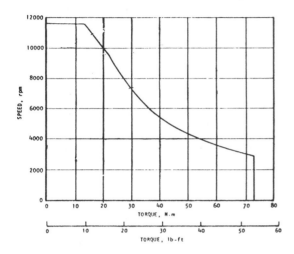

Figure 8 Motor speed-torque performance envelope.

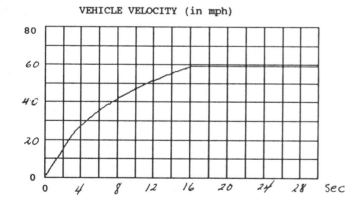

Figure 9a Velocity vs. time with the two electric motors operating on the boundary of their performance envelope.

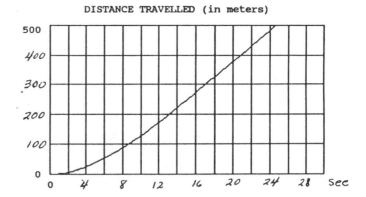

Figure 9b Distance vs. time with the two electric motors operating on the boundary of their performance envelope.

For the purposes of this Challenge, the two motors acting together are deemed adequate. However for a more practical HEV, faster acceleration and certainly a higher top speed are required. These changes can be accomplished by using more motor power and a change of gear ratio after initial low-gear acceleration. For illustrative purposes, if each motor had a peak power rating of 48 kW and a peak torque of 144 N-m, which are double the actual values, then the 100 m distance would now be covered in 6.4 sec. and the peak velocity of 58 mph is reached in 7.2 sec. If a gear change is also made to make each ratio half of the original values then a top speed of around 110 mph could be achieved with only slight increases in 0-60 mph and 0-100 m times. If this gear change were made at 30 mph then these times increase to 7.6 sec. and 6.5 sec., respectively, with each motor still controlled at its operational limits. These are negligible increases.

A very interesting aspect of this calculation is that the 0-60 mph time of approximately 7.6 sec. for a 3812 lb. vehicle would certainly require an ICE with at least twice the 96 kW of the two electric motors. This result illustrates a key advantage of electric motors over ICEs as vehicle drive elements, namely that electric motor can produce their peak torque at low speeds. With an ICE peak torque is developed at much higher vehicle speeds even in the lowest transmission gear ratio. Thus larger more polluting engines are required to produce suitable low speed performance.

4.3. Motor Control

The two electric motors are controlled as if they were a single motor as shown in Fig. 10. The two armature windings and two field windings are each wired in series. The controller designed by the Wayne Team uses some high current contactors and a field circuit chopper removed from a second DOE donated vehicle. This vehicle is known as the Audi Mule, and was part of the HTV-1 DOE sponsored hybrid vehicle research program. The control aspects of this program were handled by the General Electric Company. The controller in the Waynescort includes one stage of battery switching. As shown in Fig. 10, the parallel switches denoted as P put the two 120 V battery strings in parallel. For higher speed operation, the P switches are opened and the S switch connects the strings in series to apply 240 V to the armature circuit. The high current contactors used to implement switches P and S are both electrically and mechanically interlocked to prevent simultaneous closure, which would short the batteries thus blowing the protective fuses.

The armature current controller also uses electromechanical contactors whose actuation is coordinated with the battery parallel/series contactors based on signals representative of accelerator pedal position and vehicle velocity. Since the motors are mechanically connected to the rear wheels through a fixed gearing transaxle, the motor shaft speeds are directly related to the vehicle velocity. The primary purpose of the armature controller is to limit armature current over low speed operation, up to 13.6 mph. Beyond this speed the controller has essentially zero resistance and the battery is in a series configuration at 240 V.

The field current controller is the primary control of motor torques. A reversing switch in its output circuit allows for reverse motion of the vehicle in its ZEV mode. This electronically based controller is a conventional down-chopper circuit using a Darlington pair as the main switching element. Accelerator pedal position and vehicle velocity signals are also required for proper

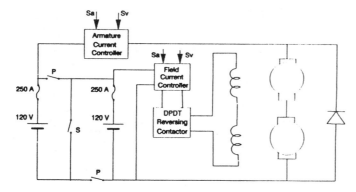

Figure 10 Schematic diagram of the motor control circuit.

operation of this field current controller. In addition the field current controller has an armature current limiting control loop. This loop becomes automatically active when the armature current is greater than 250 A. The action of this feedback loop maintains sufficient field current to maintain the armature current at this 250 A boundary.

The coordination of the battery switching contactors, and the armature and field controllers is performed in the Waynescort by a specially designed logic circuit. A prime aspect of the design of this sequential logic is to make its operation completely immune to the large magnetic fields unavoidable with very high current motor currents and the switching of these currents. Table 4 summarizes the effective states of the main aspects of this coordination. The designation of increase/decrease under the field current controller means that the controller operates to increase/decrease the field current, respectively, as the accelerator pedal is pushed further down. Figure 11 illustrates the effect of the field controller for the last stage in Table 4 with 240 V on the armature and vehicle speeds greater than 13.6 mph. Figure 11a shows how the vehicle velocity increases with decreasing field current. Similarly Fig. 11b shows how the armature current increases with decreasing field current. Operation at 55 mph is seen to require a field current of 4.5A at a steady armature current of 54A.

Table 4
Coordination Logic for Motor Controller

Accel. pedal	Vehicle speed (mph)	Series/ Parallel	Arm. Control (ohms)	Field Control
up	any	off	—	—
down	0-2.8	P	high	increase
down	2.8-5.3	P	low	increase
down	5.3-9.4	S	high	increase
down	9.4-13.6	S	low	decrease
down	> 13.6	S	0	decrease

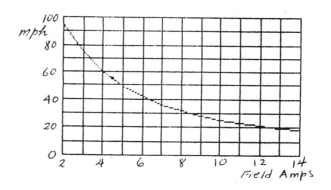

Figure 11a Vehicle speed as a function of field current for speeds > 13.6 mph at an armature voltage of 240 V.

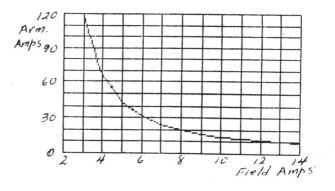

Figure 11b Motor armature current as a function of field current for speeds > 13.6 mph at an armature voltage of 240 V.

5. Emission Control

The complete emissions control system on the stock Escort has not been altered. Thus no changes have been made to the fuel delivery system except to slightly reshape the standard fuel tank to allow for the mounting of the rear transaxle. The only other change involved a slight rerouting of the filler hose. All other evaporative return lines are of stock design. The controls on the

Ford 1.9 liter engine are already optimized relative to performance and emissions, so no changes have been made. Also the exhaust system is completely stock except again for some rerouting of the connecting pope from the catalytic converter to the muffler to avoid interference with the right side half-shaft.

6. Fuel and Electrical Power Consumption

The fuel consumption of the Waynescort should be similar to the EPA Fuel Economy figures of 30 mpg City and 37 mpg Highway. The Waynescort has a gross vehicle weight (GVW) at the allowable limit which should reduce these fuel efficiency values due to increased rolling resistance which is proportional to the GVW. However, the rear tires have been changed to a larger size having a dynamic rolling radius increase of 2.26 inches, which decreases the rolling resistance. Also we plan to operate the Waynescort at an elevated tire pressure, which also decreases rolling resistance. These compensating factors should result in ICE operation such that the EPA Fuel Efficiency values are expected.

The electrical efficiency of the vehicle is estimated as follows. From Fig. 11, the armature current, and field current as a function of vehicle speed can be determined. Thus the power drawn from the battery going into the armature and field circuit, and into battery heating losses can be determined. Also we estimate the transaxle efficiency to be 92%. Now the total road power load required to overcome rolling resistance and aerodynamic resistance can be computed as a function of vehicle speed. Table 5 shows the results of this efficiency calculation.

Table 5
Electric Drive Computed Performance

Speed (mph)	Road Load (kW)	Elec. Input (kW)	Efficiency (%)
40	6.7	7.9	84.8
45	8.3	10.0	83.0
50	10.1	12.4	81.5
55	12.2	15.2	80.3

As a comparison of the cost of operating each drive system, we assume that gasoline has a price of $1.10/gal. and electric energy costs $.10/kw-h. Now if we further assume that the EPA Highway figure of 37 mpg corresponds to 55 mph operation, then the costs of operation for each drive are:

Electric Drive: $1.52/h

ICE Drive $1.64/h

Thus the ZEV mode of operation at a maximum speed of 55 mph appears roughly equal to the cost of ICE engine operation at this same speed.

7. Vehicle Structural Modifications

Two major structural modifications were made to the Waynescort. These involved cutting both rear crossmembers to allow for mounting of the rear wheel electric drive transaxle case. The front cross member is replaced by a horizontal bar mounted inside the vehicle above and slightly behind the location of the original front

cross member. This new upper cross member is constructed of 0.125 x 3.5 inch cold-rolled 1018 steel plate welded into a T cross section. Two end plates 3.5 x 5.0 x 0.312 inch of the same material are welded to the bottom side wall of the strut towers. The T section cross member is then welded between these end plates. In addition to maintaining the transverse integrity of the body, this cross member is also used to support the front of the rear transaxle case. The T-cross section is used to prevent any tendency of this replacement cross member to twist. A steel box structure similar in design to the original cross member would be lighter and of adequate strength. The T cross section steel was chosen for its simplicity and availability.

The second lower cross member, located under the vehicle in-line with the axis of the rear wheels, serves two primary functions. The first function involves maintaining the integrity of the two main longitudinal box rails. The second function involves supporting the lower control arms holding the rear knuckle in position. The stabilizer bar is also held in position by clamps on this lower cross member. In order to position the half-shafts at a high efficiency zero-degree angle with respect to the transaxle-clutch shaft axis and the wheel axis, the lower cross member needed to be cut. In addition, the cross member needed to be slotted such that the half-shafts could pass through in joining the differential output to the wheels. Figure 12 shows the half-shaft passing through a slot cut in the end section of the original cross member. This redesign keeps the outer ends of the original cross member in order to provide the required suspension lower control arm mounting points. The removed center section is replaced by a 5x1.5x0.188 inch structural steel channel mounted on steel pads placed on the two retained cross member ends. Gussetts are also welded as added strengthening elements for this redesigned cross member. This steel channel is shown below the cross member ends, the clutch housing, and transaxle case in Fig. 12. Again an additional weight is being added above what would result from a more optimal design.

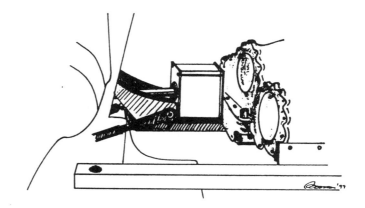

Figure 12 Detail view of half-shaft passing through a slot cut in the outer section of the original cross member.

An additional structural modification involved cutting a 20 x 36 inch section of the sheet metal in the spare-tire well section in the rear of the vehicle. This removal allows for ready access to assemble the rear drive. A light-weight aluminum box re-closes this area. The structural integrity of the vehicle is not greatly influenced by the removal and replacement of this sheet metal.

8. Suspension Redesign and Vehicle Handling

The front suspension and steering of the vehicle is unmodified from the stock Escort. All of the modifications were made to the rear suspension, as described in previous sections.

8.1. Rear Knuckle Design

As mentioned in Section 3 the two rear knuckles are fabricated by welding the top half of a standard front knuckle to the bottom half of the original rear knuckle, as shown in Fig. 13. This design allows for the connection of the two links to the bottom of the knuckle with the top half now having a hole for the drive shaft, which the original rear knuckle did not have. Figure 14 shows this rear knuckle with the suspension lower control arms connected to the lower half and the drive shaft coming through the upper half from the CV-joint at each rear wheel. Another advantage of this design is that the front disk brakes can now be readily mounted to the top of the fabricated knuckle. Stress analysis shows that Nickle welding gives a 1.67 safety factor.

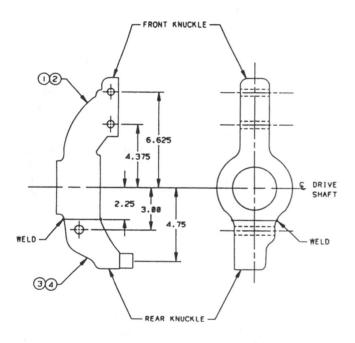

Figure 13 Detail view of the redesigned rear knuckle consisting of the top of a standard front knuckle and the bottom of a standard rear knuckle.

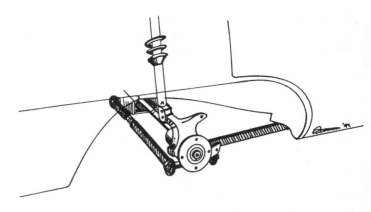

Figure 14 Passenger side rear knuckle showing the connection of all suspension linkages with the added drive shaft.

8.2. Stabilizer Bar Design

As the original lower half of the rear knuckle is still being used, the original stabilizer bar can readily be connected. The only problems were to consider the bar's integrity with a much heavier vehicle, and to reposition the supporting brackets on the lower cross member so as not to interfere with the driving half shafts. The stabilizer bar will be in a maximum load when the car is in turning. At the turning condition, the lateral forces will lift the outer radius of the car. This lifting is then neutralized by the stabilizer bar by creating reacting torsion on the bar that will force the car's body to real form (not the deformed formation.)

The analysis of the stabilizer bar can be started with the free body diagram (in turning condition) as below:

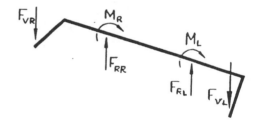

Summing up the moments and setting them equal to zero gives 11550 lb-in moment at the bracket. The reaction forces are found out to be 1050 lbs. Using the parallel axis theorem, the active inertia of the bar can be calculated. The symmetrical property of the bar simplifies the calculations. The value for the inertia is found to be 34.46 inches During the worst turning case, the maximum stress can be calculated from:

$$\sigma_{max} = \frac{Mc}{I}$$

This formula gives the stress as 3867 psi. Compared to the value of the yielding stress of the material, the number is very small. Thus the stabilizer bar still can be used safely with new loads.

The deflection caused by the loads on the bar can be calculated with:

$$\text{deflection} = \frac{FL}{AE}$$

The value is found to be 6.40E-04 inch or 0.0163 mm. This is a very small deflection. The above calculations are based on static forces. Considering dynamic forces and using the same formulas, the value of maximum stress increases to 4598 psi and the deflection to be 0.0219 mm. These values show that the original bar is very adequate.

8.3. Strut and Spring Design

Two physical changes were made to the rear struts. The first involved filling the lower end of the strut with weld material, grinding to achieve the proper shape, and redrilling mounting holes. These changes adapted the strut such that mounting to the top of the redesigned rear knuckle described in Section 8.1 could be accomplished. The second modification involved adding spring helpers to the existing strut spring.

Initial estimates concluded that the load on each rear strut spring would increase from 730 lbs. to 1220 lbs. Thus to maintain equal travelling distance (which is 3.90 inches), Hooke's law requires an increase in spring stiffness by a factor of 1.67. This increase is achieved by inserting spring helpers. Our considerations regarding fatigue and buckling of the spring indicated adequate safety factors with these spring helpers in place.

9. Choice of Materials

A variety of materials were used in constructing the HEV Waynescort from a stock Escort stationwagon. These are summarized as follows:

1. *Battery Enclosure* - The battery enclosure is constructed of plywood lined with sprayed-on fiberglass. The fiberglass is used to prevent spilled acids from interacting with the wood and also to add strength particularly to the vented base supporting the 640 lb. battery weight. In a production vehicle a lighter molded plastic enclosure would be a preferred design.

2. *Roll Bar* - The roll bar is constructed of 1.5 inch o.d., 0.120 inch wall thickness mild steel seamless tubing.

3. *Clutch Housings* - The clutch housings on the rear electric drive are machined from 6061-T6 aluminum stock.

4. *Shafts* - The half-shafts and clutch coupling shafts are machined from 4041 steel and then heat treated for added strength.

5. *Structural Cross Members* - The two structural cross members are constructed from cold rolled 1018 steel plate and structural steel channel. A production vehicle would use much lighter steel box structures.

10. Vehicle Manufacturability

When designing an automobile, Design for Manufacturing and Assembly (DFMA) must be strongly considered. A good design that cannot be easily manufactured or assembled is inconvenient and can develop defects. Such a design must be considered to be a bad design. An easily manufacturable and assembled product, however, is convenient and leads to less defects--hence, a higher quality product.

With the Waynescort, DFMA was not strongly considered because the Waynescort is a prototype and conversion vehicle, not a production vehicle. It is very difficult to implement an entirely new system on a vehicle that, before conversion, has all its components conveniently placed according to DFMA. Consequently, many of the Waynescort's components, such as the electric motors, batteries, and rear transaxle, are positioned in awkward places throughout the vehicle. In addition many of the key components used in the Waynescort's electric drive such as the motors and rear transaxle are taken from other research vehicles. Thus, these components have configurations which are not readily adaptable to the stock front wheel drive Escort.

In order to actually manufacture a HEV utilizing our independent front-wheel ICE drive and rear-wheel electric drive, significant redesign of the stock Escort body structure from the B-pillar to the rear end of the vehicle must be accomplished. The key tasks for this redesign are:

1. The battery pack must be located in a compartment under the floor of the vehicle probably in the rear-most section where the present spare-tire well is located.

2. The electric motors and their transaxle coupling to the rear wheels must also not be inside the stationwagon's cargo area. With proper controls, a design using one motor on each rear wheel may be feasible with reduction gearing and clutching integral to each motor, thus eliminating the present transaxle and differential.

Such a redesign is considered well beyond the scope of this present conversion project. Section 12 considers an alternate HEV concept which appears to be very favorable from a manufacturability standpoint.

11. Body styling and Ergonomics

The Waynescort is a conversion of a stock Escort stationwagon to a HEV to meet a set of specifications defined by the Challenge Regulations. These specifications precluded all significant body styling modifications. The Waynescort has oversized 15 inch rear wheels to change the motor to rear wheel drive ratio. However, this change also tends to level the vehicle, considering the fact that its weight is at its maximum allowable value. Also the appearance is slightly altered by these larger rear wheels. No other body styling changes were considered.

Ergonomic changes included removing the original front seats and replacing them with plastic racing seats. This change was made to give some added space for the battery pack and to achieve some weight reduction. The operation of the electric drive is extremely simple with the driver simply pressing a conventional spring-loaded accelerator pedal to go, and alternately a brake pedal to stop in the usual manner when driving on automatic transmission. The additional switches and instruments added in the dash area would certainly not all be included in a production vehicle. Our consideration in this project was to view the Waynescort as an experimental prototype intended to show the benefits of the HEV concept. Ergonomic considerations are very important, but in our view not at this early research and development stage.

12. Future Work On An Alternate HEV Design

As described in the Introductory Section 1, the Waynescort was designed such as to have a ZEV operating mode. Because the total energy which can be stored in batteries is severely limited, the range in ZEV mode is also very limited. The HEV Team's original research into HEV designs, predating the announcement of the Challenge, led to the conclusion that a vehicle acceptable to the U.S. driving public must have operating characteristics similar in performance to present-day vehicles. Even the need to constantly refuel a battery-electric vehicle by returning to a recharging station after every 50-75 miles of driving seems like an unacceptable necessity. Consequently, the only configuration whereby enough energy can be stored on-board the vehicle and involves a relatively short refueling time with available technology is the use of chemical fuel either as liquid or a gas. The conversion of this fuel to driving energy involves some heat-engine based process, and thus, does not exhibit zero emissions. However, heat engines, particularly ICEs, have the interesting property that when operating at one particular speed producing one particular output torque, they are very efficient and their emissions, though not zero, are substantially reduced when compared to operation over a comprehensive ICE map.

The concept the HEV Team proposes for a future HEV is to incorporate a small heat engine operating at constant speed and torque driving an electric generator, thus producing the average power needed to operate the vehicle. An additional amount of power would be produced by the heat engine, to be used to recharge an energy storage unit, such as a battery bank. The vehicle is driven by electric motors directly through power electronic controllers from the generator output. The energy storage unit must only be able to supply additional peaking power to the motors to allow for adequate vehicle acceleration response. This configuration, known as a series HEV, is shown in Fig. 15.

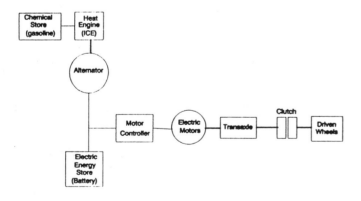

Figure 15 The series HEV drive.

Comparing the series configuration to the parallel HEV shown in Fig. 1, the key difference is simply the removal of the mechanical linkage between the heat engine and the driven wheels. The removal of this linkage removes the constraint between the speed of the heat engine and the speed of the vehicle, allowing the heat engine to always operate at its optimal speed joint. The key design problem is to properly size the heat engine such that its torque output also matches the optimal torque point.

Figure 16 illustrates a typical map of constant BSFC (brake specific fuel consumption in g/kW-h) in a plane of mep (mean effective pressure which is related to engine torque) vs. engine

speed. Also plotted are contours of constant engine power as well as typical fixed gearing constraint curves. Now to see the basis of the concept, consider that the ICE is operating at 2800 RPM in 4th gear at a relative power level of 8, as indicated by point A in Figure 16. The BSFC at point A is about 365 g/kW-h for an efficiency of 22.4% using a gasoline heat content of 44 Mj/kg. Shifting to 5th gear moves the engine at a constant relative power of 8 to point B at 2200 RPM and a BSFC of 330 g/kW-h for an efficiency of 24.8%, thus gaining 11%. However, note that operation could move at the same relative power level to point C at 1300 RPM with a decreased BSFC of 290 g/kW-h for an efficiency of 28.2%, thus gaining an additional 14% over point B. By decoupling the engine speed from the vehicle speed, there are no constraints restricting movement to point C, thus effecting an overdrive higher than 5th gear, yielding a much lower engine speed.

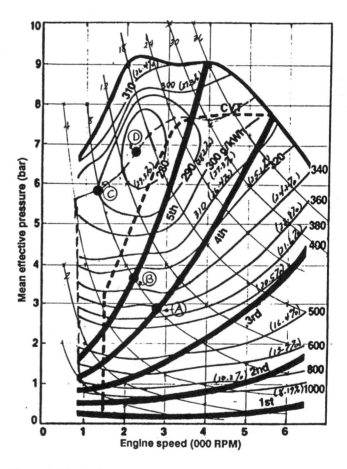

Figure 16 Typical map of ICE performance characteristics showing constant BSFC/efficiency, relative power, and 5-speed gearing constraint contours.

However, a more optimal operating point exists at point D with a BSFC of around 270 g/kW-h for an efficiency of 30.3%. In common usage, over widely varying speeds, most ICE's average an efficiency of 20% (or less) in converting gasoline to shaft power. Thus there is a potential 50% gain. However, the mechanical to electrical to mechanical conversions of the series HEV scheme, involving a generator, controller, motor, produces an efficiency factor of 72.9%. This factor assumes an efficiency for each of the three cascaded components to be about 90%. Thus, the overall gain of the series HEV over a conventional ICE vehicle is 36.5%, which takes a 28 mpg vehicle to 38.3 mpg. However, of potential greater importance, is that at constant speed, without transient operation, a heat engine produces much reduced emissions, particularly when engine designs can be entirely optimized for a single operating state.

Unfortunately, the new State legislation requiring ZEV operation precludes this series hybrid design, primarily because the energy store has to be unnecessarily large to give adequate ZEV range. Thus, the series HEV concept appears very attractive for ultra low level emissions, but is deemed not suitable for the ZEV requirements of this Challenge, which stem from State legislative requirements.

13. Acknowledgements

The Wayne State Team thanks the Ford Motor Company, the U.S. Department of Energy, and the Society of Automotive Engineers for sponsoring this HEV-Challenge. In addition we thank the many corporate sponsors whose funds and equipment gifts made our work possible. In particular, we are grateful to T.B. Woods & Sons, Mt. Pleasant, MI. for donating hydraulic clutches, and to United Technologies, Dearborn, MI. for their help in the high current circuitry. Lastly, we wish to thank Mr. David M. Meisel of Meisel Industries, Troy, MI. for his council, inventiveness, and overall expertise in helping with the difficulties faced throughout the finishing stages of this project.

Weber State University - WILDCAT

David A. Erb, Lawrence C. Garcia, and Reid H. Leland
Weber State University

ABSTRACT

An interdisciplinary team of Weber State University students designed and built "Wildcat," a practical entry for the 1993 Ford Hybrid Electric Vehicle Challenge. The car is simple and cost-effective, with good performance for commuting and highway driving. Team members gained valuable experience in a number of relevant areas.

INTRODUCTION

Recent emissions regulations have accelerated the interest in hybrid and electric vehicles. Weber State University (WSU) is proud to be part of the inaugural Ford Hybrid Electric Vehicle (HEV) Challenge, an activity which should hasten the availability of economical, reliable, and efficient HEVs.

The WSU vehicle development team includes members from Mechanical, Manufacturing, Automotive, and Electronics Engineering Technology. The HEV project is also supported by the Technical Sales and Computer Information Systems programs. Team members have gained valuable experience, not only in automotive design and development, but also in teamwork and time management.

PROJECT OVERVIEW

The WSU HEV team wanted a practical conversion with significant potential to cut emissions. The team considers market penetration to be the most important parameter in the emissions reduction potential of any HEV. Thus, the team's main goal was low cost; its motto, KISS ("Keep it Sweet and Simple"). The resulting design is discussed below.

POWERTRAIN CONFIGURATION

The primary design criteria of the powertrain were:

1. simplicity,
2. manufacturability,
3. easy installation, and
4. low cost.

The resulting design is a parallel system that meets all these criteria (see Figure 1).

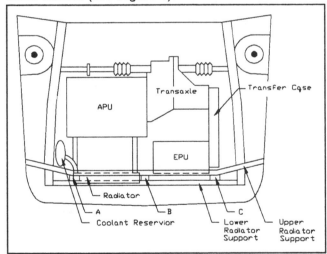

Figure 1 Drivetrain configuration and support members A, B, and C.

Two driving modes are possible with this configuration, electric power unit (EPU) and auxiliary power unit (APU). These operating modes are independent of one another. No attempt is made to run in a combined mode.

The EPU was selected based on an acceleration goal of 0 to 45 MPH in 15 seconds and a cruising speed goal of 40 MPH for at least 40 miles. Power estimates for these tasks are 30 Kw for acceleration and 10 Kw for cruise. An Advanced DC Motors model 000-256-

4001 electric motor and Curtis PMC model 1221B controller were selected for their ability to operate within these parameters. This system had the best mix of lightness, proven reliability, and cost effectiveness of the alternatives investigated.

Electrical power is provided by twelve Trojan SCS-200 lead acid batteries. These are wired in a parallel/series configuration which provides 72 VDC. The batteries have an 80% discharge cycle life of at least 300 cycles and a total weight of approximately 750 pounds.

A wiring diagram is shown in Appendix A, identifying the following:

1.   high voltage connections to the drive system,
2.   low voltage connections for accessories, and
3.   all systems safety devices.

The EPU transfers power to the wheels via the existing Escort transaxle. A simple transfer case links the electric motor to the transaxle. The overdrive and cover were removed from the transaxle tailshaft and replaced with a 3/8-inch aluminum plate to locate and support the electric motor. The transfer case contains a Morse type HV chain drive. A one-inch wide chain with 3/8-inch pitch connects two 3.5-inch pitch diameter sprockets. This system is designed to handle 96 HP, well above the expected service of about 60 HP. The sprocket on the electric motor is a press fit with a 1/4-inch key. The sprocket on the transaxle (in place of the fifth gear) is splined to match the existing shaft. Splines on the sprocket were matched to the shaft by electron discharge machining (EDM). For a one-off job, EDM worked very well and proved to be less costly than broaching. The case cover was made with 20 gage sheet metal and welded to a 1/4-inch thick by 1-inch wide steel flange.

The auxiliary power unit (APU) is the stock Escort engine. This enables the use of stock mountings, emissions controls, and other existing systems. This commonality offers large cost savings in production.

CONTROL STRATEGY

One objective was retention of stock control characteristics in both drive modes. Except for the mode selector switch, power switch, and clutch lockout, driving the Escort HEV is very similar to driving the stock Escort.

To operate in EPU mode, the link between the gasoline engine and the transmission is disengaged with a clutch lockout. The driver uses the foot pedal to release the clutch, as in a normal gear change. A cable control mounted in the vehicle dashboard operates a cam which holds the clutch release fork in the disengaged position. The EPU then drives the transmission main shaft independent of the internal combustion engine.

A three position switch was used for the mode selector. Mode switch positions correspond to EPU, APU, and off. In EPU mode, the main 12-volt power cable is isolated and the APU cannot be started by the starter motor. A main power switch equipped with an integral circuit breaker connects the battery pack to the electric motor. Both switches are accessible to the driver and passenger.

With the clutch locked out, the mode selector switch in EPU, and the main power switch on, the HEV is ready to drive in EPU mode. In EPU mode, shifting is accomplished without a clutch by modulating the throttle to match gear speeds. Due to the relatively low inertia of the motor, the synchronizers match gear speeds quickly. Shifting is very smooth and, with a little practice, is easier than shifting with the clutch.

APU operation is nearly identical to the stock Escort. With the clutch lockout disengaged, the main power switch on, and the mode selector in APU, the Escort can be started and driven in stock fashion. The original ignition switch and the functions associated with it remain operational. Isolating the starter power cable through the mode selector enables all electrical accessories to operate as stock in both modes.

Per rule 11.19, the vehicle is equipped with a circuit breaker capable of handling full current from the batteries. The car has also been equipped with two mushroom "Panic" buttons. These buttons cut the control power to the main contactors located just outside of the battery box. With the control power off, the contactors open and disrupt drive system power.

A 600 amp sparkless fuse has been located in series with the electric drive system, per rule 11.16.3.

EMISSIONS CONTROL

The Escort HEV is powered in APU mode by the stock engine, equipped with all stock emissions controls. The 1993 Escort is very similar to the 1992 model, and complies with California Transitional Low Emissions Vehicle standards (TLEV). A production version of the Weber State HEV would be equipped with 1993 Escort emissions controls.

COOLING

Three main areas required cooling:

1. gasoline engine,
2. electric motor, and
3. electrical components.

A 1979 Ford Fiesta radiator was installed to provide space for the electric motor. Radiator capacity was increased by replacing the stock core with a three row, high efficiency core. The filler, inlet, and outlet locations were altered to improve coolant flow. A ten inch, 500 cfm electric fan was mounted on the radiator to ensure proper air flow.

The electric motor is cooled by an internal fan which draws ambient air, filtered at the intake. Three separate air boxes are mounted to the EPU. Intake air flow area is ten square inches. Exhaust air flow area totals 8.25 square inches. Air intake boxes are detachable for servicing the EPU and the foam air filter elements.

The electric motor controller and the DC to DC converter also require cooling. The controller is cooled by a heat sink and radiator system. An electric pump moves liquid coolant through the heat sink to a dedicated radiator located in the engine compartment. The DC to DC converter rejects heat through an aluminum mounting plate. All other heat-producing components are cooled by natural convection.

FUEL AND ELECTRIC POWER CONSUMPTION

Electric power estimates were based on data provided by the HEV Hotline and the battery supplier. Weights of 2500 and 3500 lbs. were assumed for the stock and converted Escorts, respectively.

Road load at 50 mph was given as 4.7 Kw for aerodynamic drag, with a total of 7.9 Kw. Since non-aerodynamic road load is fairly linear with weight, the total HEV road load at 50 mph was estimated as 9.2 Kw.

The battery pack consists of twelve Trojan model SCS200 12-volt deep cycle batteries. A capacity chart for the SCS200, shown in Appendix B, was used to estimate the EPU range of the vehicle. The 50 mph power of 9.2 Kw was used as a proxy for the range event requirement. In a 72 VDC system, this represents 128 amps. The parallel battery wiring implies that a single battery must provide 64 amps. Appendix B indicates battery capability of 65 amps for 1.04 hours. Thus, the batteries should allow an EPU range of 40 miles at 40 mph.

The significant variables in fuel usage are engine

BSFC, vehicle aerodynamics, tires, and weight. The WSU HEV employs an unmodified Escort engine and body, with stock tires. Weight reduction was already a priority, for numerous reasons. Thus, there was no incentive to estimate fuel usage during design. Actual data were used in plotting contest strategy.

BATTERY PLACEMENT AND ENCLOSURE

The battery enclosure was designed and sited based on the following criteria:

1. passenger safety,
2. light weight,
3. low center of gravity, and
4. even front/rear weight   bias.

The enclosure can be described by four main components:

1. box,
2. restraints,
3. mounting, and
4. ventilation.

The battery box has fourteen individual battery cubicles (see Figure 2).

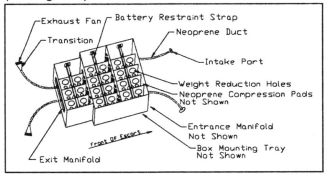

Figure 2 battery enclosure

An airtight lid was built to facilitate ventilation. The box was manufactured from 20 gage sheet steel using standard sheet metal fabrication processes including punching, bending, spot welding, and rivetting. To minimize weight, holes were punched in the partitions and inside walls. Total battery enclosure weight is approximately 110 lbs. The battery weight adds to the enclosure weight to give a total electrical power pack weight of approximately 850 lbs. A finite element model of the box was used to verify structural integrity (see Appendix C).

Battery containment and passenger safety in an accident were primary considerations in the battery box design. A piece of 1/8-inch by 1-inch strap steel holds each row of batteries in place. Attached to the strap steel are neoprene pads that apply a vertical force on the top of each battery. These pads keep the batteries from rotating in a vertical plane and from gaining momentum in a collision. Securing the strap steel at each partition and side wall increases restraint strength and safety (see Figure 2). Neoprene pads are glued to the front and back of each cubicle to hold each battery in compression on the long axis of the battery. These pads keep the batteries from rotating in a horizontal plane and from gaining momentum in a front or rear end collision.

The box is mounted as far forward as possible to reduce the effects of the added weight on the rear axle. This mounting position produces a nearly even front/rear weight bias of 49%/51%. An angle iron (1.5-inch by 1.5-inch by 1/8-inch) tray is used to mount the box to the floorboard. The box is secured to the tray with twenty-nine 5/16-inch roundhead bolts. The tray is mounted to the floorboard with twenty-one 5/16-inch bolts and four 8 mm bolts. The 5/16-inch bolts fasten to threaded inserts and the 8 mm bolts fasten to existing seat belt mounting holes. This bolt pattern has an approximate pull through strength of twenty times the battery enclosure weight. The 20 G rating is for a tensile pull through. Because the bolts are in several planes, a pure tensile pull through is highly unlikely. In an accident a great deal of energy would be absorbed by the sides of the tray and any bending. The use of bolts in mounting the battery enclosure allows for periodic service of the fuel filter and cleaning of the box.

The battery enclosure is vented for hydrogen gas removal. Air is drawn through the box using two 12 cfm brushless DC fans. These fans are mounted at the ventilation system exhaust ports (see Figure 2). This fan location creates a negative pressure in the box and ventilation ducts. Any microholes in the box or ducts will draw air into the system due to the negative pressure gradient. Hydrogen gas leaks inside the car are thus minimized. Ventilation ducts are made from 1.5-inch diameter neoprene-lined flexible tubing. Manifolds on the front and back of the battery box create an even flow of air through the box. Ventilation intake ports utilize existing holes located beneath the front seats. Intake ports are equipped with air filters and are easy to service. Exhaust ports are located underneath the rear bumper on the body side wall. The bumper baffles the exhaust ports from water and road grit.

VEHICLE STRUCTURAL MODIFICATIONS

The center and side vertical members (members A, B, and C in Figure 1) between the lower and upper radiator supports were removed to make room for the electric motor and radiator. Three brackets were made from 20 gage steel to replace the members that were removed. The new brackets are of equal or greater size and strength than those removed.

Twenty-one 1/2-inch diameter holes were drilled in the floorboard. Threaded inserts were secured in these holes for mounting the battery box.

Two 2.25-inch diameter holes were punched in the body, one on each rear quarter panel underneath the bumper. These holes are used for battery box ventilation exhaust ports.

SUSPENSION MODIFICATIONS

Increased weight required that the suspension be modified. Suspension modification objectives were:

1. stock ride height, and
2. simplicity.

New springs were specified to meet modification objectives. Spring constants were calculated for a 1000 lb. increase in rear axle weight and a 400 lb. increase in front axle weight. Spring wire diameters were calculated based on the following:

1. increased axle weight,
2. stock coil end configuration, and
3. stock number of coils.

The new front and rear spring constants are 201 and 165 lb./in., respectively. Linear springs replaced the stock variable springs. The resulting shear stresses of 84 and 74 ksi are within the manufacturer specification of 90 ksi. Corresponding spring free lengths are 11.4 and 15.0 inches. Steering and suspension geometry, mounting points, and linkages remain stock.

CHOICE OF MATERIALS

Materials used in manufactured parts were chosen based on the following:

1. performance,
2. manufacturability, and
3. cost effectiveness.

Three materials were used; steel, aluminum, and neoprene.

Twenty gage sheet steel was used throughout the car, especially in the battery box. A finite element model of the box was used to determine material thickness (see Appendix C). The corrosion characteristics of aluminum preclude its use around batteries. Composites were also considered but ruled out because of equipment limitations. Sulfuric acid-resistant polyurethane coating was used to protect the battery box.

Twenty gage sheet steel was also used in the transfer

case cover. This choice proved providential when the cover required modifications.

Other parts built with 20 gage sheet steel include:

1. duct transitions,
2. electric motor restraining strap, and
3. radiator support brackets.

Twenty-eight gage galvanized sheet steel was used for the cargo box, ballast boxes, and electric motor air ducts. Light weight and manufacturability were the main reasons for this selection.

The roll bar was made of 4130 seamless tubing. Strength, weight, and SCCA guidelines were primary reasons for this choice.

Aluminum was chosen for the transfer case plate and electrical components mounting plate. Weight considerations ruled out the use of steel for the transfer case plate. Heat generated by the electrical components required that the mounting plate also serve as a heat sink. Aluminum's high thermal conductivity made it an obvious choice for this application.

Neoprene was used extensively in the battery enclosure, due to its corrosion resistance and elasticity.

VEHICLE MANUFACTURABILITY

Design centered around in-house fabrication capabilities wherever possible. The main manufacturability criterion was simplicity. To facilitate design and construction, conversion was separated into three main areas:

1. transfer case,
2. battery pack, and
3. wiring-electrical.

By keeping the manufacturing processes simple, fabrication was faster, easier, and less expensive. This allowed earlier completion of the vehicle, extending the test time under actual operating conditions. Simple processes also allow quicker recovery when components fail during testing.

ERGONOMICS

Very few ergonomic changes were made in converting the Escort. Stock items that remained unchanged include the front seats, carpeting, side panels, dash board, and steering wheel. The rear seat was removed to provide room for the battery box. The vehicle also has the original heater/defroster which functions normally in APU mode but lacks heat in EPU mode. Air conditioning is not provided.

The stock clutch, brake, and throttle pedals; gear shift; and emergency brake lever are used for their original functions. An electric vacuum pump assists power braking in EPU mode.

Additional levers, switches, and gauges were selected and mounted for function, safety, ease of use, and appearance. These additions include a fire extinguisher activation handle, located in the coin tray between the seats. This location provides easy access and decreases the chance of accidental discharge. Emergency stop buttons are located just inside the front corner of the side windows, accessible to the driver, passenger, and course workers. They disconnect all electric power when depressed. An electric motor overheat light is mounted on the dashboard to the left of the steering wheel, visible to the driver. Voltage and amperage gauges are mounted below the climate control panel. The clutch lockout lever replaces the cigarette lighter. The mode selector switch is located between the seats, behind the hand brake.

SUMMARY

The Weber State team excelled in production of the HEV "Wildcat." The motif of KISS has led to lower cost and higher manufacturability. Identification of three main conversion areas (battery pack, transfer case, and electrical-wiring) facilitated design and construction. Safety and performance were maintained in the conversion. Team members have developed valuable teamwork skills and increased engineering confidence.

Appendix A

WIRING DIAGRAM

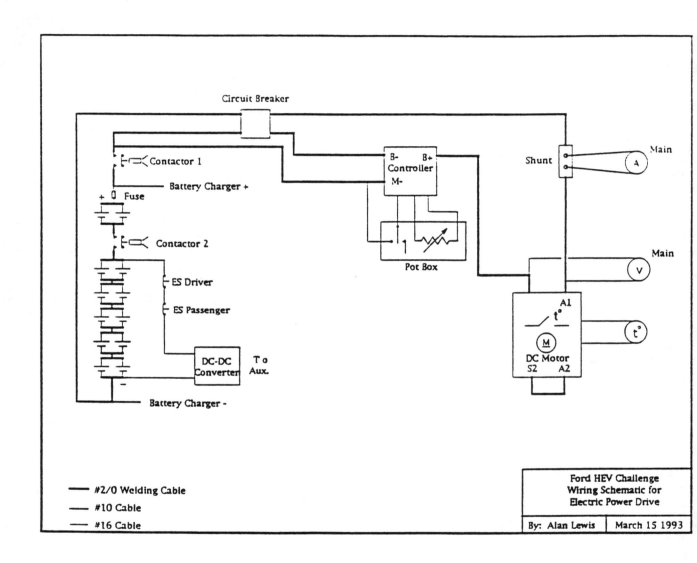

Appendix B

CAPACITY CHART FOR TROJAN SCS-200 BATTERIES

Current (amps)	Time (minutes)	Time (hours)	Capacity (amp-hours)
5	1422.92	23.72	118.58
10	611.19	10.19	101.87
15	372.82	6.21	93.20
20	262.53	4.38	87.51
25	200.00	3.33	83.33
30	160.14	2.67	80.07
35	132.70	2.21	77.41
40	112.77	1.88	75.18
45	97.68	1.63	73.26
50	85.91	1.43	71.59
55	76.48	1.27	70.11
60	68.79	1.15	68.79
65	62.39	1.04	67.59
70	57.00	0.95	66.50
75	52.40	0.87	65.50
80	48.44	0.81	64.58
85	44.99	0.75	63.73
90	41.96	0.70	62.94
95	39.28	0.65	62.20
100	36.90	0.62	61.50
105	34.77	0.58	60.85
110	32.85	0.55	60.23
115	31.12	0.52	59.64
120	29.55	0.49	59.09
125	28.11	0.47	58.56
130	26.80	0.45	58.06
135	25.59	0.43	57.59
140	24.48	0.41	57.13
145	23.46	0.39	56.69
150	22.51	0.38	56.27
155	21.63	0.36	55.87
160	20.81	0.35	55.48
165	20.04	0.33	55.11
170	19.32	0.32	54.75
175	18.65	0.31	54.40
180	18.02	0.30	54.07
185	17.43	0.29	53.74
190	16.87	0.28	53.43
195	16.35	0.27	53.13
200	15.85	0.26	52.83

Appendix C

FINITE ELEMENT MODEL OF BATTERY BOX

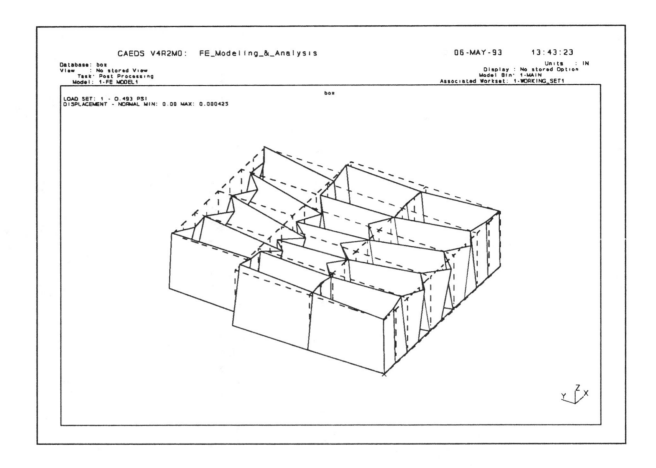

The University of Wisconsin-Madison Paradigm Hybrid Electric Vehicle

John J. Moskwa, Patrick Barber, Scott Costello, Barton Heldke,
Clark Hochgraf, Robert Rossi, and C. Thomas Wiesen
University of Wisconsin-Madison

ABSTRACT

The University of Wisconsin's entry into the 1993 Ford Hybrid Electric Vehicle Challenge is a stock-production, 5-speed Ford Escort Wagon modified to operate as a hybrid electric vehicle. The Escort's original powertrain has been removed and replaced with a series-configuration hybrid electric drivetrain consisting of a 100 HP 220V 3-phase AC induction motor and a 20 HP 4-stroke, 2-cylinder engine modified to burn M85. This paper discusses the vehicle's powertrain configuration, control strategy, design modifications, efficiency, materials selection, and vehicle manufacturability.

INTRODUCTION

Personal high-speed transportation has grown deep roots in society. Although today's pure gasoline or diesel engine vehicles produce excessive tailpipe emissions, they dominate the ever-growing vehicle market. As communities become aware of the direct health impacts of automotive pollutants, legislation is being created to force the development of zero emission vehicles. The problems with present-day zero emission vehicles include inferior driving ranges and lengthy battery recharging times. Hybrid electric vehicles are attractive because they offer greater ranges than standard electric vehicles and at the same time lower emissions than standard automobiles.

In its simplest form, hybrid electric vehicles reduce the total emissions per mile by allowing for a number of zero emissions miles to be driven. Beyond this, the dual power sources in an HEV can be strategically controlled to further minimize emissions when the engine is operating. The horsepower rating and size of the engine in an HEV can be much smaller than those in a standard car. The Hybrid Electric Vehicle Project Team at the University of Wisconsin, Madison has designed and built a series HEV which demonstrates the benefits and the implications of a hybrid drivetrain.

Team Paradigm recognizes that in the process of building a product, the needs of the customer must be considered. Team Paradigm viewed the HEV Challenge organizers as its "customer." The HEV Challenge organizers defined their requirements by way of the official HEV rules. Of 1,000 points available in the challenge, 750 points deal directly with performance characteristics and engineering design of the vehicle. These rules were analyzed using a multi-attribute utility model to define the vehicle's design criteria and provide a guide for choosing component and configuration options. The model used subjective analysis to assign the 750 contest points to specific significant aspects of the vehicle design (59 points for high battery capacity, 53 points for high motor horsepower, 40 points for weight bias, and so on.).

Along with the multiattribute utility model, some component and configuration decisions were made based on the results of computer simulations. Various simulated vehicles with different components and configurations were pitted against each other in computer simulations of the challenge's dynamic events. The results were in the form of challenge points and were used as a guide for selecting components and system configurations.

POWERTRAIN CONFIGURATION

HYBRID ELECTRIC DRIVETRAIN CONFIGURATION OPTIONS - Hybrid electric vehicle (HEV) drivetrain configurations may be generally classified as either "parallel" or "series" systems. In a "series" drivetrain, only the electric motor is directly linked to the transmission; the engine drives a generator, which in turn charges the vehicle's battery or supplies energy to the electric drive system. In this configuration the engine is not directly connected to the transmission. In contrast, a "parallel" drivetrain consists of both an electric motor and an internal combustion engine each having a direct mechanical link to the vehicle's transmission.

TEAM PARADIGM'S DRIVETRAIN SELECTION - The two configurations described above were evaluated based on their estimated ability to contribute points to the team's score in each event of the competition. This was done by assessing the impact of each relevant factor affected by the configuration choice (e.g. total acceleration, lateral stability, etc.) on the probable outcome of each event. Each factor was broken down into measurable attributes (peak engine power, drive motor torque, etc.), in order to quantify the importance of each factor in a mathematical sense. After a detailed analysis and a great deal of discussion, the Paradigm Team chose a series drivetrain configuration.

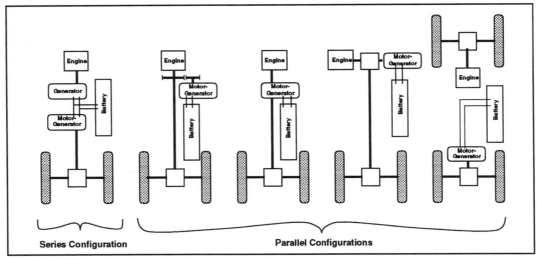

Figure 1. Various types of Hybrid Electric Drive configurations.

Well-designed parallel configuration drivetrains offer better vehicle acceleration and efficiency than their series counterparts. However, the high complexity and the difficulty involved in lowering emissions from a parallel configuration made such a system less desirable relative to a series configuration, who's engine could be easily maintained at a constant power level. Furthermore, the HEV Challenge's emissions testing rules strongly favored a series configuration. Parallel-configured entries are required to run emissions tests with the APU only. No electric power can be used to drive the vehicle. To satisfy this requirement with a parallel drivetrain would have required a 50 HP (or larger) engine.

ELECTRIC DRIVETRAIN OPERATING VOLTAGES - Team's Paradigm's choice of a three-phase 220 VAC electric drive system was driven by the need to maximize the efficiency and reduce the weight of the electric portion of the powertrain. Although a 220 VAC system requires 330 VDC from the battery pack, a requirement which proved difficult to satisfy, the high voltage also provides better performance and better efficiency than the 100 VDC motors used in most electric vehicles on the road today.

POWERTRAIN BATTERY SYSTEM - As with most electric vehicle projects, the main obstacles constraining Team Paradigm's efforts to build a high-performance electric vehicle were the weight, volume, and storage capacity limitations common to almost all commercially-available battery systems. Two batteries were chosen for use in the *Paradigm HEV*, the first being a desirable but immature molten-electrolyte lithium technology. The second battery, a less intimidating but more fully-developed starved-electrolyte lead/acid system served as a back-up option to cover the high risk involved in obtaining the lithium battery. The range of practical battery choices available to us was significantly reduced by our selection of a 220VAC motor, and thus the requirement of a 330 VDC battery bus voltage; most batteries designed for use in electric vehicles assume a 100 VDC platform, and are intractably large for use in a high-voltage system.

LiAl / FeS2: High Temperature Lithium-Aluminum / Ferric Disulfide - After investigating and considering a wide array of available battery chemistries, both common and exotic, a lithium-aluminum/ferric disulfide system was selected for use in Paradigm on the basis of its exceptional power and energy storage capabilities. LiAl / FeS_2 batteries have four times the energy density of conventional lead/acid batteries, and allow Paradigm to carry 20 kWh of electric energy in a compact package weighing under 400 lbs (182 kg).

The LiAl / FeS_2 battery chemistry utilizes a high-temperature, molten salt electrolyte. The active materials are lithium and sulfur, but both species are incorporated into chemical compounds in order to significantly reduce the operating and fabrication problems associated with the pure materials. The lithium-aluminum anode is a nearly equimolar alloy of lithium and aluminum, and remains solid at the battery's 400°C (752°F) nominal operating temperature. It is significantly safer than pure lithium and easier to process. The ferric disulfide cathode is also a solid at the battery operating temperature, and is less reactive and less volatile than pure sulfur. The electrolyte is a mixture of molten lithium salts providing exceptional electrical conductivity, thus giving the battery excellent power density characteristics.

The battery is brought up to operating temperature by means of electrical heating elements located inside the battery housing. The heat generated by the cells internally during normal use (due to I^2R losses on both charge and discharge) is adequate to maintain the battery's operating temperature. The battery can stand for at least 48 hours without requiring auxiliary heating, so regular commuter use of the *Paradigm HEV* would preclude the need for concern over the battery's temperature; if the vehicle were used on a semi-weekly or weekly basis, it would be necessary to either allow time for preheating the battery, to use some of the battery's energy to keep it warm, or to connect the battery's heating elements to an external power source.

The safety of this battery system has been thoroughly considered, and it compares very favorably with that of any currently-available battery technology, including lead/acid. The lithium-aluminum electrode is only mildly reactive and essentially non-toxic. It will not explode or burn violently in air, humid air, or water. If an accident of large enough magnitude ruptures both the battery housing and one or more of the individual steel-encased cells, the electrolyte system's design would minimize the threat posed to the vehicle's occupants by the hot liquid electrolyte: because there is no free liquid in the system, electrolyte splatter would be minimal. No hazardous fumes or chemical fire would normally develop in a catastrophic collision; the main danger would be physical contact of the occupants and fuel tank with the hot cell assemblies. The battery is sealed, and does not vent any gasses on discharge or recharge. The individual cells nearly always fail in short circuit mode, which is not a hazard but in fact an advantage (Ref. 1, Cornu) because the battery pack as a whole will continue to operate normally even if an individual cell fails. The battery requires no regular maintenance beyond the previously-discussed thermal management.

Lead/Acid Backup Battery System - The most widely-used battery in electric vehicles today is the lead/acid battery. It has proven to be reliable and inexpensive, with many different sizes and voltages to choose from. Being modular, lead/acid batteries can be connected in series or parallel to provide a wide range of voltage and capacity combinations, while still displaying versatility for placement into a vehicle. It was this versatility and low cost that persuaded the Paradigm team to select a lead/acid system as the "contingency" battery for the HEV Challenge.

Team Paradigm's back-up battery pack consists of 31 12-Volt UPS 12-95 modules donated by Johnson Controls, Inc. of Milwaukee, WI. The total battery pack weight is approximately 920 pounds. The battery pack has an open circuit voltage of 394 volts DC when fully charged (2.12 volts per cell) and a rated energy storage capacity of 9.8 kWh at a three-hour discharge rate. Johnson Control's in-lab testing results indicate that the UPS 12-95 system is capable of 300 cycles to 80% depth of discharge at a five-hour discharge rate.

THE ENGINE - On any vehicle, the average power demand (or energy consumption) of the drivetrain is considerably lower than the peak power demand. At cruising speeds, the drag force on the vehicle is mainly due to aerodynamic drag. The average power consumption of a moving vehicle is given by:

$$P = v\left(C_d \cdot A_f \cdot \frac{1}{2}\rho v^2 + W \cdot Cr\right)$$

where:
- v = vehicle velocity (ft/sec)
- C_d = vehicle body drag coefficient
- A_f = projected frontal area of the vehicle
- ρ = the density of air
- W = the vehicle weight
- C_r = coefficient of rolling resistance

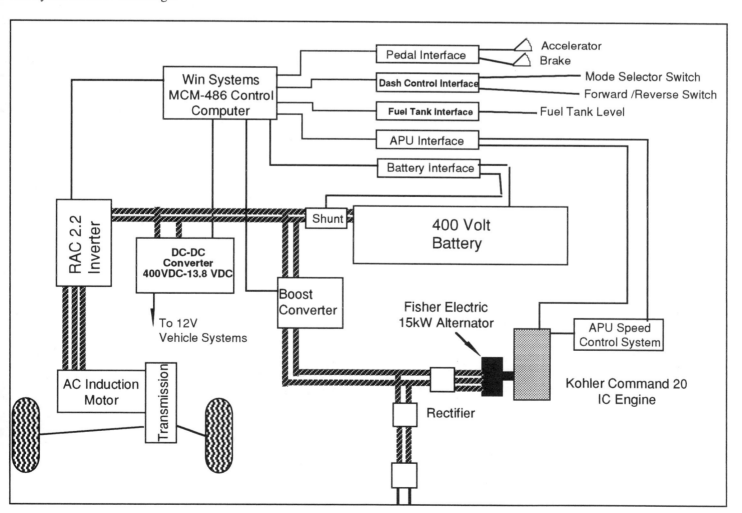

Figure 2. The Team Paradigm series drivetrain schematic.

313

Only 14 HP is required to maintain a 50 MPH cruise speed. Although far greater power is required to provide adequate acceleration, the <u>average</u> energy drain on the powertrain at cruising speed will generally be less than 16 HP. The engine in Paradigm's series-configuration drivetrain is operated so as to produce only slightly more power than the vehicle consumes when cruising at a steady speed. The vehicle draws the power needed for acceleration from the main battery pack, even when the engine is running and set up to charge the battery. On a time-averaged basis, the power put out by the engine slowly charges the battery pack.

The *Paradigm HEV*'s engine is a Kohler Command 20, manufactured by the Kohler Corporation of Kohler, WI. This overhead-valve, 624cc V-twin engine is typically used in garden tractors and engine generator sets. It was selected over comparable engines from Briggs & Stratton, Kawasaki, and others on the basis of:

- the engine's overhead valve, compact V-twin design
- the availability of technical support from Kohler
- the availability of financial support from Kohler
- Kohler's Wisconsin-based location and work-force
- Kohler's UW alumni contacts

The Command 20 has been modified to burn M85 fuel (85% methanol, 15% unleaded gasoline) with the installation of a sequential-port electronic fuel injection system, a modified version of the 1300 series EFI system manufactured by Pacer Industries of St. Louis, MO. This software-controlled system allows us to change fuel injection and spark advance maps to maximize engine performance and efficiency.

THE ALTERNATOR - A 15 kW, 310 V three-phase AC alternator manufactured by Fisher Electric Motor Technology Inc. of St. Petersburg, FL is attached to the output shaft of the engine to convert its mechanical output into electrical energy. The alternator has a permanent magnet design and provides a peak efficiency of 94%.

The alternator mounts directly to the engine; the stator mounts directly to the engine case, with the rotor mounted directly to the output shaft of the engine. Since under-hood space was at a premium, rare earth (neodymium) magnets were used to reduce the alternator's size and weight. The entire engine/alternator unit is located under the hood of the Paradigm HEV, in front of the electric motor and transmission. This location allows for effective cooling of both the alternator and the engine.

THE POWER ELECTRONICS - Power Electronics are used in the extensively in an HEV to control tractive effort, on-board generation of electricity, and battery charging. The *Paradigm HEV* utilizes two major power electronic control devices: a torque-controlled AC motor drive and a boost converter. Smooth control of the vehicle's acceleration and regenerative braking is achieved using a power electronic motor drive. The traction load of the engine is decoupled from the alternator load using the boost converter. By utilizing the ability of these converters to rapidly control power flow, it is possible to increase efficiency and reduce engine emissions.

Paradigm's motor drive system, a modified Rexroth-Indramat RAC 2.2 industrial torque-controlled inverter, converts the battery system's DC power into the AC power required to run the motor. This drive uses a flux vector torque control scheme, which avoids the jerking phenomenon known as "cogging ." The drive is rated for 100 HP when using a 380 VAC input. It has been modified to accept 330 VDC power from the batteries, and in its current configuration can provide 74 HP and 90% peak electrical efficiency when connected to the battery.

For smooth natural operation under high accelerations, the precise control of torque is useful. With such a torque controlled drive, regenerative braking can be readily implemented up to the torque limits of the drive. High quality torque control is important at low speeds to ensure safe operation while parking and maneuvering the vehicle.

The boost converter is a current-regulating power supply, designed and built by the Paradigm team. This device is used to decouple the alternator load from the transient powertrain demands of the vehicle, allowing the engine to operate at a continuous load level and thus substantially reducing engine emissions. Fluctuations in battery voltage during regeneration and hard acceleration will not affect the engine load.

The boost converter serves a dual role as an on board intelligent charger when the car is parked. It accepts a DC input from the charge port and injects a controlled charging current into the battery.

THE ELECTRIC MOTOR - Paradigm's 220 VAC three-phase induction motor was manufactured by Electric Apparatus Co. of Howell, MI. Capable of providing 100 HP, this custom-built motor weighs only 214 pounds and provides a peak torque output of 102 ft-lbs. The motor has a maximum speed of 12,000 rpm and a base speed of 5000 rpm. Team Paradigm chose to utilize a high speed motor in order to obtain an improved power-to-weight ratio and also to allow single-speed transmission gearing.

For single speed operation, the motor must be able to work over a wide speed range. In choosing between AC or DC motors, field weakening operation became an important issue. Permanent DC motors can not be easily field weakened and are also structurally speed limited to around 9000 RPM. AC machines, on the other hand, have good controllability, a wide speed range, and good efficiency at high speeds. A two-pole AC induction motor design was chosen over a 4-pole design because of its higher efficiency and wider speed range in the field weakening region.

THE TRANSMISSION - The Paradigm HEV utilizes the original Escort transmission, but it has been rotated 90° such that the bell housing is now located above the driveshafts. This rotation was necessary in order to provide more room in the engine compartment for other components.

The first two speeds of the original 5-speed transmission are used. First gear provides high acceleration and performance, with a top speed of 65 MPH. Second gear provides high powertrain efficiency and a higher top speed.

Due to the transmission's new orientation and high speed, an oil distribution and external cooling system has been added. The system pumps oil to the high speed input shaft, thus supplying adequate gear lubrication, and uses an external electric gerotor pump and a 3" x 7" oil cooler to lower the oil temperature.

CONTROLLER STRATEGY

THE NEED FOR A CONTROLLER - A standard automobile utilizes two torque control interfaces: an accelerator and a brake pedal. The Paradigm Team wanted the same devices to provide torque control in our HEV, such that the *Paradigm HEV* would have the driving feel of a "regular" car. These specifications required special control electronics, due to the intricacies involved in achieving variable torque control of a three-phase induction motor.

CONTROLLERS USED - The *Paradigm HEV* uses two powerful computers to control its drivetrain and several other critical systems. The first is a Motorola 68000 microprocessor, integrated into the control electronics of the Indramat RAC 2.2 electric motor drive. It provides precision torque control for acceleration and regenerative braking. The second computer is an on-board 50 MHz Intel 80486-based MCM-486DX computer manufactured by WinSystems of Arlington, TX. The MCM-486 is used to monitor on-board systems, inform the driver of the vehicle's status, and provide top-level control of several systems. It oversees and pre-conditions the driver's brake and accelerator input to the motor drive, and is also the brains behind the engine's on-off strategy, the battery charging strategy, and the battery pack's thermal control system.

THE CONTROL STRATEGY - Paradigm's over-all vehicle control system was designed with efficiency, low emissions, practicality, and safety as primary objectives. It was desired that Paradigm HEV drive consistently and predictably, while the control system worked to provide high energy efficiency and minimize engine emissions.

BATTERY CHARGING - Using the boost converter as a charging unit allows implementation of computer-based current-controlled battery charging. The MCM-486 has been equipped with voltage and current sensors to monitor the battery pack's condition during routine operation; these same sensors allow the MCM-486 to be used as an intelligent charging unit, capable of following almost any charging strategy.

ENGINE SPEED, TORQUE, AND ON-OFF CONTROL Simple control schemes are used to control the engine's torque, speed, and ignition. Paradigm has three user-selectable operating modes:

- Zero Emission mode (ZEV)
  Electric only
- Hybrid Electric mode (HEV)
  Electric + Engine as needed
- Engine On (APU ON)
  Electric + Engine on full-time

In HEV mode, the MCM-486 computer monitors the battery's current and voltage output, and starts the engine when the battery's state of charge drops below a specified level. It turns the engine off again as the battery approaches its fully-charged capacity. When the engine is running, the MCM-486 analyzes the vehicle's powertrain output and selects an engine power level appropriate to the current driving conditions. The optimum engine torque and speed appropriate to this power level are set by sending a current command to the boost converter and a speed command to a Kohler speed control system on the engine.

In APU ON mode, the engine remains on regardless of the battery's state of charge. This mode is required for emissions testing in the HEV Challenge. In contrast, ZEV mode keeps the engine shut down regardless of battery's state of charge.

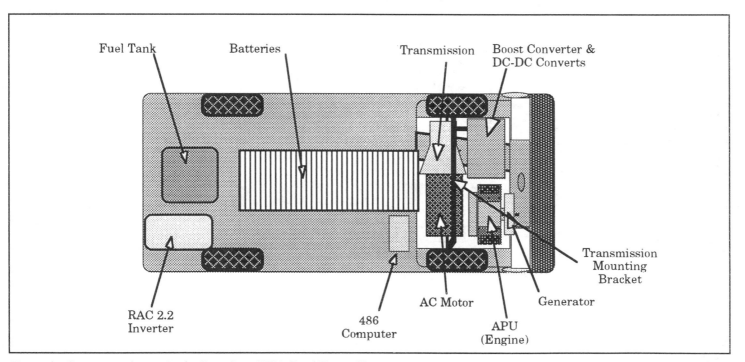

Figure 3. Component layout in the Paradigm HEV Ford Escort Wagon.

Paradigm HEV at a Glance

GENERAL
Frame Type
1992 Ford Escort Wagon LX
Weight
3650 Lb.
Tires
Goodyear Invecta P185 70R13
Chassis Material
Steel
Fuel Type
M85 (85% Methanol, 15% Reformulated Gasoline), 12 Gallon Capacity
Wheelbase
98.4"
Track Width
56.5"

HEV Strategy
Series Configuration, Single Drive Motor, Power from Battery or APU APU - Engine / Generator Set
Braking system
Electric Regeneration Braking with Hydraulic Assist

APU
Engine
Model / Manufacturer
Kohler Command 20, Kohler Corp. Kohler, WI
Engine Type
624CC, V-Twin, Overhead Valve w/ Hydraulic Lifters
Fuel type
M85 - 85% Methanol, 15% Reformulated Gasoline
Fuel Delivery
Sequential port electronic fuel injection.
Power Output
15 kW (20 hp)
Fuel consumption
N/A
Cooling
Forced Air
Weight
92 lb.

Generator
Model / Manufacturer
Fisher Electric Motor Technology, St. Petersburg, FL
Construction
Permanent Magnet AC Alternator
Output voltage
310 VAC at 3000 RPM
Power Rating
15 kW

Magnets/ excitation
Neodymium Permanent Magnet
Weight
26 Lb

DRIVELINE
Electric Motor
Model / Manufacturer
UW - 1, Electric Apparatus Co., Howell, MI
Motor type
3-phase, AC Induction, 2 pole, low leakage inductance for wide speed range
Speed Rating
Maximum speed: 12,000 rpm
Base Speed: 5,800 rpm
Voltage
220 VAC, 3 - phase
Power Rating
Continuous: 37.3 kW (50 hp)
Peak: 74.5 kW (100 hp)
Torque Rating
102 Ft.-Lb
Weight
214 lb
Cooling
Liquid Cooling, 50% water, 50% Ethylene Glycol, 5 gal/minute
Power consumption
Cooling fan and Pump consume 200 W
Surface area
Radiator provides over 50 M^2 of surface area
Pump type
Impeller

Transmission
Model / Manufacturer
1992 Ford Escort
Type
5-speed manual, Modified to accommodate Electric motor
Weight
74 lb
Lubrication
External Dry Sump with Oil cooling

BATTERY
Model / Manufacturer
UW HEV -1, Manufacturer *Wishes to remain anonymous*
Construction
LiAl-FeS2 (Lithium Aluminum - Ferric Disulfide)
Number of Modules
N/A
Module Voltage
N/A

Energy Capacity
20kWh
Open Circuit voltage
398 VDC
Weight
500 lb
Cycle Endurance
1000 cycles @ 80% DOD

POWER ELECTRONICS
Model / Manufacturer
RAC 2.2, Rexroth Indramat
Construction
Bipolar Transistor
Control Scheme
Vector Flux Torque Control
Max Current rating
172 Amperes
Switching Frequency
1.8 kHz
Power Rating
55.6 kW
Output voltage
220 VAC, 3 - phase
Weight
100 Lb.

CONTROL COMPUTER
Model / Manufacturer
MCM-486, Win-Systems
Operating System
QNX 2.4, Quantum Software
Items controlled
APU on / off strategy, pedal - inverter interface, driver feedback systems

PERFORMANCE
0-50 MPH
N/A
Top Speed
70 MPH (Estimated)
Braking Strategy
Series Regeneration with Hydraulic assist . First 2 inches of pedal travel to control regeneration, remaining pedal travel allows for hydraulic braking system (unmodified stock Escort braking system)
Zero Emission (ZEV) Range
60 miles
Hybrid (HEV) Range
210
Fuel Economy
13.3 MPG

USER CONTROL INTERFACES - Dash-mounted switches allow Paradigm's driver to "shift" the vehicle between forward, reverse, and neutral and to select the vehicle's operating strategy (ZEV, HEV, or APU ON). Both of these switches are monitored and acted on by the MCM-486. A large panic button on the dash may be used to disconnect the main battery pack in an emergency.

THE ACCELERATOR AND BRAKE INTERFACE - The Escort's original accelerator and brake pedals have been modified to send torque commands to the RAC 2.2's drive electronics via the MCM-486 with the addition of a linear potentiometer to each pedal. The free travel of the brake pedal was increased, such that the first two inches of brake pedal travel provide pure regenerative braking. After the first two inches, the hydraulic and regenerative brakes work in parallel, and full hydraulic braking power is still available. Routing these signals through the 486 allows for adjustment of the pedal interface gains, as well as implementation of the logic required for reverse "gear", safety overrides, and reverse torque cut-off near zero speed.

EMISSION CONTROL STRATEGY

TAILPIPE EMISSIONS - The engine's non-transient operation allows for reduced emissions because the fuel injection system may be run under closed loop air-fuel mixture control. Pollutant concentrations are directly related to the air-fuel ratio. Therefore, maintaining a nearly stoichiometric air-fuel ratio minimizes pollutant concentrations. (Ref. 2, Bosch)

A 3-way catalyst was chosen for the exhaust system. The PTX-4, manufactured by Englehard Industries of Iselin, NJ, is specially designed for low sulfur fuel such as M85.

Implementation of other pollution control strategies, in particular exhaust gas recirculation (EGR), was not feasible due to development time constraints and the number of modifications needed to adapt such systems to work with the Kohler Command 20.

EVAPORATIVE EMISSIONS - Evaporative emission control will be used on this vehicle. The original activated charcoal canister from the Escort will be used to lower evaporative emissions from the fuel tank. Positive crankcase ventilation is also being used to lower these evaporative emissions.

CHOICE OF FUEL - M85 was chosen as the fossil fuel source primarily for its favorable emissions characteristics. Relative to reformulated gasoline, M85 generally provides equal CO, NOx, and NMOG emissions. However, M85 has a reduced Reactivity Adjustment Factor (RAF). The RAF is an adjustment of the fuel's mass NMOG (non-methane organic gas) emissions. The factor is based on the ozone-forming potential and mass of the emissions constituents. Gasoline has an RAF of 1.0, wheras M85 has an RAF of 0.41. This lower RAF favors the use of M85 in the contest.

FUEL AND ELECTRICAL POWER CONSUMPTION

Currently only estimates are available for fuel and electrical power consumption. Models of the *Paradigm HEV* indicate that the vehicle will require approximately 6.7 kW to maintain

40 MPH. The following efficiencies were used to estimate the range of the *Paradigm HEV*:

Battery efficiency:	80%
Inverter efficiency:	85%
APU Efficiency:	21%

From these efficiencies, we estimate a range of about 60 miles in ZEV, 210 miles in HEV.

VEHICLE STRUCTURE AND DESIGN MODIFICATIONS

BATTERY LOCATION - As is with most electric cars, the hybrid electric vehicle has a large battery weight burden. Not only do the batteries have high weight, they also take up a considerable amount of space. The batteries must be placed in the vehicle along with the electric motor, IC engine, and many other systems. The batteries must be safely placed in the vehicle, while still providing room for the driver, passengers, and cargo. All the space found in the vehicle is valuable.

There are several different configurations to hold a large amount of batteries. The Ford Escort Wagon has a cargo area in back as well as a back seat area. Batteries could be placed in these areas with little or nothing done to the structure of the vehicle. However, vehicle handling would be compromised due to the extra weight in the rear of the vehicle.

The original front-rear weight bias of the Ford Escort was 59% front, 41% rear. This is advantageous for a front-wheel drive vehicle, such as the Escort, because weight in the front provides traction on the front driving wheels. It gives the steering a good "feel" and also provides for better braking, since during braking, greater force is present on the front wheels.

Placing the batteries in the back seat and cargo areas would have placed a large load on the rear of the vehicle, changing the front-rear weight bias to 50% front, 50% rear, or worse. For a front-wheel drive car, this would create reduced understeer thus causing the steering to be unresponsive (and perhaps dangerous).

The *Paradigm HEV* has its batteries running along the centerline of the car, spanning from the front drive suspension sub-assembly to the rear axle suspension sub-assembly. This keeps the front-rear weight bias as close to the original weight bias as possible as well as keeping the center of gravity low. This also leaves the rear seat and cargo area free from batteries, providing plenty of space for equipment and extra passengers. Figure 3 illustrates the position of the batteries in the vehicle.

THE BATTERY CASE - The function of the battery case is to provide adequate protection of the batteries, using a minimal amount of internal space in the car. Secondary functions of the battery case include providing added structural rigidity to the car, protecting the passenger compartment from the high voltage of the batteries, and adequately supporting the battery weight.

A rectangular section of the floor of the car was removed, equidistant from the centerline of the vehicle. This hole, measuring 15 by 80 inches, spans from the firewall to the rear axle. In its place is a large, 16-guage sheet metal cover, 18 inches in height. This is welded to the floor and reinforced with sheet metal ribs on the underside. This provides a cover for the battery tray and replaces the floor that has been removed, adding stiffness to the overall cross-sectional shape of the chassis.

The battery tray itself is constructed from 6061-T6 aluminum angle. This material provides high strength at reduced weight over a comparable tray made of structural steel angle. There are two layers of batteries, with 20 batteries in the bottom tray and 11 on the top tray. These batteries are protected from the elements by a large, removable polypropylene cover. The polypropylene provides toughness and has a high heat distortion temperature, so it will not deform under discharge temperatures. The batteries are secured in place with flat braided nylon straps, holding the batteries securely in place in the event of a roll-over.

To give the battery tray adequate strength as well as provide for torsional rigidity, A36 structural steel was selected for the main supports. It is tough, inexpensive, easily welded, and readily available. The aluminum battery tray is bolted to the main structural steel members. Cross members on the main structural beams run lengthwise under the chassis and are bolted in four positions to the underside of the vehicle. The front structural member bolts through a main structural box section and through the vehicle floor. Reinforcing steel sheets provide extra strength on the top of the floor where the battery case is bolted. The rear structural member bolts to an extension of the same structural box section just in front of the rear trailing arm mounts.

GAS TANK - The fuel container used in the Paradigm HEV is a racing-type fuel cell manufactured by Aero Tec Laboratories of Ramsey, NJ. The cell consists of a molded, seamless, plastic bladder placed in a custom-built steel container located in the rear of the vehicle. This puncture-resistant fuel cell is also equipped with a foam baffling and a filler safety check valve.

The fuel cell is located in the former spare tire well. The well was modified to allow for the cell's installation, and a sheet metal cover isolates the tank from the passenger compartment.

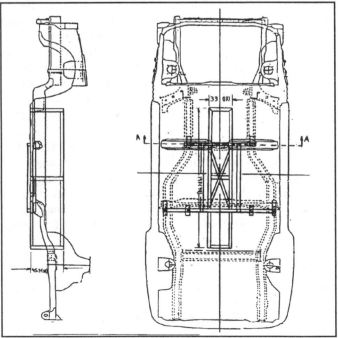

Figure 4. Battery location Schematic

The close proximity of the fuel tank to the rear of the vehicle has been of significant concern to the Team. To alleviate the hazard posed by a rear-end collision, a crush zone has been established to help absorb impact energy, consisting an aluminum honeycomb matrix located between the rear bumper and the fuel cell.

ROLL BAR - Under normal circumstances, the Escort pillar system can support the weight of its structure if its cargo contents are not securely fastened to the chassis. With the additional weight of the batteries secured to this vehicle, a roll bar was added to provide structural support for the vehicle in case of roll-over, protecting the passengers from failure of the existing pillar system.

The roll bar also provides extra torsional stiffness to the vehicle chassis. The chassis stiffness is lost due to the installation of the batteries in the floor of the vehicle. The frame bolts to the chassis in four positions. The rear mounts are located on the rear strut towers. The front mounts are on the floor just behind the front seats. This front mount was placed as close as possible to the floor frame rail without compromising the strength of the frame rail.

POWERTRAIN STRUCTURAL CHANGES - The original stock engine and its major subsystems systems; i.e. ignition electronics, fuel delivery system, cooling system and computer control, were removed from the car, leaving only the original transmission. The design of the coupling between the motor and transmission was designed to be permanent. Gears for forward and reverse are not needed because all that is required to shift into these modes is to reverse the flow of electricity into the motor. The clutch pedal was also removed from the car.

POWER SWITCH - The power from the batteries to the drive motor flows through a 400 Amp DC-rated circuit breaker mounted in the engine compartment. A hole was cut through the firewall to allow the switch to be trigerred from inside the passenger compartment in order to provide emergency manual cut-off of the battery.

SEAT BELTS - As stipulated in the HEV Challenge rules, a 5-point racing harness was installed for the driver and front passenger. The two rear seatbelts were kept as originally manufactured.

SUSPENSION MODIFICATIONS

Due to added weight of the batteries, the *Paradigm HEV's* curb weight exceeds 3200 lb. After adding passengers and cargo, the gross vehicle weight is in excess of 3600 lb. This is 150 lb. greater than the rated GVW of 3466 lb.

The greatest problem with this added weight is the accompanying reduction in vehicle stability. The Paradigm HEV Team's response to this problem was to add stiffer springs to the front and rear suspensions. The added suspension stiffness will help the *Paradigm HEV's* handling.

CHOICE OF MATERIALS

The materials chosen for the Paradigm HEV were selected on the basis of cost and availability. One of the Intentions of the HEV Challenge was to produce a practical vehicle. This practical approach limited the use of exotic materials, such as composites, in the construction of the vehicle.

The following is a list of basic materials used in the construction of the vehicle:

- Steel: Battery cover,
             Fuel tank cover
             Driveline mounting
             Seats
- 6061 T6 Aluminum:
             Battery tray
- 3003 Aluminum:
             Engine Intake manifold components
- High density Polyethylene tubing:
             Fuel line
- Aluminum Honeycomb:
             Crush Zone
- Polypropylene:
             Battery terminal covers
             Waterproof cases for:
                     Boost converter
                     Main battery switch
- Copper
             Battery bus bars

MANUFACTURABILITY

The figure of merit used in determining manufacturability was that the chosen components chose should have a demonstrated history of volume manufacturing. The industrial three-phase AC vector flux dased drive system used in this vehicle is a well-established industrial product. It is much simpler to construct than an inverter using massively paralleled MOSFET's, each of which must be individually matched.

The AC induction motor has a long history of volume manufacturing and reliable operation in harsh environments. The DC machines considered be the team required permanent magnets costing around $80 per pound, which would be difficult to reliably mount in the large rotors required for high horsepower machines.

The chassis modifications needed to produce this Escort HEV version can easily be incorporated into the manufacturing process. The following areas would be need to be added or modified for its assembly: the battery box, engine compartment, fuel tank, inverter mounts, electrical displays, and added control buttons.

BATTERY BOX - For future vehicle development, the main battery box would most likely be made either from stamped sheet steel or of a recyclable plastic composite. Due to the limited manufacturing resources available here at the University, the battery box was produced by spot welding steel sheet metal. The box is welded directly to the center forward part of the car's frame without the bottom side. The bottom side of the box is modified with steel tubing and is designed to hold the weight of the batteries. The bottom mounts directly to the car's body.

Construction of the battery case would best be accomplished in two pieces, the main battery box and the bottom battery sled. The main battery box would best be produced through stamping operation in the same manner that the bottom of the car's chassis was produced. This would be more economical and time efficient than by welding the sides together. This main battery case would be directly welded to the car's frame when the body is being welded together. For appearance and safety, the battery case would be covered with either a plastic vinyl sheet or carpeting similar to the car's interior.

The bottom of the battery case would be constructed with a large sheet of steel with a tubular steel structure to mount and support the weight of the batteries. This would bolt directly into the car's frame on its underside.

ENGINE COMPARTMENT - The engine compartment would only include the original transmission and would required the addition of an APU, electric motor and the respected mounts.

The electric motor is located between the car's engine fire wall and the APU unit. The motor consist of mounts, main motor with outside water cooled jacket and external radiator. The three mounts for the motor are attached directly to the car's frame and would be attached during the main body welding for the car. The motor and radiator would be attached after the transmission and before the addition of the APU.

Mounts for the APU would consist of two steel tubes mounted to the front and rear engine compartment. Two L-shape steel beams with two holes drilled on one side are fitted over the steel tubes and are able to be adjusted from the front to rear of the engine compartment on the front left side. The mounts would best be added when the car's body is being welded together.

The APU rest on the mounts in an upright position. This allow easy placement of the engine from the top of the engine compartment. Gas lines enter under the original cars designs. A electrical generator is added to the front of the engines shaft located about where the original engine's radiator. The electrical output wires feed through the underside of the car to the inverter located in the trunk.

FUEL TANK - In the manufacturing of the fuel tank, it would best fit between the original tire storage compartment and battery box under the car. Their would have to be some design modifications made in the existing tire storage compartment but the basic manufacturing operations would be the same.

STRUCTURAL ADDITION - For safety during the contest, an roll bar was a required to be installed in the car. If it is determined that the existing weight of the car with battery can support the top of the car in event of a roll over, than the addition of a roll bar would not be needed. If a roll bar is needed, it could be assembled by bending and adding mounts to a large steel tube mounted directly to the car's frame. Assembly of the roll bar would happen in the main welding of the car body before addition of the roof.

ELECTRONICS DISPLAYS - Because of the nature of this prototype car, their were numerous sensors required the monitor different systems condition. An LED screen and 486 computer was required to monitor these systems.

The screen for these system was added the dash just right of the console and the 486 unit was placed in the glove box. In a final production version of the car, the LED would be placed in the original console and the 486 placed under the passenger's seat. Placing of the LED screen would be feasible because a majority of the original monitoring sensors would not be needed for the new car production and hence the screen size would be minimal. Their are two reasons the original computer was placed in the glove box, these are due to the size of the test system and the need to have good accessibility to the unit for repair and modifications. The size of the unit could be reduced significantly in future models allowing for its placement under the passenger's seat. The unit would be installed at the same time the wire harness is added to the car.

INVERTER- The inverter was placed in the rear of the car due to its size and the desire to simplify weatherproofing of the unit. This allows for good maintenance for servicing and in installing in the car during manufacturability. The main unit was made from a modified unit bought off the shelf.

ERGONOMICS

DASH DISPLAY - The dash display will not change in location or design but a addition 8"x5.5" back lit black and white LED will be added on the dash between the driver and passenger. Operating parameters need in testing the car are to be displayed there.

DASH CONTROLS - Most of the existing controls in the car were left alone except for the addition of a mode selector button, shifting, main power shut off(battery) and fire suppression system .

The mode selection button consist a simple rotary dial switch with four possible choices. The position of the wording is placed directly above the need position for the switch. No pictorial icons were used in order to allow the driver a clear understanding of the exact function of its position. In future modifications, these wording need to be back lit for easy viewing at night. The location is placed on the right side of the steering wheel which allows for easy viewing by the driver and for its operations. The switch is designed so that the driver only has to rotate its position and not have to perform any other operation in changing modes.

Shifting of the car is accomplished by an electrical actuator attached at the transmission to the shift lever. A forward-neutral-reverse switch is mounted on the dash to allow easy visibility and driver accessibility. The 486 computer acts as a watchdog and locks out a direction reversal when the car is moving.

The main fire suppression system control is located on top of the battery box between the driver and passenger 5 inches from the dash. The system is manually operated to ensure that it works even when the car is not in operation or in the event of a power failure. It is also located between the front seat so that the passenger can operate it during the contest if the driver is busy controlling the car or is unable to operate the system. The handle is made up of and red T-shape and is clearly market fire suppression system.

CONTROLS DISPLAY - Due to the number of different subsystems needed to be monitored by the driver and passenger during the contest, a back-lit LCD screen was added. The system is designed to display information quickly and accurately. The screen allows the system designer the flexibility to add or remove needed information as required by the driver for a particular event. The screen also enables viewing at night.

WARNINGS - Warnings of problem systems will be done

two ways, audio and visual. Their will be three different levels for audio signals: one, two and three beeps. The number and duration of beeps increase as the severity of the problem increases. The one beep will be for situations in which a reading is about to enter a critical region. Once the reading enters a critical region, two beeps lasting one second will occur. For systems about to fail, one long beep lasting 1 second out of every 3 sec. will be initiated. Visual signal will be displayed on the LED screen and with red lights on the original dash. The display reading will blink with the lettering alternating black and white. Addition red lights will be installed in the original dash to warn the driver of critical systems.

HEATING SYSTEM - The original heating element was removed from the car and was replaced with a gas heater system. The reason a gas heating system was installed is due to the large electrical draw that is required with the existing and similar type systems. The car lacked air conditioning when we received it and will not have a system installed. The original ductwork was removed and new heating ducts were added to allow for window de-frosting.

ACCELERATOR & BRAKE PEDAL - The accelerator & brake pedals have been placed left of their original position because of the battery box and the seats being moved to accommodate it. This helps keep the alignment of the drivers right leg straight with the pedal. The size and movement of the pedals are the same as the original.

SEATS- The front seats were cut down 2.5 in. in their breadth because of the battery box. For future car production, either the car's width will have to be increased and the battery box decreased in the width. This provides a problem for the driver because he is no longer center with the steering wheel. The floor petals have been adjusted to still be center with the drivers legs. The forward and backward movement and tilt control of the front seats were maintained for the front passenger and driver.

Due to the width of the battery case, the front seats were narrowed and remounted. The back seats had a 14.5" X 8" section moved from the center of the seat. The front seats were narrowed by 2.5" to accommodate the battery case. The seat frames were cut and then welded back together and the cloth seats were tailored to fit the new seats.

PARKING BRAKE -The location of the parking brake has been moved the floor behind the driver's feet. The location still allows for the driver to apply good upward pressure to activate the system. A disadvantage with its position is that is does not allow for good visibility by the driver during operations of the car.

OTHER ISSUES -

Light - The lighting system was not modified for either the outside or inside interior for the car.

Noise - The car is expected to operate at levels less than the 100 dB limit required for the HEV Challenge.

REFERENCES

1. Cornu, J. P., et al, "Electric Vehicle Battery Options: Present and Future," SAFT Research Literature, 1990, page 5.
2. Bosch, Robert, Automotive Electric / Electronic Systems, Robert Bosch, 1988.

West Virginia University

Parviz Famouri and Chris Atkinson
West Virginia University

ABSTRACT

This paper presents the design and specifications of West Virginia University's (WVU) entry in the Hybrid Electric Vehicle (HEV) Challenge that was held in Dearborn, Michigan from June 1 - 5,1993. Several major criteria were considered in designing the vehicle. The vehicle is readily manufacturable in the short term and has a practical, low cost design. Environmental issues played an important role in the design, namely in the choice of batteries and in the design of the auxiliary power unit. This paper also includes a brief summary of the vehicle performance and WVU's team experiences at the competition.

INTRODUCTION

The Ford Motor Company developed the HEV Challenge to ignite student interests in current environmental issues, namely air pollution. Today's automobiles have created a significant air pollution problem in metropolitan areas. Thirty colleges and universities from across the United States were chosen to compete in the competition. All schools were asked to develop an HEV that meets or exceeds the requirements associated with the challenge. Teams had the option of converting a 1992 Ford Escort Station Wagon or building a vehicle from the ground up.

WVU chose to convert a Ford Escort Wagon. Our vehicle has an electric motor drive system as a main power source and incorporates an alternator driven by an internal combustion (IC) engine as a supplemental energy source (see Figure 1 in Appendix A). This vehicle is capable of operating in zero emissions mode (ZEV), which utilizes only battery power, for operation within city limits. Outside city limits, the vehicle uses the hybrid mode to extend its range.

POWER TRAIN

CONFIGURATION - This design utilizes a series hybrid configuration. A diagram detailing all power connections of the vehicle is shown in Appendix A (Figure 2). While a true series hybrid has the auxiliary power unit (APU), batteries, and the motor connected as a "linear" string of components, hybrid series has the APU directly connected to both the batteries and the electric motor. This differs from the usual series configuration as well as from a parallel configuration where the IC engine and motor are separately coupled to the transmission, or the wheels.

The disadvantages of a series configuration are a relatively poor efficiency and power to weight ratio. However, the advantages include being able to attain the maximum efficiency with the lowest emissions for the IC engine. Also, the series configuration minimizes the number of mechanical connections and hence mechanical losses.

The IC engine was designed to produce a constant 18 kW output at 3200 rpm. The engine is close-coupled to a 3 phase AC generator, the output of which is connected to a rectifier to convert the alternating current to a direct current. A computer keeps the APU output power constant by controlling the power flow to or from the batteries in HEV mode.

BATTERY SELECTION - The main factors taken into consideration when the battery selection was made were weight, cost, energy storage, environmental impact, safety, and recyclability. The two main categories of batteries considered were nickel cadmium batteries and lead acid batteries.

Five batteries were selected for final overall consideration, four lead acid and one nickel cadmium. A battery comparison is shown in Appendix B (Table 1).

Based on Table 1, the Optima 800 battery provided the maximum voltage and energy storage available for the lowest cost, making it the obvious choice. The manufacturer's specification states that the Optima can withstand vibrations at 4 g's (33 Hz) (for over twelve hours) and at 6 g's (for four hours), making it one of the best batteries for the heavy duty application of the HEV Challenge.

From environmental perspective, the spiral wound Optima battery has the ability to undergo 1300 charge-discharge cycles as compared to approximately 400 life cycles of most other lead-acids, ensuring three times the life between replacements. These batteries can be recycled using the existing industrial infrastructure for recycling lead acid batteries in the United States.

From the safety perspective, the Optima 800 has a sealed-gel cell construction with absorbed electrolytes that need no water and will not corrode or leak under normal use. Hazards involved in charging have been minimized due to a forced air circulation system within the battery compartment. The combination of materials provide quicker charge acceptance and less sulfating of the terminals. This unique construction allows for discharge at high current without damage and a greater resistance to damage caused by electrical accessory drainage. The Optima can withstand low temperatures due to air spaces in the separator that allow for water to expand safely without damaging the battery.

WVU's battery configuration consists of three parallel strings of eight batteries per string. Since each battery supplies 12 V, a total of 96 V is obtained from 24 batteries.

MOTOR SELECTION - The vehicle was calculated to require approximately 5 - 8 kW of power to operate at a steady 45 mph, depending on aerodynamic factors, small variations in road grade, rolling resistance and internal mechanical losses. Up to 40 kW of power would be required to achieve acceptable acceleration for short periods of time. This required an electric traction motor with relatively high transient peak power compared to continuous or long term maximum power. These considerations along with our general philosophy of producing a high reliable, readily manufacturable and low cost vehicle, prompted us to specify a series-wound DC motor of 14 kW continuous and 51 kW peak power rating at 120 V DC and approximately 40 kW at 96 V DC. This motor, from Advanced DC, has the advantage of low cost and high reliability with a weight and efficiency penalty (compared to an AC induction motor for example). This motor has a relatively similar speed range (0 - 3600 rpm) to the original Ford Escort engine (0 - 5500 rpm), making the use of the existing transmission both feasible and practical.

ALTERNATOR SELECTION - The alternator selected for the vehicle is a custom-made Permanent Magnet Synchronous (brushless) Alternator from Fisher Electric Motor Technology, Inc. The alternator is constructed of a rare earth type permanent magnet with a high coercive force which allows for a high efficiency and a high power to weight ratio. The alternator has a power output of 18 kW with an efficiency of approximately 91-95%. Weighing 16.3 kg, the alternator is equipped with 106 volt and 145 volt taps. The voltage regulation for the alternator, determined by taking the difference between the no-load voltage and the full load voltage and dividing it by the no-load voltage, is 27.5%.

ENGINE SELECTION - The criteria for selecting the IC engine for the APU were based on four main factors. The team wanted an engine that was efficient, produced low emissions, had a good power to weight ratio and a reasonable cost. Four types of engines were analyzed based on these criteria. These were 2-cycle piston, 4-cycle piston, rotary, and turbine engines.

It was found that the 2-cycle and rotary engines produced greater exhaust emissions than the other engine types considered. It was also found that small gas turbines were much too costly. Therefore it was concluded that the choice would be a 4-cycle gasoline engine to be converted to run on M85 fuel.

The 4-cycle engine chosen was the motorcycle derivative small utility engine Kawasaki FD620D. The FD620D was chosen because it was the most efficient (being a recent design) and the lightest of all the engines looked into and its cost was very reasonable.

TRANSMISSION ADAPTER PLATE - One of the most important decisions made in the design of the conversion of the Ford Escort to a hybrid electric vehicle was the decision to use the existing Ford transmission in combination with the electric motor to drive the front wheels of the car. In order to match these two components, it was necessary to design an

adapter plate to connect the two. This was achieved by taking two, 2.5 cm thick aluminum plates and designing one to fit on the transmission and the other one to fit on the electric motor. Then the remaining sides of the two plates were milled to mesh together with one another. Finally, the plates were mounted to each of the components, meshed and bolted together to complete the adaptation of the existing transmission and the electric motor.

CONTROLLER

CONTROLLER SETUP - There are two controllers being used; a Power Flow Controller (PFC) and a motor controller. The PFC receives electrical power from both the batteries and the APU for delivery to the motor controller, through which the driver controls the DC motor.

The present controller setup is a load leveling configuration and allows for trickle charging of the batteries in the hybrid mode if the power required by the motor is less than the power produced by the APU. Tests have been run to examine this load leveling effect. A simulated APU was run at 15 kW with the electric motor using only 10 kW of power. The other 5 kW of power went to charge the batteries. A test was also performed with only 5 kW power coming from the APU and an extra required 5 kW was drawn from the batteries, resulting in a combined 10 kW power flow to the motor.

POWER FLOW CONTROLLER - The PFC is the heart of the Hybrid Electric Vehicle. It controls the magnitude of power delivered to or from the batteries in the vehicle. There were two main factors for the basic design of the PFC.

The first is that the APU has to run at a constant rpm. This allows the IC engine to be optimized for best performance at the lowest emission levels. The PFC has the function of isolating the APU from changes in the load (the power demanded by the DC motor, which changes with driving conditions and driver demand). This is achieved by directing current out of (or into) the batteries to make up the deficit (or surplus) of power available from the APU. An IBM compatible computer controls the PFC to direct the power flow in the HEV mode.

The design of the PFC is a versatile, yet very complicated control strategy. The main unit in the PFC is the Pulse Modulated Controller Unit (PMC). This converts a DC power supply from the rectifiers on the APU into a pulse train by chopping the DC signal. The magnitude of the power delivered to the batteries is then controlled by the pulse width of the pulses in the train. As the pulse width increases, the average power diverted to the batteries increases.

The computer keeps a constant source into the PFC of 18 kW. This is done by reading the voltage and the current out of the APU to obtain the power.

ENGINE CONTROLLER - The IC engine originally had a carburetor but was converted to accommodate an electronic fuel injection system to improve combustion and therefore reduce emissions. The WVU engine employs a fully electronic controller for the injection of M85. The controller uses inputs from the manifold air pressure (MAP) sensor, coolant sensor (CLT), and an exhaust gas oxygen (EGO) sensor to determine the proper pulse width for the injectors under all operating conditions.

Once the engine is "warm" (65 °C), the controller goes into a closed loop feedback with the EGO directing changes in the injection system. The EGO is kept "off line" for the first twenty seconds or so of engine operation until it heats up.

VEHICLE STRUCTURE

Major modifications made to the vehicle structure included the construction of a heavy gauge battery box (see Figure 3 in Appendix A) capable of containing 450 kg of batteries, the addition of a roll bar for roll-over protection and the removal of the spare tire well for fuel tank relocation.

BATTERY BOX - The floor of the vehicle in the vicinity between the rear cross-member and the rear of the front seats, and in the middle of the two unibody supports was removed to accommodate the battery box. The existing middle cross-member of the vehicle was kept completely intact to keep the frame structurally sound. The only material removed was two sections of floor panel, and these were replaced by a heavy-duty high strength steel battery box. Two 0.32 cm x 2.54 cm x 5.08 cm steel C-channels were used as hangers running down from the rear cross member and across to the underneath of the intact floor below the front seats. The bottom of the battery box was kept at the same height as the floor of the vehicle. The floor of the battery box was constructed of 0.32 cm steel while the walls were of 16 gauge steel. The bottom of the box holds fifteen batteries, while the bracketing system, fabricated of 14 gauge aluminum, accommodates nine batteries on a second level. All of the batteries are held in place using a nylon webbing system to tie the batteries down. The lid of the battery box was fabricated of 16 gauge aluminum. The battery box also included four safety blowout discs that were designed to fail in the event of a pressure build up inside the box.

ROLL BAR INSERTION - Roll over occupant protection was achieved by a SCCA approved roll bar, manufactured by Autopower Industries. It consists of a single hoop with aft supports and cross braces, as shown in Figure 4 (Appendix A). The hoop mounts directly to the chassis rails behind the front seats, while the rear supports drop from the top of the hoop at an angle 55 degrees from the vertical and mount to the rear strut towers. Specifically designed cross braces were placed to avoid interference with the battery box and to provide adequate mounting for the five point harness. This design exceeds the specifications imposed by the HEV regulations.

The addition of the battery box and roll bar has, from the results of finite element modeling, considerably increased the structural integrity, rigidity and strength of the converted vehicle over the original.

CPU MOUNT - The CPU box was fabricated from aluminum sheet metal and is approximately 40 cm x 22 cm x 22 cm. The entire box weighs 11.3 kg and there are four mounts to support it and to control vibrations. The mounts are low cost Novibra Type M7A Rubber Cup Mount type. These mounts are specifically designed to isolate low frequency vibrations in all three planes. The Novibra Type was designed to give resilience for low loads and high deflections, and is very lightweight and easy to install.

For mounting the CPU, the top of the mounts are connected to each of the four corners of the CPU box. Each mount takes a minimum of 1.5 kg to cause a static deflection of 1.2 mm. The CPU is flush against the tire well and the fuel tank.

EMISSIONS CONTROL

EXHAUST SYSTEM - The exhaust system was designed to adhere to the environmental aspect of the competition regulations. The system is completely leak free and heat shielded for passenger safety. The exhaust system was rerouted to accommodate the addition of a battery box and fuel tank. A 3.8 cm diameter alloy pipe was used to allow for easy flexibility and all joints were welded to insure full containment of exhaust gas.

CATALYST - The existing three way catalyst could not be used due to the conversion from gasoline to M85. Instead, a flexible fuel catalytic converter was purchased from General Motors and installed with the exhaust system. A heated catalyst was considered, but because of cost constraints and time limitations, it was not considered feasible.

EVAPORATIVE EMISSIONS - The total emissions system in the production 1992 Escort consists of two separate systems: a rearward system which tapped vapor not yet in the fuel lines, and a forward system which controlled vapors in the engine compartment.

The rearward system consisted of piping that ran from the gas tank to a vapor collection tube that was located by the fuel filler. Vapor would leave the gas tank through its own separate line and be piped into the vapor tube where it condensed back to liquid. The liquid was then returned through a second line to the fuel tank.

The forward system consisted of a carbon canister and piping that was positioned between the fuel filter and the intake manifold. A solenoid in the line directed the flow of the vapor from the incoming fuel line to the carbon canister, where the vapor was filtered. When the car was started, a second solenoid opened on the outlet side of the carbon canister, injecting the vaporized fuel into the intake manifold. This volatilized fuel was then burned.

The standard evaporative emissions system was retained intact in the converted vehicle.

FUEL SYSTEM

The M85 fuel system consists of eight components that are essential to the engine's operation. This, in addition to certain engine modifications make up the basis for the total fuel conversion. The components of the system are the fuel tank, fuel pump, fuel filter, stainless steel fuel rail, two fuel injectors, an intake manifold, pressure regulator, and Teflon tubing fuel lines with stainless steel braiding. All components are M85 compatible.

FUEL CHOICE - The team chose to use M85 as the fuel source for the internal combustion engine for several reasons. First, methanol has a higher octane rating than reformulated gasoline (106 vs. 92) which allows for an increased compression ratio. Secondly, methanol has a higher latent heat of vaporization, high flame speed, and wide flammability limits which offer opportunities for increased thermal efficiency and engine performance.

FUEL TANK - A fuel tank had to be designed to be resistant to the corrosive nature of the M85 fuel used as well as light weight. The tank also had to be large enough to carry enough fuel to meet the HEV Competition criteria. The HEV criteria requires that the vehicle travel approximately four hours in hybrid mode. The amount of fuel required to travel this time with a calculated maximum injector flow rate of 1.95 gm/s is 28.12 kg of fuel. The amount of fuel required for this trip is approximately 37.9 Liters, which meets the competition criteria of minimum amount of fuel (19.8 liters).

The type of fuel tank used was the Aerotec Labs (ATL) Sports Cell. This tank has a volume of 45.4 liters, and dimensions of 51.4 cm x 44.8 cm x 24.0 cm. Structural modifications have been made to accommodate the fuel cell in what was the spare tire well of the original vehicle.

FUEL INJECTORS - The fuel injectors for this system were sized according to the mass flow rate consumption of the IC engine. For this Kawasaki 620 cc engine, the calculated mass flow rate of fuel required while operating at 3600 rpm is 1.44 gm/s. Because this calculation assumes the unrealistic complete mixture of fuel with the available air, the actual flow rate is somewhat higher. For this reason, it was decided to upgrade the flow rate of the injectors to 1.95 gm/s per injector. The injectors were designed by Kinsler and are of the peak and hold type with a low impedance. They have a peak current of 4 amps and require 1 amp to hold the injector open, while maintaining a resistance of 1 ohm. The injectors are static flow injectors that deliver a constant flow rate of 1.95 gm/s for a line pressure of 344.7 kPa. The injectors are pintle style that utilize double o-ring seals for greater performance and efficiency.

FUEL COMPONENTS - Selection of the fuel pump, fuel filter, and pressure regulator were crucial to the project because these components will see a lot of wear and tear from the highly corrosive M85. The governing criteria were based on the specifications of the IC engine.

The fuel pump, fuel filter, and pressure regulator were specifically designed for use with M85 and purchased from Kinsler Fuel Injection. The fuel filter has replaceable filter linings due to the corrosive nature of M85. The pressure regulator is designed to maintain a constant pressure of 344.7 kPa in the fuel line.

FUEL RAIL - The fuel rail acts as a fuel reservoir for the injectors. The size of the fuel rail is 15.24 cm long with a 15.9 mm inside diameter. The injector mounts were machined out of the same 15.9 mm stainless steel and welded to the custom intake manifold that was fabricated for this project. The fuel lines are constructed of Teflon, and have a stainless steel shield on the outside. The lines running from the fuel tank have a 11.1 mm inside diameter, and the lines running from the fuel rail to the injectors have a 9.5 mm inside diameter.

COOLING SYSTEM - The cooling system for the IC engine consists of an oil cooler (which is being used as a radiator) and a small DC electric fan. The cooling unit is rated for a 20 kW engine, and has the dimensions 3.81 cm x 13.34 cm x 38.1 cm. The fan is rated to cool up to a 2 liter engine and has a 26.2 cm diameter. Both components were purchased from Dunham Bush of Ontario, CA.

SUSPENSION

The suspension system on the original vehicle is a coil over strut arrangement and is used on all four corners of the vehicle. Since changes to the suspension have to be documented for safety, design efforts have been focused on redesigning the coil over strut system to support the added vehicle weight.

The original Escort model had a curb weight of 1090 kg with a weight distribution of 59/41 front to rear. The coil over strut arrangement had a spring constant of 15.2 kg/cm. The original length of the spring was 37.3 cm. The conversions to HEV have caused the weight of the vehicle to rise to 1730 kg, with a 50/50 weight distribution. Changes have been made to the chassis of the car, lowering the lowest point on the vehicle by an additional 5.1 cm.

These modifications caused the ride height of the rear of the vehicle to drop considerably to approximately 7.6 cm. To remedy this problem, a redesign of the rear springs was undertaken.

To simply change the spring constant to compensate for the additional weight was not an option, as the constant would rise to 35.7 kg/cm, creating an unacceptable ride. It was therefore decided that the spring constant should be increased slightly, and the physical dimensions of the spring changed.

A survey of aftermarket springs available for the Escort revealed that a spring constant of 24.1 kg/cm would allow for additional weight to be carried, while not drastically affecting ride quality. A spring of the standard length was found to be insufficient to correct the ride height deficiency.

A spring was then designed using the 24.1 kg/cm spring as a model. The result is a spring that has the same number of turns, wire thickness, and outer diameter, but different pitch. By adding 1 cm to the pitch, the height capabilities of the spring were enhanced, allowing for height rules to be satisfied as well as providing an acceptable ride. The total length of the new spring is 37.6 cm, and it should pass all applicable buckling tests adequately.

To reduce the amount of motion in the rear suspension, struts with a higher coefficient of dampening are being sought. Ideally, these struts will be slightly longer than those presently on the vehicle to compensate for the change in the free length of the spring.

The loading on the front suspension has not changed radically. Therefore, there have been no modifications made to this system.

VEHICLE MANUFACTURABILITY

One of WVU's goals was to design a vehicle that could go into production within a short period of time. To accomplish this goal WVU decided to modify the Ford Escort Wagon. The main components of the car removed during the modification were the engine, the rear seat, and the floor under the rear seat. These components were replaced by a DC motor, smaller IC engine, alternator (replacing the engine), and a battery box (replacing the rear seat and floor). The transmission, braking system, steering, and suspension system were kept largely intact and used in the modified vehicle.

Another major point of concern when examining the design of the vehicle for short term production was the cost. The majority of the conversion cost was due to a few components. These components include the IC engine, the DC motor, the power flow controllers, the alternator, and the battery pack. These components are available at a relatively fixed price with the exception of the battery pack. In the case of the batteries, the price varies depending on the type of battery chosen. There were many factors involved when choosing the batteries, but the one factor that swayed the overall decision to use lead acid batteries was their recyclability. Since the environment is the overall issue in this competition, it is only wise to use a battery that can be recycled. We believe that our design achieves the manufacturability goals set for the team.

INSTRUMENTATION

Many instrumentation changes have been made to the HEV. The dash instrument cluster has been upgraded to the Escort GT specification and other gauges have been added to the center console to monitor power flow and other electrical systems. Additional parameters are also monitored by the CPU.

The speedometer retains the original connection to the transmission. The fuel gauge displays the M85 fuel level. The analog temperature gauge monitors the IC engine coolant temperature, and the tachometer reads the electric motor speed using a diode-photo transistor setup.

Several other gauges are displayed on the middle console. A voltmeter measures the voltage across the battery pack. An ammeter displays current going into the batteries over time, and a state of charge meter displays power integrated over time going into or out of the batteries.

Several other system temperatures are monitored by the CPU: three thermocouples on the batteries, one on each of the PMC and motor controller, one on the alternator, and another on the IC engine. By utilizing and expanding the existing instrumentation we have allowed the driver and passenger complete monitoring of the HEV systems.

SUMMARY OF THE EVENT

The first day, qualifying event, went as the team anticipated. The vehicle was over weight by about 68 kg as expected. The alternatives were to accept over weight penalty points or to remove some batteries from the vehicle. The team decided on the later and one string of eight batteries was removed from the vehicle. The vehicle entered the competition approximately 72 kg below the allowable weight. The team's vehicle experienced a succession of frustrating APU malfunctions during the rest of the competition. These included the EGO sensor which was not M85 compatible and several computer software bugs which had not been discovered in limited prior testing. Apart from these minor problems, the rest of the vehicle subsystems performs as expected. At the competition the team received many compliments about the level of safety that they had designed into the vehicle.

CONCLUSION

Future plans are to optimized the performance of the APU, improve the vehicles system pakaging and under hood aesthetics, as well as incorporating many other minor changes.

WVU's Ford Escort Station Wagon met all the specifications and requirements of the 1993 HEV Challenge. Being a converted vehicle (as opposed to a ground up vehicle), the car can be easily manufactured, and is just as structurally sound and reliable as the original Escort. Because the vehicle produces low emissions and uses recyclable batteries, it is environmentally safe, a major requirement that will pave the way for the acceptance of future hybrid electric vehicles.

ACKNOWLEDGMENTS

The West Virginia University Hybrid Electric Vehicle Team would like to thank our chief sponsor, the Monogahela Power Company, a division of the Allegheny Power System, for their support throughout this project.

325

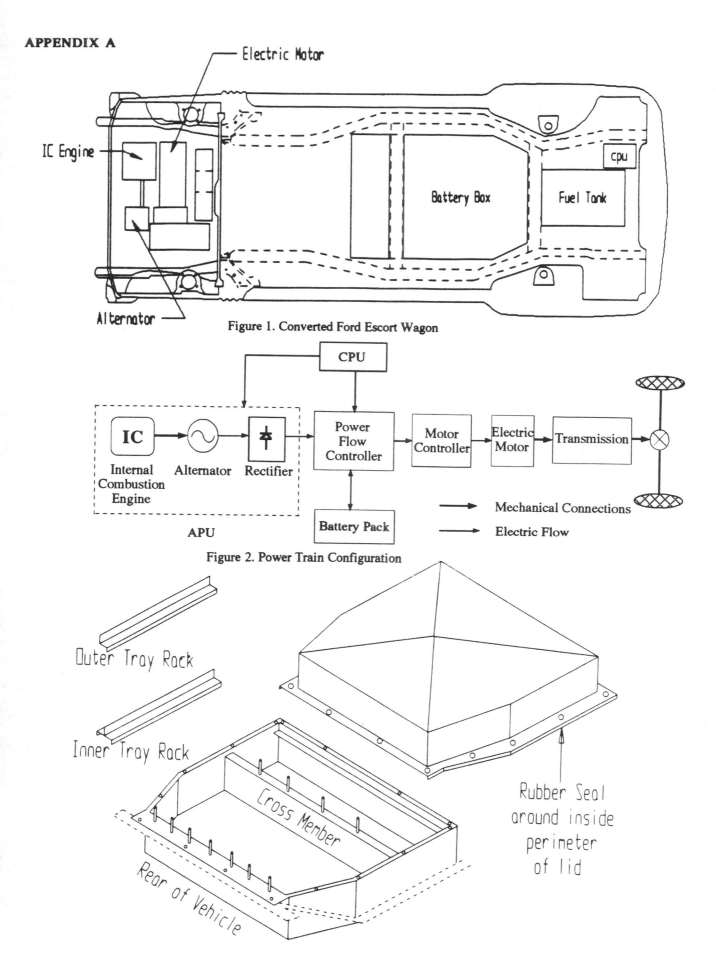

Figure 1. Converted Ford Escort Wagon

Figure 2. Power Train Configuration

Figure 3. Battery Box

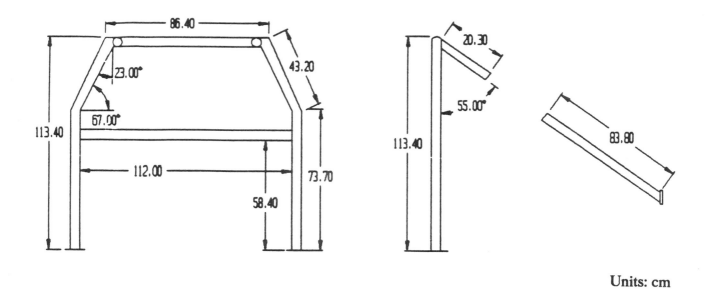

Units: cm

Figure 4. Roll Bar

APPENDIX B

BATTERY	TYPE	VOLTAGE (per battery)	WEIGHT (kg/pack)	ENERGY STORAGE (kW - hr)	COST (projected)
Optima	Pb Acid	12	428.6	14.4	$7200
Trojan J250	Pb Acid	6	566	14.21	$7105
Trojan T-125	Pb Acid	6	479	13.3	$6655
GC12V100	Pb Acid	12	522.5	9.79	$4896
SAFT 5-200	NiCd	6	374.5	14.4	$13440

Table 1.   Battery Specification Comparison